About Pearson

Pearson is the world's learning company, with presence across 70 countries worldwide. Our unique insights and world-class expertise come from a long history of working closely with renowned teachers, authors and thought leaders, as a result of which, we have emerged as the preferred choice for millions of teachers and learners across the world.

We believe learning opens up opportunities, creates fulfilling careers and hence better lives. We hence collaborate with the best of minds to deliver you class-leading products, spread across the Higher Education and Test Preparation spectrum.

Superior learning experience and improved outcomes are at the heart of everything we do. This product is the result of one such effort.

Your feedback plays a critical role in the evolution of our products and you can contact us at reachus@pearson.com. *We look forward to it.*

CLASS

10

Trishna's

PEARSON FOUNDATION

Biology

Seventh Edition

CLASS

10

Trishna's

PEARSON FOUNDATION

Biology

Seventh Edition

2025

Pearson

Photo Credits

Chapter 1 Opener: nobeastsofierce / Shutterstock
Chapter 2 Opener: Rost9 / Shutterstock
Chapter 3 Opener: venars.original / Shutterstock
Chapter 4 Opener: Salparadis / Shutterstock
Chapter 5 Opener: ebastian Kaulitzki / 123RF
Chapter 6 Opener: Mopic / Shutterstock
Chapter 7 Opener: Giovanni Cancemi / Shutterstock
Chapter 8 Opener: Andrii Vodolazhskyi / Shutterstock
Chapter 9 Opener: vchal / Shutterstock
Chapter 10 Opener: Wlad74 / Shutterstock
Chapter 11 Opener: Kichigin / Shutterstock
Chapter 12 Opener: Diyana Dimitrova / Shutterstock

ISBN 978-93-615-9847-0

First Impression

Published by Pearson India Education Services Pvt. Ltd, CIN: U72200TN2005PTC057128.

Head Office: 1st Floor, Berger Tower, Plot No. C-001A/2, Sector 16B, Noida - 201 301, Uttar Pradesh, India.
Registered Office: Featherlite, 'The Address' 5th Floor, Survey No 203/10B, 200 Ft MMRD Road, Zamin Pallavaram, Chennai – 600 044.
Website: in.pearson.com, Email: companysecretary.india@pearson.com

Compositor: Satish Kumar Shrivastava
Printed in India by Pushp Print Services

Brief Contents

Preface		*xiii*
Chapter Insights		*xvii*
Chapter 1	**Cell—The Basic Unit of Life**	**1.1**
Chapter 2	**Cell Division and Cell Cycle**	**2.1**
Chapter 3	**Life Processes in Plants**	**3.1**
Chapter 4	**Reproduction in Lower Organisms and Plants**	**4.1**
Chapter 5	**Life Processes in Human Beings–I (Digestive and Excretory System)**	**5.1**
Chapter 6	**Life Processes in Human Beings–II (Respiratory and Circulatory Systems)**	**6.1**
Chapter 7	**Reproduction in Human Beings**	**7.1**
Chapter 8	**Control and Coordination**	**8.1**
Chapter 9	**Genetics**	**9.1**
Chapter 10	**Evolution**	**10.1**
Chapter 11	**Ecology**	**11.1**
Chapter 12	**Management of Natural Resources**	**12.1**
Glossary		*G.1*
Photo Credits		*PC.1*

Contents

Preface xiii

Chapter Insights xvii

CHAPTER 1 CELL—THE BASIC UNIT OF LIFE **1.1**

Introduction **1.3**

Cell **1.3**

Cell Theory 1.3

Pioneers in the Study of Cells 1.3

Structure of a Cell **1.4**

Membranes Covering the Cell 1.4

Transport of Substances through the Plasma Membrane 1.7

Cytoplasm **1.9**

Cell Organelles 1.9

Nucleus **1.12**

Structure 1.13

Functions 1.13

Structure of DNA 1.14

Functions of DNA 1.15

Structure and Function of RNA 1.16

DNA and Chromatin Material 1.16

Structure of Chromosome 1.16

Practice Questions 1.22

Answer keys 1.28

Hints and Explanations 1.29

CHAPTER 2 CELL DIVISION AND CELL CYCLE **2.1**

Introduction **2.3**

Significance of Cell Division **2.3**

Growth of the Body 2.3

Maintenance and Repair of Cells 2.3

Replacement of Dead and Damaged Cells 2.3

Formation of New Individuals by Reproduction 2.4

Modes of Cell Division 2.4

Mitosis 2.4

Meiosis 2.10

Cell Cycle **2.13**

Practice Questions 2.17

Answer keys 2.24

Hints and Explanations 2.26

CHAPTER 3 LIFE PROCESSES IN PLANTS **3.1**

Introduction **3.3**

Nutrition **3.3**

Autotrophic Nutrition 3.3

Heterotrophic Nutrition 3.3

Nutrition in Green Plants **3.4**

Mechanism of Photosynthesis 3.7

Structure and Adaptations of Leaves for Facilitating Photosynthesis 3.11

Factors Affecting Photosynthesis 3.12

Transportation in Plants **3.14**

Absorption of Water and Minerals by the Roots 3.14

Transportation of Water Through Xylem 3.15

Transportation of Food in Plants 3.16

Respiration and Transpiration **3.17**

Respiration **3.18**

Types of Respiration 3.18

Mechanism of Exchange of Gases During Respiration in Lower Plants 3.19

Excretion in Plants **3.21**

Transpiration 3.21

Practice Questions 3.27

Answer keys 3.35

Hints and Explanations 3.37

CHAPTER 4 REPRODUCTION IN LOWER ORGANISMS AND PLANTS **4.1**

Introduction **4.3**

Asexual Reproduction **4.3**

Fission 4.3

Budding 4.4

Spore Formation 4.6

Regeneration 4.6

Fragmentation 4.7

Vegetative Reproduction 4.8

Sexual Reproduction in Angiosperms **4.13**

Structure of a Typical Flower 4.13

Process of Sexual Reproduction 4.15

Pollination 4.18

Fertilization Phase 4.23
Post-fertilization Changes 4.24
Practice Questions *4.30*
Answer keys *4.38*
Hints and Explanations *4.40*

CHAPTER 5 LIFE PROCESSES IN HUMAN BEINGS–I (DIGESTIVE AND EXCRETORY SYSTEMS) 5.1

Introduction 5.3
Need for Digestive System 5.3
Role of Enzymes 5.3
Digestive System 5.4
Alimentary Canal or Digestive Tract 5.5
Associated Digestive Glands 5.5
Alimentary Canal 5.6
Mouth 5.6
Pharynx 5.8
Oesophagus 5.9
Stomach 5.10
Small Intestine 5.10
Large Intestine 5.11
Associated Digestive Glands 5.12
Salivary Glands 5.12
Pancreas 5.13
Liver 5.13
Process of Digestion 5.15
Digestion in Mouth 5.15
Digestion in Stomach 5.16
Digestion in Small Intestine 5.17
Absorption of Food 5.18
Assimilation of Food 5.18
Egestion 5.19
Excretory System in Humans 5.20
Wastes Generated in Human Body 5.20
Excretory Organs in Humans 5.21
Lungs 5.21
Skin 5.22
Liver 5.23
Kidneys 5.23
Blood Supply to the Kidney Through Nephrons 5.26
Osmoregulation 5.29
Haemodialysis 5.29
Practice Questions *5.32*
Answer keys *5.40*
Hints and Explanations *5.41*

CHAPTER 6 LIFE PROCESSES IN HUMAN BEINGS–II (RESPIRATORY AND CIRCULATORY SYSTEMS) 6.1

Introduction 6.3
Respiratory System 6.3
Need for Respiration 6.3
Energy Needs in Organisms 6.3
Role of Glucose 6.4
Types of Respiration 6.4
Parts of Respiratory System 6.6
Process of Respiration 6.9
Mechanism of Respiration 6.11
Control of Respiration 6.12
Capacities of the Lungs 6.12
Effect of Altitude on Breathing 6.13
Respiratory Disorders 6.13
Circulatory System 6.15
Need for Circulatory System 6.15
Components of Circulatory System 6.16
Blood 6.16
Tissue Fluid 6.17
Composition of Blood 6.17
Cellular Components 6.17
Functions of Blood 6.23
Blood Vessels 6.24
Heart 6.26
Circulation of Blood 6.30
Blood Pressure 6.31
Blood Groups 6.31
Hepatic Portal System 6.32
Lymphatic system 6.33
Practice Questions *6.37*
Answer keys *6.45*
Hints and Explanations *6.46*

CHAPTER 7 REPRODUCTION IN HUMAN BEINGS 7.1

Introduction 7.3
Modes of Reproduction in Animals 7.3
Asexual Reproduction 7.3
Sexual Reproduction 7.4
Reproductive System In Humans 7.4
Male Reproductive System 7.4
Female Reproductive System 7.10
Biological Processes Involved in Reproductive Cycle 7.16

Menstrual Cycle 7.16
Role of Hormones of Pituitary Gland in Reproduction 7.17
Fertilization 7.19
Embryogenesis 7.20
Embryonic Membranes 7.21
Parturition and Childbirth 7.25
Reproductive Health 7.26
Practice Questions *7.29*
Answer keys *7.37*
Hints and Explanations *7.39*

CHAPTER 8 CONTROL AND COORDINATION **8.1**

Introduction **8.3**
Nervous System **8.3**
Need for Nervous System 8.3
Parts of Nervous System 8.3
Neuron 8.3
Conduction of Nerve Impulse 8.6
Synapse 8.7
Nerves 8.8
Central Nervous System 8.8
Peripheral Nervous System 8.13
Autonomic Nervous System 8.14
Reflex Action 8.15
Endocrine System **8.17**
Need for Endocrine System 8.17
Characteristics of Hormones 8.17
Pituitary Gland 8.18
Thyroid Glands 8.20
Adrenal Glands 8.20
Pancreas 8.22
Feedback Control of Hormone Secretion 8.24
Control and Coordination in Plants **8.27**
Phototropism 8.27
Geotropism 8.27
Hydrotropism 8.28
Chemotropism 8.28
Practice Questions *8.31*
Answer keys *8.39*
Hints and Explanations *8.40*

CHAPTER 9 GENETICS **9.1**

Introduction **9.3**
Heredity and Variation **9.3**
Units of Heredity 9.4
Cell Division and Heredity 9.5
Mechanism of Variation 9.6
Mendelian Inheritance **9.7**
Reasons for Choosing Pea Plants for Mendel's Experiments 9.7
Mendel's Experiments 9.7
Mendel's Monohybrid Cross 9.9
Mendel's Dihybrid Cross 9.12
Applications of Genetics **9.16**
Sex Determination 9.16
Genetic Disorders 9.19
Pedigree Analysis 9.21
Practice Questions *9.28*
Answer keys *9.37*
Hints and Explanations *9.39*

CHAPTER 10 EVOLUTION **10.1**

Introduction **10.3**
Origin of Universe **10.3**
Big Bang Theory 10.3
Origin of Life 10.4
Biological or Organic Evolution 10.4
Theories of Evolution **10.14**
Lamarckism 10.14
Neo-Lamarckism 10.16
Theory of Darwinism 10.16
Modern Theory of Evolution 10.17
Illustration for the Modern Theory of Evolution 10.18
Evolution as the Basis of Classification of Living Organisms 10.19
Evolution of Man 10.20
Evolution of Cabbage 10.22
Practice Questions *10.25*
Answer keys *10.33*
Hints and Explanations *10.35*

CHAPTER 11 ECOLOGY **11.1**

Introduction **11.3**
Ecosystem **11.3**
Components of Ecosystem 11.4
Classification of Ecosystems 11.4
Classification of Biotic Components of Ecosystems 11.5
Flow of Energy in Ecosystem 11.6
Environmental Pollution **11.9**
Types of Pollution 11.9
Air Pollution 11.10
Water pollution 11.17
Soil/Land Pollution 11.20
Noise Pollution 11.21

Radioactive Pollution 11.22
Worldwide Implications of Environmental Pollution 11.24
Practice Questions *11.30*
Answer keys *11.37*
Hints and Explanations *11.38*

CHAPTER 12 MANAGEMENT OF NATURAL RESOURCES 12.1

Introduction 12.3
Natural Resources 12.3
Managing Resources: The Need 12.4
National Mission for Clean Ganga 12.4
Sustainable Development and Conservation of Environment 12.5
Forest and Wildlife 12.6
Use 12.7
Sustainable Management 12.9
Water Resources 12.9
Water for Agriculture and Power Generation 12.10
Exploitation of Water Resources 12.10
Global Climate Change 12.10
Conservation 12.11
Sustainable Management 12.11
Dams 12.12
Problems 12.12
Water Harvesting 12.12
Water Harvesting Techniques 12.13
Water Saving Techniques 12.14
Coal and Petroleum Resources 12.15
Uses 12.16
Mining 12.16
Exploitation 12.16
Conservation and Sustainable Management 12.17
Renewable Energy Resources 12.17
Saving Environment–Reduce, Recycle, Reuse and Reforest 12.18
Practice Questions *12.21*
Answer keys *12.33*
Hints and Explanations *12.35*

Glossary *G.1*
Photo Credits *PC.1*

Preface

"If you have a great ambition, take as big a step as possible in the direction of fulfilling it. The step may only be a tiny one, but trust that it may be the largest one possible for now."

Mildred McAfee

Pearson Foundation Biology Series has been created keeping in mind the learner's ambition to excel in a competitive examination like NEET and other Biology Olympiads. The series can be used in addition to the books studied in school to attain that extra edge required to strengthen the concepts and prepare well for future endeavours.

Why Start Early with Pearson Foundation Series

Classes VI to X are the base years of a learner's academic life. In these years learner explore their interests and determine the goals they wish to attain. *Pearson Foundation Biology* series is filled with interactive learning that not only nurtures a learner's interest in science and mathematics but also strengthens their concepts.

The series uses real-life examples and application-based problems to teach theoretical concepts. The objective of this series is to help learners cultivate an analytical mind.

Most of the lessons to be learnt are introduced to the learners in the books for class VI. As they get promoted to higher classes, new topics are added to these lessons. This additive method helps the learners' span their learning over four standards, from VI-X. Thus, learners are not overwhelmed by the introduction of completely new lessons every time they are promoted to a new class.

While their learning is being spanned across five years, so is their ability to resolve doubts for further conceptual clarity. For instance, they can use concepts learnt in class VI to solve questions in class VII. If, in case, they get stuck while answering a question, the learners can infer for themselves that they might be lacking in conceptual clarity. They can then approach their teachers, requesting them to explain the concept once again. This helps the learner to clarify their concepts while revising the lessons previously learnt.

Since classes VI-X are deemed to be a student's formative years, we, at Pearson, aim to provide a foundation level course which serves more than just a standard curriculum.

Here is how it makes a difference to a learner's overall learning ...

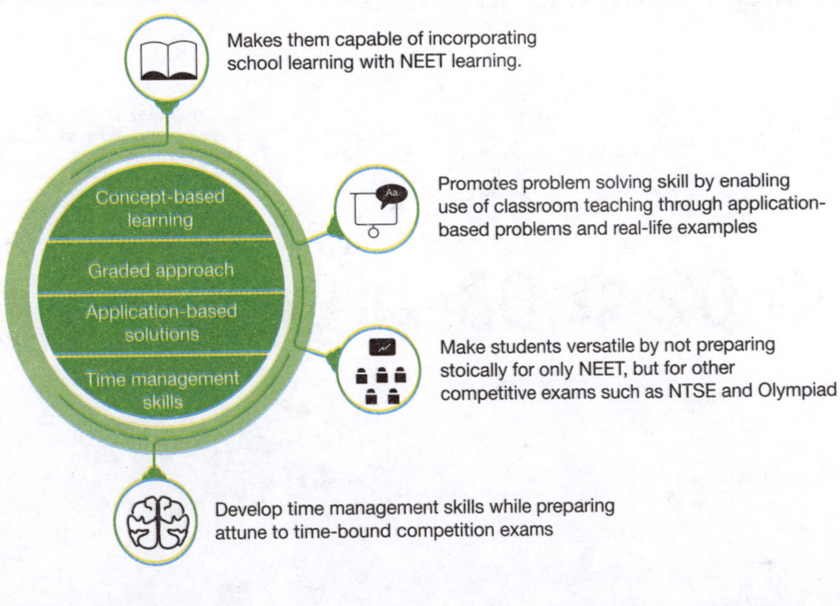

Other Uses of the Series

Instead of limiting themselves to NEET, a learner can also use this series to prepare for several other competitive examinations such as NSTSE, National and International Olympiads, BITSAT, etc. This series offers a level of concept learning that empowers learners to handle the challenging nature of questions posed in these examinations. Moreover, this will also allow the learners to have an early insight into their key strengths as well as improvement areas and help them work on them selves.

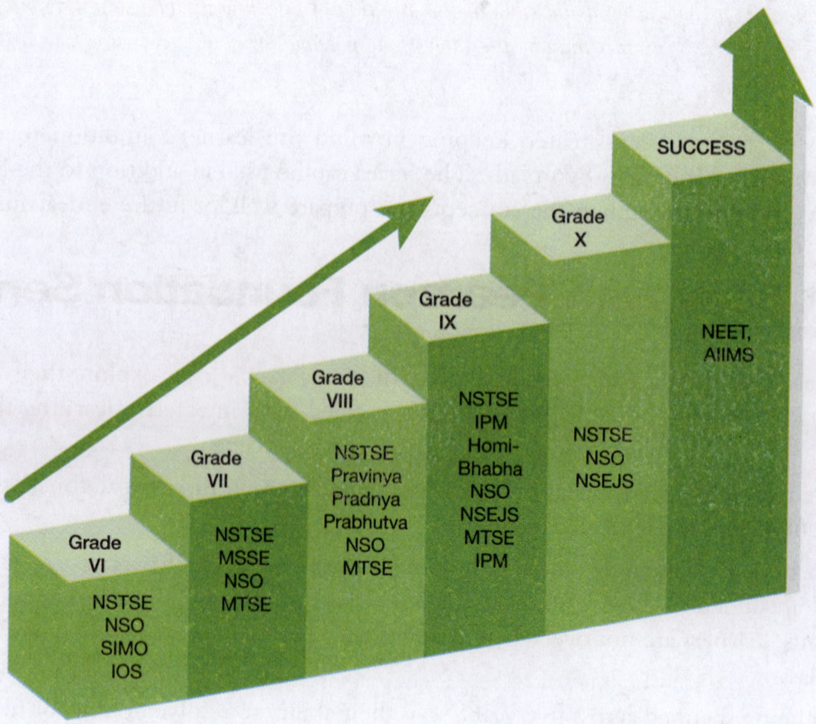

[IMO: International Mathematics Olympiad; NSO: National Science Olympiad, IOS: International Olympiad of Science, NSTSE: National Level Science Talent Search Examination, MTSE: Maharashtra Talent Search Examination, RMO: Regional Mathematical Olympiad, PPP: Pravinya Pradnya Prabhutva, NSEJS: National Standard Examination in Junior Science, IIT: Indian Institute of Technology, IISc: Indian Institute of Science, NIT: National Institute of Technology.]

Highlights of the Series

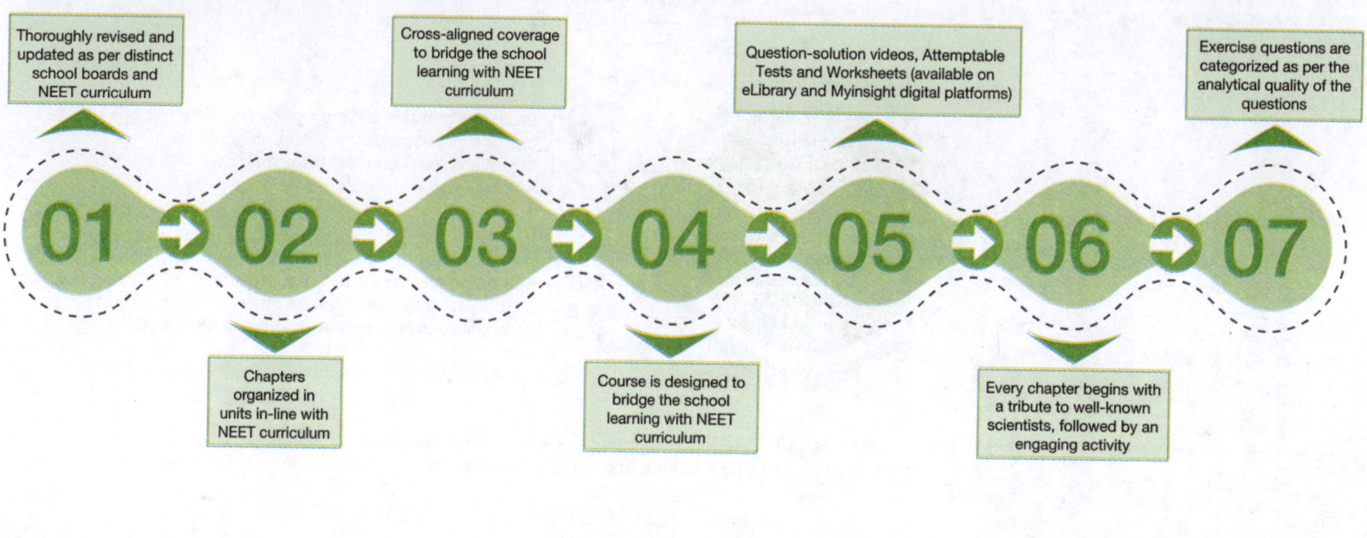

Pearson Foundation Biology series provides a perfect blend of learning through theory and practice questions with a fusion of school and NEET curriculum. It is imperative to note that this series would be as profound as you want it to be. Therefore, to get maximum benefit from this book, we recommend following the given study plan.

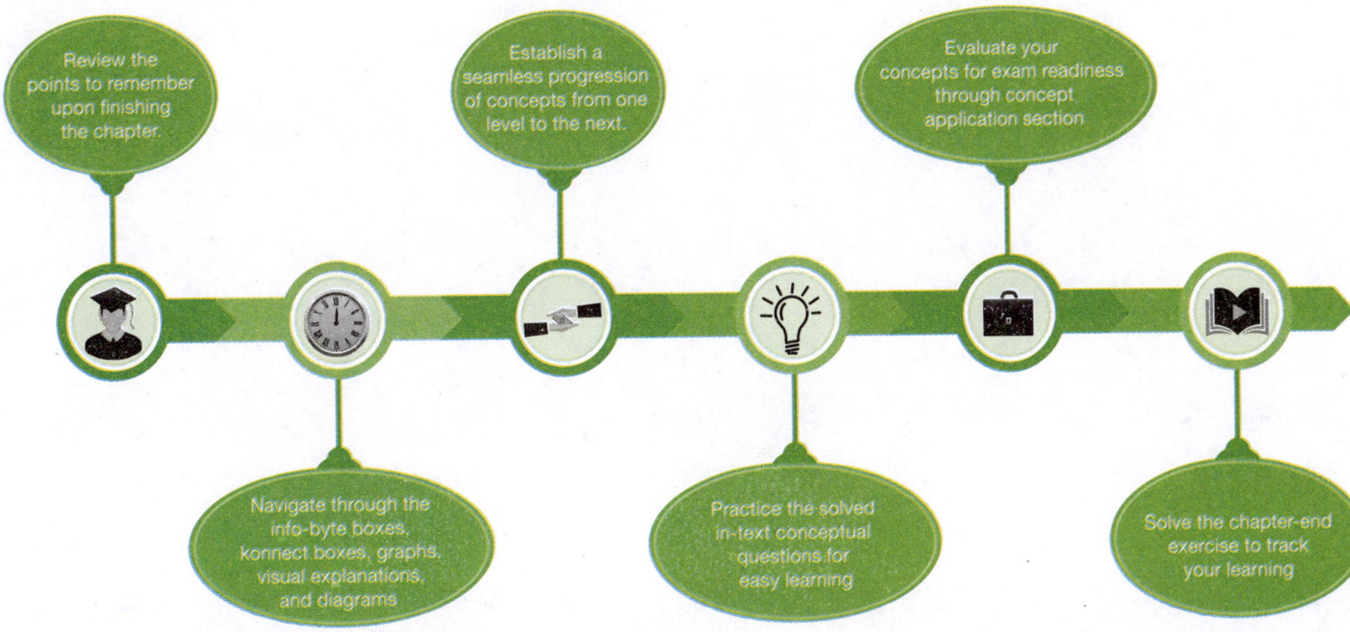

To provide a graded learning approach, the exercise part of each chapter is categorized by using four icons for question tagging. The question categorization helps the learners assess their own problem-solving and analytical skills and motivates them to improve to reach their objectives.

The following icons are used to categorize the questions with specific meanings:

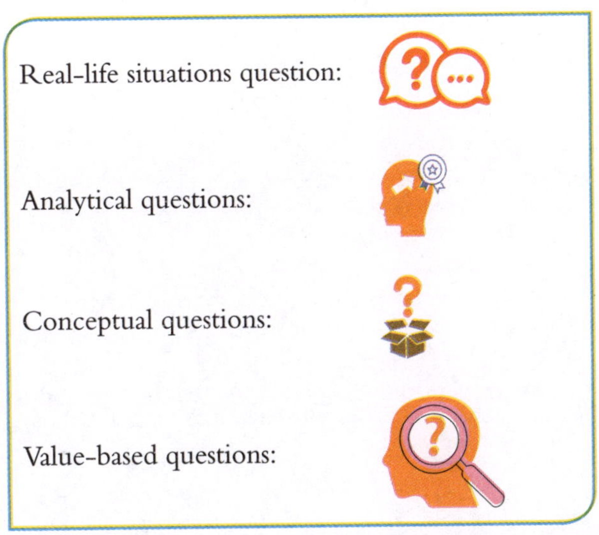

With this refined and well-tuned course from Pearson, students will become more confident when they enter the competitive world for actual NEET preparation. The effort put in today will transform into a valuable asset, contributing to success in future competitive examinations.

Chapter Insights

Remember

Before beginning this chapter, you should be able to:

- Recall the basic structure and functions of major cell organelles
- Remember the structure and important

Remember section will help them to memorize and review the previous learning on a particular topic

Key Ideas

After completing this chapter, you should be able to:

- Explain the structure and function of cell membranes
- Understand transport of substances through plasma membrane

Key points will help the students to identify the essential points in a chapter

INTRODUCTION

The cells are the fundamental building blocks of all living organisms. All activities are carried out by the cells that keep the organisms alive. Cell is defined as the basic structural, functional and hereditary unit of all living organisms. In unicellular organisms, all activities are carried out by a single cell. In multicellular organisms, the life of an organism starts from a single cell called zygote which undergoes repeated cell divisions to form a number of cells. In all higher organisms such as plants and animals, the cells formed in this way organize themselves into groups of similar cells performing specific tasks. In the course of development, these cells become specialized to perform specific functions.

Introduction section helps to lay the foundation of the following chapter and leads the way for further learning

Scientific Crypt

A Tribute to Jan Ingenhousz (1730–1799)

Jan Ingenhousz (1730–1799), a notable scientist and physician of his time, deserves special recognition for his pivotal work in uncovering plant life processes. Ingenhousz discovered the crucial process of photosynthesis in the 18th century. He demonstrated that plants absorb carbon dioxide and, in response to sunlight, emit life-sustaining oxygen, a discovery that profoundly influenced scientific perspectives on ecological balance.

The discoveries of Ingenhousz went beyond botany. He had a strong interest in medicine and contributed significantly to the understanding of diseases and immunisation.

His meticulous and rigorous experiments demonstrated the beautiful, symbiotic relationship between flora and fauna, emphasising the critical role of sunlight in the survival of life on Earth.

FUN TIME

CROSSWORD

Scientific Crypt provides information about well-known scientists related to the chapter. The engaging activity is also given in the form of a crossword to keep the learners interested.

Excretion in Plants

Excretion is the life process through which waste and toxic products are expelled from the body of an organism.

Plants generate different excretory products during execution of their life processes. **Carbon dioxide** is the product obtained during respiration. This gas is consumed in the process of photosynthesis during daytime but at night it is expelled through the **stomata**. Oxygen gas generated by photosynthesis is partially consumed during respiration, but rest of its part is excreted through the **stomata**. Certain waste products in plants are accumulated in the vacuoles of cells of old leaves. These wastes are eliminated when leaves get detached from the plants. **Resin, gum, latex**, etc., are the excretory products of plants which ooze out of the bark of trees and are shed in due course of time. Another process of excretion in plants is **transpiration**. Through which excess water is eliminated from the plant

Concepts are explained in a well-structured and lucid manner

Konnect

The number of stomata varies significantly between leaves of different plants and there may be as many as 40,000 per square centimetres on some leaves.

Konnect boxes are some add-on information of related topic

Info bytes are interesting trivia and facts that engage young minds and keep the grey cells ticking!

Info Bytes!

Leaves change colour in autumn because plants slow down the process of photosynthesis.

Quick Recap

✔ **Mitochondria are known as the cell's powerhouse. Explain the significance of its double-membrane structure in terms of function.**

Mitochondria have a unique double-membrane structure with an outer and inner membrane. This distinction is critical to its operation. The outer membrane allows ions and molecules to pass through, while the inner membrane is selectively permeable and contains the electron transport chain and ATP synthase, both of which are required for oxidative phosphorylation.

✔ **The Golgi apparatus and the ER are both important in protein modification and transport. Compare and contrast their roles in protein maturation and subsequent cellular release.**

Both the Endoplasmic Reticulum (ER) and the Golgi apparatus are important components of the cell's endomembrane system. The ER is in charge of initial protein synthesis and folding. These proteins are packaged into vesicles and transported to the Golgi apparatus after being synthesized. Proteins undergo additional modifications

Quick Recap section will help to review all important concepts, discussed in that particular chapter

Each section contains detailed diagrams, images, real life microscopic views for better understanding and conceptual clarity.

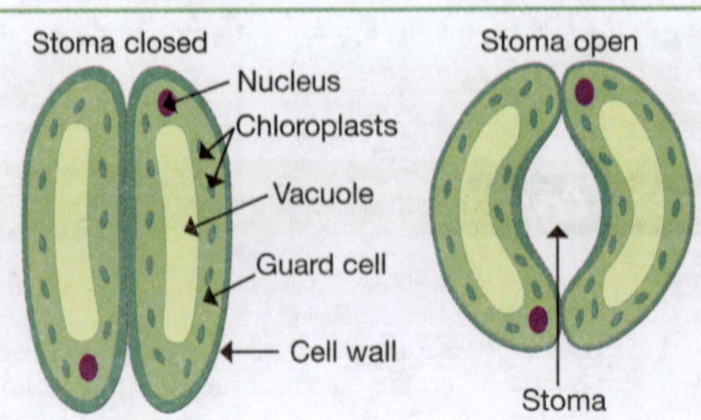

Figure. 3.5 Opening and closing of stomata

POINTS TO REMEMBER

✔ The sum total of the process through which an animal or plant takes in food substances and utilizes them is known as nutrition.

✔ A series of processes by which an organism prepares its own food from simple inorganic materials collected from the environment is called autotrophic nutrition.

✔ A mode of nutrition in which an organism depends on the other organisms for its food is

✔ Respiration can be divided into two categories based on its occurrence in the presence or absence of oxygen, i.e., Anaerobic and Aerobic Respiration.

✔ During the process of glycolysis, glucose, a 6-Carbon sugar gets converted to a 3-Carbon compound called pyruvate, and energy is released.

✔ During fermentation, ethanol and carbon

Points to remember summarises the concepts and topics presented in each chapter

PRACTICE QUESTIONS CLASSROOM WING

Very Short Answer Type Questions

Directions for questions from 1 to 5:
Fill in the blanks.

1. The organisms that produce their food by utilizing energy from chemical reactions and not by sunlight are called ____________.
2. _________ is the green-coloured pigment responsible for trapping sunlight.
3. The pores on the lower surface of the leaves responsible for the intake of CO_2 are called ____________.
4. Thylakoids serve as the site for one phase of photosyn-

(c) Sugar Concentration Theory
(d) ATP Concentration Theory

10. The absorption of what kind of energy initiates the photosynthesis reaction in chlorophyll?
    (a) Thermal energy
    (b) Chemical energy
    (c) Solar energy
    (d) Wind energy
11. Where in a plant cell does photolysis of water primar-

Short Answer Type Questions

Direction for Questions from 27 to 61:
Answer the following questions.

27. Differentiate between autotrophs and heterotrophs.
28. How are autotrophs classified?

Essay Type Questions

62. Describe the importance of photosynthesis not just for plants, but for life on Earth as a whole. Consider factors like oxygen production, food chains, and carbon sequestration.

Different typologies of questions have been included in the *Classroom Wing* which help students to develop the problem-solving skill

PRACTICE QUESTIONS COMPETITION WING

Competition Wing has been integrated chapter-wise in the exercise part to prepare students for various competitive examinations.

Level 1: Apply your Concepts

Directions for questions from 1 to 11:
Fill in the blanks.

1. Photolysis of water produces hydrogen ions and ________ ions.
2. NADP is reduced to ________ during photosynthesis.

13. Which cells surround the sieve tube elements in the phloem?
    (a) Epidermis (b) Companion cells
    (c) Xylem cells (d) Cortex cells
14. Which process occurs in the cytoplasm of a cell during aerobic respiration?
    Krebs Cycle

Graded as per complexity: Level 1; Level 2; and Level 3

Level 2: Review your Concepts

37. How does the accumulation of photosynthetic end products affect the rate of photosynthesis?
38. Explain the significance of the Calvin Cycle in the dark phase of photosynthesis.
39. How does light intensity influence the rate of photosynthesis?

Level 3: Assess Your Concepts

44. How might changes in global climate patterns affect stomatal regulation and by extension, plant survival?
45. Clear division of labor is seen within a chloroplast. Give reason.
46. How does the structure of a leaf reflect the evolutionary pressures of balancing water conservation with the gas exchange? Discuss the role of the cuticle.

32. How are spindle fibres formed during cell division? What is their importance?
33. All the somatic cells in the body of an individual have exactly identical DNA. Why?
34. Mitosis helps in cellular regeneration. Give reason.

Direction for Questions from 35 to 36:
Answer the following questions.

35. What is cell differentiation?
36. What is a nucleosome?

Essay Type Questions

37. Elaborate on the significance and roles of the various phases in the cell cycle. How does each phase prepare the cell for mitosis, and why is this preparation crucial?
38. (i) Mention the phase of mitosis that is shown in the below figure and label the parts A, B, C and D. Mention the changes taking place in the given phase.
    (ii) Observe the figure and answer the questions that follow.

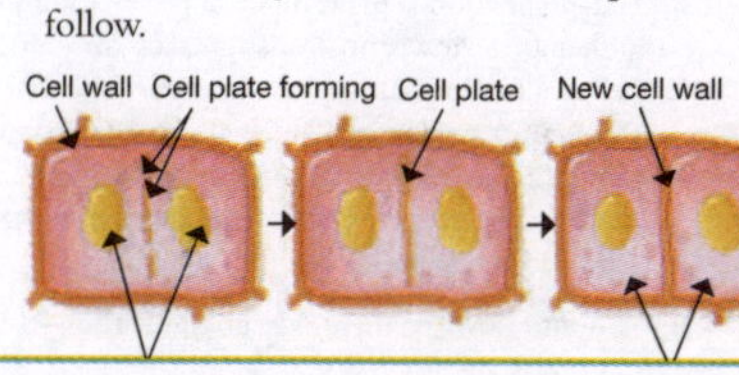

The icons are used for categorisation of the questions in Classroom Wing and Competition Wing

PRACTICE QUESTIONS NEET SPECIAL WING

Multiple-Answer Type Questions

Questions number 1 to 5 are multiple-choice questions. Each question has FOUR options (a), (b), (c), and (d). ONE OR MORE THAN ONE of these four option(s) is/are the correct answer(s).

1. If the male gamete of an organism with diploid somatic cells contains 36 chromosomes. Identify the correct statement from the following-
   (a) The zygote will have 72 autosomes and 2 X

(c) 40 cells are produced by division of 5 megaspore mother cell.
(d) 40 cells are produced by division of 10 megaspore mother cells.

Comprehension-Based Questions

A. Read the paragraph given below and answer the questions number 6 to 11:

6. Which of the following plants produces cleistogamous flowers?

NEET Special Wing is curated specifically for targeted preparation of NEET examination

Hints and Explanations

CLASSROOM WING

Short Answer Type Questions

17. Cytoplasm is a jelly-like substance that contains membrane-bound cell organelles and non-living substances called cytoplasmic inclusions. Cytoplasm without cell organelles is known as cytosol.
18. As cells die or get damaged, they need to be replaced for the organism to function properly. Additionally, for species to reproduce and continue, cell division is fundamental.
19. The composition of the cell wall varies among organisms. Cellulose is the main component in most plants, whereas fungi have chitin.
20. This selective nature is crucial for maintaining the balance of substances within the cell and protecting it from external threats.

develop. Because of this specialization, not every cell must perform every function, resulting in increased efficiency. As a result, tissues, organs, and systems emerge, each contributing to the overall function and well-being of the organism in a coordinated fashion.

25. A typical cell, regardless of organism, has characteristics in common. It has protoplasm at its core, which includes the nucleus and cytoplasm. The genetic information is stored in the nucleus, which serves as the control centre. The cytoplasm is home to a variety of organelles, each with a specific function ranging from energy production to waste management. Non-living cytoplasmic inclusions can be found here as well. The plasma membrane surrounds the protoplasm and regulates the entry and exit of substances, ensuring a balance between the cell's internal and external environments.

Hints and Explanations for key questions of classroom wing, competition wing and NEET special wing along with highlights on the common mistakes that students usually make in the examinations

COMPETITION WING

Level 1: Apply your Concepts

6. While hormones indeed don't catalyze reactions like enzymes do, their primary role is as chemical messen-

15. Whenever plant cells are stimulated by light, auxin hormone moves to the side of the shoot which is away from the light.
    Since auxins are involved in growth, the shady part of the shoot grows longer.
    Thus, shoot of the plant bends towards the light.
    Hence, the correct option is (b)

Level 2: Review your Concepts

22. In myelinated neurons, the exit and entry of potassium ions and sodium ions respectively take place through the nodes of Ranvier whereas it takes place throughout the axon in nonmyelinated neurons. So, action potentials are generated only at the nodes

NEET SPECIAL WING

Multiple-Answer Type Questions

Questions number 1 to 5 are multiple-choice questions. Each question has FOUR options (a), (b), (c), and (d). ONE OR MORE THAN ONE of these four option(s) is/are the correct answer(s).

1. If a male gamete has 36 chromosomes, then it has 35 autosomes and 1 Y gamete. When it fuses with the egg, the zygote will have 70 autosomes and 1 X and 1 Y chromosome. The germ cells will also have 35 pairs or 70 autosomes and 1 pair of allosomes.
2. 1 megaspore mother cell produces 8 haploid cells after its various divisions. Thus, 40 haploid cells will be produced by the division of 5 megaspore mother cells. From each haploid cell 1 egg is produced, so from 40 haploid cells 5 eggs are produced.
3. The megaspore mother cells are diploid and undergo

of a bisexual flower attain maturity together. For exar ple, wheat, rice, *Mirabilis*. Cleistogamy is observed non-opening flowers since the pollen grain is confin inside the flower and can pollinate the stigma of t same flower. For example, underground flowers *Commelina benghalensis*.

7. The flower of a sweet pea plant has fragrance, produc nectar and is bright in colour. Thus, it attracts bees. is a bee-pollinated flower.
8. Self-pollination is the transfer of pollen grains from t anther of a flower to the stigma of the same flow Self-pollination takes place in some bisexual flowe Parental characteristics are maintained. Production pollen grains in large quantity is not required. Flow need not be attractive as insects are not required to attracted for pollination.
9. In some flowers, there is a physical obstacle that

CHAPTER 2: WORKSHEET

Directions for questions from 1 to 5.

Answer the following questions in one word.

1. The process through which cytoplasm undergoes division during cytokinesis.
2. Primitive mode of cell division, which normally takes place in lower organisms.
3. The stage of mitosis in which the cell becomes ready for cell division.
4. This mitosis phase is marked by the initiation of the condensation of chromatin material in the nucleus.
5. The life of every organism starts from this.

Directions for questions from 6 to 10.

Answer the following questions.

6. What is the role of kinetochore during metaphase?
7. Which of the mitosis phases is the shortest? What happens in this phase?
8. During Karyokinesis, when does reformation of cell organelles take place?
9. What is centrifugal cytoplasmic division? Where is this division normally seen?
10. What is the difference between meiosis-I and meiosis-II?

DW

DW: Downloadable worksheets supplementing textual exercises for hand-on learning

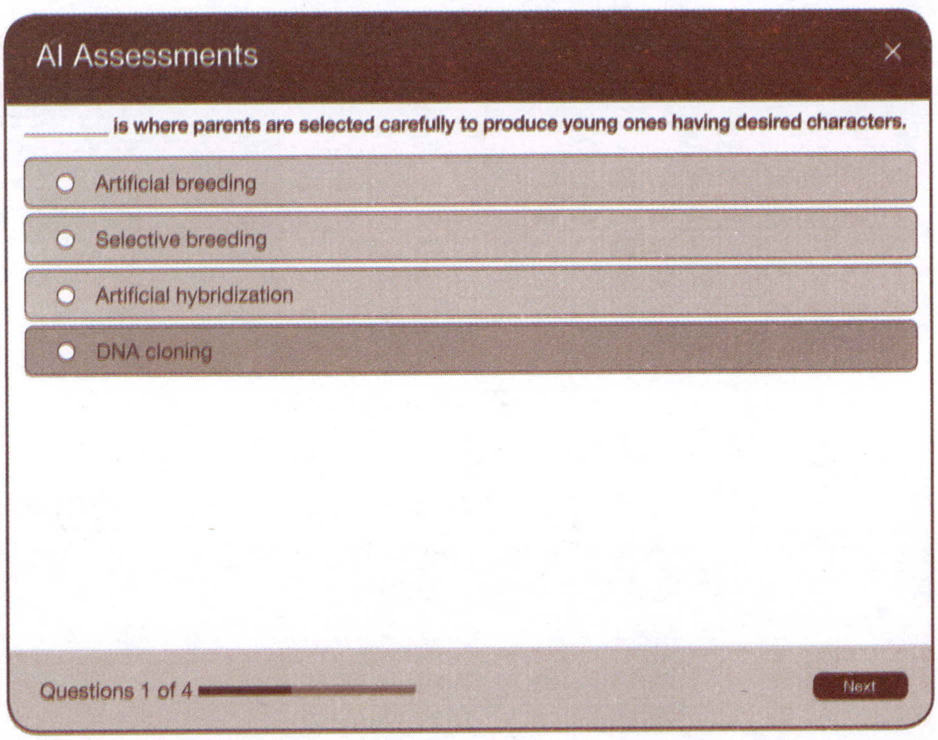

AT

AT: Attemptable Tests for assessing understanding of concepts and getting a clear picture of your exam readiness

29. What are the basic requirements for the survival of animals in the ecosystem? Explain.
30. How do biomedical wastes affect our environment?
31. What is auditory fatigue? How does it occur?
32. Define the following:
    (a) Biomass
    (b) Ecosystem
    (c) Food web

Video icon: Audio and visual learning to difficult questions for effective learning and retention

CHAPTER

1

Cell—The Basic Unit of Life

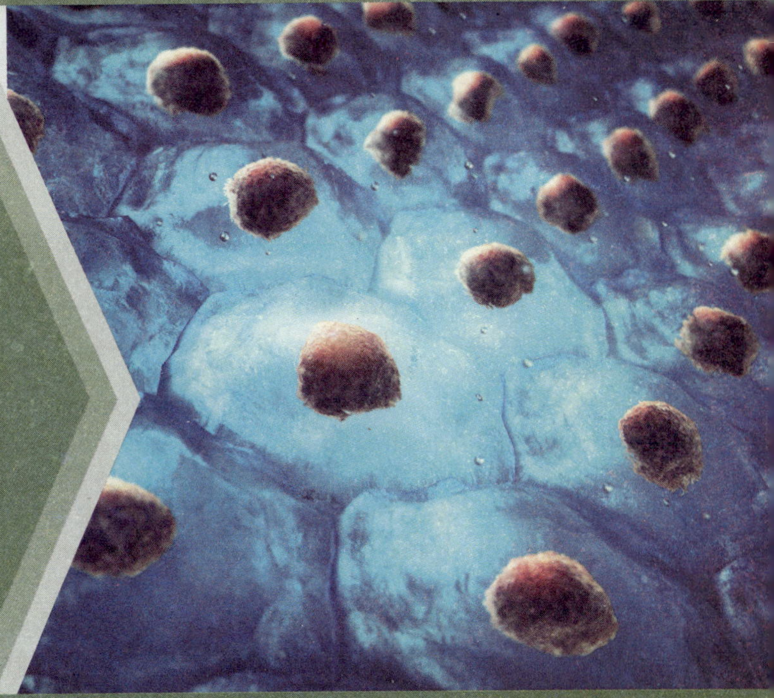

Remember

Before beginning this chapter, you should be able to:

- Recall the basic structure and functions of major cell organelles
- Remember the structure and important components of nucleus

Key Ideas

After completing this chapter, you should be able to:

- Explain the structure and function of cell membranes
- Understand transport of substances through plasma membrane
- Describe the structures and functions of different cell organelles
- Know the structure and function of DNA
- Understand the significance of chromosome number and their function

A Tribute to James Watson (born 1929) and Francis Crick (1916–2004)

In 1953, James Watson (born 1929) and Francis Crick (1916-2004) discovered the double-helix structure of DNA, revealing the deep relationship between heredity and cell functional and structural organization.

James Dewey Watson exhibited an early penchant for birdwatching, which stoked his initial interest in genetics. By the age of 15, he joined the University of Chicago under an experimental scholarship program, which offered him the milieu to further fuel his passion. Meanwhile, across the ocean, Francis Harry Compton Crick, in Northampton, England. with an innate inquisitiveness for the natural world, he pursued physics at University College, London. World War II disrupted his studies, but it was during this hiatus that Crick became enamoured with the enigmas of biology.

Both Watson and Crick held significant positions that shaped their contributions to science. Watson, after obtaining his Ph.D. from Indiana University, ventured to the University of Cambridge, landing a spot at the revered Cavendish Laboratory. Concurrently, Crick had transitioned from physics to biology, marking the serendipitous confluence of their paths at the same institution.

They established how the sequence of nucleotide bases in DNA encodes the instructions for protein production, molecular machinery, and cell structural components. This discovery was critical in demonstrating how cells grow, develop, and reproduce, as well as offering a chemical explanation for cellular activities and heredity.

FUN TIME

CROSSWORD

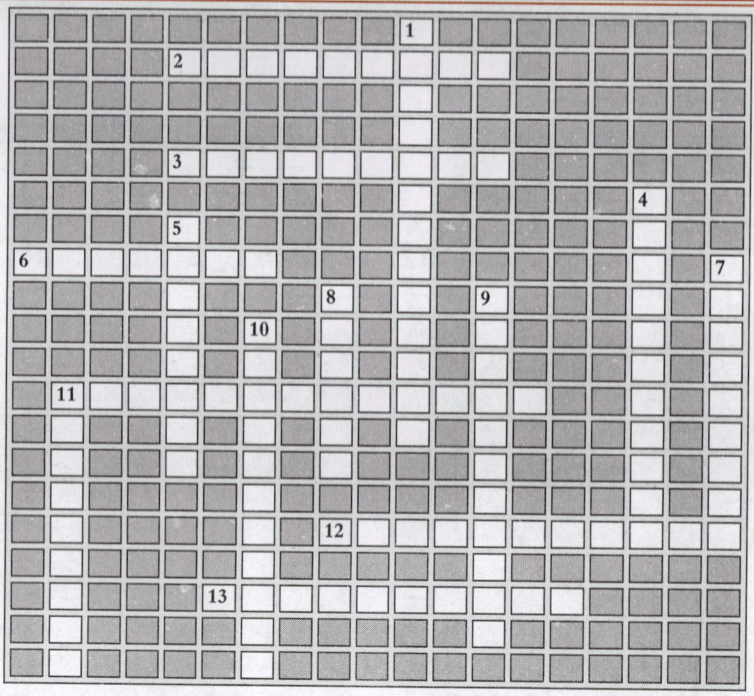

Across

2. Ribosome factory of the cell
3. The other name for sex chromosomes
6. Cytoplasm excluding the cell organelles
11. The process of synthesis of RNA transferred to ribosomes for the synthesis of proteins
12. The maintenance of a stable and constant environment in a living cell
13. Swelling of the cell due to the passage of water molecules from the outside into the cell

Down

1. The structures which connect the cells in plants
4. The biological term which means cell drinking
5. The type of solution in which no osmosis occurs when a living cell is placed in it
7. The membranous sacs which are budded off from the Golgi bodies
8. The number of chromosomes in a set in the cells of an organism
9. The process by which the pathogens make an entry into the cells in that region
10. The basic units of chromatin material
11. The membrane surrounding the vacuole in a cell

INTRODUCTION

The cells are the fundamental building blocks of all living organisms. All activities are carried out by the cells that keep the organisms alive. Cell is defined as the basic structural, functional and hereditary unit of all living organisms. In unicellular organisms, all activities are carried out by a single cell. In multicellular organisms, the life of an organism starts from a single cell called zygote which undergoes repeated cell divisions to form a number of cells. In all higher organisms such as plants and animals, the cells formed in this way organize themselves into groups of similar cells performing specific tasks. In the course of development, these cells become specialized to perform specific functions.

Cell

The process by which a cell becomes specialized in order to perform a specific function in course of time is known as cell differentiation. The groups of cells formed in this way are known as tissues, which can be defined as a group of cells having a common origin and similarity in structure and performing similar functions is known as a tissue. For example, animal tissues such as blood, muscles and bones, and plant tissues such as xylem and phloem. The formation of different types of tissues in plants and animals eventually results in the body organization with various organs and then organ systems performing various activities in a coordinated manner. This is called division of labour.

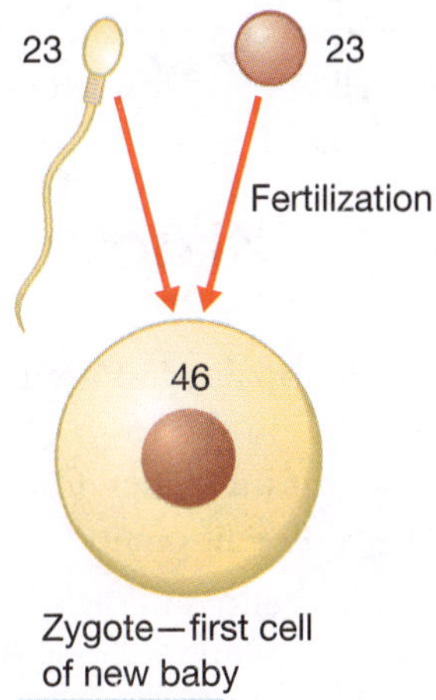

Figure 1.1 Formation of zygote (a single cell) which grows to form a multicellular organism

For example, digestive system, blood vascular system, respiratory system and excretory system perform different vital functions in coordination with each other. Therefore, cell division is the main characteristic phenomenon that takes place in the living cells that are responsible for the growth and development of an individual. Since the cells die and get damaged from time to time, they need to be replaced. Hence, cell division is an ongoing process in all the living organisms. Also, cell division is responsible for the reproduction of organisms and is essential for the continuance of the generations. The formation of zygote followed by subsequent development of zygote into an adult individual that takes place in sexual reproduction to form a zygote again is a continuous and cyclic process, involving cell division followed by subsequent phenomena.

Cell Theory

This theory forms the very foundation of understanding how life is organized and functions at the microscopic level.

Key Points of Cell Theory

- **Life's Building Blocks:** Every living thing, from bacteria to humans, is made up of cells.
- **Function & Structure:** Cells are the functional units of life, with each type serving a unique purpose.
- **Cell Lineage:** Cells come from other cells, creating an unbroken chain of life over billions of years.

Pioneers in the Study of Cells

Some important pioneers of cytology are discussed below:

Robert Hooke (1635–1703)

Hooke's discovery began with the examination of a thin slice of cork under a rudimentary microscope. To his amazement, he observed tiny, box-like structures, which he aptly named "cells" (after the Latin word for "small rooms"). Though he only observed cell walls (as cork cells are dead), his nomenclature stuck.

Anton Von Leeuwenhoek (1632–1723)

Often dubbed the "Father of Microbiology," Leeuwenhoek was not formally educated in science, yet his homemade microscopes were the best of his time. He was the first to observe live cells, like bacteria from his mouth and protists from pond water. His detailed observations of "animalcules" (as he called them) set the stage for the study of living cells.

Robert Brown (1773–1858)

While Hooke and Leeuwenhoek were ahead of their times, it was Brown who introduced the concept of the cell nucleus in plant cells. His observations revealed a distinct central structure, which would later be understood as the control center of the cell.

Matthias Schleiden (1804–1881) and Theodor Schwann (1810–1882)

Often working in tandem, these two scientists laid the cornerstone for the cell theory we know today. Schleiden, a botanist, asserted that all plants are composed of cells. Schwann, a zoologist, extended this observation to animals. Their combined insights formed the first two tenets of cell theory.

Rudolf Virchow (1821–1902)

"Omnis cellula e cellula" - Every cell arises from another cell. With this statement, Virchow revolutionized our understanding of cell propagation, establishing the third tenet of cell theory. This insight laid groundwork for understanding diseases like cancer, where cell division goes away.

Structure of a Cell

As discussed, every multicellular organism begins its life as a single cell. Be it a fish, a mango tree or human beings, all start life in the form of one cell. Since a cell divides and is capable of growing into an organism, it is called building block of life. Therefore, understanding its internal structure will help us to appreciate how different components inside it work together and sustain life.

The cells differ widely in size, shape and function. This depends on the various aspects including the complexity of the body organization in an organism. However, the basic structure of a typical cell is more or less the same for all the organisms. All living cells invariably possess protoplasm which is the living substance, it is enclosed in the membranes. The protoplasm consists of nucleus and cytoplasm. Various structures found floating in the cytoplasm are called cell organelles. Some non-living substances are also found in the cytoplasm. These are called cytoplasmic inclusions.

> **Info Bytes!**
> Researchers have estimated that about 95% of all the cells in human body are bacteria.

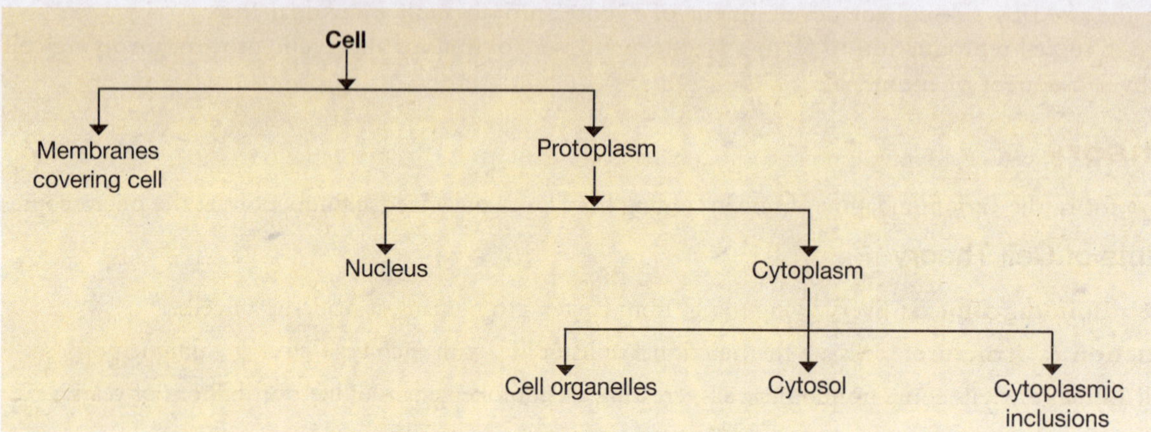

Figure 1.2 Composition of a typical cell

Membranes Covering the Cell

Every cell has an intricate internal composition. It is important for a cell to maintain a balance between its outer and inner environment. In doing so, it allows certain substances to come inside it and does not allow some to do so. This feature of a cell can only be realized if it is surrounded by a membrane that helps in maintaining a balance of its constituents. Two major cell coverings have been discussed as follows:

Plasma Membrane

The plasma membrane of a cell is an arrangement of macromolecules—lipids and proteins that form the boundary between a cell's internal composition and the outside environment. It is also called membrane. It is semi-permeable in nature that means, it allows certain molecules or ions to pass through it and controls the movement of substances that enter and exit the cell. The principal function of the plasma membrane is to protect the cell from its surrounding. The cells of all living organisms have plasma membranes.

Permeability

Plasma membranes are semi-permeable meaning that only certain molecules can pass through them. Molecules such as water, oxygen and carbon dioxide can easily pass through it. Usually, ions and polar molecules cannot pass through the membrane and they require specific channels or pores in the membrane. Hence, the membrane can control the rate at which certain molecules enter or leave the cell.

Cell Wall

The protective semi-transparent membrane surrounding the plasma membrane is known as cell wall. It is present in plant cells, bacteria and fungi. The cell wall is always present associated with the cell membrane. Cell wall is freely permeable and allows substances in the form of solution to enter and leave the cell without hindrance. The composition of cell wall is variable depending on the type of organisms. In most of the plants, cell wall is generally made up of a fibrous polysaccharide (complex carbohydrate) called cellulose. In fungi, it is generally made up of chitin.

The cell wall is multilayered with usually three layers. The three layers are middle lamella, primary cell wall and secondary cell wall. All plant cells invariably possess middle lamella and primary cell wall. Secondary cell wall may or may not be present.

Middle Lamella

- Outermost layer of cell wall.
- Composed of a polysaccharide, pectin which contains calcium and magnesium.
- Pectin helps in cell adhesion (binding) and hence this layer acts as a cementing layer which binds the cell walls of the adjacent cells.
- Cytoplasmic strands arise from the middle lamella and form interconnections between the cells. These strands are called plasmodesmata.
- The plasmodesmata facilitate the transport of proteins and other materials between the cells.

Primary Cell Wall

- It is the Layer inner to the middle lamella.
- It is mainly formed in the growing plant cells between middle lamella and plasma membrane.
- Thin, elastic and extensible layer of growing cells containing large proportion of water.
- It is composed of cellulose fibres within a gel-like matrix made of cellulose and pectin.
- It provides strength and flexibility, required to allow the growth of cells.

Secondary Cell Wall

- It is a tough and rigid layer formed after the cell reaches maturity.
- It is formed inside the primary cell wall by the deposition of materials over the existing surface.
- The composition of secondary cell walls is variable.
- In some cases, a substance called lignin may be deposited on the secondary walls of some cells. This process is known as lignification.
- In some regions, the deposition of a substance called suberin on the walls makes the walls impermeable to water.

Konnect

All living cells have cell membrane, cytoplasm and some genetic material (DNA/RNA)

Functions of a Cell Wall

Following are the primary functions of cell wall:

- It provides a framework to the cell.
- It provides definite shape to the cells.

- It gives rigidity and support to the tissues in plants.
- Cell wall gives mechanical strength to the cell to facilitate the plant to support its long and tall body.
- It helps in balancing and maintaining osmotic pressure, and prevents bursting of cells.
- It protects protoplasm against infections.
- It helps in the transport of water and minerals over long distances.

Table 1.1 Characteristic features and functions of membranes covering the cell

Membrane Covering the Cell	Characteristic Features
Plasma Membrane Structure 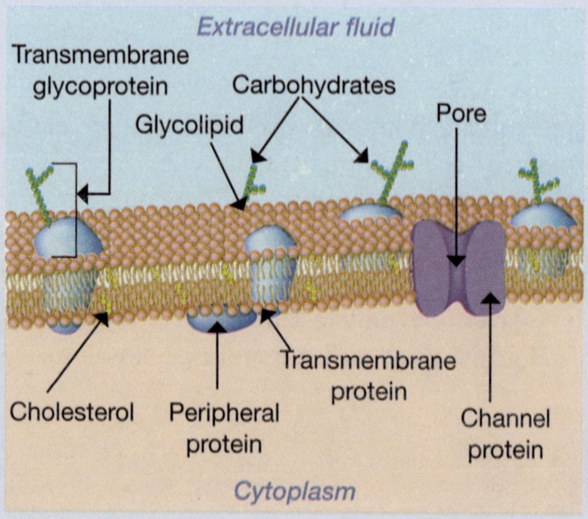	• Present in both plant and animal cells • Outermost covering of an animal cell • Semi-permeable membrane • Elastic, delicate and flexible • Made of lipids and proteins **Functions:** • Cell membrane gives shape to the cell • Serves as a mechanical barrier and protects the cell from injury • Regulates the movement of various materials into the cell and out of the cell • Maintains a stable and constant environment inside the cell. This is called homeostasis.
Cell Wall Structure 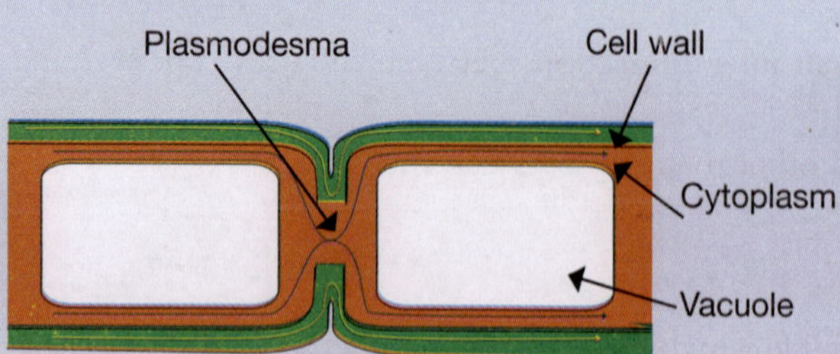	• Semi-transparent membrane surrounding the plasma membrane • It is multicellular usually having three layers 1. Primary cell wall 2. Middle lamella 3. Secondary cell wall • From the middle lamella, plasmodesmata arise which connect one cell to another **Functions:** • Provides a framework to the cell • Provides definite shape to the cells • Gives rigidity and support to the tissues in plants • Gives mechanical strength to the cell • Helps in balancing and maintaining osmotic pressure • Prevents bursting of cells • Protects protoplasm against infections • Helps in the transport of water and minerals over long distances

Transport of Substances through the Plasma Membrane

The passage of substances across the cell membrane takes place by three ways, which are listed as follows.

1. Passive transport
2. Active transport
3. Bulk transport

Passive Transport

Passive transport is a mode of transport that takes place without the expenditure of energy. It takes place by either diffusion or osmosis.

Diffusion

Diffusion is the process in which movement of molecules takes place from higher to lower concentrations until the concentrations become equal. It is generally applicable to the movement of gaseous substances. With diffusion, the plants take in carbon dioxide from the air and release oxygen during the process of photosynthesis. The taking in of oxygen into the blood from lungs and the release of carbon dioxide from the lungs into the blood also take place by diffusion.

Konnect

Osmosis is vital to many body processes, including the functioning of the kidney and the nerves.

Osmosis

The movement of solvent (water) molecules from a solution of higher water concentration to a solution of lower water concentration through a semipermeable membrane is called osmosis. In living systems, the process of osmosis is affected by the external environment. If a cell is in an environment of a hypertonic solution (solution of lower water concentration), the movement of water molecules takes place from the cell into the outside solution. This process is called exosmosis or plasmolysis. This leads to shrinkage of the cell. If a cell is placed in a hypotonic solution (solution of higher water concentration), the movement of water molecules takes place from the outside solution into the cell. This process is called endosmosis or imbibition. This results in swelling of the cell. If the cell is placed in an isotonic solution (same concentration), no osmosis takes place in either direction.

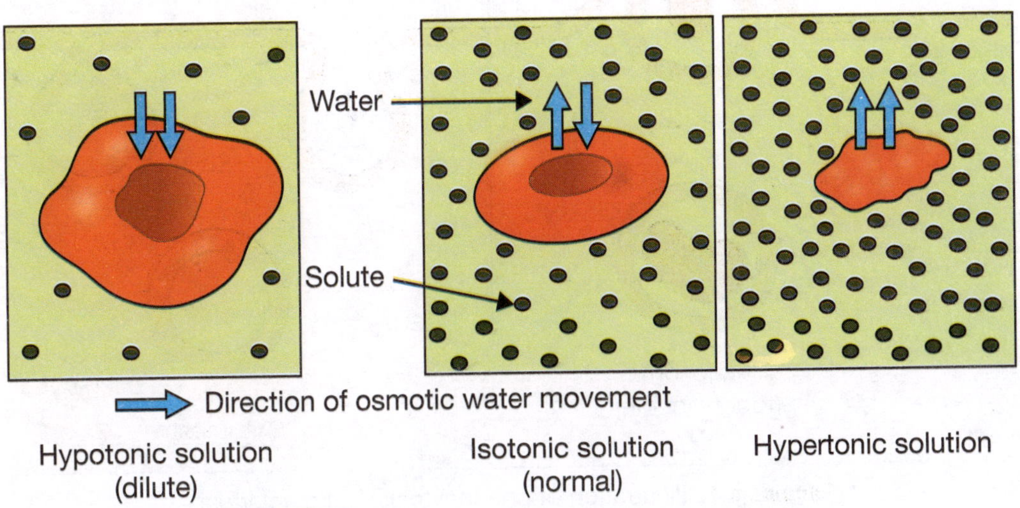

Figure 1.3 Direction of osmotic water movement

Active Transport

Active transport is the movement of ions and electrolytes that takes place across the membrane by utilizing energy produced by the cell. For example, movement of ions into the cell or out of the cell.

In general, molecules move from an area of their higher concentration to an area of their lower concentration without the expense of energy by diffusion or osmosis. Active transport occurs when molecules move across a cell membrane from a region of their lower concentration to a region of their higher concentration. In order to get molecules move against the concentration gradient, work must be done, hence energy is required.

Bulk Transport

Bulk transport involves the movement of macronutrients such as proteins and polysaccharides that can pass through only ruptured plasma membrane. This takes place by utilizing the energy produced by the cell. There are two processes that involve bulk transport and those are exocytosis and endocytosis.

Exocytosis

The process through which materials move from inside to outside the cell is known as exocytosis. This is useful in release of the secretory and excretory materials from the cell. For example, release of the proteins and other materials formed in the cell to outside the cell.

> **Info Bytes!**
>
> Pinosome and phagosome collectively known as endosomes.

Endocytosis

The process through which materials move into the cell by engulfing food and other substances from the external environment is known as endocytosis. For example, engulfing of foreign substances, dead cells, pathogens, etc. Endocytosis is an umbrella term that describes two processes: phagocytosis and pinocytosis.

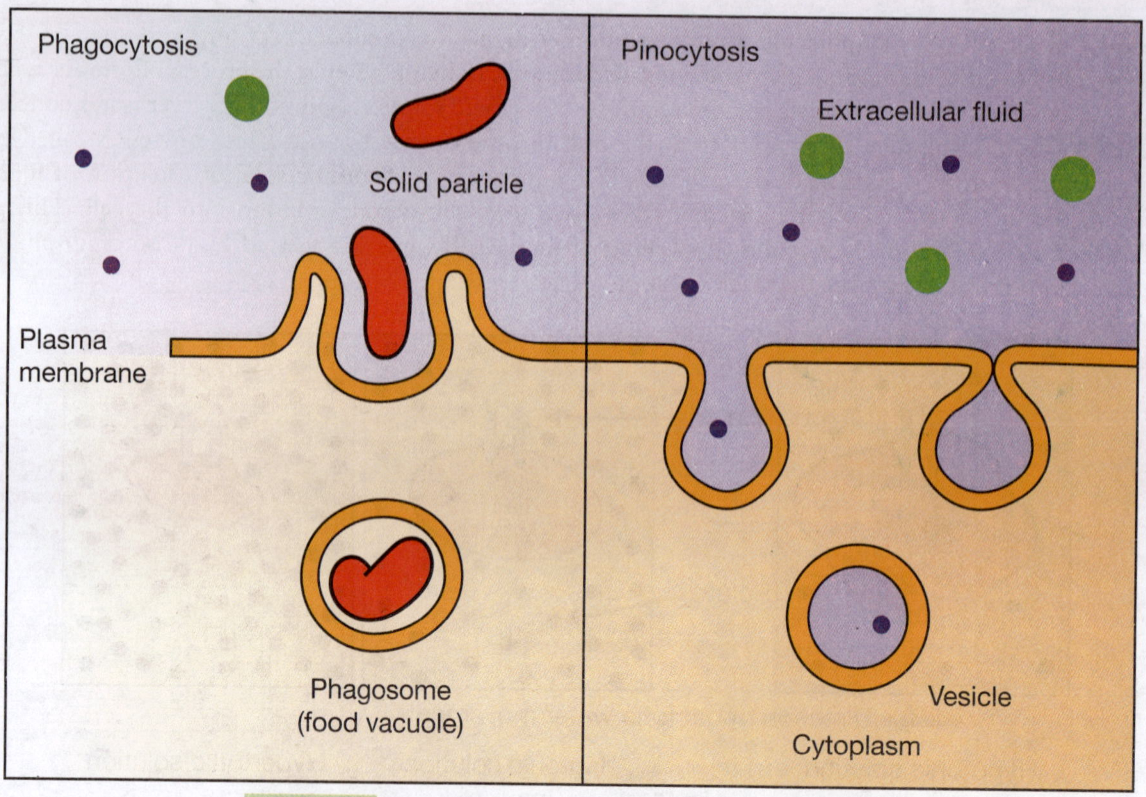

Figure 1.4 Illustration of phagocytosis and pinocytosis

1. **Phagocytosis:** It means 'cell eating'. In this process, large particles, such as cells or macromolecules, are taken in by a cell. For example, when microorganisms invade the human body, neutrophils (type of WBCs) will engulf and eventually destroy them.
2. **Pinocytosis:** It means 'cell drinking'. In this process, bulk transport of fluid matter takes place across the cell membranes by forming small vesicles.

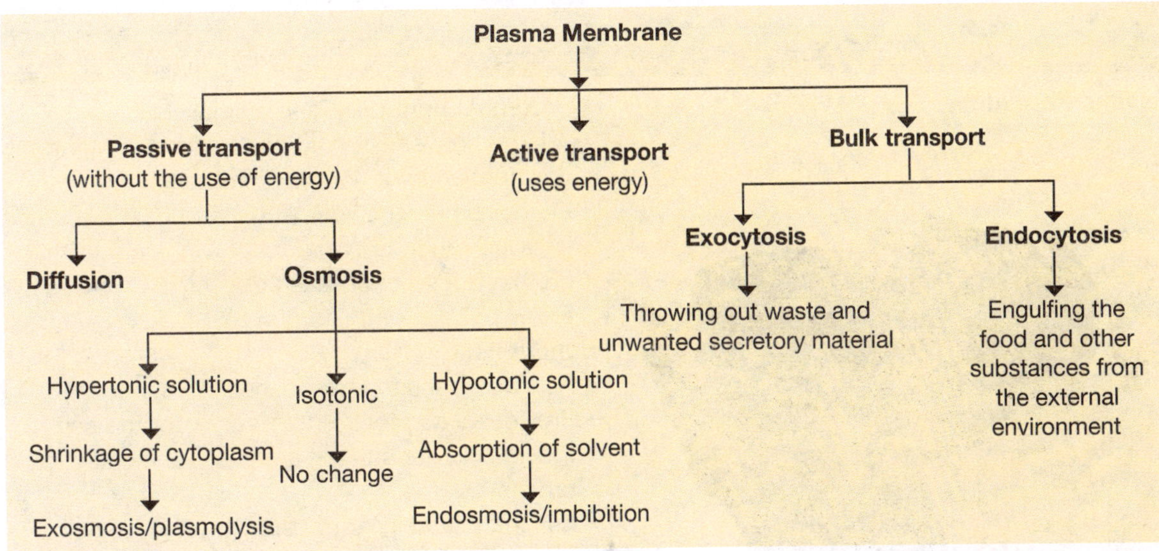

Figure 1.5 Transport function of plasma membrane

Cytoplasm

Cytoplasm is a living, colourless semi-liquid, homogeneous substance. It occupies a major part of the cell and is constantly moving. It is limited on the outside by the cell membrane. The cytoplasm is made up of 90% water and the remaining are amino acids, vitamins, enzymes, fats and carbohydrates. Many specialized, living cell organelles are found floating in the cytoplasm. Each cell organelle performs a specific function. The plant and animal cells differ with respect to the presence or absence of some of the cell organelles.

Info Bytes!

The cytoplasm which is present immediately next to the cell membrane is called ectoplasm or plasmogel or cell cortex and the cytoplasm which is close to the nucleus is known as the endoplasm or plasmosol.
The cytoplasm in the animals cells is more than that in the plant cells.

Cell Organelles

Some organelles are common to both plant and animal cells. These are explained in a table given below:

Table 1.2 Structure and function of cell organelles found in both plant and animal cells

Cell Organelle	Structure and Functions
Mitochondria 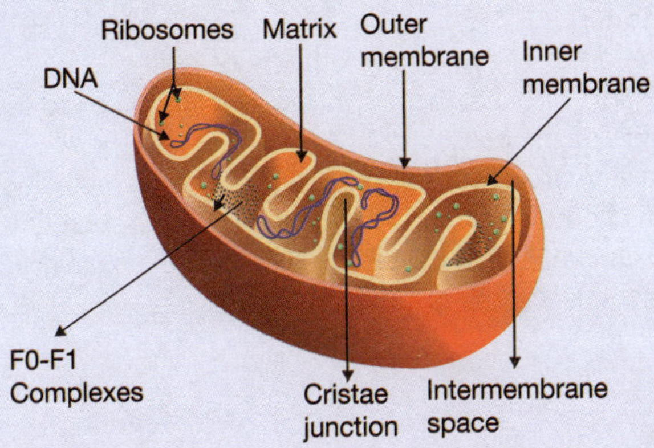	• Known as Powerhouse of Cell. • Present in both plant and animal cells. • Continuous with the plasma membrane on the outside and the nuclear membrane on the inside. • Rod-shaped structures surrounded by a double membrane • Outer membrane is smooth and porous. • Inner membrane is thrown into finger-like projections known as cristae. • The mitochondria contain their own DNA, known as mitochondrial DNA. **Functions:** • Site for cellular respiration thereby releasing energy in the process energy is stored as adenosine triphosphate (ATP) molecules. • Synthesis of respiratory enzymes. • Regulation of calcium ion concentration in the cells.

Cell Organelle	Structure and Functions
Endoplasmic Reticulum 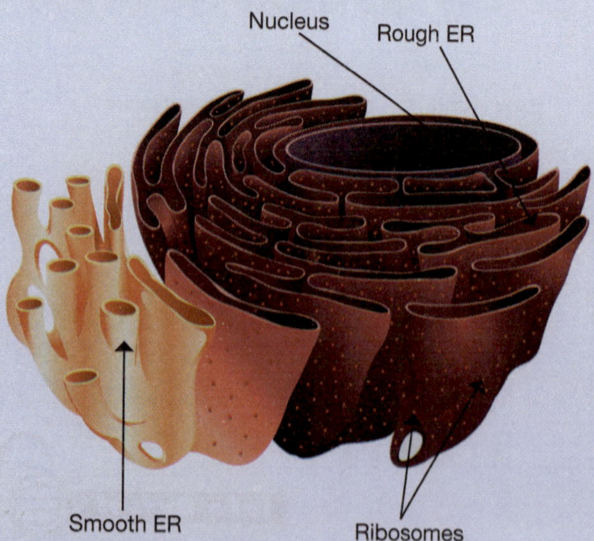 	• Present in both plant and animal cells. • A large network of fluid-filled interconnecting tubules. • Surrounded by a double membrane. • Endoplasmic reticulum (ER) that possesses ribosomes is called rough ER. • ER that does not possess ribosomes is called smooth ER. **Functions:** • Acts as "Transporting Channels" of the cell. • Provides a supportive framework for the cell. • Provides larger surface area for the metabolic processes. • It is the intercellular transport system of cell Rough ER: synthesis and transport of proteins. Smooth endoplasmic reticulum: synthesis of lipids. • Detoxification of drugs and unwanted substances in liver cells.
Ribosomes 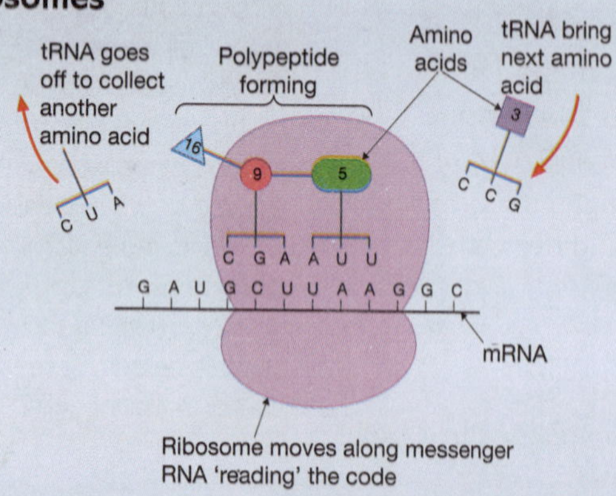 	• Present in both plant and animal cells. • Attached to the rough ER and also found in free form in the cytoplasm of the cell. • Dense, spherical bodies as small granules. • Composed of a smaller subunit and a larger subunit. • Each subunit is made up of ribonucleic acid (RNA) and proteins called ribonucleoproteins. **Functions:** • Site for protein synthesis of enzymes.
Golgi Complex 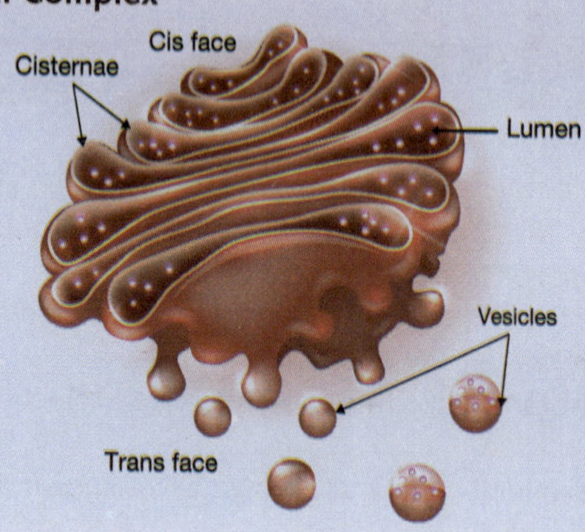 	• Commonly called "Packaging and dispatching unit" of the cell. • Stacks of flattened double-walled membrane sacs. • Fluid is present between both the membranes known as dictyosomes in a plant cell. **Functions:** • Secretion of enzymes and other substances. • Transport of substances synthesized in the cell to the outside of the cell. • Formation of lysosomes, cell wall and plasma membrane. • Production of vacuoles that contain cellular secretions, for example, enzymes, proteins, cellulose, melanin pigment, lactoprotein (milk protein), etc.

Cell Organelles Present Only in Plant Cells

There are some organelles which are found only in plant cells. They are explained below in Table 1.3.

> **Info Bytes!**
>
> Vacuoles also help with destroying and recycling broken proteins that build up in cells.

Table 1.3 Structure and function of cell organelles found only in plant cells

Cell Organelle	Structure
Plastids (i) Chloroplasts 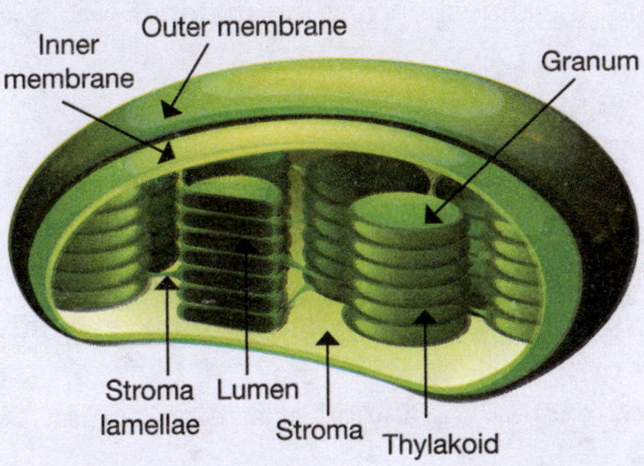 	• Present in green parts of the plants • Double-membraned structure • The inner membrane possesses more proteins • The outer membrane maybe attached to ER • Contains a green pigment known as chlorophyll • The matrix or stroma is a semifluid, colourless and colloidal complex • The matrix contains DNA and RNA • Membrane-bound, flat sac-like structures known as thylakoids run through the stroma • The green pigment chlorophyll is located within the thylakoid membrane • Thylakoids arranged one over the other forming a stalk, known as 'grana' (singular: granum) **Function:** • Trapping of solar energy during photosynthesis
(ii) Chromoplasts	• Contain fat-soluble red, orange and yellow pigments such as carotenoids • Present in flowers and fruits **Function:** • Impart colours to fruits and flowers
(iii) Leucoplasts	• Colourless plastids • Do not possess pigments • Present in parts not exposed to sunlight **Function:** • Storage of food
Vacuoles 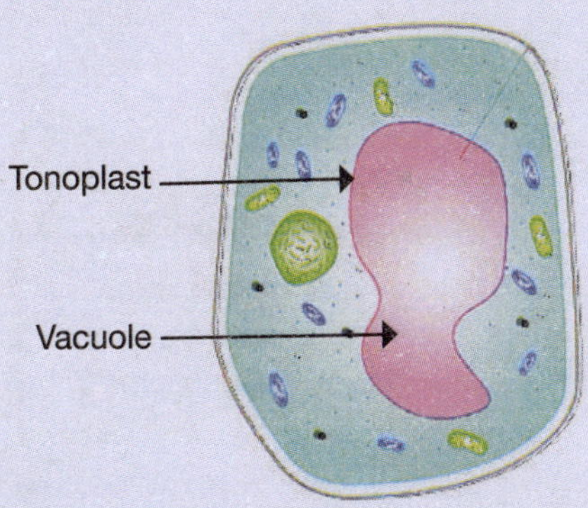 	• Large sac-like structure • Bound by a single membrane known as tonoplast • Sometimes present in animal cells also, but they are small and insignificant **Functions:** • Storage of dissolved materials such as amino acids, sugars, various organic acids and some proteins • Provide turgidity and rigidity to the cell • Help to maintain the osmotic pressure of the cell

Cell Organelles Present only in Animal Cells

There are some organelles which are exclusive to animal cells. They are explained Table 1.4.

Table 1.4 Structure and function of cell organelles found only in animal cells

Cell Organelle	Structure
Lysosomes 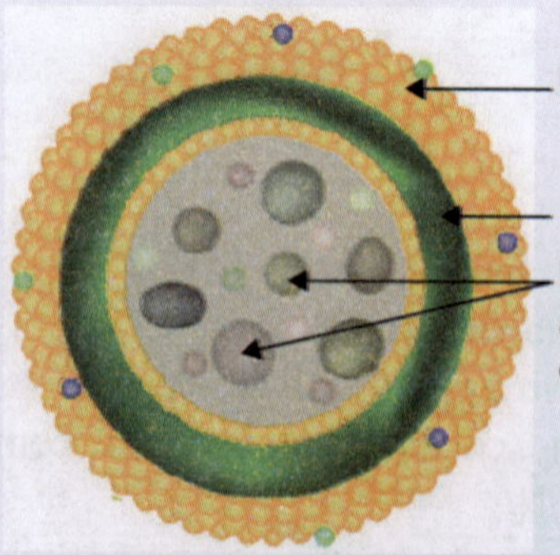 	• Membranous sacs budded off from the Golgi body • Surrounded by a single membrane • Contain powerful digestive enzymes **Functions:** • Serve as the intercellular digestive system (digestive bags of the cell) • Participate in the digestion of food material • Lysosomes burst under the diseased condition or when the cells get old or damaged and the enzymes digest their own cells • They destroy bacteria or any other foreign bodies entering the cell
Centrosome and Centrioles 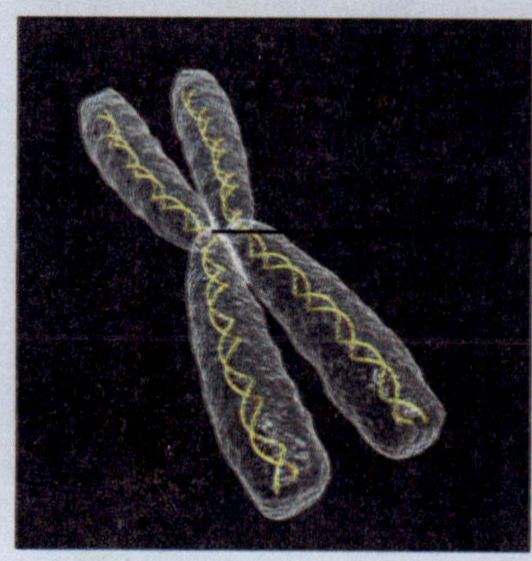 	• Centrosome is a small structure comprising granule-like structures known as centrioles • Centrioles are hollow, cylindrical structures made up of microtubules **Functions:** • Initiate and regulate cell division • During cell division, the centrioles move to the poles of the cell • They develop many spindle fibres with the help of the asters (An aster is a cellular structure shaped like a star, formed around each centrosome during cell division)

Various cell organelles perform various functions that make up the entire metabolic activity of the cell. Thus, division of labour is seen within the cell. All functions of the various cell organelles are controlled by the nucleus.

> **Info Bytes!**
> In case of frog ovum, there are hundreds of millions of ribosomes.

Nucleus

Nucleus is a large spherical body. It is generally located in the centre of the cell. Most of the cells contain a single nucleus. Such condition is called uninucleate condition. In multinucleate condition, the cell contains more than one nucleus. For example, muscle cells and cells in fungi. Multinucleate cells are produced under special cases in which nuclear division occurs without cytokinesis.

Structure

Nucleus is a large spherical body. It is generally located in the centre of the cell. Nucleus is absent in some cells, such as red blood cells in humans and sieve cells in plants. The nucleus is made up of the following components:

- Nuclear membrane
- Nuclear sap or nucleoplasm
- Nucleolus
- Chromatin material

> **Konnect**
> It takes somewhere between 4 and 8 cisternae together to form a stack. There are between 40 and 100 such stacks that make up the Golgi Body found in mammalian cells.

Components of Nucleus

Nuclear Membrane

- The nuclear membrane is a double membrane with space between the outer and inner membranes.
- It separates the nucleus from the cytoplasm.
- It is made up of lipids and proteins.
- It has minute nuclear pores that allow exchange of material between the cytoplasm and the nucleus.

Nucleoplasm

- The nucleoplasm is dense.
- Two nuclear structures known as chromatin fibres and nucleoli are suspended in it.
- It is surrounded by the nuclear membrane.

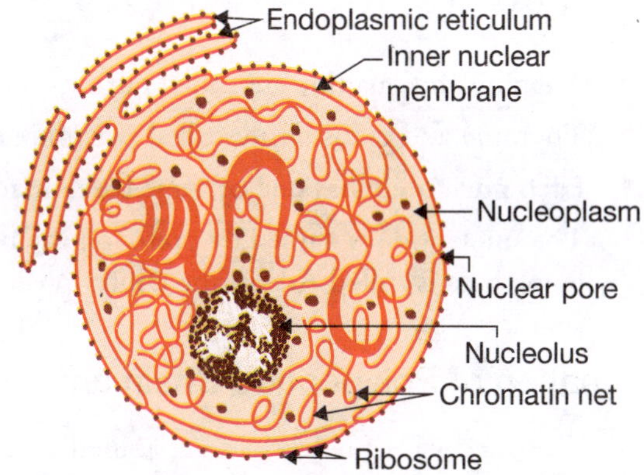

Figure 1.6 Illustration of nucleus

Nucleolus

- It is a spherical body found inside the nucleoplasm.
- It may be one or more in number.
- It is not surrounded by a membrane.
- It is rich in proteins and ribonucleic acid (RNA) molecules.
- It is a site for the formation of ribosomes. Hence, they are known as the **ribosome factory**.
- Ribosomes help in protein synthesis.

> **Info Bytes!**
> Nucleus is the largest cell organelle and holds up to 2 metres of DNA.

Chromatin Material

- The nucleus contains fine thread-like structures known as chromatin fibres.
- Chromatin fibre is composed of biomolecules known as nucleic acids and a group of proteins known as histones.
- Basically, there are two types of nucleic acids, which are:
  - Deoxyribonucleic acid known as DNA
  - Ribonucleic acid known as RNA

> **Info Bytes!**
> Mitochondria have their own DNA, which is evidence that they were once free-living bacteria that were engulfed by an ancestral eukaryotic cell.

Functions

- The nucleus is the main controlling centre of the cell.
- It plays a major role in cell division.
- As a matter of fact, the nucleus acts as a brain of the cell. The entire significance of the nucleus is in controlling the metabolic activities of the cell.

Structure of DNA

The detailed structure of DNA was provided by Watson and Crick. Hence, the structure of DNA provided by them is known as 'Watson and Crick model'.

Basic Units of DNA

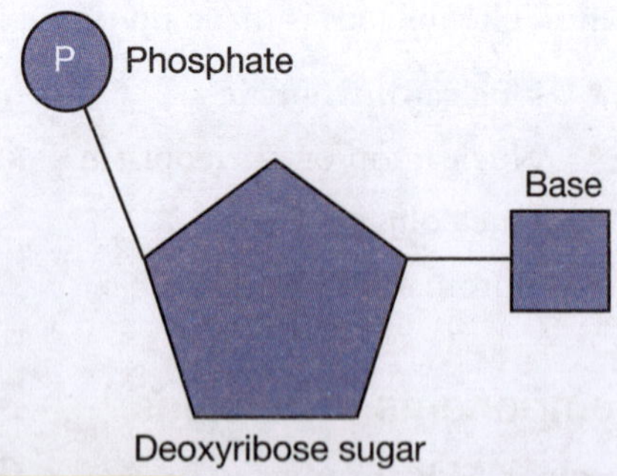

Figure 1.7 Illustration of a nucleotide

- DNA is composed of basic units called nucleotides.
- Each nucleotide contains three subunits:
  1. A molecule of pentose sugar (5-carbon sugar) known as deoxyribose sugar
  2. A phosphate group
  3. A nitrogen base
- There are four different nitrogen bases associated with the nucleotides. The four bases are:
  1. Adenine
  2. Guanine
  3. Thymine
  4. Cytosine
- Adenine and guanine are called purine bases.
- Thymine and cytosine are called pyrimidine bases.
- Each nucleotide has one of these bases attached to the pentose sugar molecule.
- The nucleotide is named by prefixing the name of the nitrogen base with it. For example, the nucleotide with Adenine base is called Adenosine triphosphate. Same is the case with the other nucleotides.

Formation of Polypeptide Chain and Complementary Base Pairing

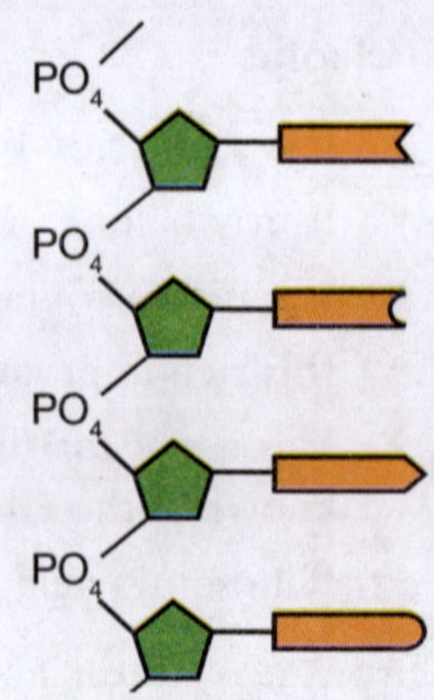

Figure 1.8 Illustration of a polynucleotide chain

- The successive nucleotides are joined to each other by a covalent bond that links the sugar molecule of one nucleotide with the phosphate group of adjacent nucleotide.
- A number of nucleotides are linked to each other in the above manner to form a long chain or strand known as polynucleotide chain or strand.
- Two such polynucleotide strands run anti-parallel to each other.
- The two strands are oriented in such a way that the nitrogen bases are towards the inside and the phosphate group and sugar molecule are towards the outside.
- This means that the nitrogen bases of the nucleotides of the two strands face each other. The purine base of one strand lies opposite to the pyrimidine base of the other strand.
- The purine base of one strand is linked to the pyrimidine base of the opposite strand by means of hydrogen bonds and vice versa.
- The adenine base is always linked to thymine base by two hydrogen bonds. The guanine base is always linked to cytosine base by three hydrogen bonds.
- This specific linkage between the respective bases is due to the structural compatibility between the particular purine and pyrimidine. For example, thymine exactly fits into adenine. Similarly, cytosine fits exactly into guanine.
- This kind of pairing of purines and pyrimidines of opposite polynucleotide strands is known as **complementary base pairing**.
- The sequence of the base pairs on the strand varies from one individual to the other. This specific sequence of base pairs makes the DNA of an individual a unique characteristic.

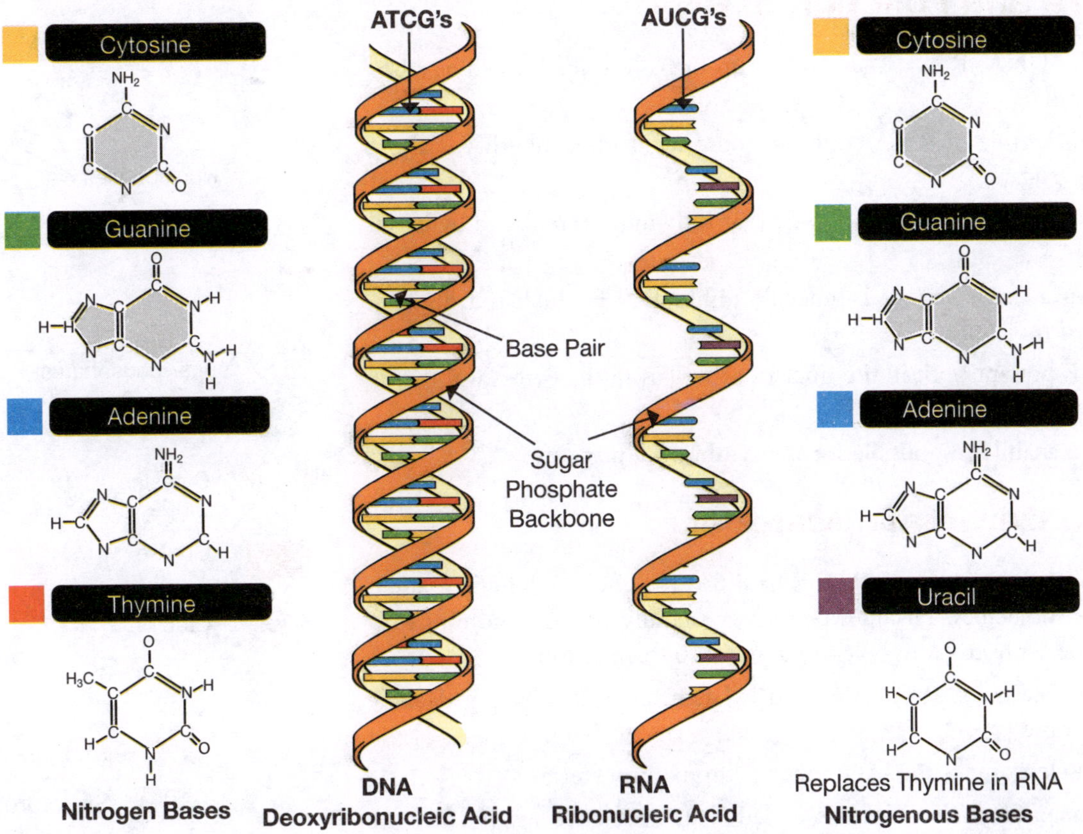

Figure 1.9 Structures of DNA, RNA and nitrogenous bases

- The fragment or region of DNA that is made up of specific sequence of nucleotides is called gene.
- Genes are the molecular units of heredity.
- These two strands are helically coiled to give rise to a structure. This structure resembles a spiral staircase or a ladder. This kind of structure is called double helix.
- Therefore, DNA is a long, double helical structure.

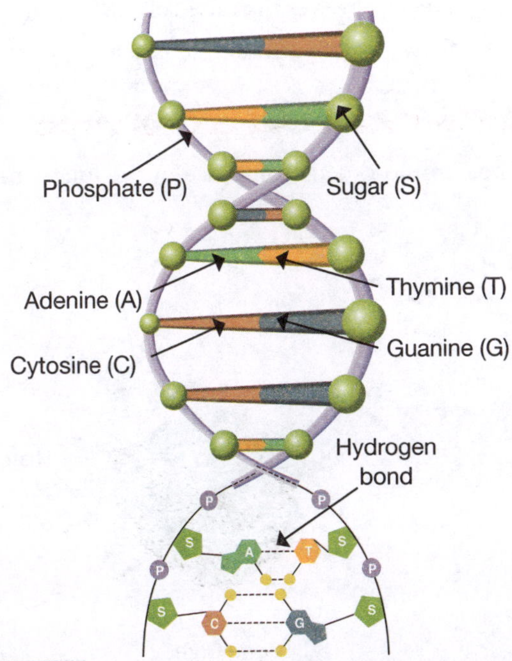

Figure 1.10 Diagram of a helical structure of DNA

Functions of DNA

The DNA performs the following functions:

- Transmission of hereditary characters from one generation to the next.
- Responsible for evolution by bringing about variations during cell division.
- Overall control of cellular metabolism. The control over cellular metabolism of DNA is attributed to the ability of DNA to provide information required for the synthesis of specific proteins. This is done by the process of transcription. Transcription is the synthesis of RNA that is transferred to the ribosomes for the synthesis of proteins.

Structure and Function of RNA

- Just like DNA, RNA is also made up of basic units known as ribonucleotides.
- The nucleotide of RNA contains ribose sugar molecule that is also a pentose sugar.
- One of the purine bases in DNA, that is thymine is replaced by uracil in RNA.
- RNA is a single-stranded molecule unlike DNA which is a double-stranded molecule.
- RNA is present both in the nucleus as well as in the cytoplasm that is located in the ribosomes.
- RNA is mainly responsible for the synthesis of proteins.

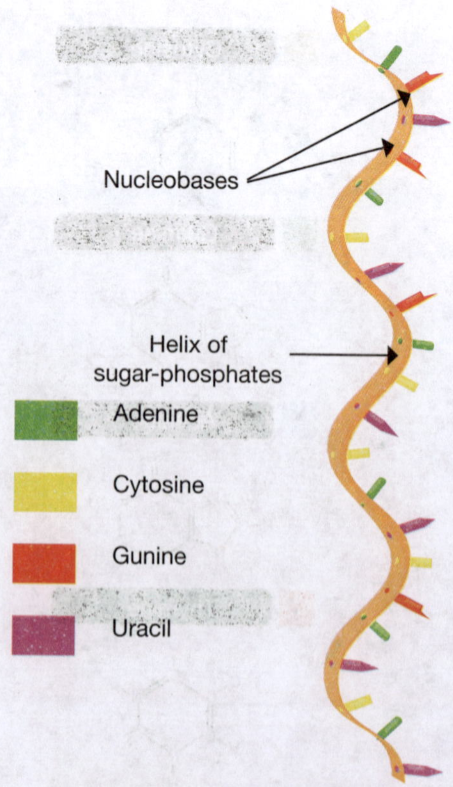

Figure 1.11 Structure of RNA

DNA and Chromatin Material

- The coiled structure of DNA is held together by a polymer of eight histone molecules. Histones belong to a family of basic proteins that combine with DNA to help condense it to form chromatin.
- The double helix of DNA bound by such histone polymer is called nucleosome.
- This nucleosome is the basic unit of chromatin material.
- A number of nucleosomes as coiled structures once again coil and forms a supercoil. The entire structure on the whole resemble a telephone wire with coils and supercoils.
- Such nucleosomes condensed together with RNA are called chromatin material.
- This chromatin material is present in the form of network of fibres floating in the nucleoplasm present in the nucleus of every mature cell.
- These chromatin fibres condense to form short, thick chromosomes during cell division.

Structure of Chromosome

The chromosome is composed of the following structures:

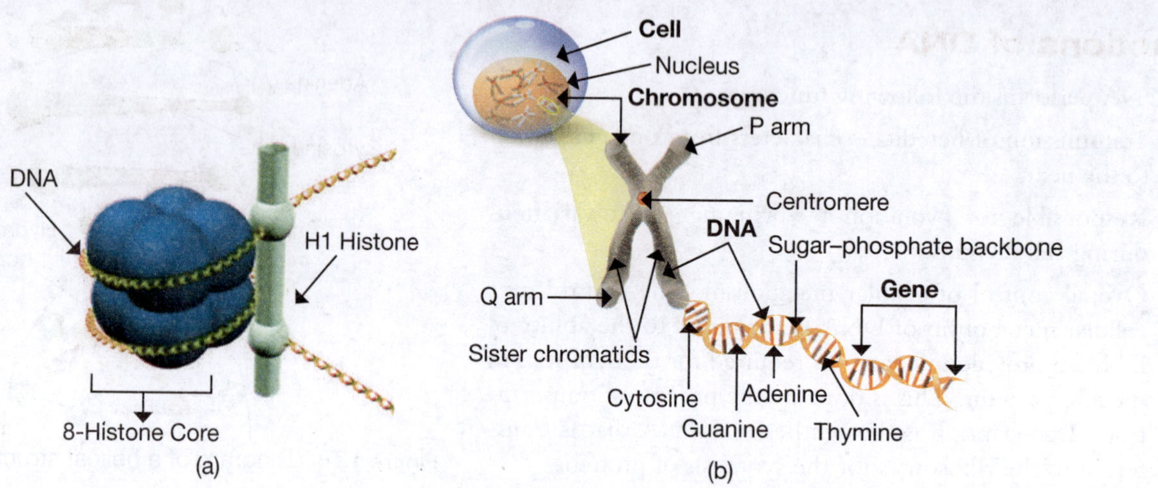

Figure 1.12 (a) Structure of Nucleosome (b) Diagrammatic representation of the structure of a chromosome, chromatin fibre and DNA

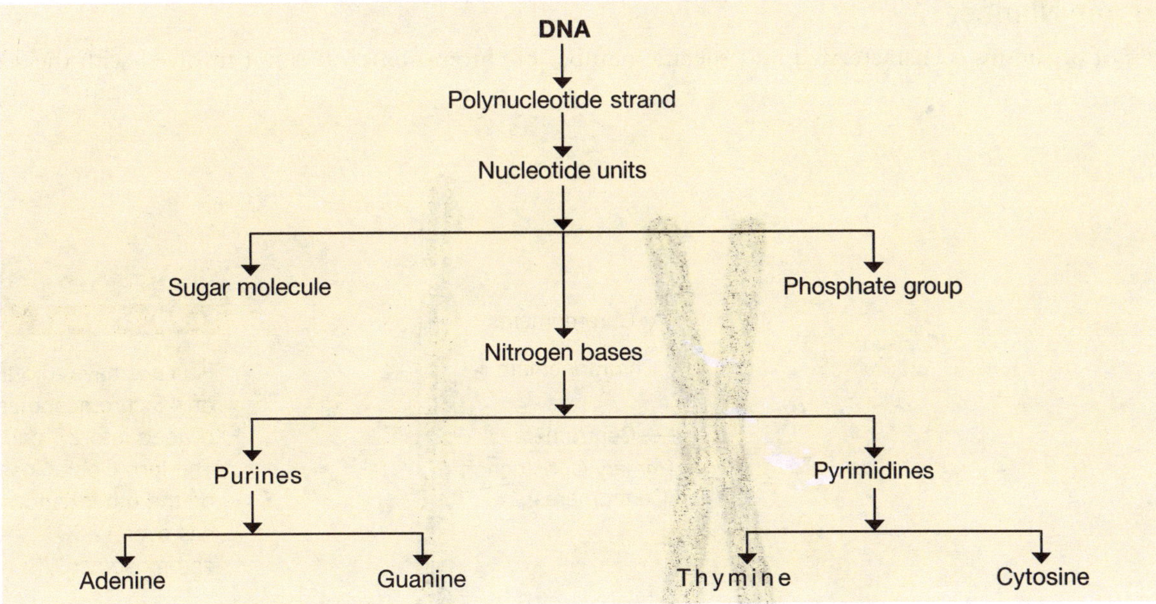

Figure 1.13 Structure of DNA—schematic representation

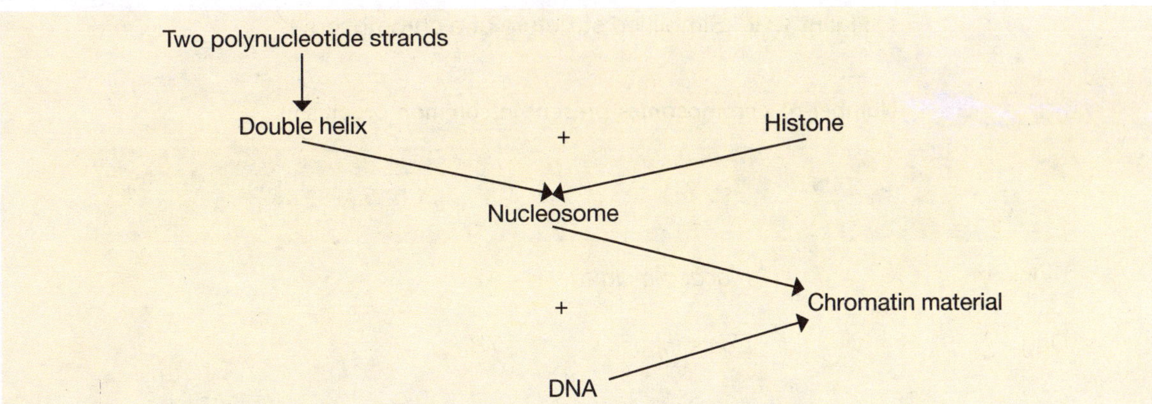

Figure 1.14 Composition of chromatin—schematic representation

Chromonema (Singular)

When chromatin fibre is in the early stage of condensation, the chromatid is called chromonema. These chromonemata are the coiled portions of the chromatin fibre. These are the gene-bearing portions of the chromatin fibre.

> **Info Bytes!**
> Organisms such as wasps, bees and ants do not have sex chromosomes.

Chromomeres

The small bead-shaped structures that appear on the chromosome are known as chromomeres. These coiled chromatins are linearly arranged along the chromosome.

Centromere and Kinetochore

Centromere is the region or point on a chromosome known as the primary constriction to which the spindle gets attached during cell division. The kinetochore is a specialized disc-like structure on the centromere to which the microtubular spindle fibres get attached during cell division.

Chromosome Number

Each species of organisms is characterized by a specific number of chromosomes. It is not involved with the size of the organism.

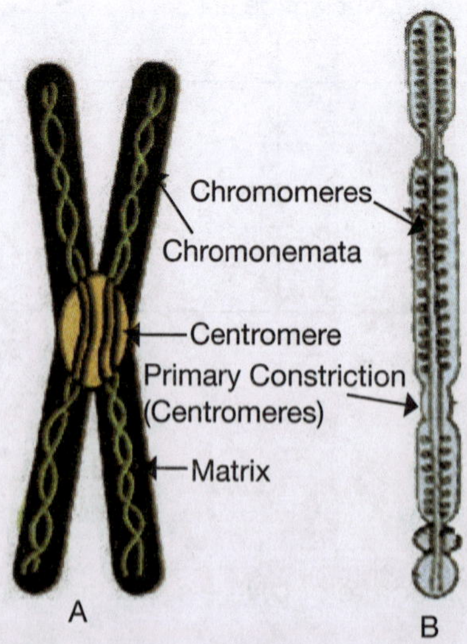

Figure 1.15 Simplified structure of a chromosome

> **Info Bytes!**
> Humans have a total of 46 chromosomes, divided into 23 pairs. The fern Ophioglossum, on the other hand, has over 1200 chromosomes.

Table 1.5 Number of chromosomes present in common organisms

Common Names of Organisms	Scientific Names	Number of Chromosomes (Diploid)
Monkey	*Macaca mulatta*	42
Dog	*Canis lupus*	78
Cat	*Felis domesticus*	38
Mouse	*Mus musculus*	40
Potato	*Solanum tuberosum*	48
Corn	*Zea mays*	20

The chromosomes can exist as sets in a cell. The number of sets of chromosomes in a cell is known as ploidy. If each cell in an organism contains two sets of chromosomes, it is considered as a diploid cell and is denoted by $2n$. If each cell in an organism contains one set of chromosomes, it is considered as a haploid cell and is denoted by n. In a diploid cell, the chromosomes occur in pairs in each cell. The two chromosomes of the pair are similar in structure (gene position) and are derived one from each parent. Such pairs of chromosomes are known as 'homologous chromosomes'. One set of homologous chromosomes is contributed from male parent (father) and one set is contributed by female parent (mother). Each homologous chromosome contains some genes and the genes represent certain characters. The two chromosomes in a homologous pair possess genes representing the same character such as height, colour of flower, etc. A cell comprises two kinds of chromosomes—autosomes and allosomes (sex chromosomes).

> **Info Bytes!**
> Y chromosomes are about one-third the size of X chromosomes.

For Example: Human cell comprises 46 chromosomes in the form of 23 pairs of homologous chromosomes. Out of these 23 pairs, 22 pairs are same in males and females. These are called autosomes. The 23rd pair of chromosomes is different in males and females. This pair is called allosomes or sex chromosomes (XY in males and XX in females). A total of 23 sets of paternal chromosomes and 23 sets of maternal chromosomes are present in each cell in human body.

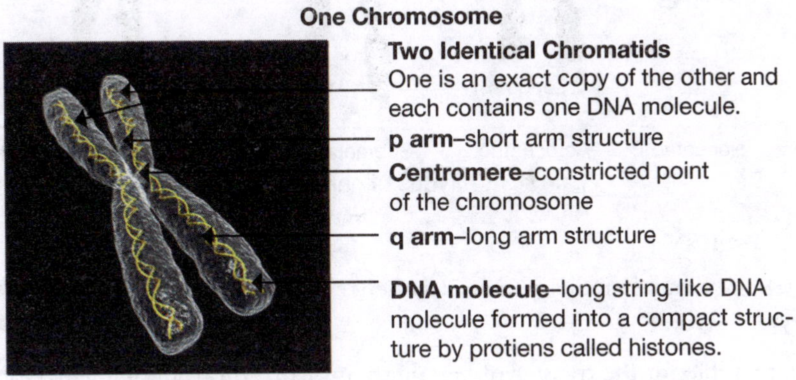

Figure 1.16 Detailed structure of one chromosome

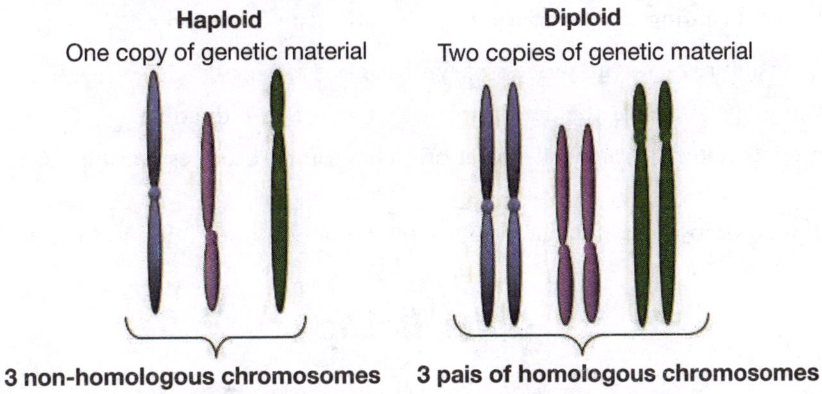

Figure 1.17 Haploid and Diploid Chromosomes

Each chromosome bears two fibres known as chromatids. The chromatids of the same chromosome are called sister chromatids. The chromatids of different chromosomes in the homologous pair are called non-sister chromatids. The region that joins the two sister chromatids is known as centromere or primary constriction. Chromosomes can be classified based on the position of centromere.

> **Konnect**
>
> Telomeres are areas of DNA located at the ends of chromosomes. They are protective caps that stabilize DNA during cell replication.

Types of Chromosomes

Following are the four types of chromosomes, based on the position of the centromere:

1. **Telocentric chromosomes:** Rod-like and have a centromere situated on the proximal end.
2. **Acrocentric chromosomes:** Rod-like and have a small, or even imperceptible arm. Centromere is situated at one end, slightly lower than the normal position.
3. **Submetacentric chromosomes:** Chromosomes having unequal arms are thus L-shaped or T-shaped. Centromere is almost in the middle position.
4. **Metacentric chromosomes:** Have equal or almost equal arms and thus are V-shaped.

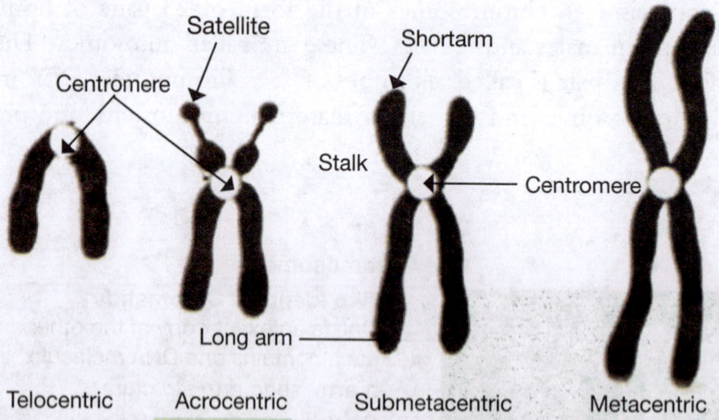

Figure 1.18 Types of chromosomes

Significance of Chromosomes

Chromosomes are the carriers of our hereditary material, hence they are indispensable for life. Following are some primary functions that they perform:

- Chromosomes are responsible for the transfer of hereditary information from one generation to the other. So, they form a link between generations.
- They are responsible for bringing about variations in the organisms of the same species.
- Chromosomes control and regulate the process of synthesis of proteins.
- Sex chromosomes are responsible for the determination of sex of an individual.
- Chromosomes can contribute to biological evolution. They can also be responsible for some genetic disorders in the organisms.
- All these functions of chromosomes are related to the phenomenon of cell division which is the basis of life.

Quick Recap

✔ **Mitochondria are known as the cell's powerhouse. Explain the significance of its double-membrane structure in terms of function.**

Mitochondria have a unique double-membrane structure with an outer and inner membrane. This distinction is critical to its operation. The outer membrane allows ions and molecules to pass through, while the inner membrane is selectively permeable and contains the electron transport chain and ATP synthase, both of which are required for oxidative phosphorylation. The intermembranous space, which exists between the two membranes, is critical for the proton gradient required for ATP synthesis. The inner membrane folds to form structures known as cristae, which increase the surface area available for oxidative phosphorylation.

✔ **The Golgi apparatus and the ER are both important in protein modification and transport. Compare and contrast their roles in protein maturation and subsequent cellular release.**

Both the Endoplasmic Reticulum (ER) and the Golgi apparatus are important components of the cell's endomembrane system. The ER is in charge of initial protein synthesis and folding. These proteins are packaged into vesicles and transported to the Golgi apparatus after being synthesized. Proteins undergo additional modifications in the Golgi, such as the addition of sugars (glycosylation) or other groups. The Golgi then sorts and packages these proteins into vesicles, which it then directs to their final destinations, which can be within the cell, at the cell membrane, or outside the cell.

✔ **Lysosomes are frequently referred to as the cell's 'suicide bags.' Explain why this name was chosen and what would happen if a lysosome ruptured within the cytoplasm.**

Lysosomes have earned the nickname 'suicide bags' due to their high concentration of hydrolytic enzymes capable of digesting biomolecules. Under normal circumstances, these enzymes are safely enclosed within the lysosomal membrane, where they break down waste and cellular debris. However, if a lysosome ruptures, these enzymes are released into the cytoplasm, where they can digest cellular components and cause cell damage or even death. Under certain conditions, the cell can use this self-destructive ability to undergo programmed cell death or autophagy.

✔ **Explain how chloroplasts in plant cells help to sustain life on Earth through the photosynthesis process.**

During photosynthesis, chloroplasts capture solar energy to convert carbon dioxide and water into glucose. This not only feeds the plant but also generates oxygen, which is essential for life on Earth.

POINTS TO REMEMBER

- ✔ The 'cells' are the fundamental building blocks of all living organisms.
- ✔ Various structures floating in the cell are called cell organelles.
- ✔ Cell membrane gives shape to the cell and is present in both plants and animals.
- ✔ The passage of substances across the cell membrane takes place by three modes: Active Transport; Passive Transport and Bulk Transport.
- ✔ Cytoplasm is made up of 90 per cent water and the remaining is amino acids, vitamins, carbohydrates and enzymes.
- ✔ Mitochondria are the site for cellular respiration, and release energy for carrying out the metabolic activities of the cell.
- ✔ Endoplasmic reticulum is a large network of fluid-filled interconnecting tubules and provides a supportive framework to the cell.
- ✔ Ribosomes are found in both plants and animals, and are the site for protein synthesis of enzymes.
- ✔ Golgi complex is responsible for the transport of substances synthesized in the cell to the outside of the cell.
- ✔ Vacuoles are large sac-like structures bound by a single membrane known as tonoplast and they are responsible for storage of dissolved material such as amino acids, sugars, various organic acids and some proteins.
- ✔ Chloroplasts are green-coloured plastids responsible for trapping of solar energy during photosynthesis.
- ✔ Lysosomes are membranous sac-like structures budded off from Golgi bodies which serve as the intercellular digestive system.
- ✔ The nucleus contains fine thread-like structures known as chromatin fibres and these fibres are composed of biomolecules known as nucleic acids.

PRACTICE QUESTIONS CLASSROOM WING

Very Short Answer Type Questions

Directions for questions from 1 to 6:

Fill in the blanks.

1. The cell is defined as the basic ________, ________ and hereditary unit of all living organisms.
2. Every multicellular organism begins its life as a ________.
3. ________ are groups of cells having a common origin, similarity in structure, and performing similar functions.
4. In multicellular organisms, life begins from a single cell known as ________, which evolves into numerous cells through repeated ________.
5. Protoplasm, the living substance inside a cell, consists of two main components: the ________ and the ________.
6. While both have important roles, the ________ allows selective passage of substances, whereas the ________ provides rigidity and support in plant cells.

Directions for questions from 7 to 13:

For each of the following questions, for choices have been provided. Select the correct alternatives,

7. What is the main distinction between unicellular and multicellular organisms concerning cellular activity?
   (a) Unicellular organisms have no cellular activity.
   (b) All activities in unicellular organisms are carried out by multiple cells.
   (c) All activities in unicellular organisms are carried out by a single cell.
   (d) Multicellular organisms begin life with multiple cells.
8. Which layer of the cell wall acts as a cementing layer binding adjacent cells together?
   (a) Primary Cell Wall (b) Secondary Cell Wall
   (c) Plasma Membrane (d) Middle Lamella
9. Why is the process of cell differentiation crucial for multicellular organisms?
   (a) It aids in energy production.
   (b) It ensures the division of cellular functions.
   (c) It increases the number of cells.
   (d) It enables specialized cells to perform general functions.
10. Within the cytoplasm, non-living substances are referred to as:
    (a) Protoplasm
    (b) Cytoplasmic inclusions
    (c) Cell organelles
    (d) Plasmodesmata
11. Which component ensures that a cell maintains a balance between its internal and external environments?
    (a) Nucleus
    (b) Cell organelles
    (c) Plasma Membrane
    (d) Cytoplasmic inclusions
12. Which of the following processes does not require the expenditure of energy?
    (a) Active transport (b) Exocytosis
    (c) Osmosis (d) Endocytosis
13. Where does cellular respiration occur, releasing energy stored as ATP molecules?
    (a) Ribosomes
    (b) Golgi Complex
    (c) Mitochondria
    (d) Endoplasmic Reticulum

Directions for questions from 14 to 16:

Match the entries of Column 1 with those of Column 2.

14.

Column 1	Column 2
A. Plasma membrane	(i) Cells of common origin
B. Cell wall	(ii) Nucleus and cytoplasm
C. Protoplasm	(iii) Prevents bursting of cells
D. Cytoplasm	(iv) Maintains homeostasis
E. Tissue	(v) About 90% water

15.

Column 1	Column 2
A. Mitochondria	(i) Harness sunlight
B. Ribosome	(ii) Food storage
C. Endoplasmic reticulum	(iii) Cellular respiration
D. Chloroplast	(iv) Intercellular transport
E. Leucoplast	(v) RNA

16.

Column 1	Column 2
A. Production of melanin	(i) Lysosomes
B. Storage of sugars	(ii) Golgi complex
C. Digestive bags of cells	(iii) Centrosome
D. Cell division regulation	(iv) Vacuoles

Short Answer Type Questions

17. What is the difference between cytoplasm and cytosol?

18. Explain the importance of cell division in ensuring the survival and continuity of species.

19. How does the structure of a cell wall differ between plants and fungi?

20. Discuss the significance of semi-permeability in the plasma membrane.

21. Explain the term 'diffusion' as it relates to gaseous substances in plants.

22. What is the significance of the presence of their own DNA in mitochondria?

23. Adenine cannot pair with cytosine. Give reason.

Essay Type Questions

24. Discuss the concept of 'division of labour' in multicellular organisms, elaborating on how differentiated cells lead to system-wide coordination and increased efficiency.

25. Delve deep into the structure of a typical cell, explaining the various components and their significance in maintaining the vitality of the cell.

26. Provide a comprehensive overview of the different layers of the plant cell wall, detailing their composition, development, and crucial functions in ensuring the cell's well-being.

27. Elaborate on the different types of transport mechanisms across the plasma membrane.

PRACTICE QUESTIONS COMPETITION WING

Level 1: Apply your Concepts

Directions for questions from 1 to 5:
Fill in the blanks.

1. The specialized, rigid layer that forms after a plant cell reaches maturity is called the ________.
2. In __________, large particles, such as cells or macromolecules, are taken in by a cell.
3. Mitochondria are also known as the __________ of the cell.
4. The process through which materials move from inside to outside the cell is known as ________.
5. The intercellular transport system of a cell is the ________.

Directions for questions from 6 to 10:
For each of the following questions, for choices have been provided. Select the correct alternatives,

6. Which organelle is referred to as the 'Packaging and dispatching unit' of the cell?
   (a) Endoplasmic Reticulum
   (b) Ribosomes
   (c) Golgi Complex
   (d) Lysosomes
7. Which of the following organelles contain powerful digestive enzymes?
   (a) Centrioles
   (b) Mitochondria
   (c) Lysosomes
   (d) Chloroplasts
8. The cytoplasm in animal cells is __________ compared to plant cells.
   (a) Less
   (b) More
   (c) Equal
   (d) Absent
9. Which of the following is NOT a component of the nucleus?
   (a) Chromatin material
   (b) Nucleolus
   (c) Golgi Body
   (d) Nuclear membrane
10. Adenine always pairs with:
    (a) Cytosine
    (b) Guanine
    (c) Thymine
    (d) Uracil

Direction for Questions from 11 to 15:
Choose the correct option.

(a) Both A and R are true and R is the correct explanation for A.
(b) Both A and R are true but R is not the correct explanation for A.
(c) A is true and R is false.
(d) A is false and R is true.

11. **Assertion (A):** Rough ER is in continuation with nuclear membrane.
    Reason (R): DNA controls the protein synthesis in rough ER.
12. **Assertion (A):** Nucleic acids are macromolecules.
    Reason (R): Polynucleotide strand is the backbone of nucleic acid.
13. **Assertion (A):** The two chromosomes of a homologous pair possess the same structure.
    Reason (R): The two chromosomes are derived from the same parent.
14. **Assertion (A):** Nucleus is not located in the centre of a plant cell unlike an animal cell.
    Reason (R): Plant cells possess chloroplasts that are not present in an animal cell.
15. **Assertion (A):** Lysosomes are called demolition squads of the cell.
    Reason (R): Lysosomes participate in the process of digestion of food under diseased condition.

Level 2: Review your Concepts

16. Explain the role of DNA in protein synthesis.
17. (a) Smooth endoplasmic reticulum is abundant in liver cells, cells in brain and the cells in the muscles of limbs. What are the functions performed by it in the respective cells?
    (b) Sarcoplasmic reticulum is the modified form of smooth ER. What is its significance?
18. (a) In what way the totipotent cells, pluripotent cells and multi potent cells differ from each other?
    (b) What are stem cells? Where are they located in human body? What is their importance?
19. Why are nucleosomes significant in the cell's nucleus?
20. Differentiate between autosomes and allosomes.
21. What makes the DNA of an individual unique?
22. Describe the significance of chromosomes in organisms.

Level 3: Assess Your Concepts

23. Diseases related to mitochondria are inherited from female parent only. Give reason.
24. Reflect on the intricate network of communication between the nucleus and other organelles within the cell. Highlight the significance of this cooperation in ensuring efficient cellular processes.
25. Eukaryotic cells, like ours, have a nucleus. This is different from simpler prokaryotic cells. Having a nucleus offers protection to our DNA and better organization, helping cells function more efficiently and adapt to various situations.
26. The nucleolus is a small part in the nucleus. It's like a factory that makes ribosomes. Ribosomes are tiny machines that read RNA (messages from DNA) to build proteins. Every cell needs proteins to work correctly, so the nucleolus is essential!

AT

PRACTICE QUESTIONS NEET SPECIAL WING

Multi-Answer Type Questions

Questions number 1 to 5 are multiple-choice questions. Each question has FOUR options (a), (b), (c), and (d). ONE OR MORE THAN ONE of these four option(s) is/are the correct answer(s).

1. Which of the following is true regarding secondary cell wall?
   (a) composition is fixed
   (b) is lignified
   (c) has suberin which makes it impermeable to water
   (d) it contains cellulose and pectin
2. Pyrimidine bases found in RNA are:
   (a) Adenine
   (b) Cytosine
   (c) Guanine
   (d) Uracil
3. The endomembrane system of a eukaryotic cell includes:
   (a) Nuclear envelope
   (b) Endoplasmic reticulum
   (c) Golgi apparatus
   (d) Mitochondria
4. Which of the following is true regarding pinocytosis?
   (a) It means cell drinking
   (b) It means cell eating
   (c) It engulfs and destroys macromolecules
   (d) Bulk transport of fluid matter takes place through vesicles
5. Which of the following is true regarding centrosome and centrioles?
   (a) They are made up of cylindrical microtubules
   (b) During cell division they move to equator
   (c) They undergo aster formation during cell division
   (d) They destroy bacteria and foreign body entering inside the cell

Comprehension-Based Questions

A. Read the paragraph given below and answer the questions number 6 to 11:

Ravi and his friends were studying about DNA and chromosome structure in their biology class. They learnt that the DNA strands are made up of sugar phosphate back bone and projecting in the middle are the nitrogen bases which consists of purines and pyrimidines. The two antiparallel DNA strands are connected by the complementary base pairing which is very specific. The two strands are coiled to form a spiral ladder like structure which is called as a double helix. The coiled DNA binds with histone proteins to form basic subunits which are supercoiled and together with RNA form chromatin material. The chromosome is observed during cell division very clearly. Chromosomes consists of different structures which are observed at different times of condensation like chromonema, chromomeres, centromere, kinetochore, etc. The chromosomes can exist as sets in a cell. The number of sets of chromosomes in a cell is known as ploidy. If each cell in an organism contains two sets of chromosomes, it is considered as a diploid cell and is denoted by 2n. If each cell in an organism contains one set of chromosomes, it is considered as a haploid cell and is denoted by n. A cell comprises two kinds of chromosomes—autosomes and Allosomes (sex chromosomes).

6. What is chromatid called in the early stages of condensation?
   (a) Chromomere
   (b) Chromonema
   (c) Chromomeres
   (d) Centromere
7. Kinetochore is:
   (a) small bead shaped structure
   (b) primary constriction
   (c) coiled portion of chromatin fibre
   (d) specialized disc like structure

8. The number of chromosomes found in *Canis lupus* is:
   (a) 42
   (a) 78
   (a) 38
   (a) 40

9. In complementary base pairing cytosine is attached to guanine by:
   (a) 2 hydrogen bonds
   (a) 3 hydrogen bonds
   (a) 1 hydrogen bond
   (a) 2 covalent bonds

10. The structure which is a point of attachment for microtubular spindle fibres during cell division is:
   (a) Chromomere
   (b) Centrosome
   (c) Centromere
   (d) Kinetochore

11. Match the column:

Column – A	Column – B
(i) Sugar+ nitrogen base + Phosphate	(a) Pyrimidine
(ii) Adenine and guanine	(b) Nucleosome
(iii) Thymine and cytosine	(c) Nucleotide
(iv) Double helix + histone	(d) Chromatin material
(v) Nucleosome + RNA	(e) Purines

B. Read the paragraph given below and answer the questions number 12 to 17:

Cell consists of cell membrane, ground substance which is cytoplasm, a nucleus and the different cell organelles. Cytoplasm occupies a major portion of the cell and 90% of it is made up of water. Embedded in the cytoplasm are the mini machineries that is the cell organelles. All the organelles perform specific function and work in tandem with each other to perform the cellular processes efficiently. Mitochondria are the power houses whereas ribosomes are required for protein synthesis. Endoplasmic reticulum make up one part of the endomembrane system of the cell. Golgi complexes are the packaging and despatching unit. Different kinds of plastids are only found in plants. Vacuoles are large and many in plant cells whereas in animal cells they are few, small or may not be present at all. Lysosomes act as digestive bags of the cell. Centrosome and centriole initiate cell division and nucleus contains the genetic material of the cell.

12. Which of the following organelles do not have a membrane?
   (a) Lysosomes
   (b) Nucleus
   (c) Golgi body vesicles
   (d) Ribosomes

13. Which of the following organelle is responsible for peptide synthesis in the cell?
   (a) Mitochondria
   (b) Ribosomes
   (c) Chloroplast
   (d) Golgi apparatus

14. Which organelle is responsible for vacuole production?
   (a) Lysosome
   (b) Ribosome
   (c) Golgi complex
   (d) Endoplasmic reticulum

15. The semifluid substance found in chloroplast is called:
   (a) Stoma
   (b) Stroma
   (c) Protoplasm
   (d) Chloroplasm

16. Which of the following is not a function of vacuole?
   (a) Maintenance of osmotic pressure of the cell
   (b) Secretion enzymes
   (c) Providing turgidity and rigidity
   (d) Storage of various substances

17. Match the column:

Column – A	Column – B
(i) F_0F_1 complexes	(a) Smooth endoplasmic reticulum
(ii) Lipid synthesis	(b) Dictyosomes
(iii) Golgi body in plant cells	(c) Deoxyribose
(iv) Sugar in DNA	(d) Mitochondria
(v) Powerful digestive enzyme	(e) Lysosome

ANSWER KEYS

Crossword

Across

2. Nucleolus 3. Allosomes 6. Cytosol 11. Transcription 12. Homeostasis
13. Imbibition

Down

1. Plasmodesmata 4. Pinocytosis 5. Isotonic 7. Lysosomes 8. Ploidy
9. Endocytosis 10. Nucleosomes 11. Tonoplast

Classroom Wing

Very Short Answer Type Questions

1. Structural, functional 2. Single cell 3. Tissues
4. Zygote, divisions 5. Nucleus, cytoplasm 6. Plasma membrane, cell wall
7. (c) 8. (d) 9. (b) 10. (b) 11. (c)
12. (c) 13. (c) 14. A → iv, B → iii, C → ii, D → v, E → i
15. A → iii, B → v, C → iv, D → i, E → ii 16. A → ii, B → v, C → i, D → iii, E → iv

Competition Wing

Level 1: Apply Your Concepts

1. Secondary cell wall 2. Phagocytosis 3. Powerhouse 4. Exocytosis
5. Endoplasmic Reticulum 6. (c) 7. (c) 8. (b)
9. (c) 10. (c) 11. (a) 12. (a) 13. (c)
14. (b) 15. (b)

NEET Special Wing

Multiple-Answer Type Questions

1. (b, c) 2. (b, d) 3. (a, b, c) 4. (a, d) 5. (a, c)

Comprehension-Based Questions

6. (b) 7. (d) 8. (b) 9. (b) 10. (d)
11. (i) → (c); (ii) → (e); (iii) → (a); (iv) → (b); (v) → (d)
12. (d) 13. (b) 14. (c) 15. (b) 16. (b)
17. (i) → (d); (ii) → (a); (iii) → (b); (iv) → (c); (v) → (e)

Hints and Explanations

CLASSROOM WING

Short Answer Type Questions

17. Cytoplasm is a jelly-like substance that contains membrane-bound cell organelles and non-living substances called cytoplasmic inclusions. Cytoplasm without cell organelles is known as cytosol.

18. As cells die or get damaged, they need to be replaced for the organism to function properly. Additionally, for species to reproduce and continue, cell division is fundamental.

19. The composition of the cell wall varies among organisms. Cellulose is the main component in most plants, whereas fungi have chitin.

20. This selective nature is crucial for maintaining the balance of substances within the cell and protecting it from external threats.

21. Diffusion is the process wherein the movement of molecules occurs from higher to lower concentrations until equilibrium is achieved. In plants, diffusion plays a crucial role in gas exchange. For instance, plants absorb carbon dioxide and release oxygen during photosynthesis via diffusion.

22. The presence of their own DNA in mitochondria suggests that they might have originated as independent organisms and later evolved to become part of eukaryotic cells. This is a key concept behind the endosymbiotic theory.

23. Adenine is a purine that is structurally compatible with the pyrimidine which is thymine. The purine, guanine is compatible with pyrimidine, cytosine.

Essay Type Questions

24. In multicellular organisms, the concept of 'division of labour' emphasises cell specialization, allowing for system-wide coordination and efficiency. Division of labour is analogous to a well-organized team, with each member performing a specific function. This ensures that the organism as a whole function properly. Cells differentiate to take on specific roles as organisms develop. Because of this specialization, not every cell must perform every function, resulting in increased efficiency. As a result, tissues, organs, and systems emerge, each contributing to the overall function and well-being of the organism in a coordinated fashion.

25. A typical cell, regardless of organism, has characteristics in common. It has protoplasm at its core, which includes the nucleus and cytoplasm. The genetic information is stored in the nucleus, which serves as the control centre. The cytoplasm is home to a variety of organelles, each with a specific function ranging from energy production to waste management. Non-living cytoplasmic inclusions can be found here as well. The plasma membrane surrounds the protoplasm and regulates the entry and exit of substances, ensuring a balance between the cell's internal and external environments.

26. The primary layers of the plant cell wall are the middle lamella, primary cell wall, and secondary cell wall. The outermost layer, the middle lamella, binds adjacent cells and is high in pectin. The primary cell wall, which is located between the middle lamella and the plasma membrane, is thin and elastic and serves to support growing cells. The secondary cell wall is a rigid layer that forms after the cell matures and provides extra support. Depending on the region and cell type, this wall may lignify or become water-impermeable through suberin deposition.

27. The cell membrane controls the movement of substances into and out of the cell. This mode of transportation can be passive or active. Diffusion and osmosis are examples of passive transport that require no energy. Diffusion is the movement of molecules from a higher concentration to a lower concentration. The movement of water across a semipermeable membrane is referred to as osmosis. Active transport, on the other hand, necessitates the use of energy and involves the movement of molecules against a concentration gradient. Bulk transport, which includes exocytosis (movement of materials out of the cell) and endocytosis (movement of materials into the cell), is another mode of transport.

COMPETITION WING

Level 1: Apply your Concepts

11. Rough ER is associated with the function of synthesis of proteins. The proteins are synthesized in the ribosomes based on the information received from the nucleus. When there is any malfunction in the ribosomes or rough ER, there is a possibility that wrong proteins are synthesized. This may lead to irreversible abnormalities in the individual. In order to avoid this, the nucleus regulates the ribosomes in the process of synthesis. For example, it can send instruction to the ribosomes to stop the synthesis of proteins. In order to have direct access to the ribosomes, rough ER is located close to the nucleus which is in continuation with the nuclear membrane.

    Hence, the correct option is (a).

12. Nucleic acids possess nucleotides as the basic units. Each nucleotide possesses a sugar molecule, a phosphate group and nitrogen bases. These nucleotides are linked to each other by means of chemical bonds forming a polynucleotide chain. Since they are polymeric molecules, they are called macromolecules.

    Hence, the correct option is (a).

13. The two chromosomes in homologous pair possess the same structure. This means that they possess genes representing the same characters. One chromosome is derived from mother and one is derived from father.

    Hence, the correct option is (c).

14. A plant cell possesses vacuole in the centre. Hence, the nucleus is pushed towards the periphery.

    Hence, the correct option is (b).

15. Lysosomes are known as demolition squads of the cell because they destroy bacteria and other foreign bodies entering into the cell. The ability of lysosomes to participate in the process of digestion of food under diseased condition is called autolysis.

    Hence, the correct option is (b).

Level 2: Review your Concepts

16. The process of protein synthesis takes place in multiple steps. The first step of the process is called transcription. Transcription is the process of generating a copy of RNA which carries the information to the site of protein synthesis, that is, ribosomes.

    Since this RNA transfers the information from DNA to the ribosomes, it is called messenger RNA (mRNA).

    Proteins are made up of amino acids. Different amino acids can be linked together by means of chemical bonds to form different kinds of proteins.

    The proteins vary from one another depending on the sequence of amino acids. The sequence of amino acids is decided by the information brought by mRNA in the form of sequence of nucleotides.

    The sequence of nucleotides in mRNA is complementary to the sequence of nucleotides in the DNA strand.

17. (a) Smooth ER in the liver cells serves the function of detoxification of drugs and metabolic wastes in the liver. Since smooth ER is associated with the function of synthesis of hormones, it is abundantly found in the organs such as testes, ovaries, glands, etc. In the muscle cells, particularly in striated muscles (muscles of limbs), smooth ER regulates the calcium ion concentration in the blood as per requirement.

    (b) The ER present in the muscle cells is called sarcoplasmic reticulum. The sarcoplasmic reticulum stores the calcium ions and releases them during the action of muscle fibre. The calcium ions released in this manner interact with the contractile proteins which utilize ATP to shorten the muscle fibre. Thus the sarcoplasmic reticulum plays a major role in the excitation and contraction of muscles.

18. (a) Totipotent cells are the cells of the zygote that can form the cells of embryo and those of the extraembryonic membranes. The embryonic cells in the first few cell divisions are the only totipotent cells. Pluripotent cells are the cells that have the ability to give rise to all the cell types in the entire body of the organism. Embryonic stem cells are pluripotent. Multipotent cells can differentiate into more than one cell type. But their activity is limited. They can differentiate into closely related family of cells. Adult stem cells are multipotent cells. Hematopoietic stem cells can become red blood cells, white blood cells or platelets.

    (b) Stem cells are the undifferentiated cells that have the ability to become any other cell types. Adult or somatic stem cells exist throughout the body after embryonic development. These are located within the respective tissues such as bone marrow, blood, liver, etc.

19. Nucleosomes, consisting of DNA wrapped around histone molecules, help condense DNA to form chromatin. This compact structure allows for the efficient packaging of DNA within the nucleus.

20. Autosomes are chromosomes that are the same in both males and females and do not determine sex. Allosomes, or sex chromosomes, differ between males and females and are responsible for determining an individual's gender.

21. The specific sequence of base pairs on the DNA strand varies from one individual to another. This unique sequence of base pairs characterizes an individual's DNA.

22. Chromosomes are crucial as they carry genetic information, ensuring the inheritance of traits from one generation to the next and playing a vital role in the growth, development, and functioning of organisms.

Level 3: Assess Your Concepts

23. Mitochondria contain DNA. The mitochondrial DNAs present in sperm cell are very few and these are destroyed by the egg cell during the process of fertilization.

    As a result, only the mitochondrial DNA of mother is present in the embryo. This means that the offspring inherits the mitochondria from the female parent only. Hence, the diseases involved with the mitochondrial DNA are inherited from the female parent only.

24. The nucleus does not function on its own. It's similar to the CEO of a company, who communicates frequently with other departments. For example, it sends RNA instructions to the cytoplasmic ribosomes. These ribosomes then use these instructions to construct the proteins that are required. Similarly, the endoplasmic reticulum and Golgi apparatus aid in protein refinement and transport, respectively. This ongoing collaboration ensures that the cell runs efficiently, with each organelle performing a specific function within the larger cellular operation.

25. The presence of a nucleus distinguishes eukaryotic cells from simpler prokaryotic cells. This nucleus functions as a vault, guarding our precious DNA. Cells evolved and became more complex as organisms evolved and became more complex. A nucleus provides a level of organization and protection that is thought to give eukaryotic cells an advantage in adapting and thriving in diverse environments.

26. The nucleolus is a specialized area within the nucleus. Consider it a specialized workshop within the larger factory. Its primary function is to put together ribosomes, which are tiny cellular machines. These ribosomes then travel to the cell's cytoplasm, where they play an important role in protein synthesis. In essence, the nucleolus ensures that the cell has all of the necessary tools to construct the proteins required for various cellular functions.

NEET SPECIAL WING

Multiple-Answer Type Questions

1. Secondary cell wall is formed inside the primary cell wall by the deposition of materials over the existing surface. Its composition is variable. In some cases, lignin deposits are present. In some regions it has suberin deposits which makes it impermeable to water
2. Cytosine and Uracil are the two pyrimidine bases found in RNA.
3. The endomembrane system is a group of membranes that work in coordination with each other to modify, package and transport proteins and lipids in eukaryotic cells. It includes nuclear envelope, endoplasmic reticulum, golgi apparatus, vesicles, lysosomes and vacuoles.
4. Pinocytosis means 'cell drinking'. In this process, bulk transport of fluid matter takes place across the cell membranes by forming small vesicles.
5. Centrosome is a small structure comprising granule like structures known as centrioles. They are made up of hollow, cylindrical structures called microtubules.

Comprehension-Based Questions

A.

6. When chromatin fibre is in the early stage of condensation, the chromatid is called chromonema. These chromonemata are the coiled portions of the chromatin fibre.
7. The kinetochore is a specialized disc-like structure on the centromere to which the microtubular spindle fibres get attached during cell division.
8. Each species of organisms is characterized by a specific number of chromosomes. It is not involved with the size of the organism. ***Canis lupus*** or Gray Wolf has 78 chromosomes in its cells.
9. There is a specific linkage between the respective bases is due to the structural compatibility between the particular purine and pyrimidine. For example, thymine exactly fits into adenine. Similarly, cytosine fits exactly into guanine. This kind of pairing of purines and pyrimidines of opposite polynucleotide strands is known as complementary base pairing. Cytosine is attached to guanine by 3 hydrogen bonds.
10. The kinetochore is a specialized disc-like structure on the centromere to which the microtubular spindle fibres get attached during cell division.
11. Match the following:

    DNA is composed of basic units called nucleotides. Each nucleotide contains three subunits:

    A molecule of pentose sugar (5-carbon sugar) known as deoxyribose sugar, a phosphate group and a nitrogen base
    (i) (c)

    Adenine and guanine are called purine bases.
    (ii) (e)

    Thymine and cytosine are called pyrimidine bases.
    (iii) (a)

    The double helix of DNA bound by histone polymer is called nucleosome. This nucleosome is the basic unit of chromatin material.
    (iv) (b)

    Nucleosomes condenses together with RNA to form chromatin material. This chromatin material is present in the form of network of fibres floating in the nucleoplasm present in the nucleus of every mature cell.
    (v) (d)

B.

12. Ribosomes are dense, spherical bodies present as small granules. They are composed of a smaller subunit and a larger subunit. Each subunit is made up of ribonucleic acid (RNA) and proteins called ribonucleoproteins. They do not possess a membrane.
13. Ribosomes are the site for protein (peptide) synthesis in a cell.
14. Golgi complex is responsible for vacuole production that contain cellular secretions, for example, enzymes, proteins, cellulose, melanin pigment, lactoprotein (milk protein), etc.
15. In chloroplast the matrix is called stroma which is a semifluid, colourless and colloidal complex and contains DNA and RNA.
16. Secretion of enzymes is one of the main function s of golgi complex. The functions of vacuoles includes storage of dissolved materials such as amino acids,

sugars, various organic acids and some proteins, providing turgidity and rigidity to the cell and maintenance of osmotic pressure of the cell.

17. Match the following:

Mitochondria is the site for cellular respiration thereby releasing energy in the process energy is stored as adenosine triphosphate (ATP) molecules. This occurs in the F1F0 machinery in the inner membrane of mitochondria.
(i) (d)

Smooth endoplasmic reticulum is responsible for synthesis of lipids.
(ii) (a)

Golgi complexes are smaller in plant cells and are known as dictyosomes.
(iii) (b)

The sugar molecule in DNA is known as deoxyribose sugar as it has one less oxygen than the ribose sugar found in RNA.
(iv) (c)

Lysosomes are membranous sacs budded off from the Golgi body. They are surrounded by a single membrane and contain powerful digestive enzymes to destroy foreign body or digest own cell in case of emergency.
(v) (e)

CHAPTER

2

Cell Division and Cell Cycle

Remember

Before beginning this chapter, you should be able to:

- Recall the different phases of mitosis and meiosis
- Remember the events in a cell cycle

Key Ideas

After completing this chapter, you should be able to:

- Understand the significance of cell division
- Describe the stages of mitosis and meiosis
- Explain the characteristic changes in different phases of cell division
- Differentiate mitosis from meiosis

A Tribute to Walther Flemming (1843–1905)

In the realm of cellular biology, a resounding homage must be paid to Walther Flemming (1843–1905), the trailblazing biologist who played a pivotal role in elucidating the mysteries of cell division and the cell cycle.

From a young age, he displayed a proclivity for the sciences, a characteristic that would eventually guide his academic and professional trajectory. For his higher education, Flemming attended the University of Rostock. It was here that he studied medicine, immersing himself in the intricacies of human biology and anatomy. After completing his studies at the University of Rostock, Flemming's academic endeavours didn't stop. Every slide he prepared, every hour he spent peering through the microscope, was a testament to his unwavering commitment to the world of cellular biology. He was driven by the profound allure of discovery.

His revolutionary work involved the first-ever comprehensive depiction of chromatin, detailing its transformative behaviour during mitosis and paving the way for profound insights into the mechanisms of cellular reproduction and genetics.

Walther Flemming's most notable academic and professional journey was primarily associated with the University of Kiel in Germany. He worked as a Professor at the University of Kiel, Germany; and, as Director of the Anatomical Institute at the University.

FUN TIME

CROSSWORD

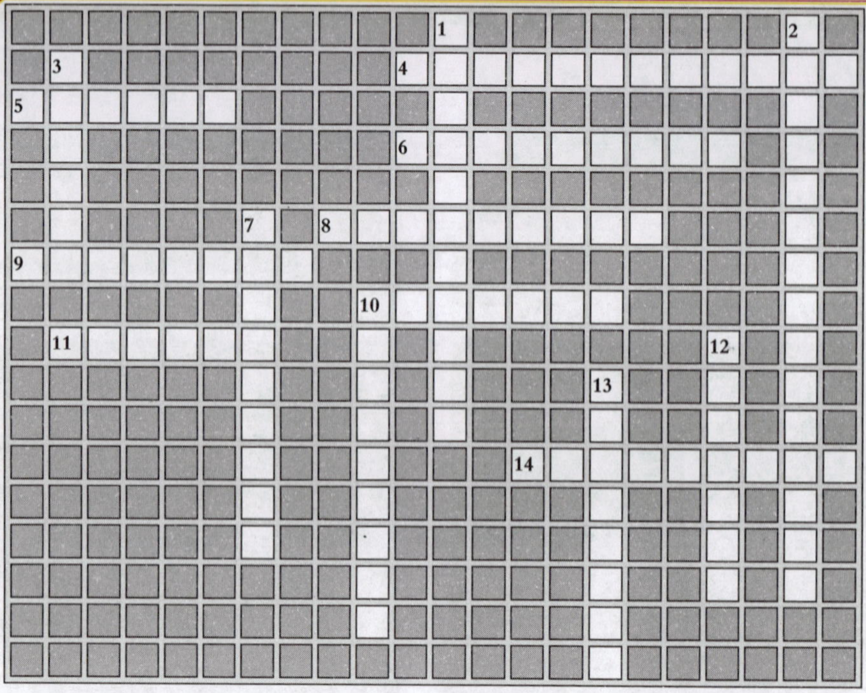

Across

4. The organelles which carry out the function of centrioles in a plant cell
5. The structures developed from gametes in haploid organisms
6. The structure formed during the cytokinesis in a plant cell
8. The last phase of mitosis cell division
9. The shortest phase of mitosis cell division
10. To transfer genetic information to the next generation
11. The single cell from which the entire organism is developed
14. X-shaped structure that connect homologous chromosomes till anaphase.

Down

1. A disc-shaped protein structure at the surface of centromeres
2. Disappearance of chiasmata at the end of prophase I of meiosis
3. The organ which destroys the worn out RBC
7. Radiating structures around the daughter centrioles during the cell division of the animal cell
10. The preparatory phase for mitosis cell division
12. The scientist who coined the term Mitosis
13. Direct cell division

INTRODUCTION

All the living organisms start their life from a single pre-existing cell. A single cell undergoes repeated divisions to form many groups of cells.

The process of formation of new cells by the division of pre-existing cells is known as **cell division.** The cell that undergoes cell division is known as **parent cell** or **mother cell.** The cells that are formed as a result of cell division are known as **daughter cells**. During cell division, each cell splits up to form two identical daughter cells that resemble their parent cell.

Significance of Cell Division

Cell division is a necessary process taking place in all the living organisms without any exception. Following are some of the points of significance explaining why cell division is essential:

- Growth of the body
- Replacement of damaged and dead cells
- Reproduction
- Repair of tissues

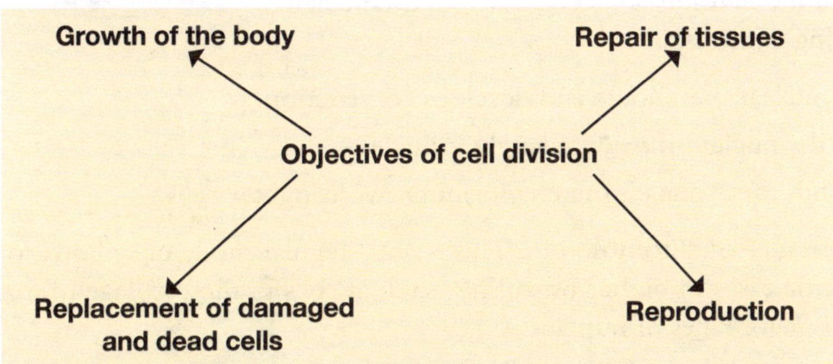

Figure 2.1 Objectives of cell division

Info Bytes!

The concept of cell division was first noted by German botanist Hugo von Mohl in 1835 when he observed cells in the process of splitting.

Growth of the Body

Growth is one of the basic activities that takes place in all living organisms. In unicellular organisms, growth results due to the increase in size and volume of the cytoplasmic contents of the cell. In multicellular organisms, the cells undergo repeated divisions to form many cells of different sizes and shapes. It is followed by other phenomena such as cell differentiation and organ formation. This ultimately results in the growth of an individual organism.

Info Bytes!

The human body replaces its entire skin surface roughly every 27 days thanks to the consistent turnover of skin cells.

Maintenance and Repair of Cells

Injuries, cuts, bruises or fractures result in the rupture of cells. The process of healing takes place by the formation of new cells in place of ruptured ones. Cell division results in the formation of new cells that fill the gaps formed at the site of injury.

Replacement of Dead and Damaged Cells

The cells may get damaged due to wear and tear in the course of time. Such damaged cells are replaced by the division of cells. The different types of cells have different life spans. The cells die after a specific period. Such cells are worn out from the body and are replaced by new cells formed by cell division. For example, the life span of RBC in blood is 120 days. These are destroyed in the spleen and are formed in the bone marrow. Cell division takes place constantly to replace the damaged or worn out cells.

Formation of New Individuals by Reproduction

In case of unicellular organisms, the nucleus of the single cell (organism) divides to produce a new individual. In multicellular organisms, both asexual reproduction and sexual reproduction take place. Asexual reproduction takes place by the nuclear and cytoplasmic division of the cells in the organism to produce new cells that form the entire organism identical to the parent organism. Sexual reproduction involves the formation of male and female gametes (sperms and ova) by cell division followed by the fusion of the male and female gametes to form a zygote. The life of every organism starts from a zygote. Zygote undergoes repeated cell divisions to develop into an organism.

Info Bytes!

Every second, nearly 2 million cells divide in our body, facilitating growth and development.

Modes of Cell Division

Depending on the method in which the division of nucleus takes place, the cell division can be of two types:

1. Direct cell division (Amitosis)
2. Indirect cell division

Info Bytes!

The record for the fastest cell division is held by certain bacteria, like *Escherichia coli*, which under ideal conditions can divide in as little as 20 minutes.

The direct cell division or amitosis is the only primitive mode of cell division. This takes place generally in lower organisms like bacteria.
Amitosis is the mode of cell division in which the division takes place within the nucleus. Following changes take place in the cell during amitosis:

- The nucleus elongates along with the nuclear membrane and develops constriction.
- This constriction deepens and divides the nucleus into two daughter nuclei.
- The cytoplasm also divides and surrounds these nuclei, thereby forming two daughter cells.

In this mode of cell division, there is no appearance of chromosomes. This is not a regular mode of cell division in higher organisms. It takes place only in certain specific cases in higher organisms, such as cells in the cartilage of mammals and cells of old tissues. It also occurs in the foetal membranes of humans.

Indirect cell division is characterized by the appearance of chromosomes. There are two modes of indirect cell division. They are:

1. Mitosis
2. Meiosis

Mitosis

The term 'mitosis' was coined by Fleming. The mitotic cell division takes place in all the somatic cells in the body of the organism. Somatic cells are the cells that are not involved with the fertilization process of sexual reproduction. A newly formed cell is not capable of cell division immediately. It undergoes a series of changes to be capable of cell division. This stage of the cell during which such changes take place and the cell becomes ready for cell division is known as interphase. Interphase which is the non-dividing preparatory phase of the cell division is followed by the mitotic phase (M phase) which is the dividing phase. Interphase is the preparatory phase for the cell division. It can be divided into three sub-phases depending upon the events taking place in the cell. They are:

1. First growth phase (G_1 phase)
2. Synthetic phase (S phase)
3. Second growth phase (G_2 phase)

Info Bytes!

Mitosis has only 1 complete sequence of chromosome division and cytokinesis.

Characteristic Changes in Respective Mitosis Phases

The characteristic changes during various stages of a cell cycle are described below.

G_1 phase (Gap Phase I)

G_1 phase is characterized by the following changes:

- Increase in the size of the cell and the nucleus
- Synthesis of RNA and proteins
- Increase in the number of cell organelles
- No change in DNA content

Info Bytes!

The liver can regenerate itself from just 25% of its original mass due to the prowess of cell division.

S phase

S phase is the most significant step in the process of cell division and is characterized by the following changes:

- Synthesis of new DNA in which the DNA content of the cell is doubled. This is called DNA replication.
- DNA replication results in the formation of duplicate set of genes without increase in the chromosome number.

Info Bytes!

Human DNA is 95% identical to the DNA of chimpanzees.

Process of DNA Replication

The process of DNA replication is explained below.

The two strands of the DNA double helix get separated. Two new strands are synthesized for the two separated strands. Each strand of the original DNA molecule serves as a template for the synthesis of a new strand as its counterpart. This newly synthesized strand will be complementary to the original strand. This means the sequence of base pairing in the new strand remains the same as the counterpart of the original DNA which got separated. This means, a duplicate copy of the same DNA is produced during this process. This entire process of synthesis of new DNA from the original DNA is called **DNA replication** or **DNA copying**. DNA replication involving complementary base pairing is responsible for the preservation of DNA sequence of the original cell (parent cell).

Example: Sequence of nucleotides of the original DNA

A A G A G G A T A A G A G G C G.........(Sequence of strand 'A'—template)

T T C T C C T A T T C T C C G C ... (Sequence of strand 'B')

Sequence of nucleotides of the newly synthesized strands of DNA

T T C T C C T A T T C T C C G C ... (Sequence of strand 'C' which is complementary to strand 'A' template)

A A G A G G A T A A G A G G C G .... (Sequence of new strand 'D' which is complementary to strand 'B' template)

Sequence of nucleotides in the new sets of DNA formed after replication

A A G A G G A T A A G A G G C G ... (Sequence of strand 'A')

T T C T C C T A T T C T C C G C ... (Sequence of strand 'C'—new)

T T C T C C T A T T C T C C G C ... (Sequence of strand 'B')

A A G A G G A T A A G A G G C G ... (Sequence of strand 'D'—new)

The daughter cells that are produced at the end of cell division possess the same DNA as the parent cell. The number of chromatids in the chromosomes gets doubled. But, the sister chromatids remain attached at the centromere. This means that the chromosomes occur in pairs. As a result, the number of chromosomes remains the same at the end of this phase. The resulting sets of chromosomes with duplication of genes are called homologous chromosomes. At this stage, chromosomes are clearly visible.

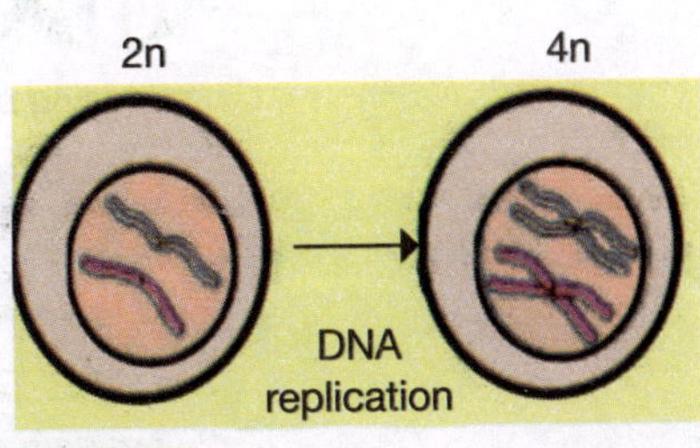

Figure 2.2 S Phase—DNA replication

The number of chromatids becomes double keeping the number of chromosomes constant. For example, in human cell, there are 46 chromosomes. At the end of S phase, there are 92 chromatids in the cell. Number of chromosomes remain same; only chromatids doubles. Synthesis of histone protein also takes place during this phase. Duplication of centrioles also takes place in animal cell. In the plant cell, centrosome is absent. Hence, microtubules play the role of centrioles. After the DNA replication, the original cell is considered to be almost ready to undergo mitotic cell division.

Info Bytes!

It will take 50 years to type the entire human genome if someone types at a speed of 60 wpm (words per minute) and works 8 hours a day.

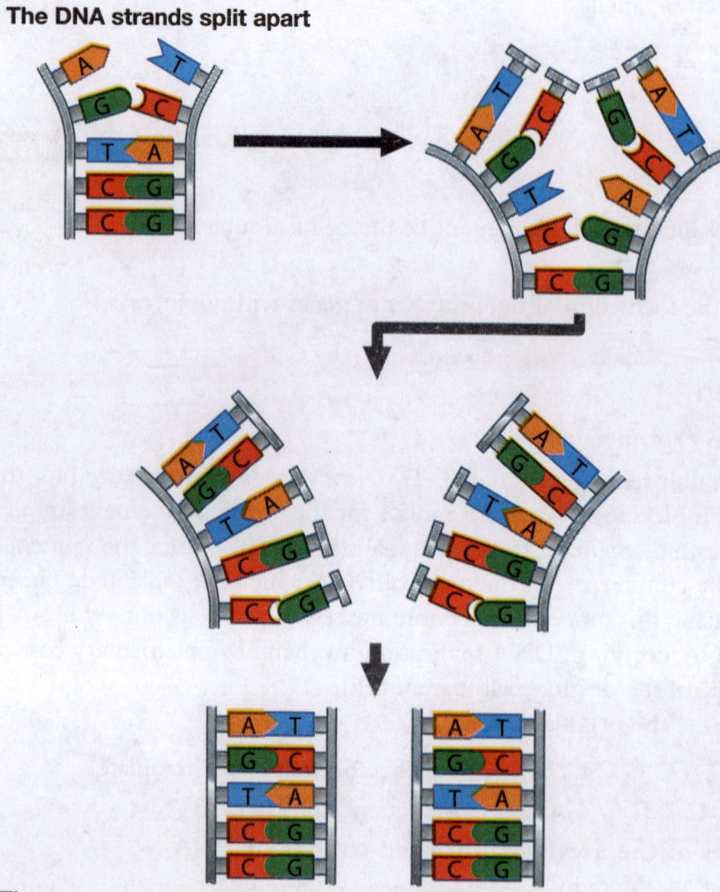

Figure 2.3 Diagram showing cell DNA replication

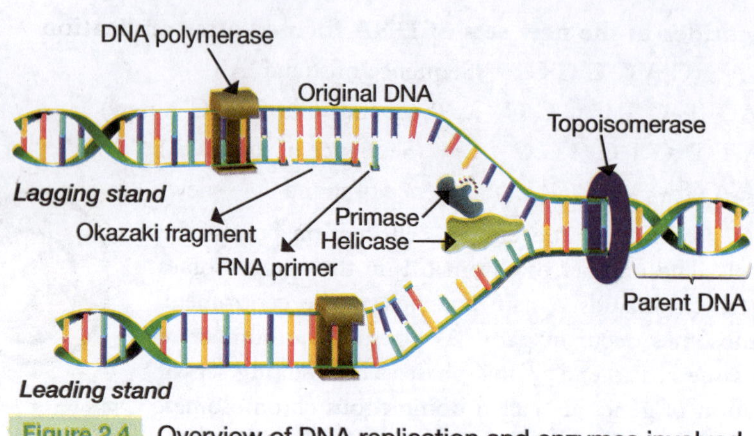

Figure 2.4 Overview of DNA replication and enzymes involved

G_2 phase

G_2 phase is characterized by the following changes:

- Continuation of synthesis of RNA and proteins
- Multiplication in the number of cell organelles
- Growth of cytoplasmic content of the cell
- Formation of spindle fibres

With G_2 phase, the interphase concludes. At the end of the interphase (G_2 phase), the cell is totally ready for entering the phase of actual cell division that is M phase. M phase of cell division is referred to as actual Mitotic Cell division or Mitosis.

M-Phase

The M phase or the actually dividing phase (Mitosis) of the cell cycle takes place in two steps:

1. Karyokinesis (division of nucleus)
2. Cytokinesis (division of cytoplasm)

Info Bytes!

Several critical steps in mitosis are controlled by phosphorylation or dephosphorylation of proteins.

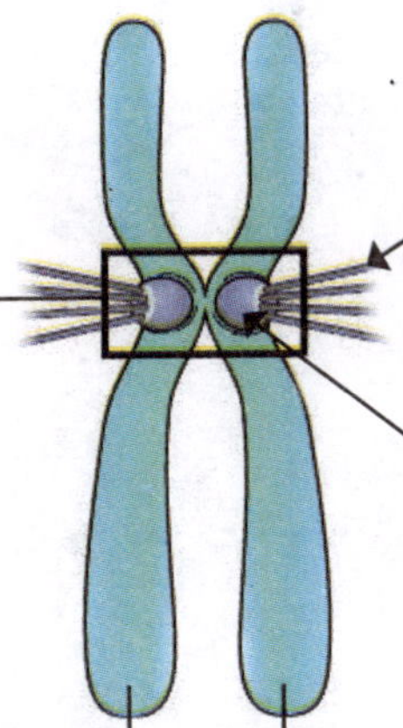

Figure 2.5 Sister chromatids each showing a kinetochore and centromere

Division of nucleus is the most significant step in the cell division as it involves the distribution of genetic material to the daughter cells. The genetic material is distributed in the form of chromosomes. Karyokinesis in mitosis takes place in four successive steps usually referred to as phases of mitosis. They are listed as follows.

1. Prophase 2. Metaphase 3. Anaphase 4. Telophase

Karyokinesis is followed by cytokinesis in which the cytoplasm of the parent cell divides eventually producing two daughter cells. These four phases of karyokinesis are explained further:

Prophase

- This phase is marked by the initiation of the condensation of chromatin material in the nucleus.
- The chromatin network becomes untangled and begins to condense becoming thick chromosomes which are prominent and visible.
- In an animal cell, the centriole that has already undergone duplication during the S phase now begins to move towards the opposite poles of the cell.
- In a plant cell, the mitotic spindle is formed with the help of microtubules.

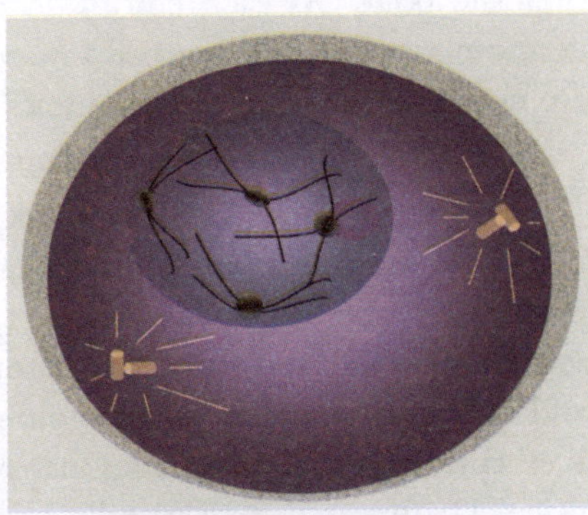

Figure 2.6 Prophase

- In animal cells, each daughter centriole is surrounded by radiating rays called **aster rays**. Spindle fibres appear between the daughter centrioles. There is no astral formation in a plant cell.
- Towards the end of prophase, the nuclear membrane disappears.
- The nucleolus, Golgi complex and endoplasmic reticulum (ER) also disappear.

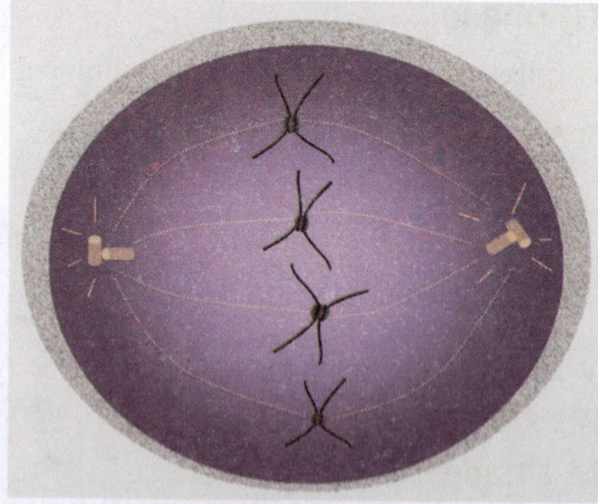

Figure 2.7 Metaphase

Metaphase

The complete breakdown of the nuclear membrane is the beginning of metaphase. The chromosomes are spread throughout the cytoplasm of the cell. A small disc-like protein structure called **kinetochore** is formed at the surface of the centromeres. This structure allows the chromatids to be attached to a spindle fibre on a chromosome. Each chromosome gets attached to the spindle fibre by the kinetochore of the centromere. The chromosomes arrange themselves at the equator plane in this phase.

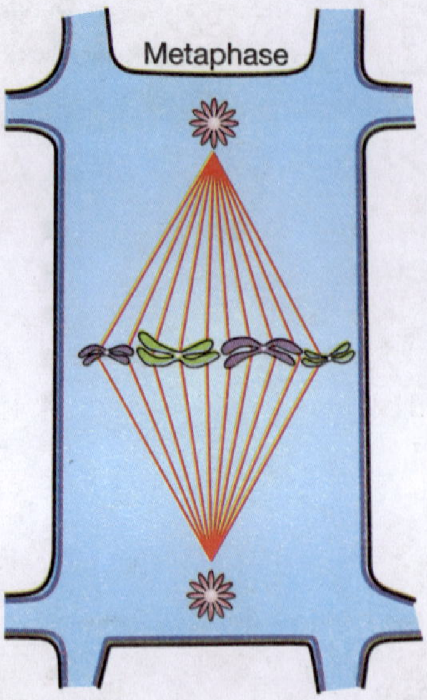

Figure 2.8 Metaphase of mitosis in a plant cell

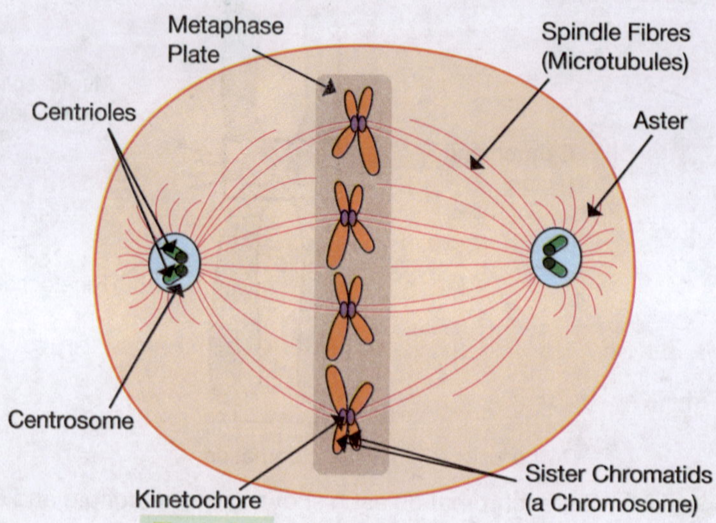

Figure 2.9 Metaphase in animal cells

Anaphase

This is the shortest phase. Each chromosome that is arranged at the equator plane gets split. Each daughter chromatid begins to migrate towards the two opposite poles. As each chromatid moves away from the equator plane, the centromere of each is pushed towards the poles. These daughter chromatids are now referred to as chromosomes of the future daughter nuclei.

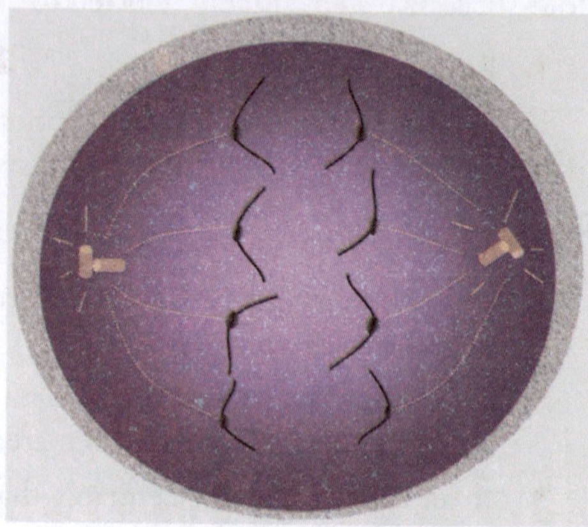

Figure 2.10 Anaphase

Telophase

This is the beginning of the final stage of mitosis. The daughter chromosomes reach their respective poles. Once they reach their poles, the chromosomes start unwinding and form the chromatin network. The nuclear membrane and nucleolus reappear and surround the respective daughter chromosomes. Reformation of cell organelles such as Golgi complex and ER in the cell takes place. Disappearance of spindle fibres and astral rays occur. The centrioles duplicate and get surrounded by centrosphere, thus producing a centrosome near each daughter nucleus. The nucleus reappears, and the two daughter nuclei begin to increase in size.

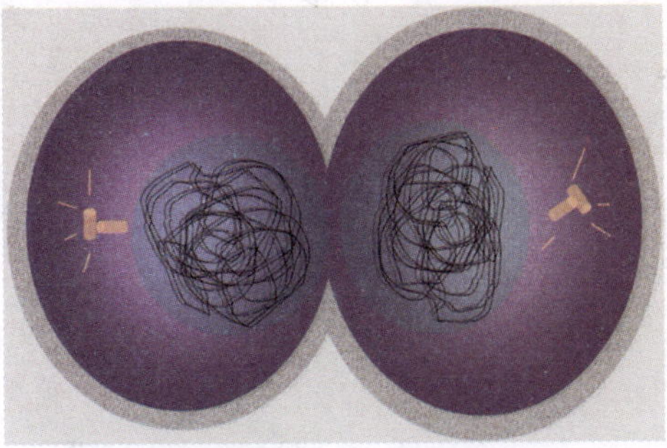

Figure 2.11 Telophase

Cytokinesis

Karyokinesis takes place more or less in the same way in both an animal cell and a plant cell. But the process of cytokinesis differs to a large extent from an animal cell to plant cell.

Cytokinesis in an Animal Cell

During cytokinesis, the cytoplasm undergoes division by a process called cleavage. This happens with the appearance of a furrow in the plasma membrane. The furrow gradually deepens and finally joins in the middle thus dividing the cell into two parts. The cell membrane starts constricting from the sides and continues inward until the mother cell is divided into two daughter cells. This type of cytokinesis is said to be centripetal as the process starts at the periphery and proceeds towards the centre.

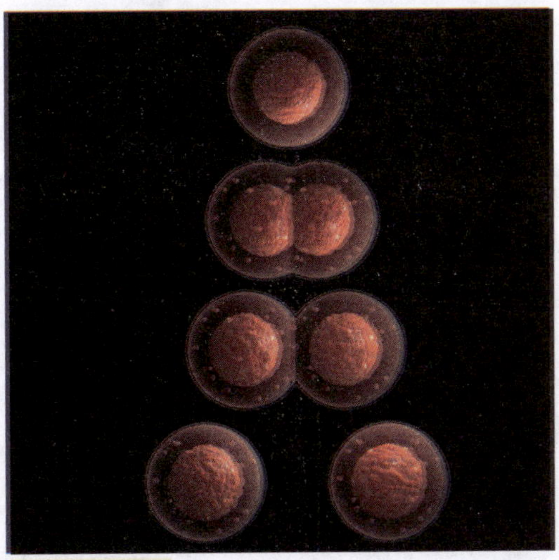

Figure 2.12 Cytokinesis in an animal cell

Cytokinesis in a Plant Cell

Plant cells undergo cytokinesis differently because the cell is bound by a rigid cell wall in addition to the plasma membrane. During telophase, a cell plate is formed across the cell, that is, a new cell wall is formed between the two membranes of the cell. During telophase, membrane-enclosed vesicles derived from the Golgi apparatus migrate to the centre of the cell to form a cell plate. Eventually, the growing cell plate fuses with the existing plasma membrane, producing two daughter cells, each with its own plasma membrane. This kind of cytoplasmic division is said to be **centrifugal** as it starts at the centre and moves towards the periphery. A new cell wall is formed between the two membranes of the cell plate. At the time of cytoplasmic division, the organelles get distributed within the two daughter cells.

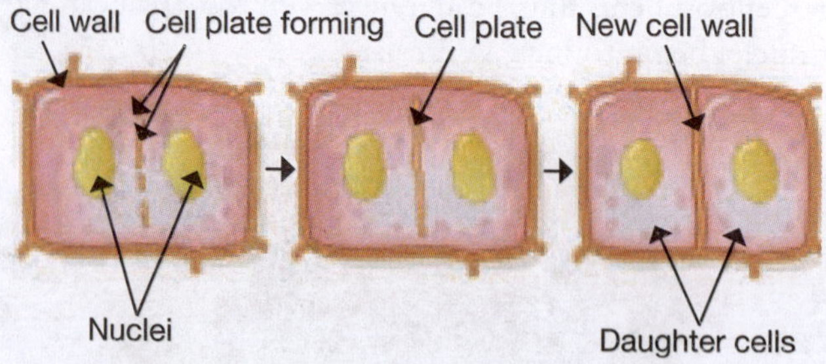

Figure 2.13 Cytokinesis in a plant cell

Significance of Mitosis

Significance of mitosis is discussed below:

- Mitosis results in equal distribution of genetic material from parent cell to the daughter cells.
- At the end of this cell division, the chromosome number is maintained same as the parent cell.
- This results in growth and development of the organisms.
- This cell division also maintains the size of the body of the organism.
- It helps in the regeneration of cells during healing of injuries.
- It helps in the replacement of old and dead cells.
- In plants, mitosis helps in the production of new plants through vegetative propagation, tissue culture, etc.
- It also helps in the production of new organisms by the technique of cloning where the parental characters are retained as it is in the new organisms.

Meiosis

The term meiosis was coined by J. B. Farmers and J. E. S. Moore. Meiosis is the type of cell division that occurs in the reproductive cells or germ cells. This is the type of cell division is involved in the formation of male and female gametes in the higher organisms. The interphase stage involving DNA replication takes place to prepare the cell for the cell division in the same way as in the case of mitotic cell division. Just like mitosis, karyokinesis is followed by cytokinesis in meiosis. However, meiosis differs from mitosis in that it involves two successive nuclear divisions during karyokinesis. The first nuclear division is known as meiosis-I and the second one is known as meiosis-II.

Info Bytes!

Siblings from same parent have different genetic make up.

Meiosis-I

Meiosis-I takes place in four phases just like mitosis. The four phases of meiosis-I are:

1. Prophase-I 2. Metaphase-I 3. Anaphase-I 4. Telophase-I

However, the events taking place during these phases are quite different from those taking place in the respective phases of mitosis. Meiosis-I may be followed by cytokinesis or may directly lead to meiosis-II. At the end of meiosis-I, two haploid daughter cells are formed from one diploid mother cell. Meiosis-II is similar to mitosis cell division. It results in the formation of two haploid daughter cells from each haploid daughter cell, formed at the end of meiosis-I. Among all the four phases.

Prophase-I

Prophase-I of meiosis is the most prolonged and complicated phase and can further be divided into five subphases:

1. Leptotene
2. Zygotene
3. Pachytene
4. Diplotene
5. Diakinesis

Leptotene

- Appearance of chromosomes as long threads
- Chromosomes show beaded appearance due to the presence of chromomeres
- Formation of homologous chromosomes

↓

Zygotene

- Pairing of homologous chromosomes known as synapsis
- Each pair of homologous chromosomes is called bivalent
- Attachment of chromosomes to nucleoprotein in lateral manner

↓

Pachytene

- Chromosomes become short and thick
- Chromatids get separated and become clearly visible
- Four chromatids form one pair of homologous chromosomes, called tetrad
- Exchange of genes between non-sister chromatids (chromatids of different chromosomes) takes place. This phenomenon is known as crossing over

↓

Diplotene

- Separation of homologous chromosomes
- Chromosomes attached only at the region of crossing over
- This point of attachment is called chiasma (plural: chiasmata)

↓

Diakinesis

- Disappearance of chiasmata known as terminalization
- Disappearance of nucleolus
- Formation of fibres from nuclear membrane
- Chromosomes acquire characteristic size and form

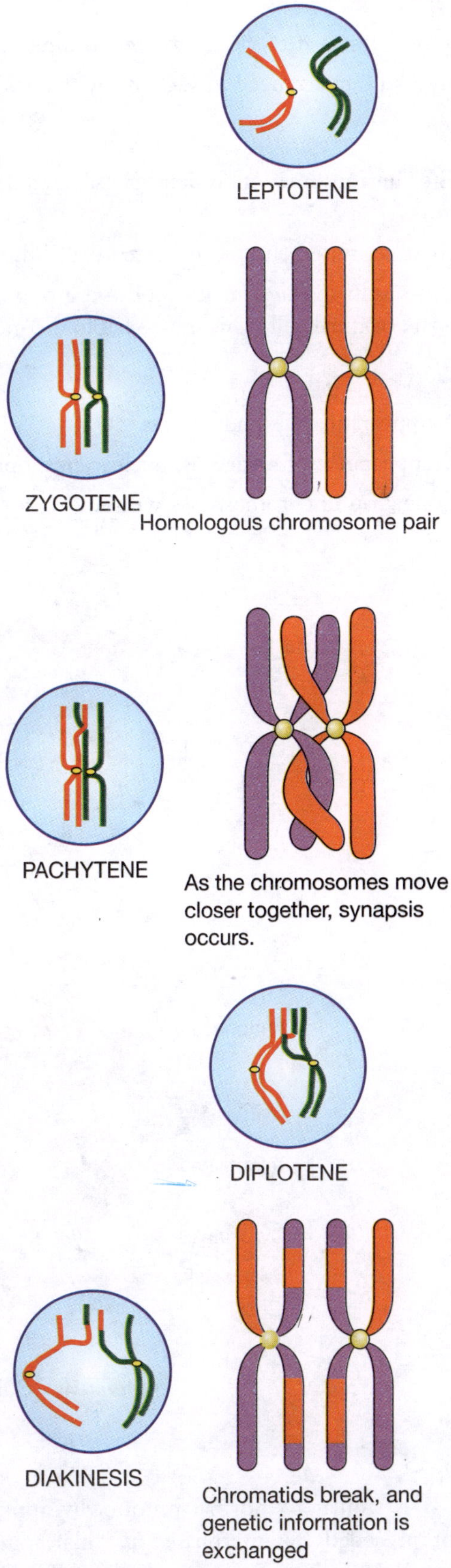

Figure 2.14 Sub-phases of prophase-I (meiosis-I)

Metaphase-I

- Spindle fibres are formed from centromere or microtubules.
- Bivalents are arranged in such a way that they form an equatorial plate.

Anaphase-I

- The chromosomes of bivalents get separated and move towards the opposite poles. This process is known as disjunction.
- These separated chromosomes are called dyads. Each dyad comprises two chromatids joined at the centromere.
- This results in the formation of two groups of chromosomes, each with half the number of chromosomes present in the original cell. This means haploid condition is attained.

Telophase-I

- Disappearance of spindle fibres
- Reappearance of nucleolus, nuclear envelope and nucleoplasm.
- Elongation of chromosomes without the formation of network

Info Bytes!

Mutation is the process of changing a DNA sequence permanently and it can occur during meiosis.

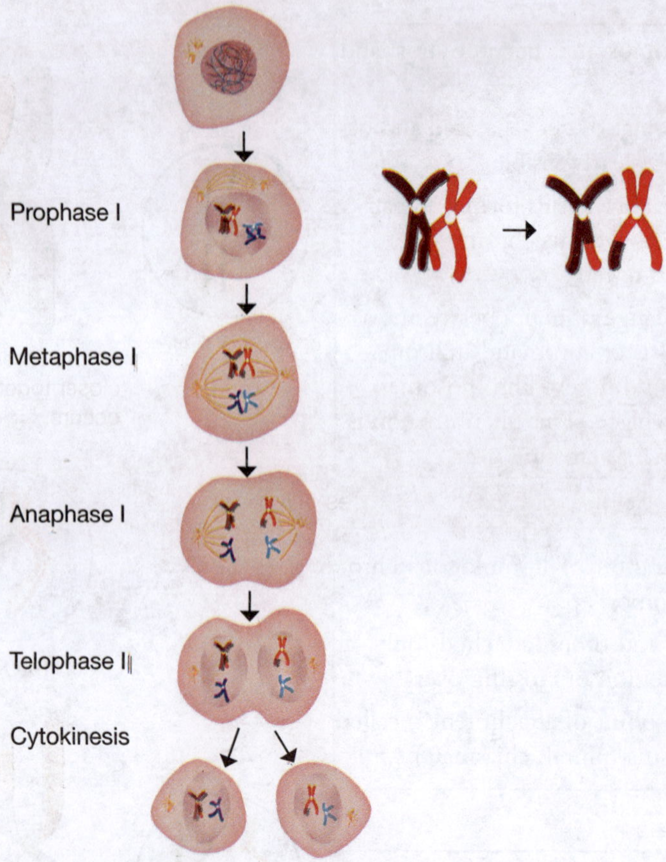

Figure 2.15 Sub-phases of meiosis-I

Info Bytes!

The record for understanding the cell cycle was set by three scientists – Leland Hartwell, Tim Hunt, and Paul Nurse – who were awarded the Nobel Prize in 2001 for their ground-breaking discoveries on the key regulators of the cell cycle.

Meiosis-II

Meiosis-II is similar to normal mitotic division in which the chromosome number is retained. However, meiosis-II is not preceded by interphase. Just like mitosis, meiosis-II takes place in four phases. They are: prophase-II; metaphase-II; anaphase-II; and telophase-II. The two stages of karyokinesis are followed by cytokinesis. This completes the entire meiotic division. The two haploid daughter cells formed at the end of meiosis-I undergo meiosis-II separately, resulting in the formation of four haploid daughter cells. This means that two daughter cells are formed from each daughter cell of meiosis-I. Meiotic cell division eventually results in the formation of four haploid daughter cells from a diploid mother cell in contrast to mitotic cell division which results in the formation of two diploid daughter cells from a diploid mother cell. On the whole, as a result of meiotic cell division of one diploid germ cell, four haploid daughter cells are formed. These haploid daughter cells are called gametes. In the case of male organisms, the male gametes (sperms) are produced by meiotic cell division of the germ cells. In the case of female organisms, the female gametes (eggs or ova) are produced by meiotic cell division of the germcells.

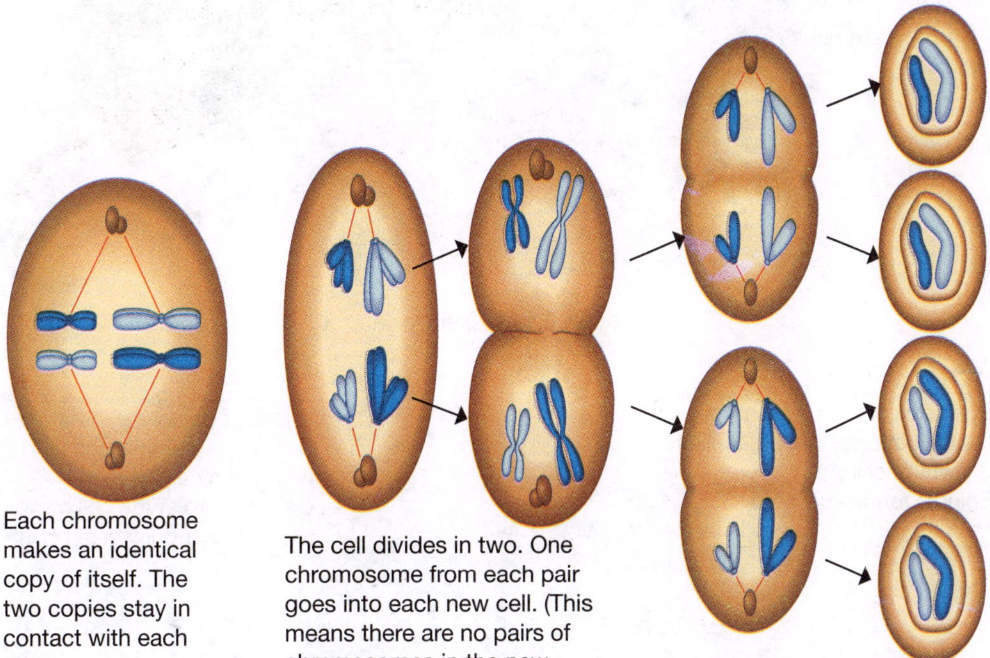

Figure 2.16 Sub-phases of Meiosis-II

Cell Cycle

The haploid male gamete fuses with the haploid female gamete to form a diploid zygote during the process of fertilization. Thus, the chromosome number is retained for the organism. The diploid zygote undergoes repeated mitotic divisions and subsequent processes resulting in the development and growth of the organism. Every mitotic division of a cell results in the formation of two new daughter cells. As the daughter cells are not ready for further cell division, they go through the interphase in which DNA replication and other events take place. Thus, the cells undergo cyclic sequence of events in the body of the organism. This is known as cell cycle.

> **Info Bytes!**
>
> If errors arise during the cell cycle, checkpoints exist to either correct them or halt the cycle, preventing the proliferation of faulty cells.

The series of events taking place in a cell involving duplication of DNA followed by the formation of two daughter cells which again follow the same series of events is known as cell cycle.

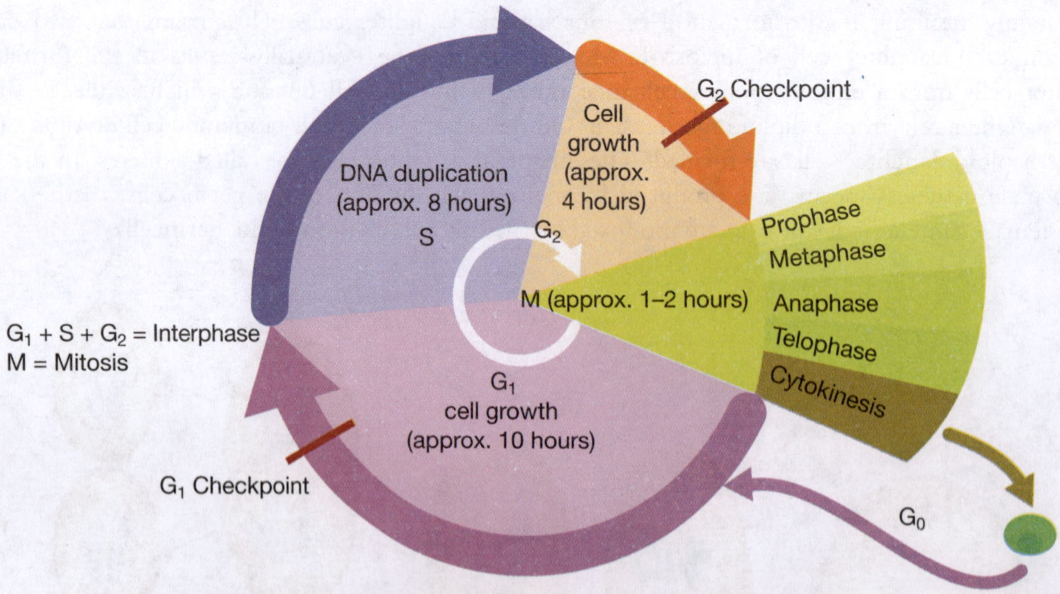

Figure 2.17 Cell cycle

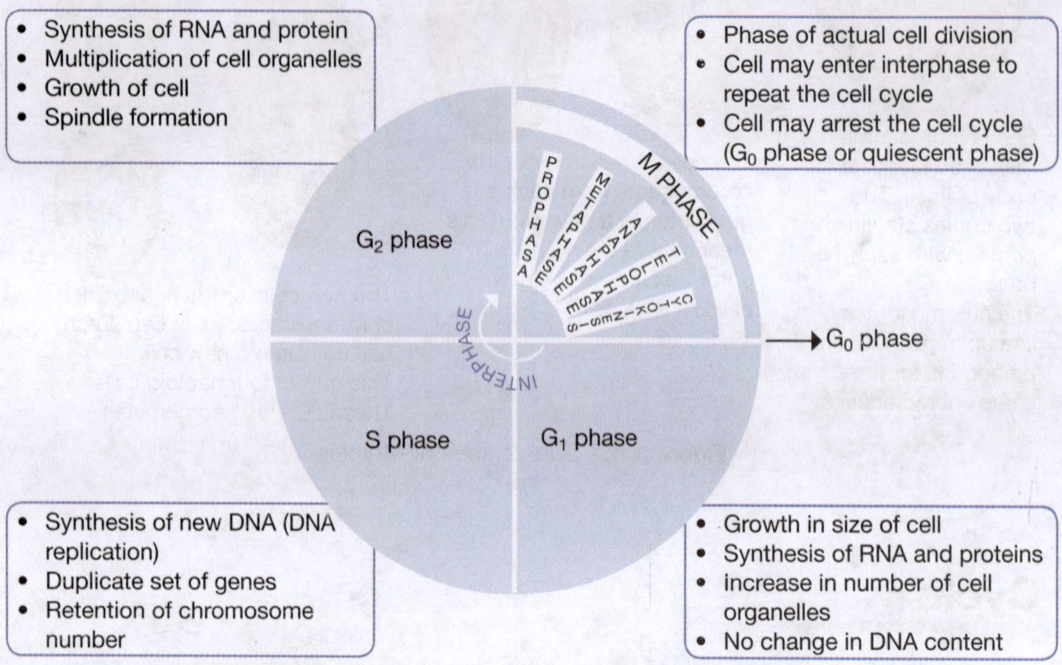

Figure 2.18 Cell cycle—Schematic representation

The cell cycle can be basically divided into two phases, namely:

1. Non-dividing interphase
2. Dividing mitotic phase

Interphase pertains to the changes taking place in newly formed cell. This is basically a preparatory phase for the cell during which the cell undergoes certain changes required for undergoing cell division by itself. Interphase (I phase) is the longest phase as it lasts for around or more than 90% of the time. This phase can further be divided into three sub-phases depending on the events taking place inside the cell. The three sub-phases include first growth phase (G_1 phase), second growth phase (G_2 phase) and synthetic phase. This is followed by mitotic phase (M phase) which is the actual dividing phase and lasts for a short span of time. After M phase, a cell again enters the interphase and repeats the cycle of cell division. During this transition from interphase to M-phase, some of the cells may take a different course. This is called G_0 phase or quiescent phase. The cell may stop further cell division due to lack of nutrients and may remain inactive or die. The period of inactivity may differ from cell to cell. The cell may not undergo cell division but remain metabolically active by undergoing a process of cell differentiation where it becomes specialized to perform specific tasks. This above process results in the formation of tissues. The cells of these tissues may undergo cell division only at the time of injury for the purpose of healing.

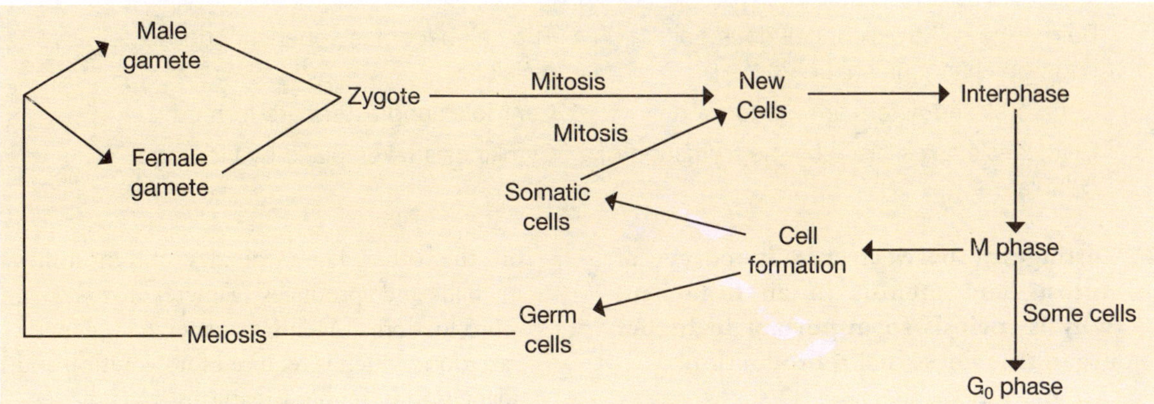

Figure 2.19 Typical life cycle of cells of a higher organism involving cell cycle

Quick Recap

✔ **Explain the significance of direct and indirect cell division in terms of the processes and outcomes. What differences do their approaches to cellular continuity have?**

Direct cell division, or amitosis, involves directly splitting the nucleus, whereas indirect cell division involves more complicated phases like mitosis and meiosis. The indirect method is more precise and controlled, whereas the direct method is faster but less precise.

✔ **Mention the differences between mitosis and meiosis.**

Mitosis	Meiosis
Occurs mainly in somatic cells	Occurs in germ cells or reproductive cells
Two daughter cells are formed which may be haploid or dipioid	Four daughter cells are formed which are always haploid
This division occurs both in asexually and sexually reproducing organisms	Occurs only in sexually reproducing organisms
DNA replication takes place only once for every cell division during interphase	DNA replication takes place only once for two cell divisions that are meiosis I and II
Daughter nuclei formed are exactly similar to that of parent cell	Daughter nuclei are formed by genetic recombinations caused due to crossing over. Hence, they are not similar to parent
Prophase is very short and simple	Prophase is elaborate and made up of sub-stages
Synapsis of homologous chromosomes and crossing over do not occur	Synapsis and crossing over take place
Synaptonemal complex is not formed	Synaptonemal complex is formed
Chromosomal number remains constant	Chromosomal number is reduced to half
Helps in growth and repair of tissues	Helps in formation of gametes

✔ **Distinguish between the mitotic cell division in plant cell and that in animal cell.**

Mitosis in plant cell	Mitosis in animal cell
Usually takes place in growing regions such as root tip, shoot tip and lateral regions of stems and roots	It takes place in almost all the regions of the body, except brain
Before the cell division, cell does not undergo change in shape	The cell becomes spherical prior to cell division
Centrioles and asters are not formed	Centrioles and asters are formed
Cytokinesis takes place by the formation of cell plate	Cytokinesis takes place by cleavage

✔ **Distinguish between the functions of mitosis and meiosis in an organism. Why is meiosis so important in higher organisms for sexual reproduction?**

Mitosis ensures cell growth and repair by producing identical daughter cells. Meiosis, on the other hand, divides chromosomes in half and produces gametes for sexual reproduction. Meiosis generates genetic variation, which is required for evolution and adaptation in higher organisms.

POINTS TO REMEMBER

- ✔ The process of formation of new cells by the division of pre-existing cells is known as cell division.
- ✔ Depending on the method in which the division of nucleus takes place, the cell division can be of two types: direct cell division and indirect cell division.
- ✔ Amitosis is the mode of cell division in which the division takes place within the nucleus.
- ✔ Mitosis takes place in all the somatic cells in the body of the organism.
- ✔ Mitosis can be divided into three sub-phases: First growth phase (G_1 phase), Synthetic phase (S phase) and Second growth phase (G_2 phase).
- ✔ Mitosis results in growth and development of the organisms.
- ✔ Meiosis is the type of cell division which is responsible for production of male and female gametes in higher organisms.
- ✔ Meiosis-I is divided into 4 sub-phases: Prophase-I, Metaphase-I, Anaphase-I and Telophase-I.
- ✔ Prophase-I of meiosis-I is the most prolonged and complicated phase and can further be divided into five subphases: Leptotene, Zygotene, Pachytene, Diplotene and Diakinesis.
- ✔ Meiosis-II is similar to normal mitotic division in which the chromosome number is retained.
- ✔ The series of events taking place in a cell involving duplication of DNA followed by the formation of two daughter cells which again follow the same series of events is known as cell cycle.

PRACTICE QUESTIONS CLASSROOM WING

Very Short Answer Type Questions

Directions for questions from 1 to 9:
Fill in the blanks.

1. In unicellular organisms, growth results due to the increase in size and volume of the _________.
2. While the DNA content of the cell is doubled during the S phase, the number of chromosomes remains _________.
3. The _________ phase of the cell cycle results in the formation of spindle fibres.
4. The ________ is responsible for the preservation of the DNA sequence of the original cell.
5. During amitosis, there is no appearance of_________.
6. Daughter chromosomes reach their poles in the ______ stage of the cell division.
7. Spindle fibres disappear in _____ phase of meiosis-I
8. ______ is the most appropriate stage to count the number of chromosomes.
9. Meiotic division of a diploid germ cell results in the formation of ______ daughter cells.

Directions for questions from 10 to 26:
For each of the following questions, four choices have been provided. Select the correct alternatives.

10. Why does cell division in unicellular organisms differ significantly from multicellular ones?
    (a) Multicellular organisms do not reproduce.
    (b) Cell division in unicellular organisms only results in growth.
    (c) Cell division in unicellular organisms leads to a completely new individual.
    (d) Unicellular organisms have simpler DNA.
11. Which of the following does not occur during the prophase of mitosis?
    (a) Formation of spindle fibres
    (b) Disappearance of the nuclear membrane
    (c) Synthesis of new DNA
    (d) Chromatin condensation
12. Which phase of the cell cycle prepares the cell for mitosis but does not involve actual division?
    (a) S phase (b) G_2 phase
    (c) G_1 phase (d) Interphase
13. The structure allowing chromatids to attach to spindle fibres is the:
    (a) Kinetochore (b) Centromere
    (c) Centrosome (d) Aster ray
14. Indirect cell division is characterized by the appearance of:
    (a) Nuclei (b) Cytoplasm
    (c) Chromosomes (d) Organelles
15. Which of the following occurs in anaphase stage of cell division?
    (a) Formation of dyads
    (b) Formation of spindle fibres
    (c) Disappearance of spindle fibres
    (d) Reappearance of nucleolus
16. Which of the following is true at the end of the mitotic cell division process regarding chromosome number?
    (a) Chromosome number in a daughter cell is less than that in the parent cell.
    (b) Chromosome number in a daughter cell is less than or equal to that in the parent cell.
    (c) Chromosome number in a daughter cell is equal to that in the parent cell.
    (d) Chromosome number in a daughter cell is greater than or equal to that in the parent cell.
17. Identify the number of chromosomes in human germ cell.
    (a) 23 (b) 46
    (c) 92 (d) 23 in males and 46 in females
18. Which stage of mitotic cell division bears V-shaped chromosomes?
    (a) Prophase (b) Anaphase
    (c) Metaphase (d) Telophase

19. Identify the cell which does not undergo meiosis.
(a) Bacterial cell
(b) Plant cell
(c) Animal cell
(d) Fungal cell

20. Identify the location in which exchange of genetic material occurs in the process of crossing over.
(a) Chromatids and non-homologous chromosomes.
(b) Sister chromatids of the homologous chromosomes.
(c) Non-sister chromatids of the homologous chromosomes.
(d) Between chromosomes.

21. In which of the following aspects, meiosis-II differs from mitotic cell division?
(a) Meiosis-II involves crossing over
(b) Meiosis-II is not followed by cytokinesis
(c) Meiosis-II gives rise to four daughter cells from one parent cell.
(d) Meiosis-II is not preceded by interphase.

22. How many daughter cells are formed after meiotic cell division from five mother cells?
(a) 40
(b) 10
(c) 30
(d) 20

23. Identify (i) and (ii) in the following chart?

Parent cell → 2 Daughter cells (i) → 4 Daughter cells (ii)

(a) (i) = 2n; (ii) = n
(b) (i) = n; (ii) = n
(c) (i) = n; (ii) = 2n
(d) (i) = 2n; (ii) = 2n

24. Which of the following are wrong statements/?
(i) Bivalents are tetrads
(ii) A bivalent means four chromatids and two centromeres
(iii) One bivalent consists of two homologous chromosomes
(iv) Bivalents are formed in zygotene
(a) (i) (ii) (iii) and (iv)
(b) (ii) only
(c) (iii) and (iv)
(d) (iv) only

25. Identify the correct sequence of cell cycle.
(a) $G_2 \rightarrow M \rightarrow G_1 \rightarrow S$.
(b) $S \rightarrow G_2 \rightarrow M \rightarrow G_1$.
(c) $G_1 \rightarrow S \rightarrow G_2 \rightarrow M$.
(d) $M \rightarrow G_1 \rightarrow S \rightarrow G_2$.

26. Which is the most appropriate stage to count the number of chromosomes?
(a) Prophase
(b) Interphase
(c) Metaphase
(d) Telophase

Directions for questions from 27:
Match the entries of Column 1 with those of Column 2.

27.

Column 1	Column 2
A. Crossing over	(i) Diakinesis
B. Pairing of homologous chromosomes	(ii) Diplotene
C. Formation of fibres from nuclear membrane	(iii) Pachytene
D. Chiasmata formation	(iv) Zygotene

Short Answer Type Questions

28. How does the role of cell division in unicellular organisms contrast with its role in multicellular organisms?

29. Give technical terms for the following.
(a) Division which brings about vegetative propagation.
(b) The stage in which bivalents are formed.
(c) The process during which meiosis occurs in human beings.
(d) Points at which two sister chromatids are held together.
(e) The process of division of cytoplasm.
(f) Proteins and RNA synthesis takes place in this stage.

30. Why might it be important for the DNA content to double during the S phase, even though the number of chromosomes remains constant?

31. Describe the relationship between kinetochore, spindle fibres, and chromatids during mitosis.

32. How are spindle fibres formed during cell division? What is their importance?

33. All the somatic cells in the body of an individual have exactly identical DNA. Why?

34. Mitosis helps in cellular regeneration. Give reason.

Direction for Questions from 35 to 36:
Answer the following questions.

35. What is cell differentiation?

36. What is a nucleosome?

Essay Type Questions

37. Elaborate on the significance and roles of the various phases in the cell cycle. How does each phase prepare the cell for mitosis, and why is this preparation crucial?

38. (i) Mention the phase of mitosis that is shown in the below figure and label the parts A, B, C and D. Mention the changes taking place in the given phase.

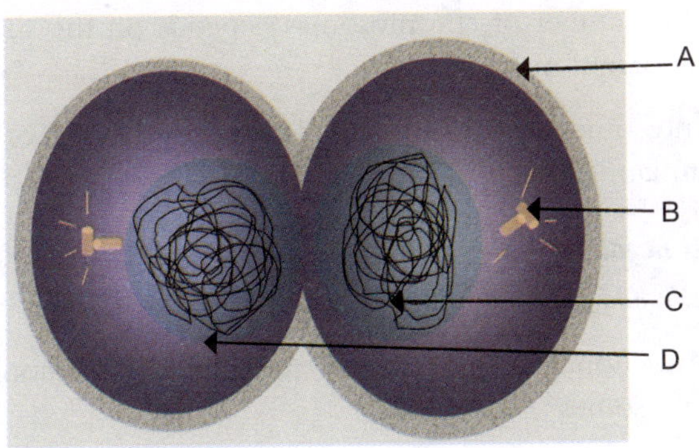

(ii) Observe the figure and answer the questions that follow.

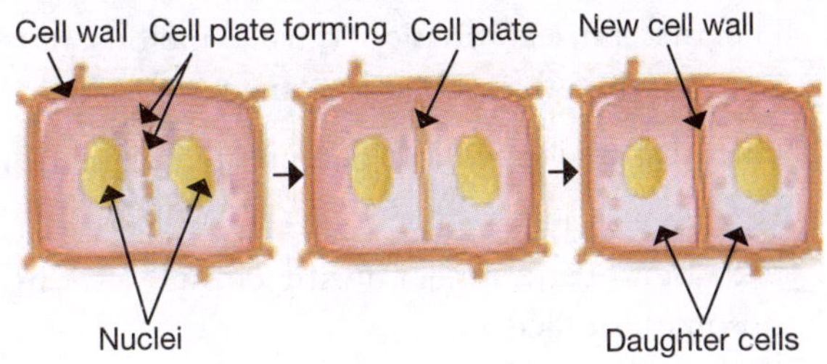

(a) Name whether this type of cell division takes place in plants or animals and why?

(b) Name and explain the phase of cell division that is shown.

39. Discuss the evolutionary significance of amitosis and mitosis. How might the complexities of mitosis offer advantages to multicellular organisms compared to the simpler amitosis?

PRACTICE QUESTIONS COMPETITION WING

Level 1: Apply your Concepts

Directions for questions from 1 to 14:
Fill in the blanks.

1. Meiosis is a type of cell division that results in the formation of ______ cells from a ______ cell.

2. The first nuclear division during meiosis is termed ______ while the second is termed ______.

3. The most prolonged and complicated phase of meiosis-I is ________.

4. The point of attachment during crossing over in chromosomes is called a ________.

5. After the process of fertilization, a ______ zygote is formed.

6. ______ is the basic structural, functional and hereditary unit of all living organisms.

7. _____ is also referred to as ribosome factory.

8. DNA is a part of _______ in nucleus.

9. Adenine and Guanine are called ______ bases.

10. The membrane by which vacuoles are bound is ______.

11. Thymine and Cytosine are called ______ bases.

12. The kind of structure of a DNA is ______.

13. The number of sets of chromosomes in a cell is ______.

14. The pair of chromosomes that are similar in structure is called _______ chromosomes.

Direction for Questions from 15 to 16:
For each of the following questions four choices have been provided. Select the correct alternatives.

15. Division of centromere and chromatids takes place between which stages of mitotic cell division?

(a) Prophase and metaphase

(b) Metaphase and anaphase

(c) Anaphase and telophase

(d) Telophase and prophase

16. The order of phases in mitosis is

(a) Metaphase, Prophase, Anaphase and Telophase

(b) Prophase, Metaphase, Telophase, Anaphase

(c) Prophase, Metaphase, Anaphase, Telophase

(d) Anaphase, Prophase, Metaphase, Telophase

Direction for Questions from 17 and 18:
Check if the given statement is correct or not, if found incorrect rewrite the correct statement.

17. The number of chromosomes depends on the size of the organism.

18. Autosomes in human cells determine the sex of the human.

Direction for Questions from 19 to 21:
Find the odd term out giving reasons.

19. Mitochondria; Endoplasmic reticulum; Chromoplast; Ribosomes

20. Endoplasmic reticulum; Chloroplast; Chromoplast; Leucoplast

21. Chromatin fibre; Ribosome; Mitochondria; Vacuoles

Direction for Questions from 22 to 24:
Write the missing correlated terms.

22. RNA → Single helix :: DNA → _____

23. Diploid : 2n :: ______ :: Haploid

24. Karyokinesis: Nuclear division :: Cytokinesis : ______

Direction for Questions from 25 to 35:
Choose the correct option.

(a) Both A and R are true and R is the correct explanation for A.

(b) Both A and R are true, but R is not the correct explanation for A.

(c) A is true and R is false.

(d) A is false and R is true.

25. **Assertion (A):** Inactive stage in the cell cycle is quiescent stage.
Reason (R): All the cells pass through quiescent stage.

26. **Assertion (A):** All the cell organelles are seen until the end of prophase.
Reason (R): Chromatids separate but remain in the centre of the cell in anaphase.

27. **Assertion (A):** Haploid cells are formed by meiosis cell division.
Reason (R): Gametes are haploid cells.

28. **Assertion (A):** Recombination and crossing over take place in meiosis I.
Reason (R): In the process of meiosis two stages of DNA replication take place.

29. **Assertion (A):** Crossing over takes place between two homologous chromosomes.
Reason (R): Crossing over is the exchange of chromosomal fragments between homologous chromosomes.

30. **Assertion (A):** Gametes formed from the same individual have exactly identical DNA.
Reason (R): Homologous chromosomes are formed by DNA replication.

31. **Assertion (A):** The cell division in a plant cell is called an astral division.
Reason (R): Cytokinesis in plant cell takes place by the formation of cell plate.

32. **Assertion (A):** All the cells in an individual possess same DNA.
Reason (R): DNA replication involves complementary base pairing.

33. **Assertion(A):** Mitotic cell division is referred to as homotypic division.
Reason (R): Mitotic cell division retains the number of chromosomes.

34. **Assertion (A):** Karyokinesis is the significant stage in cell division.
Reason (R): Crossing over takes place during karyokinesis.

35. **Assertion (A):** Chromosome number is maintained constant at the end of S phase.
Reason(R): S phase does not involve crossing over phenomenon.

Level 2: Review your Concepts

36. Why is Prophase-I of meiosis more complex than the prophase of mitosis?

37. Give importance of mitosis in embryo development.

38. Describe the role of chiasma in the process of meiosis.

39. Quiescent stage is the inactive stage. Justify.

40. Which kind of cell division leads to cancer? Explain.

Level 3: Assess Your Concepts

41. Meiosis is responsible for creating genetic diversity among sexually reproducing organisms. Discuss why genetic diversity is vital for the survival of species and how meiosis contributes to it.

42. Imagine a world where organisms reproduce without meiosis, leading to no genetic diversity among offspring. Describe how this could impact ecosystems, evolution, and the survival of species.

43. After the removal of cancerous tumor by surgical procedure, the organ is treated with chemotherapy or radiotherapy. Explain the reason with reference to the concept of cell cycle.

AT

PRACTICE QUESTIONS NEET SPECIAL WING

Multiple-Answer Type Questions

Questions number 1 to 5 are multiple-choice questions. Each question has FOUR options (a), (b), (c), and (d). ONE OR MORE THAN ONE of these four option(s) is/are the correct answer(s).

1. Which of the following is true for Pachytene stage of Prophase I?
   (a) Formation of homologous chromosomes
   (b) Crossing over
   (c) Bivalent formation
   (d) Tetrad formation

2. Which of the following is true regarding cytokinesis in plant cell?
   (a) Centrifugal division
   (b) Cleavage formation
   (c) Centripetal in nature
   (d) Preceded by cell plate formation

3. Which of the following terms are not related to the complex formed by a pair of synapsed homologous chromosomes?
   (a) Bivalent (b) Kinetochore
   (c) Equatorial plate (d) Synapsis

4. A somatic cell which has just gone through the synthetic phase of the cell cycle as compared to its gamete has:
   (a) double the DNA
   (b) four times the DNA
   (c) twice the number of chromosomes
   (d) Same number of chromosomes

5. Which of the following contain microtubules?
   (a) Spindle fibres
   (b) Mitochondria
   (c) Centrioles
   (d) Cilia

Comprehension-Based Questions

A. Read the paragraph given below and answer the questions number 6 to 11:

Meiosis is an important process for gamete formation. It is the only process through which gametes can be formed in sexual reproduction. In human body the normal cells are diploid and have 23 pairs of chromosomes. But the gametes that are formed only have half the number of chromosomes and are haploid. This reduction in the chromosome number is necessary as sexual reproduction involves fusion of the male and female gamete during fertilisation. Meiosis consists of two phases – Meiosis I and Meiosis II. Meiosis I and II both show the following phases that is Prophase, Metaphase, Anaphase, Telophase followed by cytokinesis. But the difference between Meiosis I and Meiosis II is that in the first one reduction of chromosome number takes place and in the latter proper mitotic division takes place. Prophase I of meiosis I is unique in that it consists of further five stages namely- Leptotene, Zygotene, Pachytene, Diplotene and Diakinesis. In meiosis we see a unique feature of DNA recombination which helps the organisms to adapt to the changing environment.

6. The process of female gamete formation is halted at prophase 1 of meiosis I until the female reaches puberty. So, during childhood the DNA in the female gamete consists of
   (a) 46 chromosomes, 92 chromatids
   (b) 46 chromosomes, 46 chromatids
   (c) 23 chromosomes, 46 chromatids
   (d) 23 chromosomes, 23 chromatids

7. The number of centromeres and chromatids present in bivalent is
   (a) 4 centromeres, 4 chromatids
   (b) 2 centromeres, 4 chromatids
   (c) 1 centromeres, 2 chromatids
   (d) 2 centromeres, 2 chromatids

8. Which of the following is also called as reductional division?
   (a) Meiosis I
   (b) Meiosis II
   (c) Both a and b
   (d) None of the above

9. Which is the longest phase of meiosis I?
(a) Prophase I
(b) Metaphase I
(c) Anaphase I
(d) Telophase I

10. Both ovum and sperm are formed by meiosis, which of the following statement is true regarding the process of the gamete formation?
(a) Female gamete formed is larger than the male gamete
(b) The process of meiosis is halted in both till reproductive maturity
(c) In both the processes 4 viable gametes are produced
(d) Eggs and sperms are both motile

11. Match the column:

Column – A	Column – B
(i) Pachytene	(a) Homologous chromosomes
(ii) Zygotene	(b) Crossing over
(iii) Diakinesis	(c) Bivalent
(iv) Diplotene	(d) Terminalization
(v) Leptotene	(e) Chiasma

B. Read the paragraph given below and answer the questions number 12 to 17:

The continuous series of events that take place where new cells are produced from the old ones is called cell cycle. The interphase of the cell cycle is the longest phase and consists of G_1, S and G_2 phase. G_1 and G_2 are growth phases and DNA synthesis occurs in the S phase. It is in the M or the mitotic phase that the cell divides. In mitosis first nuclear division takes place and then cytoplasmic division. The nuclear division takes place in 4 stages which include Prophase, metaphase, anaphase and telophase. In mitosis the chromosome number is retained. Mitosis is required for growth, repair and maintenance.

12. In which phase DNA synthesis takes place?
(a) G_1
(b) G_2
(c) S
(d) M

13. Colchicine prevents cell division, so in which phase of mitosis does it arrests the cell division?
(a) Prophase
(b) Metaphase
(c) Anaphase
(d) Telophase

14. The nuclear envelope starts disappearing at which phase?
(a) Prometaphase
(b) Metaphase
(c) Anaphase
(d) Telophase

15. In early prophase a diploid cell has ______ chromosomes and at telophase, it has ______ chromosomes.
(a) 23, 23
(b) 46, 23
(c) 46, 46
(d) 46, 92

16. Which of the following statement is true regarding mitosis?
(a) Spindle fibres bind to centromere and initiates the separation of homologous chromosomes.
(b) Centrosome bind to chromatids to ensure equal division.
(c) Centrioles found on chromatids to form asters.
(d) Centrioles form spindle fibres which bind to kinetochore and helps to pull the chromatids apart.

17. Match the column:

Column – A	Column – B
(i) Prophase	(a) Preparatory phase before cell division
(ii) Metaphase	(b) Aster formation
(iii) Anaphase	(c) Attachment of spindle fibres at the kinetochore
(iv) Telophase	(d) Chromatids move to the poles
(v) Interphase	(e) Nuclear membrane and nucleolus reappears

ANSWER KEYS

Crossword

Across

4. Microtubule
5. Spores
6. Cellplate
8. Telophase
9. Anaphase
10. Inherit
11. Zygote
14. Chiasmata

Down

1. Kinetochore
2. Terminalization
3. Spleen
7. Asterrays
10. Interphase
12. Fleming
13. Amitosis

Classroom Wing

Very Short Answer Type Questions

1. Cytoplasmic contents
2. Constant
3. G_2
4. Replication
5. Chromosomes
6. Telophase
7. The telophase
8. Metaphase
9. Haploid
10. (c)
11. (c)
12. (d)
13. (a)
14. (c)
15. (a)
16. (c)
17. (b)
18. (b)
19. (a)
20. (c)
21. (d)
22. (d)
23. (b)
24. (b)
25. (c)
26. (c)
27. A → (iii), B → (iv), C → (i), D → (ii)

Competition Wing

Level 1: Apply Your Concepts

1. Four haploid, diploid mother
2. Meiosis-I, meiosis-II
3. Prophase-I
4. Chiasma
5. Diploid
6. Cell
7. Nucleolus
8. Chromatin
9. Purine
10. Tonoplast
11. Pyrimidine
12. Double helix
13. Ploidy
14. Homologous
15. (b)
16. (c)
19. Chromoplast
20. Endoplasmic reticulum
21. Chromatin fibre
22. Double helix
23. 2n
24. Cytoplasmic division
25. (c)
26. (d)
27. (b)
28. (c)
29. (a)
30. (c)
31. (b)
32. (b)
33. (a)
34. (b)
35. (b)

NEET Special Wing

Multiple-Answer Type Questions

1. (b, d) 2. (a, d) 3. (a, d) 4. (b, c) 5. (a, c, d)

Comprehension-Based Questions

6. (a) 7. (b) 8. (a) 9. (a) 10. (a)

11. (i) → (b); (ii) → (c); (iii) → (d); (iv) → (a); (v) → (e)

12. (c) 13. (b) 14. (a) 15. (c) 16. (d)

17. (i) → (b); (ii) → (c); (iii) → (d); (iv) → (e); (v) → (a)

Hints and Explanations

CLASSROOM WING

Short Answer Type Questions

28. In unicellular organisms, cell division essentially leads to the creation of a new organism, functioning as a mode of reproduction. On the other hand, in multicellular organisms, cell division contributes to growth, development, repair, and in some cases, reproduction.

29. Technical terms
    (a) Mitosis
    (b) Zygotene
    (c) Gamete formation
    (d) Chiasmata
    (e) Cytokinesis
    (f) G_2 phase of interphase

30. The doubling of DNA content ensures that after the cell divides, both daughter cells receive a complete and identical set of genetic information. The number of chromosomes remains constant because each chromosome consists of two sister chromatids after replication, which get separated during cell division.

31. The kinetochore is a protein structure present in chromatids. During mitosis, spindle fibres, which emerge from the centrosomes, attach to these kinetochores. This attachment helps in the alignment and later separation of chromatids, ensuring proper cell division.

32. Microtubules are seen in the cytoplasm of cell during cell division. These give rise to fine thread-like structures called spindle fibres.

    Spindle fibres move chromatids or chromosomes apart and help them in reaching the poles of the cell.

33. DNA sequence is preserved during mitotic division because of complementary base pairing. Therefore, all the somatic cells have the same DNA sequence.

34. Any somatic tissue or cells can undergo the process of mitosis.

    Injured tissue heals by the process of mitosis.

    This cell division helps in formation of new cells at the injured part.

    Bones form new cells at the fractured region.

    Liver cells have the highest power of regeneration that takes place by cell division that is mitosis.

35. Cell differentiation is a process through which a cell changes from one type to another, to perform special functions during its development. This generally takes place during the development of multicellular organisms, as a multicellular organism changes from a simple zygote to a complex system of tissues and cell types.

36. The double helix of DNA bound by eight molecules of histone protein is known as nucleosome.

    Nucleosomes are the basic units of chromatin fibre.

Essay Type Questions

37. The cell cycle is divided into phases, each of which serves a specific purpose. Cell growth and DNA replication preparation take place during the G1 phase. The S phase is in charge of DNA replication, ensuring that the cell has two full sets of chromosomes. Cells continue to grow and prepare for mitosis during the G2 phase. These phases collaborate to get the cell ready for the mitotic phase. This preparation is critical for ensuring that cell division proceeds smoothly and produces two healthy daughter cells.

38. (i) The phase of mitosis shown in the figure is telophase

    A → Cell membrane, B → Centriole, C → Chromatids, D → Nuclear membrane

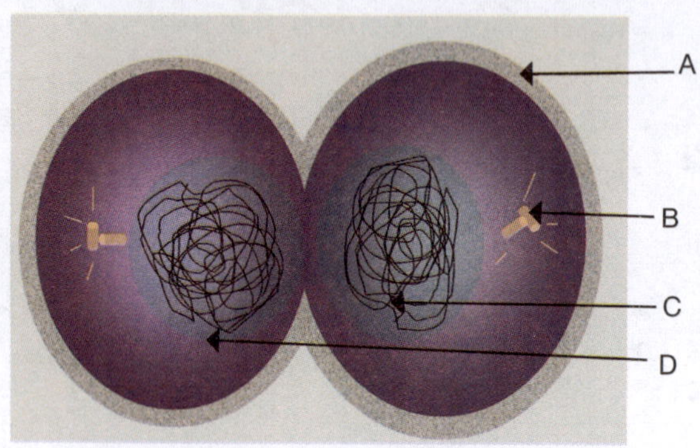

(ii) (a) The type of cell division shown occurs in plants because the cell is bound by a rigid cell wall in addition to the plasma membrane.
(b) The phase of cell division shown is cytokinesis.

Plant cells undergo cytokinesis differently because the cell is bound by a rigid cell wall in addition to the plasma membrane.
During telophase, a cell plate is formed across the cell, in other words, a new cell wall is formed between the two membranes of the cell.
During telophase, membrane-enclosed vesicles derived from the Golgi apparatus migrate to the centre of the cell to form a cell plate.
Eventually, the growing cell plate fuses with the existing plasma membrane, producing two daughter cells, each with its own plasma membrane.
This kind of cytoplasmic division is said to be centrifugal as it starts at the centre and moves towards the periphery.
A new cell wall is formed between the two membranes of the cell plate.

39. While amitosis is a more primitive form of cell division found primarily in unicellular organisms, mitosis has evolved as a more complex and regulated form of cell division found in multicellular organisms. Amitosis is faster, but it lacks the complex controls that ensure each daughter cell inherits the entire set of DNA. Mitosis' evolution could have played a role in the rise and success of complex multicellular organisms by providing mechanisms for maintaining genetic stability, facilitating growth, and repairing injuries.

COMPETITION WING

Level 1: Apply your Concepts

17. Each species of organisms is characterized by a specific number of chromosomes and is not involved with the size of the organism.

18. Autosomes are not sex-related chromosomes, and hence cannot influence the sex of an individual. Allosomes are the sex chromosomes that influence the sex of an individual.

19. Chromoplast is the odd one as this is the cell organelle which is present only in a plant cell, whereas the other three are present either in a plant cell or an animal cell.

20. Endoplasmic reticulum is the odd one as this is the cell organelle which is present either in plant or animal cell whereas the other three are the organelles that are present only in plant cells.

21. Chromatin fibre is the odd one as this is a component which is present in the nucleus of a cell whereas the other three are the organelles of the cells.

22. RNA → Single helix: DNA → Double helix

23. Diploid : $2n$ :: n :: Haploid

24. karyokinesis : Nuclear division :: Cytokinesis : Cytoplasmic division

25. All the cells do not undergo quiescent stage. Assertion is true and reason is false.

    Hence, the correct option is (c).

26. Some of the cell organelles disappear at the end of prophase. Chromatids after separation remain at the centre in anaphase. Only during telophase, they move to the periphery.

    Hence, the correct option is (d).

27. Haploid cells are formed by meiotic cell division. This is a reduction division in which the chromosomal number is reduced to half. Gametes are haploid cells. Both assertion and reason are true, but reason does not support assertion.

    Hence, the correct option is (b).

28. Recombination and crossing over takes place in meiosis I in which exchange of genetic material takes place. DNA replication in meiosis takes place only once before prophase I. After telophase I, the cycle is continuous which starts with prophase II. Assertion is true and reason is false.

    Hence, the correct option is (c).

29. Crossing over is the exchange of genetic material between two homologous chromosomes.
    This takes place in pachytene stage of prophase I in meiotic cell division. Assertion is true and supported by reason.

    Hence, the correct option is (a).

30. Gametes are formed by the meiotic cell division of the germ cell in an individual. The crossing over takes place during the course of cell division. In this, there is exchange of genetic material between the non-sister chromatids. Due to this, the gametes do not have exactly identical DNA, though DNA replication preserves the nucleotide sequence in the homologous chromosomes.

    Hence, the correct option is (c).

31. The cell division in a plant cell does not involve the formation of aster as the plant cell lacks centriole or centrosome.
    It is not because of cell plate formation during cytokinesis. Both assertion and reason are true but reason does not support assertion.

    Hence, the correct option is (b).

32. Due to the complementary base pairing during DNA replication in cell division, the daughter cells formed as a result of cell division possess the same DNA as the parent cell. Hence, DNA sequence in an individual is preserved.

    Hence, the correct option is (b).

33. The daughter cells formed during mitotic cell division have the same number of chromosomes as the parent cell. Hence it is known as homotypic division.

    Hence, the correct option is (a).

34. Karyokinesis involves the nuclear division. It involves the distribution of chromosomes that contain the genetic material. Therefore, this is the most significant stage during cell division. This pertains to both mitosis and meiosis. Crossing over takes place during karyokinesis in only meiosis. Both assertion and reason are true but reason does not support assertion.

    Hence, the correct option is (b).

35. DNA replication is the main event which takes place during S phase. The genetic material gets doubled. The number of chromatids becomes doubled. Since the sister chromatids remain attached at the centromere, the number of chromosomes remains the same.

S phase is a part of interphase which is preparatory phase for the cell. It is not the actual dividing phase of the cell. Crossing over phenomenon is related to the dividing phase of only meosis. Reason does not support assertion.

Hence, the correct option is (b).

Level 2: Review your Concepts

36. Prophase-I in meiosis is more complex because it involves the pairing of homologous chromosomes (synapsis), formation of bivalents, and crossing over among non-sister chromatids.

37. Mitosis is important in embryonic development as single cell zygote develops into embryo. This embryo undergoes mitotic cell division and gives rise to many cells. These cells form tissues, undergoes differentiation to form organs and organ systems for the normal functioning of an individual. Perfect development of embryo is not possible without mitotic cell division.

38. Chiasma is the point where two non-sister chromatids have exchanged genetic material. It's crucial for genetic diversity and ensures proper segregation of chromosomes.

39. There are certain cells in the animal body that do not divide and enter into an inactive stage. This stage is known as quiescent stage or G_0 of cell cycle.
Cells of this stage are metabolically active, but do not divide until the requirement of an organism.
They divide occasionally when needed to be replaced. For example, heart cells.

40. Normally, cells undergo cell division which is controlled by enzymes. They go through cell cycles repeatedly and at some stage, like 40–60 cycles, they become inactive and eventually die. This phenomenon is called apoptosis. But, due to some reason, when the controlling mechanism fails, the cell cycles take place rapidly and in an uncontrolled manner and the phenomenon of apoptosis fails. As a result, the cells divide abnormally producing a lump of tissues in the respective organ. This is called tumor. If the cells do not have the ability to invade other organs, it is called benign tumor. If the cells have the ability to invade other organs, it is called malignant or cancerous tumor.

Level 3: Assess Your Concepts

41. Because of genetic diversity, populations can adapt to changing environments, ensuring their survival. Meiosis, particularly crossing over in Prophase I, results in gametes with unique gene combinations. Because of this diversity, there is a greater chance that if environmental conditions change, at least some individuals will have the necessary traits to survive and reproduce.

42. There would be no genetic diversity among offspring if meiosis did not occur. Every member of a species is a clone of their parents. Because no individual would have the necessary traits to deal with new challenges in the absence of genetic variation, populations would be extremely vulnerable to diseases and environmental changes. Evolution and adaptation would be hampered significantly.

43. Once the cancerous tumor is removed by surgery, the few cells that are left over get abundant supply of nutrients in the system. As a result, they undergo cell divisions much more rapidly thereby spreading the cancerous tissue further. Therefore, these few cells are destroyed or killed by exposing them to high frequency radiation or by giving medicines which can arrest the cell divisions or kill the cells.

NEET SPECIAL WING

Multiple-Answer Type Questions

1. Four chromatids form one pair of homologous chromosomes, called tetrad. Exchange of genes between nonsister chromatids takes place and is known as crossing over

2. In plant cell cytokinesis, membrane-enclosed vesicles derived from the Golgi apparatus migrate to the centre of the cell to form a cell plate. Eventually, the growing cell plate fuses with the existing plasma membrane, producing two daughter cells, each with its own plasma membrane. This kind of cytoplasmic division is said to be centrifugal as it starts at the centre and moves towards the periphery.

3. Pairing of homologous chromosomes results in the synapsis. Each pair of homologous chromosomes is called bivalent.

4. The human gametes are haploid with 23 chromosomes. A somatic cell is diploid and has 46 chromosomes which means the somatic cell has double the number of chromosomes as compared to its gamete. Suppose the gamete has 'x' amount of DNA, then the somatic cell will have 2x amount of DNA as the number of chromosomes are also double. But since the somatic cell has gone through 'S' phase of the cell cycle, it means DNA duplication has occurred, so as a result the number of chromosomes remain same but they will have double the number of chromatids and four times the x amount of DNA which is present in the gamete.

5. Microtubules are part of the cytoskeletal structure of the cell. They are found in only eukaryotic cells and help in cell division, transport within the cell and maintenance of the shape of the cell. They are part of centrioles, spindle fibres and cilia.

Comprehension-Based Questions

A.

6. Prophase 1 is the first phase of meiosis. Here the cell has undergone DNA duplication but has not yet divided. Thus, the cell is still diploid and has 46 chromosomes. But since DNA duplication has occurred each chromosome has 2 chromatids. Thus, the number of chromatids is double the number of chromosomes and is 42 in number.

7. A bivalent chromosome is formed by the pairing of homologous chromosomes. Each chromosome is represented by a single centromere and since at this juncture DNA is doubled, each chromosome consists of 2 chromatids each.

8. Meiosis I is also called as reductional division as it is in this phase that the chromosome number is reduced to half.

9. Prophase I is the longest phase of meiosis I. Prophase I of meiosis I consists of 5 phases- Leptotene, Zygotene, Pachytene, Diplotene and Diakinesis. It is a reductional division and involves reduction in the number of chromosomes

10. Ovum is the largest cell in the human body and sperm is the smallest cell. The process of meiosis in spermatogenesis is continuous unlike the ovum formation. In spermatogenesis 4 viable gametes are formed whereas in oogenesis only 1 viable gamete is formed. Ovum is immotile whereas sperm is motile.

11. Match the following:

In Pachytene exchange of genes between nonsister-chromatids (chromatids of takes place). This phenomenon is known as crossing over.
(i) (b)

Pairing of homologous chromosomes known as synapsis takes place in the zygotene phase.
(ii) (c)

In Diakinesis phase disappearance of chiasmata takes place which is known as terminalization.
(iii) (d)

In Diplotene separation of homologous chromosomes takes place which are attached only at the region of crossing over. This point of attachment is called chiasma.
(iv) (a)

In Leptotene phase formation of homologous chromosomes takes place.
(v) (e)

B.

12. DNA synthesis takes place in the S phase or the synthesis phase of the cell cycle. Here DNA is duplicated but the chromosome number is retained.

13. Colchicine prevents spindle formation. The spindle attaches to the kinetochore of the centromeres in metaphase. So due to colchicine treatment the cell division is arrested at metaphase.

14. Just before metaphase begins (at prometaphase stage) the nuclear membrane starts to disappear. After it completely disappears, the spindle fibres are formed which attach to the kinetochore of the centromere and the chromosomes get arranged at the equatorial plane.

15. A dividing cell of mitosis during prophase and at telophase has the same number of chromosomes. Since the cell is diploid, it will have 46 chromosomes at both the stages.

16. Centrioles form spindle fibres which bind to a disc like structure called as kinetochore found on centromere. The contraction of the spindle fibres helps to pull the chromatids apart.

17. Match the following:

In animal cells during prophase, each daughter centriole is surrounded by radiating rays called aster rays. Spindle fibres appear between the daughter centrioles. There is no astral formation in a plant cell.
(i) (b)

In metaphase a small disc-like protein structure called kinetochore is formed at the surface of the centromeres. This structure allows the chromatids to be attached to a spindle fibre on a chromosome. Each chromosome gets attached to the spindle fibre by the kinetochore of the centromere.
(ii) (c)

In Anaphase, each chromosome that is arranged at the equatorial plane gets split. Each daughter chromatid begins to migrate towards the two opposite poles.
(iii) (d)

In Telophase, the chromosomes start unwinding and form the chromatin network. The nuclear membrane and nucleolus reappear and surround the respective daughter chromosomes.
(iv) (e)

Interphase pertains to the changes taking place in newly formed cell and is basically a preparatory phase for the cell during which the cell undergoes certain changes required for undergoing cell division by itself. This phase can further be divided into three sub-phases which include first growth phase (G_1 phase), second growth phase (G_2 phase) and synthetic phase.
(v) (a)

CHAPTER 3

Life Processes in Plants

Remember

Before beginning this chapter, you should be able to:

- Remember different types of nutrition
- Recall the photosynthesis process
- Understand the basic mechanism of transpiration
- Recall the respiration process in plants
- Remember basic concepts of transpiration in plants

Key Ideas

After completing this chapter, you should be able to:

- Describe and differentiate the major modes of nutrition
- Explain the process of photosynthesis
- Understand the mechanism of opening and closing of stomata
- Describe the process and types of respiration
- Understand the mechanism of exchange of gases in lower and higher plants
- Describe the process and types of transpiration

Scientific Crypt

A Tribute to Jan Ingenhousz (1730–1799)

Jan Ingenhousz (1730–1799), a notable scientist and physician of his time, deserves special recognition for his pivotal work in uncovering plant life processes. Ingenhousz discovered the crucial process of photosynthesis in the 18th century. He demonstrated that plants absorb carbon dioxide and, in response to sunlight, emit life-sustaining oxygen, a discovery that profoundly influenced scientific perspectives on ecological balance.

The discoveries of Ingenhousz went beyond botany. He had a strong interest in medicine and contributed significantly to the understanding of diseases and immunisation.

His meticulous and rigorous experiments demonstrated the beautiful, symbiotic relationship between flora and fauna, emphasising the critical role of sunlight in the survival of life on Earth.

FUN TIME

CROSSWORD

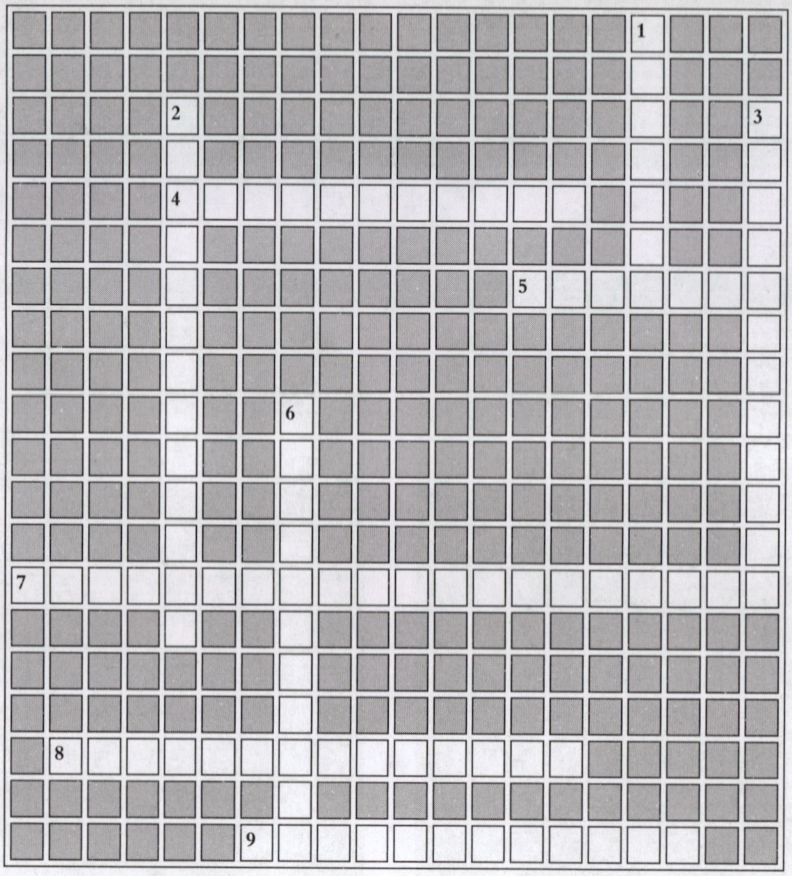

Across

4. Process by which an organism prepares food from inorganic material
5. One of the main products of photosynthesis obtained in the dark phase
7. The addition of inorganic phosphate to ADP to produce a highly energetic ATP molecule carried out by electrons excited through capturing light
8. Specialized roots emerge from waterlogged soil to aid in respiration by facilitating aeration.
9. Organism depends on other organisms for food

Down

1. Respiration that occurs in the presence of oxygen
2. Loss of water from the plant's aerial parts, primarily leaves.
3. A process where ethanol and carbon dioxide are formed along with the liberation of energy
6. Process by which Green plants make carbohydrates from atmospheric carbon dioxide and soil water in the presence of sunlight.

INTRODUCTION

Different physiological activities such as nutrition, respiration, excretion, transportation, and photosynthesis occur in the body of living organisms. These physiological activities that are essential for the survival of living organisms are known as life processes. These are also called metabolic activities. The life processes take place within one cell in unicellular organisms. However, Different organs are dedicated to specific life processes in multicellular organisms. Nutrition, one of the vital life processes, is essential for growth, development of immunity, reproduction, production of energy, etc.

Nutrition

The sum total of the process through which an animal or plant takes in food substances and utilizes them is known as nutrition. Nutrition can be of two types:

1. Autotrophic nutrition
2. Heterotrophic nutrition

Autotrophic Nutrition

A series of processes by which an organism prepares its own food from simple inorganic materials collected from the environment is called autotrophic nutrition.

Organisms involved in autotrophic nutrition are called autotrophs. Autotrophs can be further classified into two types on the basis of source of energy utilized. These are:

1. Photoautotrophs
2. Chemoautotrophs

Info Bytes!

Before photosynthesis evolved, Earth's atmosphere consisted of water vapour, methane, ammonia and other gases, but not oxygen.

Green plants are photoautotrophs as they prepare their food using light of the sun through the photosynthesis process. The organisms that produce their food by utilizing energy from chemical reaction and not by sunlight are called chemoautotrophs. For example, Archaebacteria, Cyanobacteria.

Heterotrophic Nutrition

A mode of nutrition in which an organism depends on the other organisms for its food is called heterotrophic nutrition. Organisms involved in heterotrophic nutrition are called heterotrophs. All animals and non-photosynthetic plants are heterotrophs. Unicellular organisms are also heterotrophs, for example, *Amoeba, Paramoecium*, etc.

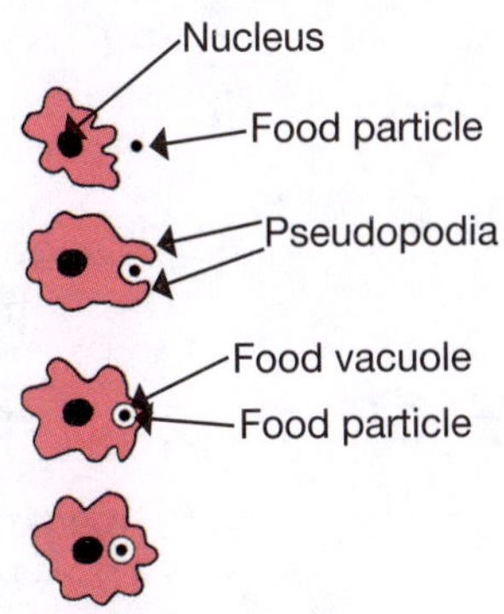

Figure. 3.1 Nutrition in Amoeba

Nutrition in Amoeba

Amoeba ingests food by encircling the food particle with the help of finger-like projections called pseudopodia present at the cell surface. Ingested food gets digested in the vacuole of the cell. Complex food particles are converted to simpler soluble substances during digestion. Undigested food is thrown out of the body by the rupture of the cell membrane.

Nutrition in *Paramoecium*

Paramoecium has fine hair-like structures known as cilia that are spread all over the surface of the body cell. *Paramoecium* ingests the food with the help of the cilia. It has a groove on one side of the body cell through which the food particle is ingested.

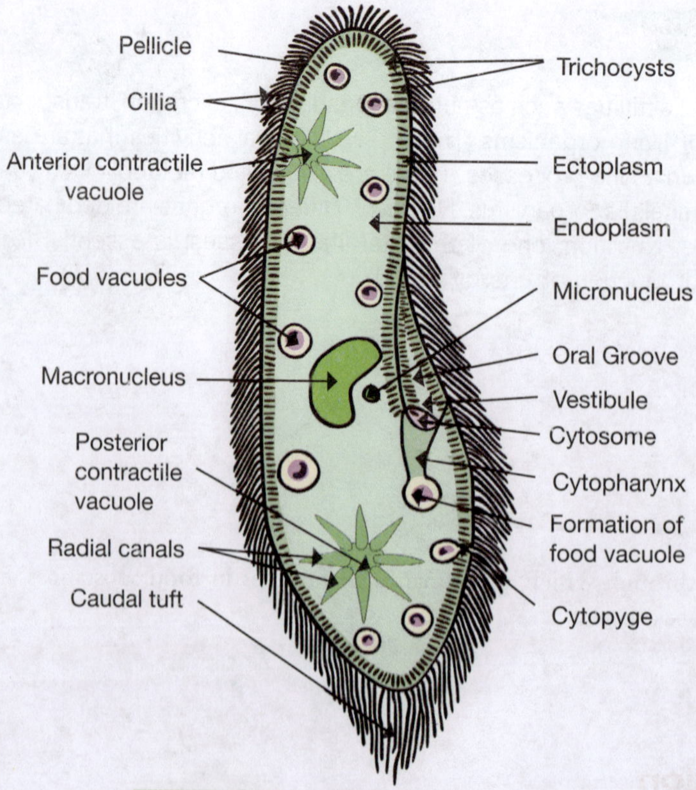

Figure. 3.2 Nutrition in *Paramoecium*

Nutrition in Green Plants

Green plants prepare their food through the photosynthesis process. The term 'Photosynthesis' originates from two words 'Photo' which means light and 'synthesis' which means put together. The process through which green plants prepare carbohydrates using carbon dioxide from atmosphere and water from the soil in presence of sunlight is called photosynthesis.

> **Info Bytes!**
>
> The giant sequoia, one of the largest living organisms, can live for over 3,000 years, showcasing the incredible resilience and longevity of plants.

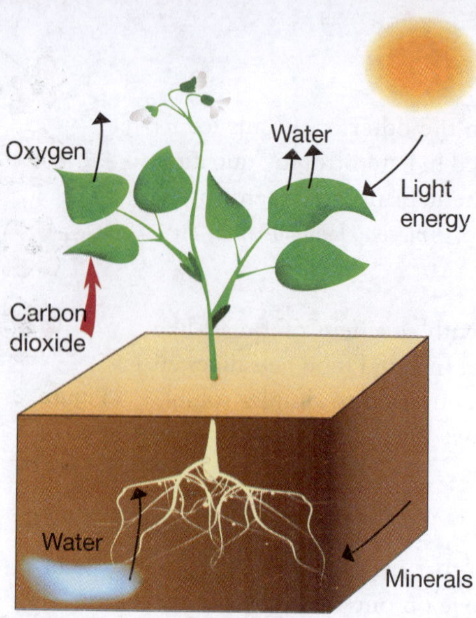

Figure. 3.3 Overview of photosynthesis

> **Info Bytes!**
>
> Heterotrophic plants rely on other plants or animals, either parasitically or through mutual benefits.Eg. cuscuta, pitcher plant (*Nepenthes rajah*),

Photosynthesis

The raw materials required for the process of photosynthesis and their sources are tabulated below. These are:

1. Carbon dioxide
2. Water
3. Solar energy
4. Chloroplasts

Konnect

Plants are green in color because of the pigment chlorophyll which absorbs deep-blue and red light and reflects green colour.

Table 3.1 Sources of the raw materials required for photosynthesis

Raw Material	Source
Carbon dioxide	Atmosphere
Water	Soil (absorption by root)
Solar energy	Sunlight
Chloroplast	Present in green parts of the plants like leaves, soft stem, etc.

Info Bytes!

While most plants are green, autotrophic bacteria might be purple, green, or even red. They use different pigments to capture light energy.

Structure of Chloroplast

Chlorophyll is the green-coloured pigment which is responsible for trapping sunlight. It is found inside chloroplast which is the actual site for photosynthesis. The structure of chloroplast is explained in detail in the following section.

Chloroplasts are small organelles found in plants and algae. They are green-coloured plastids responsible for carrying out the process of photosynthesis to prepare food for the plant. Each chloroplast can be divided into following three main parts:

1. Double membrane
2. Stroma or matrix
3. Thylakoids

Info Bytes!

Some algae conduct photosynthesis in extremely low light conditions, nearly 200 meters below the ocean's surface.

Double Membrane

The chloroplast is enveloped by a double-layered membrane composed of proteins. The outer membrane is freely permeable and the inner one is selectively permeable.

Stroma or Matrix

- Stroma is the colourless matrix present inside the double membrane.
- It is rich in proteins.
- One of the phases of photosynthesis that does not require light takes place in stroma.

Thylakoids

Thylakoids are the membrane-bound, flattened sac-like structures. Around 10–20 thylakoids are stacked one above the other. Each such stack of thylakoids is known as granum. A number of grana are present floating in the stroma. Grana contain various pigments which are the coloured substances that absorb some specific wavelengths of light and reflect the others. As a result, they impart colour to the material in which they are present. The material gets the reflected colour. Due to the presence of these pigments, thylakoids serve as the site for one of the phases of photosynthesis that requires light. The pigments present in the thylakoids are:

1. Chlorophylls
2. Carotenoids

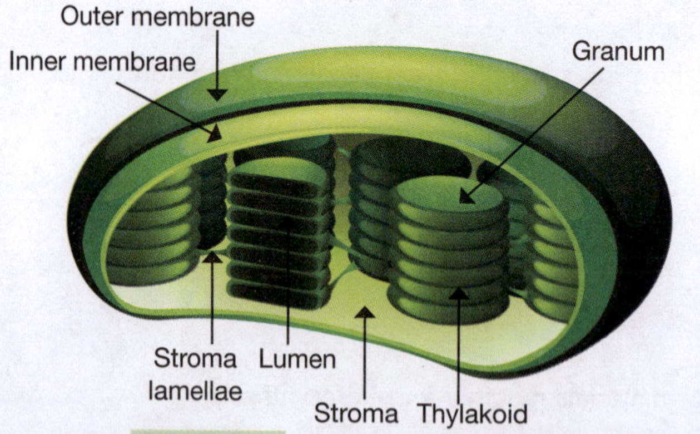

Figure. 3.4 Structure of chloroplast

Info Bytes!

The DNA of the chloroplast is located in the stroma.

There are many types of chlorophylls. The major and most abundant ones are chlorophyll-a and chlorophyll-b. There are two types of carotenoids:

1. Carotene
2. Xanthophyll

Among these, chlorophyll-**a** is the principal pigment while all others are accessory pigments. The principal pigment, chlorophyll-a is mainly responsible for the absorption of sunlight and acts as the reaction centre for the part of photosynthesis that takes place in the presence of light. Chlorophyll contains carbon, oxygen, hydrogen, nitrogen and most importantly chlorophyll-a contains magnesium in the form of Mg^{+2} ion as the central ion.

Function of Chloroplast

The principal functions of chloroplast are as listed below:

- The different pigments in chloroplast trap the solar energy of certain wavelengths such as red, green, violet, blue, etc.
- Chlorophyll is the pigment present in chloroplasts in major proportions. It absorbs blue and red lights of the spectrum and reflects green colour.
- Absorption of light energy activates the chlorophyll and thus, the photosynthesis reaction starts.
- Green plants synthesize carbohydrates in the presence of light through the process of photosynthesis.

Intake of CO_2

The CO_2 intake happens through tiny pores or openings on the lower surface of the leaves called stomatal pores or apertures. Each stomatal pore is surrounded by a pair of bean-shaped cells known as guard cells. The pores along with the guard cells constitute stomata. Stomata act as the passage for the transfer of gases from the environment to the plant and vice versa. The guard cells regulate the opening and closing of the stomata on account of the differential thickness of their cell walls, the inner wall facing the stomatal opening being thicker than the outer wall. As the plasma membrane of the cells is semi-permeable, it allows the movement of water in and out of the cells depending on the concentration of the surrounding medium. The flow of water into the cells through the plasma membrane creates an osmotic pressure in the cells. Because of this, the cells bulge and become turgid. The turgidity of the guard cells controls the opening and closing of the stomata. Two theories have been put forward to explain the mechanism of opening and closing of stomata, which are:

1. Sugar concentration theory
2. Potassium ion concentration theory

Let us study these theories in detail, one by one.

Sugar Concentration Theory

Key features of Sugar Concentration Theory are:

- Guard cells contain chloroplast which is the site for photosynthesis.
- Glucose is the product of photosynthesis.
- The formation of glucose enhances the osmotic pressure in the guard cells.
- Water from neighbouring cells enters the guard cells to reduce the osmotic pressure by means of endosmosis and as a result, the guard cells become turgid.
- Turgid guard cells help in widening of stomatal aperture.
- When the water content of neighbouring cells decreases, the reverse phenomenon called exosmosis takes place and guard cells become flaccid due to loss of water. Flaccidity of the guard cells closes the stomatal aperture.

Info Bytes!

During extremely dry periods, the stomata stay closed.

Potassium ion Concentration Theory

Key features of Potassium ion Concentration Theory are mentioned below.

- During the photosynthesis process in the guard cells, adenosine triphosphate (ATP) is produced which is the source of energy.
- ATP facilitates the entry of potassium ions from the neighbouring cells into guard cells.
- Guard cells become turgid due to the increase in concentration of potassium ions.
- Increase in turgidity of the guard cells widens the stomatal aperture.
- During night, photosynthesis and the formation of ATP stop.
- Therefore, potassium ions get transported from guard cells to neighbouring cells and this phenomenon makes guard cells flaccid. The flaccidity of the guard cells closes the stomatal aperture.

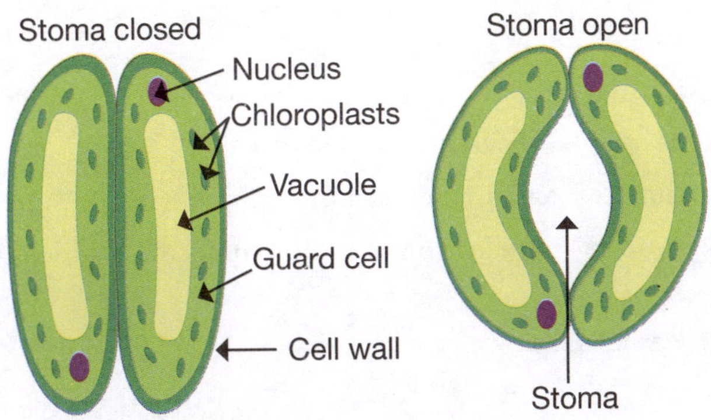

Figure. 3.5 Opening and closing of stomata

Konnect

The number of stomata varies significantly between leaves of different plants and there may be as many as 40,000 per square centimetres on some leaves.

Intake of Water

Water required for photosynthesis is absorbed by the root from the soil. When the concentration of the salts in the cells of root hair increases, the water from the soil enters those cells in the root hair by the process of osmosis. The water from the root goes to different parts of the plant for different purposes.

Mechanism of Photosynthesis

The mechanism involves a series of steps which are as explained below:

- The photosynthesis process is an oxidation–reduction reaction. The balanced chemical equation for the overall reaction involved in photosynthesis is shown as

Info Bytes!

Leaves change colour in autumn because plants slow down the process of photosynthesis.

$$6\,CO_2 + 6\,H_2O \xrightarrow{\text{Sunlight and chlorophyll}} C_6H_{12}O_6 + 6\,O_2$$

Carbon dioxide, Water → Glucose, Oxygen

Carbon dioxide undergoes reduction to form glucose whereas water undergoes oxidation to liberate oxygen. During the photosynthesis process, a series of complex reactions take place that occur in two phases, which are as follows:

1. Light reactions or light phase
2. Dark reactions or dark phase

Light Reaction or Hill Reaction

Light reactions or light-dependent reactions are a group of reactions which make use of light energy. They were discovered by the the scientist Robin Hill (1937), that is why they are also known as Hill reaction. Light reaction is a photochemical reaction that takes place in the thylakoid membrane of chloroplasts. The thylakoids possess various proteins and electron acceptor molecules along with the pigments. All of these together constitute light-harvesting systems called photosystems. The various proteins act as enzymes that catalyze the reactions. The electron acceptor molecules aid in the transfer of electrons during the reactions. These molecules are nicotinamide adenine dinucleotide phosphate (NADP) and adenosine diphosphate (ADP). The series of complicated reactions are broadly classified into following four steps:

1. Absorption of light by chlorophyll
2. Photolysis of water
3. Reduction of NADP
4. Photophosphorylation

These steps are described in the following sections.

Absorption of Light by Chlorophyll

- A photon is the basic unit of light energy.
- Chlorophyll gets energized by absorbing photons of light of certain wavelengths.
- Thus, the electrons in chlorophyll molecules attain the excited state from the ground state.
- Some of these high-energy electrons are taken up by the electron acceptor molecules, which are NADP and ADP.
- Some of the excited electrons are utilized for the splitting of water molecules.

Photolysis of Water

- After the absorption of light energy, chlorophyll molecules help in the dissociation of water molecules into hydrogen ions (H^+) and hydroxide ions (OH^-).

$$4\,H_2O \longrightarrow 4\,H^+ + 4\,OH^-$$

$$4\,OH^- \longrightarrow 2\,H_2O + O_2 + 4\,e^{-1}$$

$$\overline{2\,H_2O \longrightarrow 4\,H^+ + O_2 + 4\,e^{-1}}$$

- Some of this oxygen is used up for the respiration process.
- The remaining amount of oxygen is diffused into the atmosphere through the stomata.
- The electrons are used to convert ADP into ATP later on.

Info Bytes!

$NADPH_2$ is the reduced form of NADP.

Reduction of NADP

- NADP is nicotinamide adenine dinucleotide phosphate.
- In this step, NADP is reduced to $NADPH_2$ by the hydrogen ions released during photolysis of water and the high-energy electrons.

$$NADP + 2e^{-1} + 2\,H^{+} \longrightarrow NADPH_2$$

Photophosphorylation

- In this step, ATP is produced by the reaction between ADP and inorganic phosphate.

$$\text{ADP + Inorganic phosphate} \longrightarrow \text{ATP}$$

- ATP is the supplier of energy.
- The addition of inorganic phosphate to ADP to produce highly energetic ATP molecule is called phosphorylation. As this is carried out by the electrons excited by capturing light, it is called photophosphorylation.
- All the above reactions take place in the presence of sunlight, and hence, they are called light reactions.
- Light energy is converted to chemical energy in this phase of photosynthesis.
- At the end of the light phase, light energy is converted to chemical energy and remains temporarily stored in ATP and $NADPH_2$.
- These are transported to stroma for the transfer of this stored energy to glucose during the dark phase.

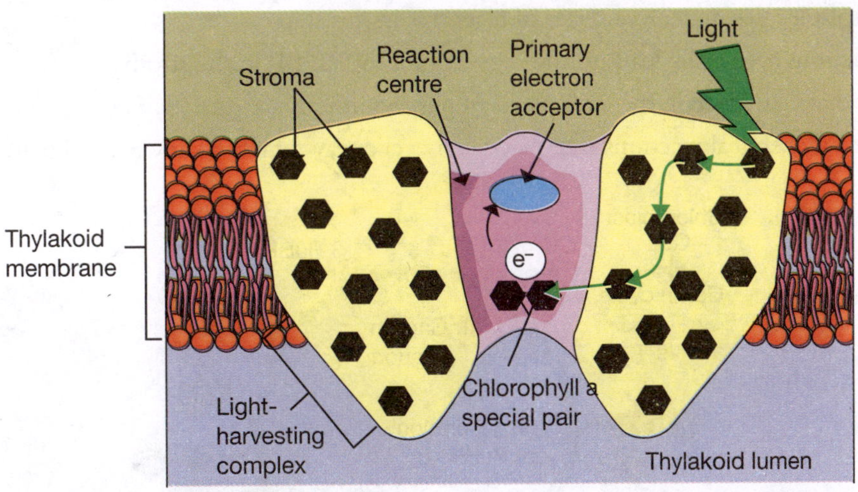

Figure. 3.6 Illustration of Light reactions (or Hill reaction)

Dark Reactions or Biosynthetic Reaction or Calvin Cycle

The scientist Calvin and his co-workers elucidated dark reactions, and hence, these reactions are called Calvin reactions. Dark reactions take place in continuation of light reactions. In these reactions, light energy is not utilized. Hence, it is called dark phase. Dark reactions are slower than the light reactions as they are purely enzyme driven. The site of dark reactions is stroma of chloroplasts. The dark reactions take place in three major steps:

1. Fixation of carbon dioxide
2. Formation of sugar
3. Regeneration of ribulose-1, 5-biphosphate (RUBP)

These steps are explained below:

Fixation of Carbon Dioxide (Carbon Fixation)

- Carbon dioxide absorbed is utilized in this step for the formation of a 3-carbon compound that is phosphoglyceric acid (PGA) as the initial product.
- Carbon dioxide combines with a 5-carbon sugar that is RUBP which is present in stroma.

$$CO_2 + \text{RUBP (5-carbon sugar)} \longrightarrow \text{PGA}$$

- In this step, carbon dioxide is reduced and the oxygen in the carbon dioxide is added to hydrogen and forms water which is a by-product.
- Therefore, the equation for photosynthesis is more appropriately represented as follows

$$6\,CO_2 + 12\,H_2O \longrightarrow C_6H_{12}O_6 + 6\,O_2 + 6\,H_2O$$

- Since water molecules are present on both the reactant and product sides, water molecules on products are ignored while writing the net balanced chemical equation. Only net number of water molecules used upside are shown on reactants side.

Formation of Sugar

- In this step, some molecules of PGA formed in the first step produce glucose, a 6-carbon sugar.
- $NADPH_2$ and ATP formed during light reaction are utilized in the series of reactions involved in the formation of glucose from PGA.

Regeneration of RUBP

- Rest of the PGA molecules undergo a series of reactions in this step.
- This series of reactions eventually leads to the regeneration of RUBP in the stroma.
- All the reactions that take place in the dark phase of photosynthesis are catalyzed by enzymes.
- In this phase, the biochemical reactions take place in a cyclic way which is shown as follows:

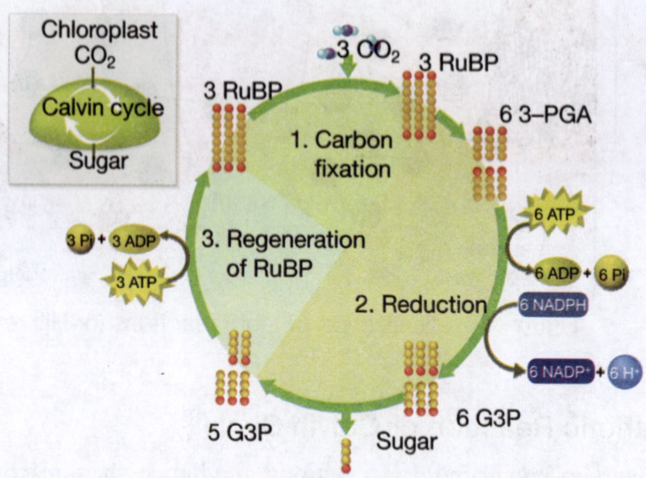

Figure. 3.7 Calvin cycle: simple schematic representation

- Thus, the main products of photosynthesis are glucose obtained in dark phase and oxygen obtained in light phase.
- Glucose formed gets converted to different complex substances, such as sucrose (cane sugar), starch and cellulose.
- These complex substances are stored by the plants in their storage organs.

Info Bytes!

Researchers have discovered a sea slug that creates its own energy through photosynthesis.

- Sucrose which is formed by the combination of two different 6-carbon sugars (glucose and fructose) is stored in sugarcane and sugarbeet.
- Starch which is obtained by joining many glucose molecules is stored in potato, sweet potato, rice, wheat, maize, etc.

Structure and Adaptations of Leaves for Facilitating Photosynthesis

Leaves of the plants undergo various adaptations to facilitate photosynthesis. Some of them are given below in the table.

Table 3.2 Adaptation of leaves for facilitating photosynthesis

Adaptation	Purpose of the adaptation
Thin structure	Easy diffusion of carbon dioxide to the site of photosynthesis
Large surface area	Effective absorption of light
Thin waxy, transparent coating on the upper surface of the leaves	Evaporation is controlled without preventing the passage of light
Presence of vascular bundle (xylem and phloem)	Transportation of water to the site of photosynthesis and the sucrose produced from the site Network-like structure of vascular bundle provides rigidity to the leaves
Palisade cells	Facilitate the movement of chloroplasts present in them and thus help in absorption of light by chlorophyll
Guard cells surrounding the stomatal pores	Help in opening stomatal pores for the entry of carbon dioxide during daytime and closing the pores during night to control loss of water
Loosely packed spongy mesophyll cells	Create spaces for efficient exchange of gases

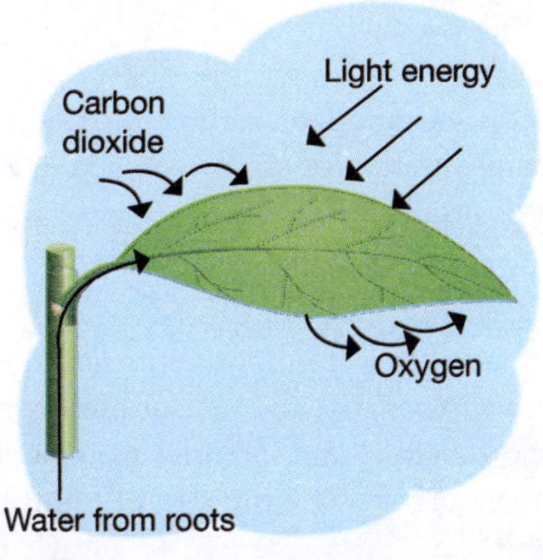

Figure. 3.8 Structure of a leaf adapted for photosynthesis

Konnect

Pine trees and other conifers have evolved over the years to grow in a triangle shape because of photosynthesis. The triangular shape exposes most of their needles to the sun, especially the ones near the top of the tree.

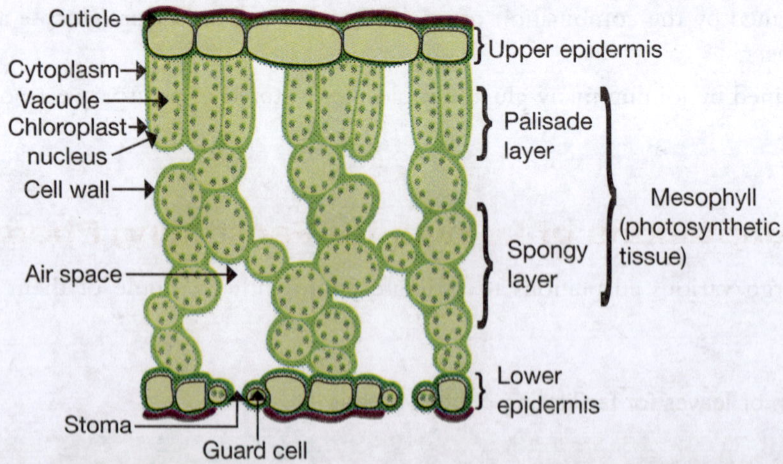

Figure. 3.9 Anatomy of a leaf facilitating photosynthesis

Factors Affecting Photosynthesis

The rate of photosynthesis is influenced by two types of factors namely internal factors and external factors.

External Factors

Major external factors are :

- Light
- Carbon dioxide
- Temperature
- Water

Light

Intensity and quality are the two characteristics of light that govern the rate of photosynthesis. If the other factors like temperature and the concentration of carbon dioxide are not limiting, the rate of photosynthesis is directly proportional to the intensity of the light. But the process of photosynthesis gets inhibited if the intensity of light is very high. Quality of light indicates the frequency or the colour of light. Most of the green plants absorb red and blue lights for the photosynthesis process. But the rate of photosynthesis is higher in red light than in blue light.

Carbon dioxide

The rate of photosynthesis is directly proportional to the concentration of carbon dioxide if other factors such as temperature and intensity of light are not limiting. Since the concentration of carbon dioxide in air is 0.03 per cent and it hardly varies, carbon dioxide itself acts as a limiting factor in this process.

Temperature

If carbon dioxide and intensity of light are not the limiting factors, the optimum temperature required for the process of photosynthesis is 35°C. In the range of temperature from 5°C to 35°C, the rate of photosynthesis becomes double for every 10° rise in temperature, if the concentration of carbon dioxide and intensity of light are adequate and do not influence the rate of photosynthesis. High and very low temperatures reduce the rate of photosynthesis drastically. But there are some exceptions. This process can take place even at 70°C.

Water

Water is one of the reactants in the process of photosynthesis. Less than 1 per cent of the total water absorbed by the root is utilized in photosynthesis. The reduction in water supply greatly influences the rate of photosynthesis. This is because the lack of water decreases the turgidity of the guard cells. This phenomenon leads to the closure of stomata and thus the intake of carbon dioxide decreases. Moreover, the diffusibility of carbon dioxide decreases because of the dryness of cells in leaves.

Internal Factors

Internal factors influencing the rate of photosynthesis are:

- Chlorophyll content
- Accumulation of end products (during photosynthesis)
- Anatomy of leaf

Chlorophyll Content

Chlorophyll content is essential for photosynthesis. Non-green parts of the variegated leaves do not undergo photosynthesis if chlorophyll is absent in them. But the rate of photosynthesis is independent of the total chlorophyll content, rather it depends on the concentration of chlorophyll.

Accumulation of End Products of Photosynthesis

The rate of photosynthesis decreases if the glucose produced during this process is not translocated. Thus accumulation of photosynthetic product affects photosynthesis.

Anatomy of Leaf

Another factor that governs the rate of photosynthesis is the anatomy of leaf. The variations of the anatomical features among different plants affect the process of photosynthesis. These are:

- **Thickness of cuticle and epidermis**—It is directly proportional to the rate of photosynthesis.
- **Size, position and distribution of stomata**—They influence the rate of photosynthesis.
- **Variation in sizes of cells in different tissues and the intercellular space**—They affect the rate of photosynthesis.

Significance of Photosynthesis

Photosynthesis is one of the most vital processes without which sustenance of life on Earth would not be possible. Some of the significances of photosynthesis are:

> **Info Bytes!**
>
> A recent study suggests the Oriental hornet performs photosynthesis using a bright yellow pigment called xanthopterin in its exoskeleton.

Food

- The indirect or direct sources of food of all sorts of animals are photosynthetic plants. In this way, ecological balance is maintained on Earth.

Balance of Carbon Dioxide and Oxygen in the Atmosphere

- Carbon dioxide is consumed and oxygen is released during photosynthesis. Thus, the photosynthesis process has the most significant role in maintaining the balance of oxygen and carbon dioxide in the atmosphere.

Storage of Energy

- The solar energy is trapped in the form of chemical energy in the photosynthetic product, that is, glucose in green plants.
- Finally, green plants get converted into petroleum, wood, coal and biomass which are the sources of conventional energy.

Transportation in Plants

The food that is produced in the plant leaves is required to be transported to different parts of the plants. The transported food, water and minerals are not only absorbed by the roots, but are also transported to different sites of the plant's body for different purposes. Hence, transportation of water, minerals and food is an important life process. The process of transportation of water and minerals is preceded by the absorption of these substances by the roots.

Absorption of Water and Minerals by the Roots

Water and soluble minerals are absorbed through root hair that provide a large surface area. The salt concentration of the cell sap in cells of the root hair is generally higher than the solution of water and salts present outside in the soil. Due to this difference in concentration, water and soluble minerals enter the cells of the root hair from outside by the process of endosmosis. From the root hair, the water along with the minerals enters the tissues of the root. Anatomy of a root of a plant includes the following five major tissues:

1. Epidermis
2. Cortex
3. Endodermis
4. Pericycle
5. Xylem

Info Bytes!

Epiphytic orchids contain velamen root specially adopted to absorb water directly from the atmosphere.

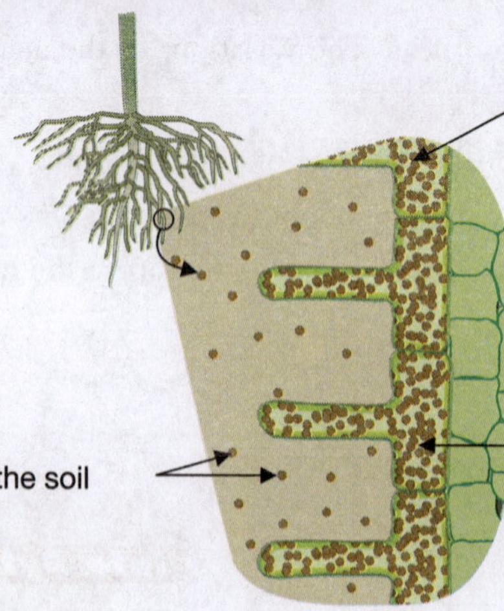

Figure. 3.10 Uptake of minerals by root hair through active transport

Info Bytes!

The Bristlecone Pine tree has roots that can keep it anchored and nourished for over 5,000 years, making it the oldest known living tree.

There are two different pathways by which water and minerals are transported from root hair to xylem. They are symplast and apoplast pathways. The passage of water and minerals through the cytoplasm of the cells is called transportation through symplast pathway. Apoplast is the intercellular space outside the plasma membrane. The passage of water and minerals through cell wall and intercellular spaces is known as apoplast pathway. This takes place by means of plasmadesmata arising from the cell walls. The initial driving force that causes the transportation of water and minerals to xylem from root hair is called root pressure.

Info Bytes!

The total number of root hair strands present in a four-month-old corn plant is approximately 14 billion or more.

Imbibition

The literal meaning of the term imbibition is the absorption of water by the solid particles of an adsorbent without forming a solution. Substances that are composed of hydrophilic material like cellulose and proteins, have a strong affinity for water, they imbibe water or moisture and get swelled up. Imbibition is helpful in seed germination, growth of seedling in soil, ascent of sap in plants, etc.

Turgidity and Flaccidity

Turgidity refers to the state of being turgid or swollen due to high fluid content. A cell is in its fully expanded condition when it is turgid. Turgidity occurs when a cell is placed in a hypotonic solution that has a low solute concentration than that of the cytoplasm. Turgidity is important for plants as it plays an essential role in opening and closing of stomata.

Flaccidity refers to the state between turgidity and plasmolysis when the plasma membrane is not pushed against the cell wall. This happens when a turgid cell is placed in an isotonic solution. During the flaccid state, there is no net movement of water across the plasma membrane.

Plasmolysis takes place when plant cells lose water after being placed in a hypertonic solution (a solution that has a higher concentration of solutes than the cell does). This causes the protoplasm to shrink away from the cell wall.

Diffusion

It is the free movement of molecules of a substance from the region of its higher concentration to the region of its lower concentration, when the two are in direct contact. Semi-permeable membrane or differentially permeable membranes allow the diffusion of only solvent particle through them while restricting the movement of solute particles. The transport of CO_2 and O_2 from the atmosphere into the plants takes place by diffusion.

Root Pressure

The water from the root hair enters cortex of the root and the cortical cells become turgid. Due to the pressure created in turgid cortical cells, water and minerals are forced to move towards the xylem. Then the cortical cells become flaccid and further absorption of water takes place. The following figure shows the symplast and the apoplast pathways for the transportation of water and minerals.

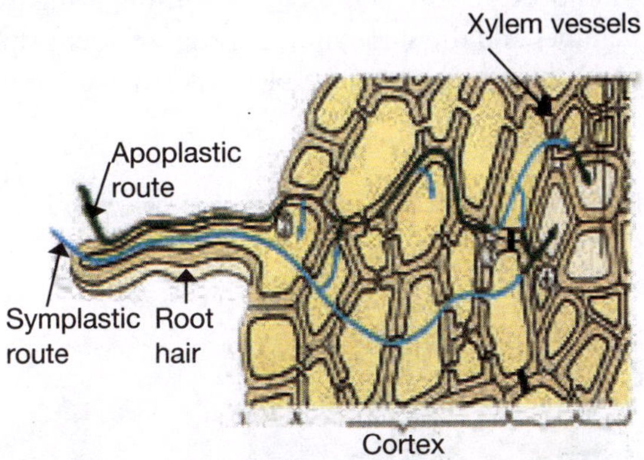

Fig. 3.11 Symplast and apoplast pathways

Info Bytes!

More than 95% of the water absorbed by the root system is operated by passive forces like DPD (Diffusion Pressure Deficit) gradient created by the transpiration pull.

The water and minerals are transported to different parts of the plants from the root through xylem tissue.

Transportation of Water Through Xylem

Xylem is a complex tissue composed of different types of cells. Vessels and tracheids of xylem present in roots, stems and leaves are interconnected. Due to this interconnectivity of cells of xylem, a network of channels is formed for the transportation of water and minerals, that is also called xylem sap. The upward movement of xylem sap is called ascent of sap. The various driving forces for the ascent of sap are as follows:

1. Capillarity
2. Cohesive force
3. Transpiration pull

All the three mechanisms mentioned above together help in the transportation of xylem sap. The diameter of xylem vessels is very minute. It ranges from 20 to 400 micrometres. Hence, water capillarity is exhibited here due to the adhesive force between cell walls of xylem and water. Then the role of cohesive force comes into existence. The force of attraction among the similar molecules is called cohesive force. Cohesive force is very strong in water. This helps in the formation of a long water column without any air gap. Next the transpiration phenomenon pulls the water column strongly in the upward direction. Transpiration is the loss of water from the surface of aerial parts of the plant mainly from the leaves. Transpiration of water through stomata in leaves creates a deficit of water in the surrounding mesophyll cells in leaves. As a result of it, water column is pulled from the xylem cells in leaf veins. Thus the transpiration pull helps the water column to move upward. This generally takes place at the expense of energy and is an active transport. The other phase of transportation in plants involves the translocation of food prepared by photosynthesis, from the leaves to the other parts of the body.

Transportation of Food in Plants

The vascular tissue, phloem is concerned with the transportation of food from leaves to the other parts of the plant. Phloem tissue transports sugar, amino acids and other organic substances in both upward and downward direction to fulfil the requirements of all parts of the plants. Translocation of these substances which constitute phloem sap takes place from leaves to phloem by the mechanism of active transport. The source of the energy required for this process is ATP which is produced during the process of respiration. Two types of specialized cells of phloem tissue, sieve tube elements and companion cells, are involved in translocation of photosynthetic product. They are sieve tube elements and companion cells. Sieve tube elements are tube-like structures connected one above the other. There are porous sieve plates between two sieve tube elements. Companion cells surround the sieve tube elements. Sugar, amino acids and other organic molecules are transported to sieve tubes through companion cells. The adjacent positions of xylem and phloem tissues facilitate the movement of water molecules from xylem to sieve tubes of phloem. The movement of water molecules from xylem to phloem takes place through the process of osmosis which is a passive transport. Thus, a high pressure is developed inside the sieve tube elements and phloem sap can transport in both the directions through highly porous sieve plates. Because of the difference in pressure between the sieve tubes and the surrounding tissues, phloem sap is translocated to the surrounding cells. Thus, photosynthetic product reaches different parts of the plant for storage, growth and generation of energy requirements to conduct different biological processes.

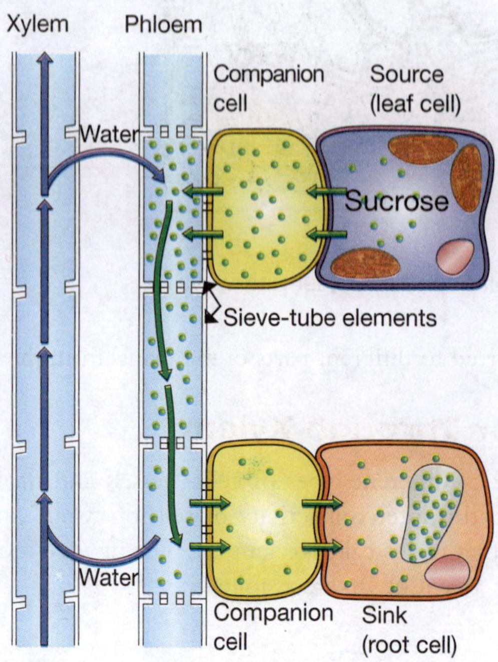

Figure. 3.12 Mechanism of transportation of food in plants

In most of the organisms, the food supplied to different parts of their body gets converted to glucose. The glucose then undergoes oxidation through the process of respiration and energy is released. The energy released during respiration is utilized for other biological activities required for the survival and propagation of life.

Quick Recap

✔ **Determine the difference between autotrophic and heterotrophic nutrition. How do these modes of nutrition meet the energy needs of various organisms?**

Autotrophic nutrition refers to organisms that prepare their food using simple inorganic materials, such as plants that perform photosynthesis. Animals, on the other hand, are heterotrophic organisms that rely on others for food. Autotrophs convert sunlight or other sources of energy into chemical energy, whereas heterotrophs consume organic substances and break them down to release energy.

✔ **Based on the balanced chemical equation for photosynthesis and the complex biochemical reactions involved in the process, answer the following questions.**

(a) How many atoms of carbon are fixed per one molecule of glucose formed?

(b) How many Calvin cycles are involved for the formation of one molecule of glucose?

(c) What is the total number of NADP and ATP required for the entire process?

(d) How can six molecules of water give six oxygen molecules at the end?

(a) One atom of carbon is fixed in each Calvin cycle. Addition of six CO_2 molecules to RUBP results in the formation of 12 PGA molecules. This requires two Calvin cycles. Out of these, two PGA molecules are utilized for the formation of one glucose molecule. The other ten are utilized for the regeneration of RUBP.

(b) Six Calvin cycles are involved in the synthesis of one molecule of glucose. The addition of each CO_2 molecule to RUBP produces two molecules of PGA. This means that the addition of six CO_2 molecules to RUBP produces 12 molecules of PGA. On the whole, two molecules of PGA are converted to glucose molecule. The other ten molecules are utilized for the regeneration of RUBP.

(c) A total of 12 NADPH and 18 ATP molecules are involved in the synthesis of one glucose molecule. Each Calvin cycle requires two NADP and three ATP molecules.

(d) Six water molecules are formed during the formation of PGA during Calvin cycle. These are formed by the reduction of CO_2 molecules. A total of 12 molecules of water are utilized during light reaction. They undergo photolysis to form six molecules of water. The net number of water molecules used is 6 and it is depicted in the final balanced chemical equation.

✔ **Dark phase is more appropriately called light-independent phase. Justify.**

Dark phase of photosynthesis involves the main process of carbon fixation to form glucose. This phase takes place throughout the day and not necessarily in night. Since it is in contrast to light phase that takes place in the presence of sunlight, it is called dark phase. Moreover, the dark phase depends on the products of light phase, namely ATP and NADPH. Therefore, it is more appropriately called light-independent phase rather than as dark phase.

Respiration and Transpiration

All living organisms be it plants or animals are required to perform certain essential functions in order to ensure the survival of species. Plants, like animals, require nourishment, a way to excrete waste material (through transpiration), a way to breathe (to take in oxygen), ways to reproduce and create new plants, and other essential life processes. Similar to respiration in humans and animals, plants also respire to produce energy by using nutrients and oxygen, and giving out carbon-dioxide and water as by product. Respiration is essentially the opposite of photosynthesis, a process by which plants produce oxygen.

Respiration

The word respiration is derived from the Latin word **'respirare'**, the meaning of which is to breathe. Respiration is the process in which food materials present in the body of the organisms are broken down chemically with the help of enzymes, with liberation of energy.

Types of Respiration

Respiration can be divided into two categories based on its occurrence in the presence or absence of oxygen. These are:

1. **Aerobic respiration (takes place in the presence of oxygen)**
2. **Anaerobic respiration (takes place in the absence of oxygen)**

Both the processes of respiration can be divided into **two** stages. The first stage of both the types of respiration is same. This stage of respiration is known as **glycolysis**.

Info Bytes!

On an average, one individual human being breathes in 11,000 L of air a day.

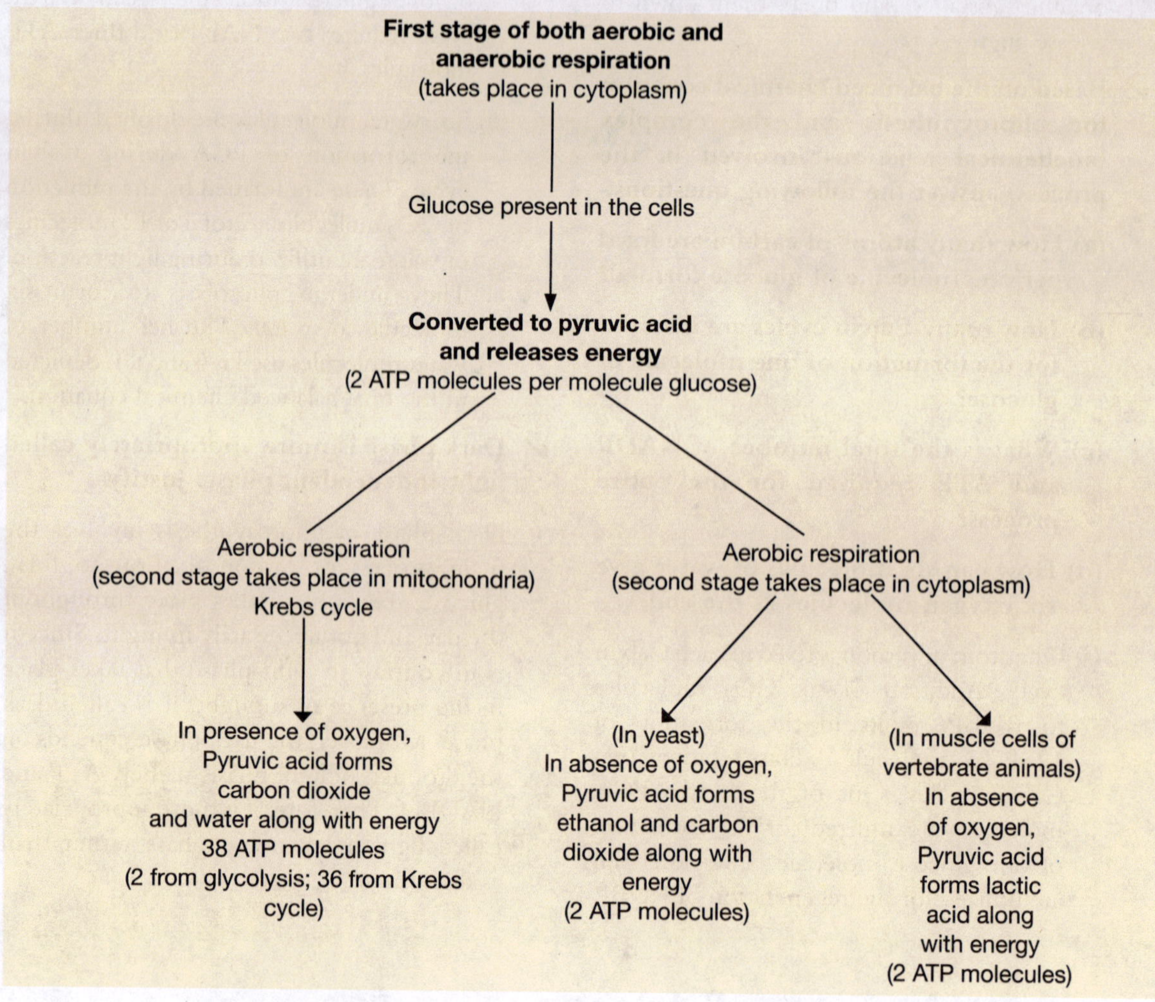

Figure. 3.13 Schematic representation of the process of respiration

Glycolysis

This process takes place in the cytoplasm of the cell. Cytoplasm of the cells contains the enzyme required for the process of **glycolysis**. The word **'glycos'** means sugar and **'lysis'** means splitting. During the process of **glycolysis**, glucose, a 6-Carbon sugar gets converted to a 3-Carbon compound called **pyruvate, and energy is released.** At the end of glycolysis, **2 ATP molecules** are formed per **glucose molecule.** After the process of glycolysis, **pyruvic acid** undergoes a series of changes and liberates energy. Unlike the first stage, the second stage of respiration is not common in both aerobic and anaerobic processes.

Anaerobic Respiration

Fermentation is a type of anaerobic respiration. **Alcoholic fermentation** is one of them and it is carried out in microorganisms like yeast and certain bacteria to fulfil their requirement of energy. The site of this stage of anaerobic respiration is also cytoplasm. In the second stage of alcoholic fermentation, ethanol and carbon dioxide are formed along with the liberation of energy. Other processes of fermentation that take place in certain bacteria produce lactic acid, acetic acid, oxalic acid and citric acid along with energy. Sometimes anaerobic respiration occurs in the muscle cells of vertebrate animals also. This process liberates energy and lactic acid is formed as the product. The organisms that completely depend on anaerobic respiration for their energy are called anaerobes or **anoxybiotic organisms**.

> **Info Bytes!**
> It is estimated that about one-third of all the food we consume is fermented.

Aerobic Respiration

This stage of aerobic respiration is also called **Krebs cycle** and takes place in mitochondria. During this process, pyruvic acid undergoes **complete oxidation** since **oxygen** is also involved in the reaction. Complete oxidation of **pyruvic acid** produces **carbon dioxide and water** as the end products along with the liberation of energy. Energy released in this process gets stored in **ATP** during its formation. At the end of this stage, **36 molecules of ATP** are produced by the oxidation of two molecules of pyruvic acid formed from **one molecule of glucose.** This means that the **total number of ATP molecules** produced **per glucose molecule** becomes 38 which includes 2 **ATP molecules** produced at the end of **glycolysis. ATP** acts as the source of energy for all cellular processes. There are three phosphate groups present in an ATP molecule. Energy is released during the separation of the last phosphate group by the reaction with water. Thus energy can be extracted from ATP. After the loss of one phosphate radical, ATP changes to **ADP.**

Mechanism of Exchange of Gases During Respiration in Lower Plants

Lower plants like algae are aquatic and remain submerged in water. Exchange of oxygen and carbon dioxide required for respiration and photosynthesis, respectively take place throughout the surface of the body of the plant. Examples are *Chlamydomonas* **and** *Spirogyra.*

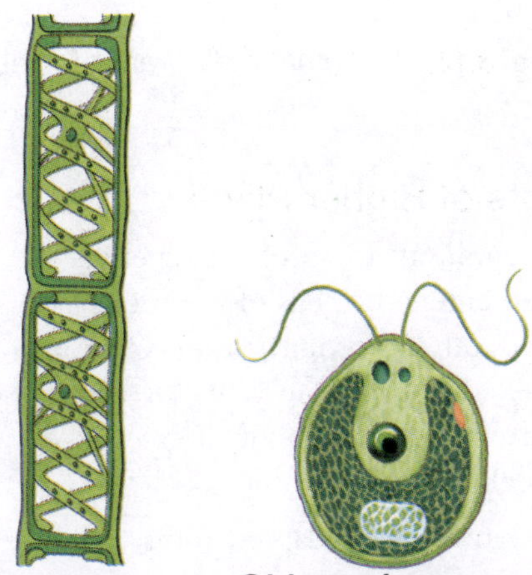

Figure. 3.14 Illustration of *Spirogyra* and *Chalamydomonas*

> **Info Bytes!**
> Krebs cycle is named after Sir Hans Adolf Krebs who is credited for its discovery.

Kreb's cycle

Citric Acid Cycle, also called Krebs cycle, is a series of chemical reactions of primary importance in all living cells that utilize oxygen during the process of cellular respiration. In these aerobic organisms, this cycle is a metabolic pathway that is an essential stage for the break down of carbohydrates, fats and proteins into carbon dioxide and water in order to generate energy. It takes place within the mitochondria in eukaryotic organisms, and in the cytoplasm in prokaryotic organisms.

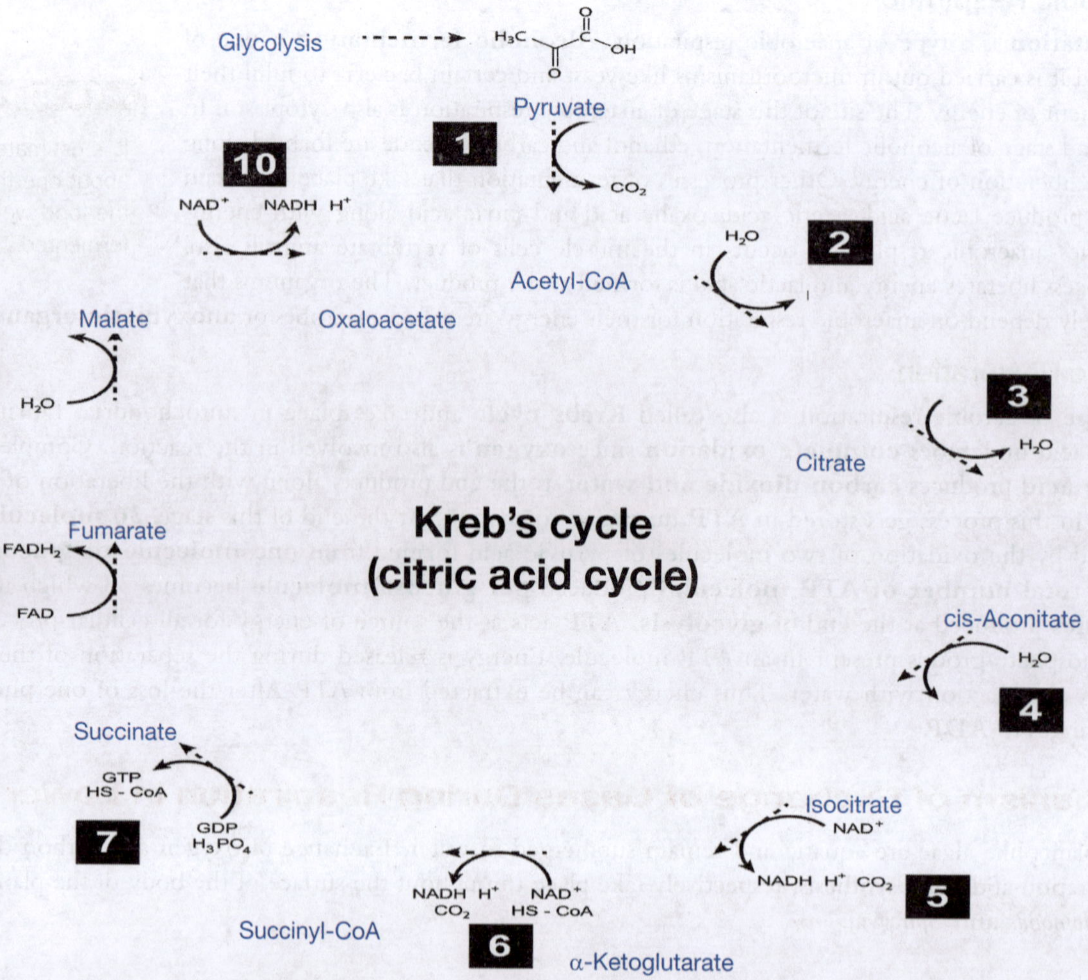

Figure. 3.15 Schematic diagram of Krebs cycle

Exchange of Gases Through Roots of Higher Plants

In young roots, root hair is present throughout its surface. Spaces between the soil particles are filled with air. Oxygen enters the cells of the root hair by the process of **diffusion** and then reaches other cells in the root. Carbon dioxide formed during respiration is expelled in the same way. **In older portion of the roots and in woody stem**, entry and exit of gases take place through small openings called **lenticels.**

Mangrove trees that grow in coastal swamps have adapted roots called **pneumatophores** for the purpose of breathing since the soil in those areas is not aerated. **Pneumatophores** are specialized roots that emerge out of the water-logged soil to facilitate the aeration required for respiration. The apical region of the pneumatophores has lenticels for the exchange of gases.

Figure. 3.16 Lenticels on bark of tree

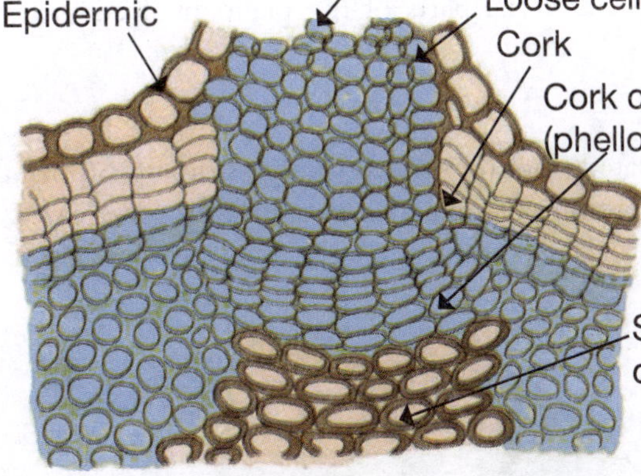

Figure. 3.17 Structure of lenticel

Figure. 3.18 Pneumatophore

In leaves and green soft stems, stomata are present that facilitate the exchange of gases. After entering through stomata or lenticels, oxygen gas reaches the cells of different parts of the plants through the diffusion process via intercellular spaces. In the same way, carbon dioxide gas produced during respiration is expelled out. Complex chemical reactions take place during different life processes in plants. These chemical reactions generate both useful and waste products. The accumulation of waste products in the body of any organism is harmful. Hence, periodical elimination of the waste products is essential and the system of processes involved is called excretion.

Excretion in Plants

Excretion is the life process through which waste and toxic products are expelled from the body of an organism.

Plants generate different excretory products during execution of their life processes. **Carbon dioxide** is the product obtained during respiration. This gas is consumed in the process of photosynthesis during daytime but at night it is expelled through the **stomata**. Oxygen gas generated by photosynthesis is partially consumed during respiration, but rest of its part is excreted through the **stomata**. Certain waste products in plants are accumulated in the vacuoles of cells of old leaves. These wastes are eliminated when leaves get detached from the plants. **Resin, gum, latex**, etc., are the excretory products of plants which ooze out of the bark of trees and are shed in due course of time. Another process of excretion in plants is **transpiration**. Through which excess water is eliminated from the plant

Transpiration

Transpiration is the process by which the elimination of water takes place from the aerial parts of the plant in the form of water vapour.

Types of Transpiration

Transpiration can be categorized based on the aerial parts of the plant involved in transpiration. Different types of transpiration are as follows:

Stomatal Transpiration

About 90 per cent of the total water is eliminated from the plants through stomata. Stomatal transpiration depends on the structure of the leaves, the number and distribution of stomata on the surface of the leaves.

Figure. 3.19 Location of stomata on a leaf

Cuticular Transpiration

Transpiration through cuticle, a waxy coating over the epidermal layers of leaves, is called cuticular transpiration. About 5–10 per cent water loss takes place through the cuticles. Cuticular transpiration is inversely proportional to the thickness of the cuticle.

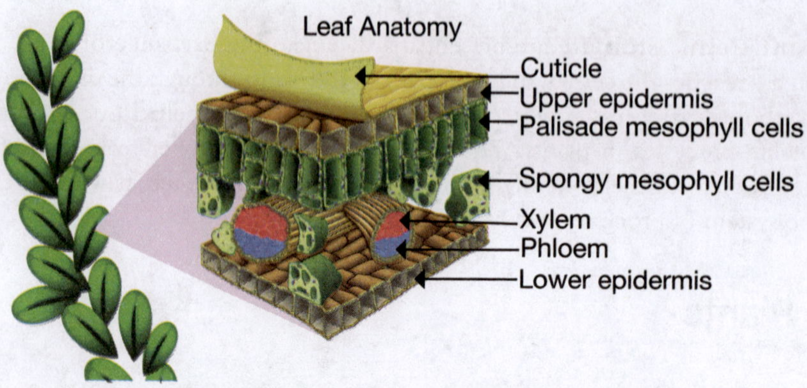

Figure. 3.20 Transpiration through cuticles

Lenticular Transpiration

Water from plants can also evaporate through small openings, called lenticels present in the woody stems. This is called lenticular transpiration. Plants transpire about 0.1 per cent water through lenticels.

Factors Affecting Transpiration

Transpiration in plants depends on following two factors:

1. Environmental factors
2. Morphology and anatomy of leaves

Environmental Factors

Following are the environmental factors that affect transpiration.

- **Intensity of Light**—Strong light stimulates opening of stomata and thus increases the transpiration.
- **Humidity**—Transpiration is inversely proportional to humidity.
- **Wind Velocity**—The higher the velocity of wind, the more is the transpiration.
- **Percentage of Carbon Dioxide in Air**—Excess carbon dioxide leads to closure of stomata and thus reduces the transpiration.
- **Temperature**—Higher temperature of the surrounding increases transpiration.
- **Atmospheric Pressure**—Increase in atmospheric pressure reduces transpiration.

Info Bytes!

75% of rainfall received by the Amazon tropical rain forest comes from plant-transpired water vapour.

Morphology and Anatomy of Leaves

Larger leaves transpire more water. Inadequate absorption of water by the root causes wilting of leaves. Wilting of leaves reduces transpiration. Transverse arrangement of leaves increases transpiration while perpendicular arrangement reduces transpiration. Succulent leaves contain latex in their tissues, and hence transpiration gets reduced. Different anatomical features such as less number of stomata, sunken stomata, presence of cuticle, compact mesophyll, etc., reduce transpiration.

Figure. 3.21 Microscopic view of leaf cells

Different Adaptations in Leaves for Reducing Transpiration

In dry regions, leaves of the plants are adapted structurally in such a way that transpiration is reduced to a great extent. Some of the adaptations of leaves are mentioned below. Thick cuticle is present over the leaves in banyan trees. Concentration of stomata is more on the bottom surface of the leaves. Stomata in plants in arid region are embedded at a greater depth of leaves. This type of stomata is called sunken stomata. For example, *Nerium*. In *Nerium*, stomata are also covered with hair to retain still air in the spaces among the hair strands. Thus transpiration gets reduced.

Figure. 3.22 Adaptation of stem and leaves in cactus

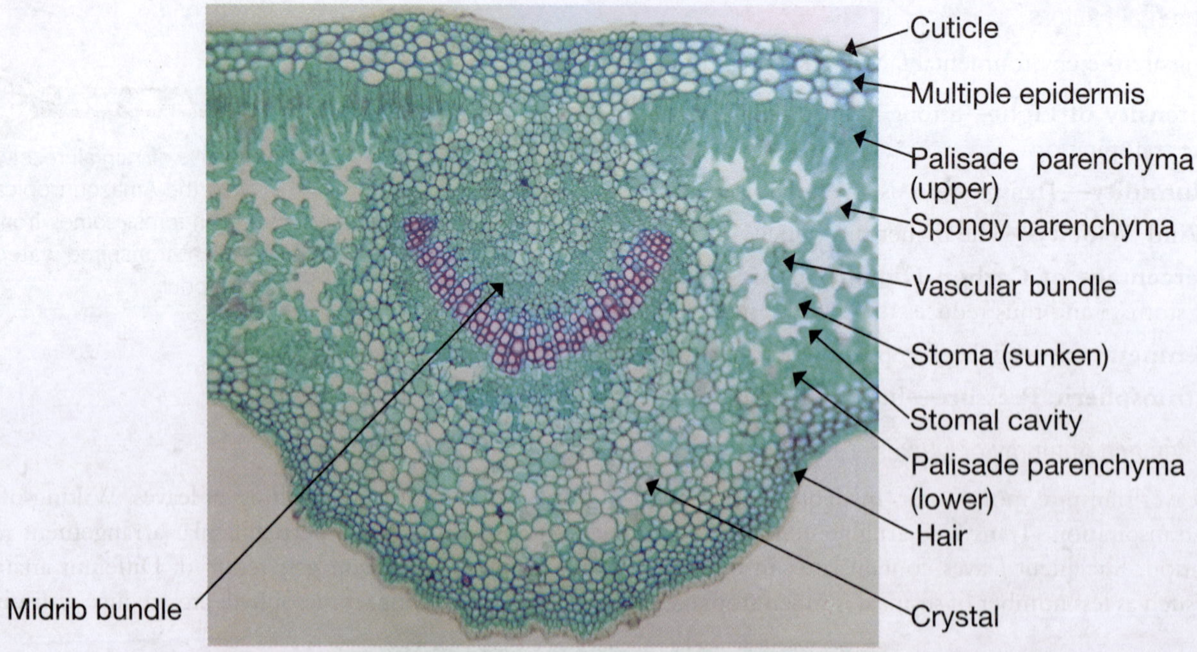

Figure. 3.23 Anatomy of *Nerium* leaf

Palisade parenchyma substitutes spongy parenchyma and thus intercellular space is reduced. This adaptation reduces transpiration. Presence of thick coating of epidermal hair over the surface of leaves reduces transpiration. For example, cucurbits. In the plants of family **Crassulaceae** which are succulent plants, stomata open only in the night when ambient temperature is relatively less and humidity is more. The carbon dioxide enters through stomata only in the night and gets stored for photosynthesis during daytime. In the daytime, stomata remain closed and thus transpiration is reduced. In cactus, leaves get modified to spines while their stem is green and swollen to carry out photosynthesis and store water, respectively.

Advantages of Transpiration

Following are the advantages of transpiration:

- Temperature of the plants remains relatively low even under intense sunlight because of transpiration.
- This process helps in translocation of water, minerals and food through vascular tissues by controlling the water content of the cell.
- It creates a suction force that helps in absorption of water by roots and thereby facilitates **ascent of sap**.
- It controls the osmotic pressure of the tissues and thus helps in different life processes.
- Transpiration has effect on climate. It also causes rain by increasing the moisture content in air.

Disadvantages of Transpiration

Following are some disadvantages of transpiration:

- Transpiration causes wilting of leaves. Persistent wilting causes permanent damage.
- Excessive transpiration affects life processes and thus prevents proper growth of the plant.
- Higher rate of transpiration leads to closure of stomata due to lack of water in plants. In response to this condition, the formation of abscissic acid takes place.
- The hormone, abscissic acid causes shedding of leaves, delay in the production of flower, etc.
- A high percentage of water absorbed by the root is lost due to transpiration. So, the energy required to absorb and translocate the water gets wasted.

Quick Recap

✔ **(a) The phenomenon of guttation indicates that root pressure causes passive mode of absorption and transport. Justify.**

(b) How is the phenomenon of bleeding different from that of guttation?

(a) Due to the root pressure created within the roots, the water enters the roots even when there is sufficient water in the cells. When the transpiration is low, transpiration pull becomes insignificant. This excess water exudes from the leaves and is seen as water droplets on the leaf margins. This phenomenon is known as guttation.

(b) When there is an injury or cut on the surface of aerial parts of the plant such as stem, the cell sap oozes out of the plant. This phenomenon is called bleeding

✔ **What is wilting?**

Wilting of leaves is the loss of rigidity in them. This happens when a plant does not receive enough water as a result of which the pressure inside the leaves drops. In other words, loss of water from the plants is more than the absorption of water in the plant. When a plant is adequately hydrated, leaves are sturdy and strong, but when a plant is not properly hydrated, the leaves lose their strength and appear drooping and withering.

✔ **Why is root pressure regarded as the 'initial driving force' in water and mineral transport?**

Water uptake by root hairs creates a positive pressure that pushes water upwards into the plant, resulting in root pressure. This provides the initial momentum for water and minerals to move to other parts of the plant, thereby assisting capillary action.

✔ **What role do pneumatophores play in plant respiration?**

Pneumatophores are specialized roots that emerge from wet soils and allow plants to access atmospheric oxygen. They have numerous pores that allow for gaseous exchange, which is critical for plants in low-oxygen environments.

✔ **Explain how cacti's structural adaptations allow them to survive in arid environments.**

For desert survival, cacti have evolved a variety of structural adaptations. Their leaves have been modified into spines, which reduces water loss through transpiration. The plant's survival during dry spells is ensured by the green and swollen stem, which performs photosynthesis and stores water.

✔ **The greater the thickness of the cuticle, the lesser the transpiration. Why?**

Cuticle is a waxy layer that is secreted on both surfaces of the leaf by epidermis. Cuticle prevents the evaporation/transpiration of water from the leaf surface, allowing transpiration only to a little extent.

POINTS TO REMEMBER

- The sum total of the process through which an animal or plant takes in food substances and utilizes them is known as nutrition.
- A series of processes by which an organism prepares its own food from simple inorganic materials collected from the environment is called autotrophic nutrition.
- A mode of nutrition in which an organism depends on the other organisms for its food is called heterotrophic nutrition.
- The process through which green plants prepare carbohydrates from carbon dioxide taken from atmosphere and water from the soil in presence of sunlight is called photosynthesis.
- Chloroplasts are green-coloured plastids responsible for carrying out the process of photosynthesis to prepare food for the plant.
- The gaseous exchange between environment and the plant happens through tiny pores or openings on the lower surface of the leaves called stomatal pores or apertures.
- The addition of inorganic phosphate to ADP to produce highly energetic ATP molecule carried out by electrons excited through capturing light is called photophosphorylation.
- The main products of photosynthesis are glucose obtained in dark phase and oxygen obtained in light phase.
- The initial driving force that causes the transportation of water and minerals to xylem from root hair is called root pressure.
- Transpiration is the loss of water from the surface of aerial parts of the plant mainly from the leaves.
- Respiration is the process in which food materials present in the body of the organisms break down chemically with the help of enzymes, and energy is liberated.
- Respiration can be divided into two categories based on its occurrence in the presence or absence of oxygen, i.e., Anaerobic and Aerobic Respiration.
- During the process of glycolysis, glucose, a 6-Carbon sugar gets converted to a 3-Carbon compound called pyruvate, and energy is released.
- During fermentation, ethanol and carbon dioxide are formed along with the liberation of energy.
- Krebs Cycle involves complete oxidation of pyruvic acid which produces carbon dioxide and water as the end products along with the liberation of energy.
- Exchange of oxygen and carbon dioxide required for respiration and photosynthesis, respectively takes place throughout the surface of the body in lower plants, and through root hairs and lenticels in higher plants.
- Pneumatophores are specialized roots that emerge out of the water-logged soil to facilitate the aeration required for respiration.
- Excretion is the life process through which waste and toxic products are expelled from the body of an organism.
- Transpiration is the process by which the elimination of water takes place from the aerial parts of the plant in the form of water vapour.
- In dry regions, leaves of the plants are adapted structurally in such a way that transpiration is reduced to a great extent.
- In cactus, leaves get modified to spines while their stem is green and swollen to carry out photosynthesis and store water, respectively.

PRACTICE QUESTIONS CLASSROOM WING

Very Short Answer Type Questions

Directions for questions from 1 to 5:
Fill in the blanks.

1. The organisms that produce their food by utilizing energy from chemical reactions and not by sunlight are called _____________.

2. _________ is the green-coloured pigment responsible for trapping sunlight.

3. The pores on the lower surface of the leaves responsible for the intake of CO_2 are called _____________.

4. Thylakoids serve as the site for one phase of photosynthesis that requires ________.

5. In the Potassium ion Concentration Theory, _______ facilitates the entry of potassium ions from neighbouring cells into guard cells.

Directions for questions from 6 to 26:
For each of the following questions, four choices have been provided. Select the correct alternatives.

6. Which of the following is not involved in autotrophic nutrition?
   (a) Amoeba
   (b) Green plants
   (c) Photoautotrophs
   (d) Chemoautotrophs

7. Where does the photosynthesis phase that does not require light occur?
   (a) Thylakoids
   (b) Stroma
   (c) Chlorophyll
   (d) Outer membrane of the chloroplast

8. What central ion does chlorophyll-a contain?
   (a) Fe^{+2} (b) Na^{+1}
   (c) Mg^{+2} (d) Ca^{+2}

9. Which theory explains the opening and closing of stomata based on sugar concentration?
   (a) Chlorophyll Concentration Theory
   (b) Potassium ion Concentration Theory
   (c) Sugar Concentration Theory
   (d) ATP Concentration Theory

10. The absorption of what kind of energy initiates the photosynthesis reaction in chlorophyll?
    (a) Thermal energy
    (b) Chemical energy
    (c) Solar energy
    (d) Wind energy

11. Where in a plant cell does photolysis of water primarily take place?
    (a) Mitochondria
    (b) Thylakoid membrane
    (c) Nucleus
    (d) Cytoplasm

12. Which adaptation does NOT facilitate photosynthesis in leaves?
    (a) Thick structure
    (b) Large surface area
    (c) Presence of vascular bundle
    (d) Palisade cells

13. Imbibition is beneficial in:
    (a) Seed germination
    (b) Closing of stomata
    (c) Formation of root hair
    (d) Movement of minerals

14. How many Calvin cycles are involved in the synthesis of one glucose molecule by photosynthesis?
    (a) 3 (b) 1
    (c) 4 (d) 6

15. Release of oxygen during photosynthesis takes place in which of the following steps?
    (a) Photophosphorylation
    (b) Reduction of NADP
    (c) Carbon fixation
    (d) Photolysis of water

16. Under which of the following conditions, the absorption of water mainly takes place by active transport?

(i) Low humidity

(ii) Low temperature

(iii) High temperature

(iv) High humidity

(a) (i), (ii) (b) (ii), (iv)

(c) (i), (iii) (d) Only (iii)

17. Match the entries of Column 1 with those of Column 2.

Column 1	Column 2
A. Chloroplasts	(i) Light reactions
B. Photophosphorylation	(ii) Transportation of water
C. Calvin reactions	(iii) Stroma
D. Xylem	(iv) Formation of sugar

(a) A → (iii), B → (i), C → (iv), D → (ii)

(b) A → (ii), B → (i), C → (iv), D → (iii)

(c) A → (iv), B → (i), C → (iii), D → (ii)

(d) A → (i), B → (ii), C → (iii), D → (iv)

18. The site for both aerobic and anaerobic respiration is ________.

(a) Cytoplasm (b) Xylem

(c) Phloem (d) Chloroplast

19. In which process pyruvic acid undergoes complete oxidation and produces carbon dioxide and water?

(a) Excretion

(b) Anaerobic respiration

(c) Aerobic respiration

(d) Transportation

20. In which part of the cell, does Kreb's cycle take place?

(a) Cytoplasm (b) Mitochondria

(c) Chloroplast (d) Both (a) and (b)

21. Identify the organism in which pyruvic acid gets converted to lactic acid in the absence of oxygen.

(a) Amoeba

(b) *Paramoecium*

(c) Fungus

(d) Vertebrate animals

22. The conversion of pyruvic acid into lactic acid or ethanol in anaerobic respiration takes place in which organelle?

(a) Mitochondria (b) Cytoplasm

(c) Chlorophyll (d) Thylakoids

23. The water droplets formed on the leaf margins in the early mornings under high humid conditions is considered as which phenomenon?

(a) Condensation

(b) Transpiration

(c) Guttation

(d) Bleeding

24. Latex in rubber plants oozes out from the stems due to which phenomenon?

(a) Bleeding

(b) Guttation

(c) Transpiration

(d) Condensation

25. Which of the following steps in cellular respiration is associated with release of maximum number of ATP molecules?

(a) Glycolysis

(b) Kreb's cycle

(c) Oxidative phosphorylation

(d) Reduction of NADP

26. Match the entries of Column 1 with those of Column 2.

Column 1	Column 2
A. Stomata	(i) Anaerobic respiration
B. Mangrove trees	(ii) Intake of CO_2
C. Woody stem	(iii) Pneumatophores
D. Yeast	(iv) Lenticels

(a) A → (ii), B → (iii), C → (iv), D → (i)

(b) A → (ii), B → (i), C → (iv), D → (iii)

(c) A → (iv), B → (i), C → (iii), D → (ii)

(d) A → (i), B → (ii), C → (iii), D → (iv)

Short Answer Type Questions

Direction for Questions from 27 to 54:
Answer the following questions.

27. Differentiate between autotrophs and heterotrophs.
28. How are autotrophs classified?
29. Define photosynthesis.
30. Name the different parts of chloroplasts.
31. Draw the structure of chloroplast.
32. Explain the main role of stomata in flower.
33. What are the different phases of photosynthesis?
34. Mention the different steps of reactions that take place during the light phase of photosynthesis.
35. Write a short note on photophosphorylation.
36. What are the factors that affect the rate of photosynthesis?
37. Explain about the nutrition in a unicellular animal which throws the undigested food by the rupture of cell membrane.
38. Where do Hill's reactions take place in the chloroplasts?
39. Write a short note on the function of the site that is used for photosynthesis.
40. Identify the reaction that takes place in stroma and mention the major steps that are involved in it.
41. How does the structure of a chloroplast relate to its function in photosynthesis?
42. How is the process of photosynthesis in green plants different from the nutrition process in amoeba?
43. How can photosynthesis in plants be seen as a 'counterpart' to respiration in animals, in terms of energy exchange and balance in the ecosystem?
44. Describe the significance of chlorophyll in the process of photosynthesis.
45. What role does the stomata play in photosynthesis?
46. What are the different pathways by which water and minerals are transported from root to the xylem?
47. What are the different mechanisms that are involved in ascent sap?
48. Do the plants on the higher altitudes undergo less transpiration? Explain.
49. Explain the different types of transpiration.
50. Respiration is a slow process in plants. How?
51. Name the stage which is common for both the types of respirations.
52. Define nutrition and mode of nutrition.
53. Define cellular respiration.
54. What is the chemical reaction that takes place in yeast? Mention the condition.

Essay Type Questions

55. Describe the importance of photosynthesis not just for plants, but for life on Earth as a whole. Consider factors like oxygen production, food chains, and carbon sequestration.
56. It's hypothesized that chloroplasts in plant cells were once free-living bacteria. Explore this theory and discuss the implications it has for understanding symbiotic relationships in evolution.
57. Delve into the adaptive evolution of these pigments, considering factors like light intensity, angle, and the underwater environment.
58. How is transpiration minimized in crassulaceae plant?
59. Explain the reason why some trees in the coastal swamps have their roots emerged outward.

PRACTICE QUESTIONS COMPETITION WING

Level 1: Apply your Concepts

Directions for questions from 1 to 11:
Fill in the blanks.

1. Photolysis of water produces hydrogen ions and ________ ions.
2. NADP is reduced to ________ during photosynthesis.
3. The main products of photosynthesis are _______ obtained in the dark phase and _______ obtained in the light phase.
4. Chlorophyll captures light energy to excite its electrons, transitioning them from a _________ state to an ________ state.
5. The step where ATP is produced by the reaction between ADP and inorganic phosphate is termed as ____________.
6. The site where dark reactions of photosynthesis occur is called the ________ of the chloroplast.
7. ________ and ________ pathways are the two different ways by which water and minerals are transported from root hair to xylem.
8. The vascular tissue responsible for the transportation of food from leaves to other parts of the plant is ________.
9. Respiration in plants is essentially the opposite of ___________, a process by which plants produce oxygen.
10. Roots adapted for aeration, especially in water-logged soils, are known as ____________.
11. _____ transpiration accounts for about 90% of the total water loss in plants.

Direction for Questions from 12 to 17:
For each of the following questions four choices have been provided. Select the correct alternatives.

12. Which among the following forces does not help in the transportation of xylem sap?
    (a) Capillarity (b) Cohesive force
    (c) Transpiration pull (d) Root pressure
13. Which cells surround the sieve tube elements in the phloem?
    (a) Epidermis (b) Companion cells
    (c) Xylem cells (d) Cortex cells
14. Which process occurs in the cytoplasm of a cell during anaerobic respiration?
    (a) Krebs Cycle
    (b) Photosynthesis
    (c) Glycolysis
    (d) Calvin Cycle
15. Lenticels are crucial for:
    (a) Photosynthesis
    (b) Transpiration
    (c) Gas exchange in older parts of roots and woody stem
    (d) Anaerobic respiration
16. Which of the following factors decreases transpiration?
    (a) Increased light intensity
    (b) Decreased humidity
    (c) High wind velocity
    (d) Excess carbon dioxide
17. Which plant shows an adaptation where stomata open only at night to reduce transpiration?
    (a) Cactus (b) Banyan
    (c) Nerium (d) Crassulaceae

Direction for Questions from 18 to 22:
Correct the following statements.

18. Transpiration is directly proportional to humidity.
19. Transpiration through waxy coating over epidermal layers of leaves is known as lenticular transpiration.
20. The decrease in concentration of potassium ions leads to increase in turgidity of the guard cells.
21. Calvin reactions take place in grana of the chloroplast.
22. During night, the plants release major proportion of carbon dioxide.

Direction for Questions from 23 to 26:
Write the missing correlated terms.

23. Cyanobacteria : __________ : : *Paramoecium* : Heterotrophs.

24. Grana : __________ : : Stroma : Calvin reactions.

25. Surface respiration: *Chlamydomonas*: Mangrove trees: __________.

26. Lenticels: lenticular respiration: : __________ : Cuticular respiration.

Direction for Questions from 27 to 36:
Choose the correct option.

(a) Both A and R are true and R is the correct explanation for A.

(b) Both A and R are true but R is not the correct explanation for A.

(c) A is true and R is false.

(d) A is false and R is true.

27. **Assertion (A):** Chlorophyll is green in colour.

Reason (R): Chlorophyll absorbs green light from visible spectrum of light.

28. **Assertion (A):** The rate of photosynthesis increases with increase in light intensity only up to a point.

Reason (R): Photosynthesis includes dark phase.

29. **Assertion (A):** Leaves of different plants possess variable shades.

Reason (R): Chlorophyll contains complex structure with magnesium as the central atom.

30. **Assertion (A):** The cells in mesophyll are loosely packed with air spaces.

Reason (R): Photosynthesis takes place even when stomata are closed.

31. **Assertion (A):** Water molecules move from xylem to phloem during transportation process.

Reason (R): The source of energy for this process comes from the respiration in the form of ATP.

32. **Assertion (A):** In *Cuscuta*, stomata remain open during night.

Reason (R): *Cuscuta* is a hydrophyte.

33. **Assertion (A):** Physical exercise is usually followed by muscular pain.

Reason (R): Anaerobic respiration results in the production of less number of ATP molecules.

34. **Assertion (A):** In prokaryotes, anaerobic respiration takes place.

Reason (R): Prokaryotes possess indistinct nucleus.

35. **Assertion (A):** In woody plants, cuticular transpiration takes place.

Reason (R): In woody plants, epidermis is replaced by cork cambium.

36. **Assertion (A):** Kreb's cycle takes place in the cristae of mitochondria.

Reason (R): Cristae possess DNA and ribosomes.

Level 2: Review your Concepts

37. How does the accumulation of photosynthetic end products affect the rate of photosynthesis?

38. Explain the significance of the Calvin Cycle in the dark phase of photosynthesis.

39. How does light intensity influence the rate of photosynthesis?

40. Explain the main difference between the symplast and apoplast pathways for the transportation of water and minerals.

41. The energy released in anaerobic respiration is much less than aerobic respiration. Give reason.

42. Explain the primary role of companion cells in the translocation of photosynthetic products.

43. Stomata are abundant on the under surface of the-leaves. Give reason.

Level 3: Assess Your Concepts

44. How might changes in global climate patterns affect stomatal regulation and by extension, plant survival?

45. Clear division of labor is seen within a chloroplast. Give reason.

46. How does the structure of a leaf reflect the evolutionary pressures of balancing water conservation with the need for gas exchange? Discuss the role of the cuticle, stomata, and the arrangement of mesophyll tissues in this context.

47. Given that chlorophyll primarily absorbs light in the blue and red parts of the spectrum, why do most plants appear green? Discuss the potential evolutionary reasons behind this apparent inefficiency.

48. The water and minerals are usually transported in the roots by apoplast pathway up to endodermis, but later transported by symplast pathway. Give reason.

AT

PRACTICE QUESTIONS NEET SPECIAL WING

Multiple-Answer Type Questions

Questions number 1 to 5 are multiple-choice questions. Each question has FOUR options (a), (b), (c), and (d). ONE OR MORE THAN ONE of these four option(s) is/are the correct answer(s).

1. Which features are included in the Sugar-Concentration Theory?
   (a) Turgid guard cells increases the stomatal aperture
   (b) Flaccid guard cells increases the stomatal aperture
   (c) Increase in glucose concentration increases the osmotic pressure in the guard cells
   (d) Decrease in glucose concentration decreases the osmotic pressure in the guard cells

2. Identify the events of Hill reaction from the following:
   (a) Absorption of light by chlorophyll
   (b) Photolysis of CO_2
   (c) Reduction of NADP
   (d) Photo oxidation

3. What happens to oxygen which is released during photolysis of water used up?
   (a) Used up for respiration process
   (b) Used up for photosynthesis process
   (c) Diffused into atmosphere
   (d) Takes part in excretion

4. Which of the following are favourable adaptations for carrying out photosynthesis?
   (a) Large surface area of leaves
   (b) Tightly packed spongy cells
   (c) Thick structure of the leaves
   (d) Guard cells surrounding the stomatal pores

5. Transpiration can take place through:
   (a) Hydathode (b) Lenticels
   (c) Stomata (d) Cuticle

Comprehension-Based Questions

A. Read the paragraph given below and answer the questions number 6 to 11:

Photosynthesis in plants is a process which takes place with the help of green pigment called chlorophyll. The chlorophyll is contained within a green coloured plastid called chloroplast. The process of photosynthesis takes place in two phases- that is the light phase and the dark phase. In the light phase which is also known as Hill reaction absorption of light takes place by chlorophyll. The products of light reaction are used in the dark reaction or Calvin cycle where carbon dioxide fixation takes place with the help of RUBP. There are various adaptations shown by the plant to aid the process of photosynthesis. Light, CO_2, temperature and water are the various factors which affect photosynthesis.

6. Magnesium as a central ion is present in:
   (a) Carotene
   (b) Xanthophyll
   (c) Chlorophyll-a
   (d) Carotenoid

7. Which lights of the spectrum are absorbed by chlorophyll?
   (a) Red
   (b) Blue
   (c) Green
   (d) Both a and b

8. The high energy molecules are accepted by electron acceptor molecules like:
   (a) ATP
   (b) ADP
   (c) NAD
   (d) H_2O

9. Reduction of NADP occurs by:
   (a) Hydrogen ions released from photolysis of water
   (b) High energy electrons
   (c) Inorganic phosphate
   (d) Both a and b

10. The process of addition of inorganic phosphate to ADP in order to produce ATP is called:
   (a) Phosphorylation
   (b) Photophosphorylation
   (c) Oxidation
   (d) Photooxidation

11. Match the column:

Column – A	Column – B
(i) Carbon fixation	(a) Glucose
(ii) 5 carbon sugar for CO_2 fixation	(b) PGA
(iii) Product of photosynthesis in dark phase	(c) Oxygen
(iv) Product of photosynthesis in light phase	(d) Light
(v) Factor affecting photosynthesis	(e) RUBP

B. Read the paragraph given below and answer the questions number 12 to 17:

Respiration can be divided into two categories based on its occurrence in the presence or absence of oxygen. These are: Aerobic respiration (takes place in the presence of oxygen) and Anaerobic respiration (takes place in the absence of oxygen). Both the processes of respiration can be divided into two stages. The first stage of both the types of respiration is same. It takes place by the breakdown of glucose by glycolysis to produce Pyruvic acid. The next step is different in Anaerobic respiration and Aerobic respiration. Fermentation is a type of anaerobic respiration. It is carried out in microorganisms like yeast and certain bacteria to fulfil their requirement of energy. The site of this stage of anaerobic respiration is also cytoplasm. Anaerobic respiration can also take place in muscle cells of vertebrates but the by products are different. In Aerobic respiration Kreb's cycle takes place and produces a large amount of energy. Exchange of gases in plants in different regions takes place via different modes like stomata, lenticels, cuticles and even pneumatophores.

12. Why does anaerobic respiration in muscle cells of vertebrate animals produce less energy than aerobic respiration?
(a) Energy is stored in lactic acid
(b) Energy is stored in ethanol
(c) Energy is lost to O_2
(d) Energy is lost to CO_2

13. Which of the four-word equations represents anaerobic respiration in yeast?
(a) Carbon dioxide + water → glucose + oxygen
(b) Glucose → ethanol + carbon dioxide
(c) Glucose → lactic acid
(d) Glucose + oxygen → carbon dioxide + water

14. Which conditions are required by green plants for respiration?

	Bright sunlight	Darkness
A.	Yes	Yes
B.	Yes	No
C.	No	Yes
D.	No	No

(a) A (b) B
(c) C (d) D

15. Which reactions can occur in the muscle cells of vertebrates?
1. Carbon dioxide + water ⟶ glucose + oxygen
2. Glucose ⟶ ethanol + carbon dioxide
3. Glucose ⟶ lactic acid
4. Glucose + oxygen ⟶ carbon dioxide + water

(a) 2 and 3
(b) 1 and 3
(c) 3 and 4
(d) 1 and 4

16. Which processes take place through the action of enzymes or bio catalysts?

1. Digestion
2. Osmosis
3. Respiration
4. Diffusion

(a) 1 and 2
(b) 1 and 3
(c) 2 and 4
(d) 3 and 4

17. Match the column:

Column – A	Column – B
(i) Exchange of gas in Mangroves	(a) Lenticels
(ii) Exchange of gas in woody stems	(b) Pneumatophores
(iii) Exchange of gas in young roots	(c) Diffusion through surface
(iv) Exchange of gas in green soft stems	(d) Cytoplasm
(v) Kreb's cycle in prokaryotes	(e) Stomata

ANSWER KEYS

Crossword

Across

4. Autotrophic 5. Glucose 7. Photophosphorylation 8. Pneumatophores
9. Heterotrophic 11. Glycolysis 12. Excretion 13. Anaerobic 16. Respiration
17. Stomata

Down

1. Aerobic 2. Transpiration 3. Fermentation 6. Photosynthesis 10. Chloroplasts
14. Nutrition 15. Cactus

Classroom Wing

Very Short Answer Type Questions

1. Chemoautotrophs 2. Chlorophyll 3. Stomatal pores or apertures 4. Light
5. ATP 6. (a) 7. (b) 8. (c) 9. (c)
10. (c) 11. (b) 12. (a) 13. (a) 14. (d)
15. (d) 16. (c) 17. (a) 18. (a) 19. (c)
20. (b) 21. (d) 22. (b) 23. (c) 24. (a)
25. (c) 26. (a)

Competition Wing

Level 1: Apply Your Concepts

1. Hydroxide (OH^-) 2. $NADPH_2$ 3. Glucose, oxygen 4. Ground, excited
5. Photophosphorylation 6. Stroma 7. Symplast, apoplast 8. Phloem
9. Photosynthesis 10. Pneumatophores 11. Stomatal 12. (d) 13. (b)
14. (c) 15. (c) 16. (d) 17. (d)
23. Chemoautotroph 24. Hill reactions 25. Pneumatophores 26. Cuticles 27. (c)
28. (a) 29. (b) 30. (a) 31. (c) 32. (c)
33. (b) 34. (b) 35. (d) 36. (c)

NEET Special Wing

Multiple-Answer Type Questions

1. (a, c) **2.** (a, c) **3.** (a, c) **4.** (a, d) **5.** (b, c, d)

Comprehension-Based Questions

6. (c) **7.** (d) **8.** (b) **9.** (d) **10.** (a)

11. (i) → (b); (ii) → (e); (iii) → (a); (iv) → (c); (v) → (d)

12. (a) **13.** (b) **14.** (a) **15.** (c) **16.** (b)

17. (i) → (b); (ii) → (a); (iii) → (c); (iv) → (e); (v) → (d)

Hints and Explanations

CLASSROOM WING

Short Answer Type Questions

27.

Autotrophs	Heterotrophs
The organisms that prepare food on their own by a series of processes are known as autotrophs, for example, plants.	The organisms that depend on other organisms for their food are known as heterotrophs, for example, *Amoeba*.

28. Autotrophs are classified into two types, namely:
   (a) **Photoautotrophs**—Green plants are photoautotrophs since they prepare their own food.
   (b) **Chemoautotrophs**—These organisms produce their food by utilizing energy from chemical reaction and not by utilizing sunlight, for example, cyanobacteria.

29. Photosynthesis is a process through which green plants prepare carbohydrates after taking in carbon dioxide from the atmosphere and water from the soil in the presence of sunlight.

30. Each chloroplast can be divided into there main parts:
   (a) Double membrane
   (b) Stroma
   (c) Thylakoids

31.

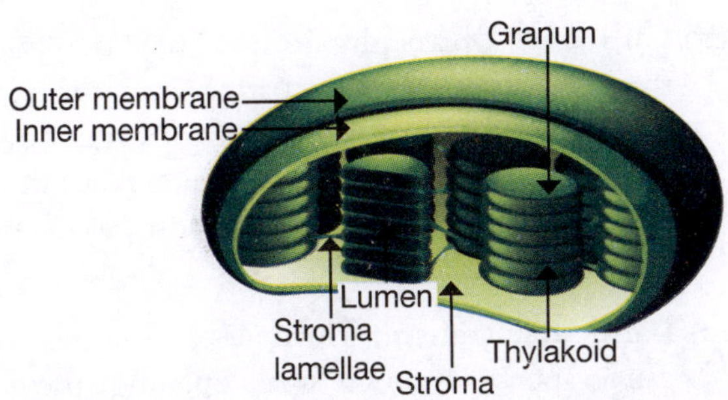

32. (a) The tiny pores or openings on the lower surface of the leaves are called stomata.
   (b) Stomata act as the passage for the transference of gases from the environment to the plant and vice versa, for example, taking in carbon dioxide for photosynthesis.

33. Photosynthesis is not a single-step process. It is a series of complex reactions that occur in two phases, which are:
   (a) Light reactions
   (b) Dark reactions

34. Light reactions were discovered by the scientist named Hill, and this is the reason why they are known as Hill reactions. These reactions occur in four different steps as follows:
   (a) Absorption of light by chlorophyll
   (b) Photolysis of water
   (c) Reduction of NADP
   (d) Photophosphorylation.

35. The synthesis of adenosine triphosphate (ATP) with reaction between adenosine diphosphate (ADP) and inorganic phosphate is called phosphorylation. ADP + inorganic phosphate—ATP. Since this reaction takes place in the presence of light, it is called photophosphorylation. ATP molecules are energy suppliers and the ATP formed in this way during the light phase is utilized during the dark phase.

36. There are two types of factors that influence the rate of photosynthesis, which are:
   (a) External factors
      (i) Light
      (ii) Carbon dioxide
      (iii) Temperature
      (iv) Water
   (b) Internal factors
      (i) Chlorophyll content
      (ii) Accumulation of end products of photosynthesis
      (iii) Anatomy of leaf

37. The unicellular organism *Amoeba* ingests the food by encircling the food particle with the help of finger-like projections of the cell surface. Ingested food gets digested in the vacuole of the cell. During digestion, complex food particles are converted to simpler sub-

stances. Undigested food is thrown out of the body by the rupture of the cell membrane.

38. Light reactions were discovered by a scientist named Hill; therefore, they are also known as Hill reactions. These reactions are photochemical reactions that take place in the grana of the chloroplast.

39. Chloroplast is the site for photosynthesis. These are green-coloured plastids containing a green pigment called chlolrophyll. Each chloroplast can be divided into three main parts:

    (a) **Double membrane**: The chloroplast is enveloped by a double membrane and the outer membrane is more permeable and the inner one is selectively permeable.

    (b) **Stroma**: It is a colourless matrix inside the double membrane and is rich in proteins. Dark reactions take place in stroma.

    (c) **Thylakoids**: These are the stacks of membrane-bound flattened sac-like structures. Each flat-like structure is known as grana. Grana contain chlorophyll and are also the site for the Hill reactions or light reactions.

40. Dark reactions or the Calvin reactions occur in stroma. These reactions occur in three major steps which are:

    (a) Fixation of carbon dioxide

    (b) Formation of sugar

    (c) Regeneration of RUBP

41. The chloroplast's structure is tailored to its role in photosynthesis. It has chlorophyll within thylakoids to capture sunlight, and a stroma wherein the light-independent reactions take place.

42. Green plants use photosynthesis, a process of converting light energy to food energy, whereas amoebas consume food particles directly, encircling them with pseudopodia.

43. Photosynthesis and respiration: Photosynthesis absorbs sunlight energy and stores it in glucose, whereas respiration in animals releases this stored energy. It's a cyclical exchange in which the output of one process becomes the input of the other.

44. Chlorophyll is vital for photosynthesis as it captures and absorbs light energy. When it absorbs photons, electrons in chlorophyll molecules transition from a ground state to an excited state. This energy is then used to drive the chemical reactions that convert carbon dioxide and water into glucose.

45. Stomata are tiny openings on the leaf surface that allow for the exchange of gases. During photosynthesis, they open to let in carbon dioxide from the atmosphere and release the by-product oxygen. They are essential for the efficient functioning of the photosynthesis process.

46. There are two different pathways by which water and minerals are transported from root hair to the xylem, which are:

    (a) **Symplast pathway**: The passage of water and minerals through the cytoplasm of the cells is called transportation through symplast pathway.

    (b) **Apoplast pathway**: These are the intercellular spaces outside the plasma membrane. The passage of water and minerals through the cell wall and intercellular spaces is known as apoplast pathway.

47. The different mechanisms that are involved in ascent sap are:

    (a) Capillarity

    (b) Cohesive force

    (c) Transpiration pull

48. At higher altitudes, atmospheric pressure is very low as compared to the ground level. As increase in atmospheric pressure reduces transpiration, at higher altitudes due to very less atmospheric pressure transpiration will by high.

49. There are three types of transpiration such as:

    (a) **Stomatal transpiration:** In this type of transpiration, 90 per cent of water gets eliminated from the plants through stomata. This depends on the structure of the leaves and the number of stomata on the leaves.

    (b) **Cuticular transpiration:** The transpiration through cuticle, awaxy coating over the epidermal layers of leaves is called cuticular transpiration. Only 5–10 per cent water loss takes place through the cuticle. It is inversely proportional to the thickness of the cuticle.

    (c) **Lenticular transpiration:** Water from plants also can evaporate through small openings present in the woody stems. This is called lenticular transpiration. Only 0.1 per cent of water is lost through lenticels.

    - Plants do not have any specific respiratory organs.
    - There are large intercellular spaces filled with air in their bodies

50. Plants are stationary and their energy requirement is less. So, the process of respiration is slow.

51. Glycolysis is the first stage of respiration and is common for both aerobic and anaerobic respiration.

52. Nutrition can be defined as the process of intake of nutrients and its utilization by an organism. Mode of nutrition can be defined as the way by which an organism receives its food.

53. Cellular respiration is a biochemical process in which the simple nutrients such as glucose are oxidized within the cells to release energy.

54. Glucose → Pyruvate → Ethanol + Carbon dioxide + Energy (2 ATP molecules)
The condition required is the absence of oxygen.

Essay Type Questions

55. Photosynthesis is essential to life on Earth, primarily producing oxygen and converting solar energy into usable chemical energy. Plants absorb carbon dioxide and release oxygen, which is required for the respiration of most living organisms. The repercussions of this are far-reaching; without photosynthesis, atmospheric oxygen would deplete, rendering Earth uninhabitable for aerobic organisms. Furthermore, the glucose produced during photosynthesis serves as the primary energy source for a wide range of organisms, forming the foundation of the food chain. Herbivores eat plants and are then eaten by carnivores, and so on. On a larger scale, photosynthesis acts as a natural regulator of Earth's carbon levels, assisting in climate stabilisation by continuously consuming carbon dioxide. With growing concerns about global warming and rising CO_2 levels, the role of plants as carbon sinks has never been more important.

56. The endosymbiotic theory provides an intriguing glimpse into the possible evolution of eukaryotic cells. Chloroplasts, like mitochondria, are thought to have evolved from free-living bacteria that were engulfed by ancestral eukaryotic cells. Instead of being digested, these bacteria developed a symbiotic relationship with their host cell, benefiting from its defences and resources over time. In exchange, the bacteria, which could photosynthesize, supplied glucose to the host cell. The presence of a double membrane in chloroplasts, indicating an engulfment event, lends support to this theory. Furthermore, chloroplasts have their own DNA that is distinct from the cell nucleus and closely resembles bacterial DNA. This mutually beneficial relationship transformed Earth's life, allowing the proliferation of diverse plant life forms that shaped ecosystems and paved the way for terrestrial life.

57. Light is essential for photosynthesis, and plants have evolved a plethora of adaptations to effectively harness it. Plants are exposed to different light intensities and wavelengths depending on their environment. Plants in sun-drenched deserts or tropical rainforests, for example, have high chlorophyll concentrations to capture the abundant sunlight. Plants in shaded environments or deeper waters, on the other hand, may have different pigments, such as phycobilin, to absorb the wavelengths that penetrate these environments. Aquatic plants, in particular, are confronted with a dual challenge. Because water absorbs and scatters sunlight, these plants frequently have pigments capable of capturing diffused light. This evolutionary dance between plants and light demonstrates life's resilience and adaptability.

58. *Crassulaceae* are succulent plants and their stomata opens only in the night when ambient temperature is relatively low and humid. The carbon dioxide enters through stomata only in the night and gets stored for photosynthesis during daytime. In day time, the stomata remains closed and thus transpiration is reduced.

59. As the soil in the coastal swamps is not much aerated, hence for the purpose of breathing some trees like mangrove trees have specialized roots, such as pneumatophores which emerge out of water-logged soil.

COMPETITION WING

Level 1: Apply your Concepts

18. Transpiration is inversely proportional to humidity.

19. Transpiration through waxy coating over the epidermal layers of leaves is known as cuticular respiration.

20. The increase in concentration of potassium ions leads to increase in the turgidity of the guard cells.

21. Calvin reactions take place in stroma of the chloroplast.

22. During night, the plants release a major proportion of carbon dioxide. Whereas, during daytime, both photosynthesis and respiration take place simultaneously. So, both oxygen and carbon dioxide are released.

23. Cyanobacteria : Chemoautotroph : : *Paramoecium* : Heterotrophs.

24. Grana : Hill reactions : : Stroma : Calvin reactions.

25. Surface respiration : *Chlamydomonas* : : Mangrove trees : Pneumatophores.

26. Lenticels : lenticular respiration : : cuticles : cuticular respiration.

27. Chlorophyll appears green in colour as it absorbs red and blue lights of the visible spectrum

    Hence, the correct option is (c)

28. The final product of photosynthesis is glucose. This actually takes place during the dark phase that does not require light. But this is carried out by utilizing the precursors formed during the light phase, which are ATP and NADPH. Hence, intensity of light affects only some part of the photosynthetic process.

    Hence, the correct option is (a)

29. Chlorophyll in leaves is a complex substance having a number of pigments. This is the reason why the leaves possess variable shades. Chlorophyll-a is the principal pigment with magnesium as the central atom. Both are correct statements, but reason does not support assertion.

    Hence, the correct option is (b)

30. In addition to making the gaseous exchange more efficient, the air spaces present in the mesophyll trap some amount of carbon dioxide in them. This facilitates some photosynthesis even when the stomata are closed.

    Hence, the correct option is (a)

31. The movement of water from xylem to phloem takes place by means of osmosis. This is a passive mode of transport which does not require energy.

    The correct answer is (c)

32. *Cuscuta* is a succulent plant that stores water in the thickened stems. In these plants, stomata remain open during night when the temperature is less. This is to reduce water loss by transpiration. Stomata remain open during night as the air is cool and humid.

    Hence, the correct option is (c)

33. During vigorous physical exercise, the oxygen in the cells gets exhausted. Therefore, anaerobic respiration takes place in the muscle cells for the immediate need of extra amount of energy. During this process, lactic acid is formed as the end product. This causes muscular pain. Though anaerobic respiration results in the production of less amount of energy, it is not the reason for the given assertion.

    Hence, the correct option is (b)

34. In prokaryotes, anaerobic respiration takes place as the cells do not possess mitochondria. Though prokaryotes possess indistinct nucleus, this is not the reason for the given assertion.

    The correct answer is (b)

35. In woody plants, due to the activity of lateral meristematic tissue, cork cambium is formed. It is mostly made up of dead cells and is present as the outermost layer of plants. The stomata on epidermis usually aid in transpiration in non-woody plants. But, in woody plants, the stomata are not exposed out. In the cork cambium, some openings called lenticels are present. They carry out the function of transpiration, which is called lenticular transpiration.

    Hence, the correct option is (d)

36. DNA and ribosomes are present in the matrix of mitochondria. DNA possesses genes that are responsible for the synthesis of enzymes required for the process of cellular respiration (Kreb's cycle). The actual Kreb's cycle takes place in the cristae of mitochondria as the cristae provide large surface area for the various complicated biochemical reactions involved in Kreb's cycle.

    Hence, the correct option is (c)

Level 2: Review your Concepts

37. Accumulation of photosynthetic end products, like glucose, can decrease the rate of photosynthesis. If glucose produced is not transported or used, it can act as a feedback inhibitor, signalling the plant to slow down the photosynthetic process.

38. The Calvin Cycle, also known as the dark reactions or biosynthetic phase, is where the fixed carbon dioxide is converted into glucose using the ATP and NADPH2 produced in the light phase. It ensures the continuous conversion of atmospheric carbon dioxide into energy-rich glucose molecules.

39. Light intensity is directly proportional to the rate of photosynthesis up to a certain point. When other factors like temperature and carbon dioxide concentration are non-limiting, as light intensity increases, the rate of photosynthesis also increases. However, at extremely high light intensities, the process may get inhibited.

40. The symplast pathway involves transportation through the cytoplasm of the cells, while the apoplast pathway involves the passage of water and minerals through the cell wall and intercellular spaces.

41. In anaerobic respiration, glucose is not completely oxidized to carbon dioxide, but it is partially oxidized. During the process of glycolysis, two ATP molecules are produced. It does not involve Krebs cycle and oxidative phosphorylation which are normally associated with the formation of large number of ATP molecules. Therefore, less amount of energy is released.

42. Companion cells surround sieve tube elements and facilitate the transportation of sugar, amino acids, and other organic molecules into the sieve tubes, aiding in their translocation throughout the plant.

43. Stomata are present under the surface of leaves in case of land plants. This is to reduce water loss by transpiration as they are less exposed to the sunlight. This also facilitates greater diffusion of carbon dioxide into the leaves as CO_2 is a heavier gas.

Level 3: Assess Your Concepts

44. Stomata, or minute pores on plant leaves, serve as entry points for gas exchange and water vapour release. Their opening and closing processes are finely tuned and influenced by environmental factors. Some plants' stomatal density appears to be decreasing as CO_2 levels rise due to climate change. This makes evolutionary sense: if there is more CO_2 available, plants may not require as many stomata to absorb it, resulting in less water loss through transpiration. Reduced transpiration, on the other hand, can have a domino effect on local climates, affecting humidity and temperature. Some plants may adapt to these changes, but others, particularly those in already vulnerable ecosystems, may face extinction. The interdependence of stomatal regulation, photosynthesis, and global climate highlights the delicate balance of life processes on our planet.

45. Chloroplast has two membranes. Thylakoids present in the grana carry out the initial phase of photosynthesis. Stroma is concerned with the dark phase in which the actual product of photosynthesis that is glucose is formed. The enzymes and coenzymes required for the process are synthesized by ribosomes as per the instructions given by DNA. Thus, division of labour is seen in chloroplast.

46. Over millennia, plants have experienced various environmental pressures, leading to the evolution of sophisticated leaf structures. The external waxy cuticle conserves moisture while stomata, tiny adjustable pores, regulate gas exchange. Internally, mesophyll tissues differentiate into spongy and palisade cells, each playing distinct roles in photosynthesis. These adaptations reflect nature's finesse in balancing essential processes. The coexistence of hydration, respiration, and photosynthesis in leaves is a testimony to nature's grand design and the struggle for survival.

47. Why are most plants green? This foundational question delves into the absorption spectrum of chlorophyll. While chlorophyll molecules absorb light most efficiently in the blue and red spectra, they reflect green light. Evolution might have favoured this seeming 'inefficiency' for multiple reasons. Over-absorption can lead to cellular damage, and green light might not offer sufficient energy. Additionally, the green hue could serve protective or deterrence roles in specific ecosystems, reducing herbivory or minimizing heat absorption.

48. The pathway outside plasma membrane is not free beyond endodermis. This is due to the obstruction by Caspian strip made up of waterproof material called suberin in the pathway.

NEET SPECIAL WING

Multiple-Answer Type Questions

1. According to sugar concentration theory during the day, increase in glucose concentration due to photosynthesis results in endosmosis in the guard cells. The guard cells become turgid and this helps to increase the stomatal aperture. At night reverse occurs, the guard cells become flaccid and the stomatal aperture closes.
2. Light reactions or light-dependent reactions are a group of reactions which make use of light energy. They were discovered by the scientist Robin Hill, that is why they are also known as Hill reaction. The series of reactions occurring in Hill reaction are broadly classified into four steps:

   Absorption of light by chlorophyll, Photolysis of water, Reduction of NADP and Photophosphorylation.
3. After the absorption of light energy, chlorophyll molecules help in the dissociation of water molecules into hydrogen ions (H^+) and hydroxide ions (OH^-). Some of this oxygen is used up for the respiration process. The remaining amount of oxygen is diffused into the atmosphere through the stomata.
4. Leaves of the plants undergo various adaptations to facilitate photosynthesis. They have thin structure for easy diffusion of carbon dioxide to the site of photosynthesis. They also have guard cells surrounding the stomatal pores which help in opening stomatal pores for the entry of carbon dioxide during daytime and closing the pores during night to control loss of water.
5. Transpiration can be categorized based on the aerial parts of the plant involved in transpiration. About 90 per cent of the total water is eliminated from the plants through stomata. About 5–10 per cent water loss takes place through the cuticles which is a waxy coating over epidermis of leaves. Water from plants can also evaporate through small openings, called lenticels present in the woody stems. Plants transpire about 0.1 per cent water through lenticels.

Comprehension-Based Questions

A.

6. The principal pigment, chlorophyll-a is mainly responsible for the absorption of sunlight and acts as the reaction centre for the part of photosynthesis that takes place in the presence of light. Chlorophyll contains carbon, oxygen, hydrogen, nitrogen and most importantly chlorophyll-a contains magnesium in the form of Mg^{+2} ion as the central ion.
7. Chlorophyll is the pigment present in chloroplasts in major proportions. It absorbs blue and red lights of the spectrum and reflects green colour.
8. Chlorophyll gets energized by absorbing photons of light of certain wavelengths. Thus, the electrons in chlorophyll molecules attain the excited state from the ground state. Some of these high-energy electrons are taken up by the electron acceptor molecules, which are NADP and ADP.
9. NADP is reduced to $NADPH_2$ by the hydrogen ions released during photolysis of water and the high energy electrons.
10. The addition of inorganic phosphate to ADP to produce highly energetic ATP molecule is called phosphorylation.
11. Match the following:

    Carbon dioxide absorbed is utilized in this step for the formation of a 3-carbon compound that is phospho glyceric acid (PGA) as the initial product.
    (i) (b)

    Carbon dioxide combines with a 5-carbon sugar that is RUBP which is present in stroma. This brings about CO_2 fixation and PGA is produced.
    (ii) (e)

    The main products of photosynthesis is glucose obtained in dark phase.
    (iii) (a)

    The main products of photosynthesis are glucose obtained in dark phase and oxygen obtained in light phase.
    (iv) (c)

    Intensity and quality are the two characteristics of light that govern the rate of photosynthesis. If the other factors like temperature and the concentration of carbon dioxide are not limiting, the rate of photosynthesis is directly proportional to the intensity of the light.
    (v) (d)

B.

12. In muscle cells of vertebrate animals due to lack of oxygen, anaerobic respiration takes place where lactic

acid is produced along with 2 ATP. Most of the energy is trapped within lactic acid molecule and hence less energy is released in this process.

13. Glucose ⟶ ethanol + carbon dioxide
This is the chemical equation which takes place during anaerobic respiration in yeast cells.

14. Respiration in green plants can take place continuously with or without the presence of light.

15. In muscle cells in vertebrates, during anaerobic respiration lactic acid is produced and during aerobic respiration carbon dioxide and water is produced along with energy in the form of ATP.

16. Digestion and respiration are the processes which are dependent on enzymes or catalyst to carry out the biological reactions in very specific conditions. Osmosis and diffusion are dependent on the concentration gradient and do not depend on the action of enzymes to take place within the plant body.

17. Match the following:
Mangrove trees that grow in coastal swamps have adapted roots called pneumatophores for the purpose of breathing since the soil in those areas is not aerated. Pneumatophores are specialized roots that emerge out of the water-logged soil to facilitate the aeration required for respiration.
(i) (b)

In older portion of the roots and in woody stem, entry and exit of gases take place through small openings called lenticels.
(ii) (a)

In young roots, root hair is present throughout its surface. Spaces between the soil particles are filled with air. Oxygen enters the cells of the root hair by the process of diffusion and then reaches other cells in the root. Carbon dioxide formed during respiration is expelled in the same way.
(iii) (c)

In leaves and green soft stems, stomata are present that facilitate the exchange of gases. After entering through stomata or lenticels, oxygen gas reaches the cells of different parts of the plants through the diffusion process via intercellular spaces. In the same way, carbon dioxide gas produced during respiration is expelled out.
(iv) (e)

Krebs cycle, is a series of chemical reactions of primary importance in all living cells that utilize oxygen during the process of cellular respiration. It takes place within the mitochondria in eukaryotic organisms, and in the cytoplasm in prokaryotic organisms.
(v) (d)

CHAPTER
4

Reproduction in Lower Organisms and Plants

Remember

Before beginning this chapter, you should be able to:

- Understand the significance of reproduction
- Recall basic methods of reproduction
- Remember major fertilization and post-fertilization events in plants

Key Ideas

After completing this chapter, you should be able to:

- Describe asexual and sexual modes of reproduction
- Understand various methods of vegetative propagation in plants
- Discuss role of flowers in reproduction
- Explain post-fertilization events in plants

A Tribute to Gregor Johann Mendel (1822–1884)

Gregor Johann Mendel (1822–1884) is widely regarded as the 'Father of Genetics,' and his ground-breaking work is the foundation of modern genetic research. Mendel, who was born in Heinzendorf, Austria, was an Augustinian friar and scientist who conducted ground-breaking experiments on pea plants in his monastery garden between 1856 and 1863. His careful observation and analysis revealed the fundamental principles of inheritance.

Mendel's research established the existence of paired elementary units of inheritance (now known as genes) as well as the laws of segregation and independent assortment. These laws explain how traits are inherited and have broad implications, illuminating our understanding of reproduction not only in plants but also in lower organisms. He established the concept of dominant and recessive traits by demonstrating that offspring inherit one allele for each trait from each parent.

Though Mendel's extraordinary discoveries were not widely recognised during his lifetime, the scientific community recognised his invaluable contributions after his death.

FUN TIME

CROSSWORD

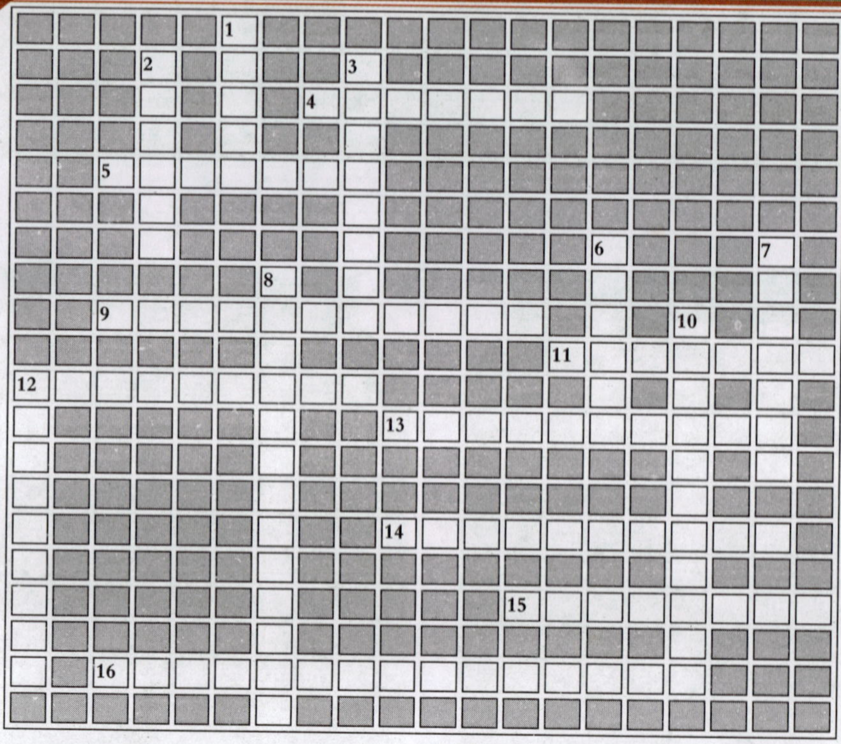

Across

4. The method of asexual reproduction found in yeast
5. The part of the seedling which gives rise to shoot system
9. The condition of flower in which the style and stamen are of contrasting heights
11. The location where the nucellus attaches to the integuments in the embryo sac
12. The globular structures which release spores in lower plants
13. Third whorl of a flower
14. The structures of seed which form the first leaves after germination
15. The flat disc like structure present above the pedicel of the flower
16. Pollination by means of bats

Down

1. The mark of the scar which remains when the seed gets detached from the stalk
2. the stems that grows just below the soil surface or just on the surface of the ground.
3. Nutritive tissue of the embryo formed after fertilisation
6. Thread like projections developed in Rhizopus
7. The name given to root modification in turmeric
8. The method of asexual reproduction in which the broken thallus grows into a new individual
10. The condition in which the flower remains without opening and drives self-pollination
12. Two other cells other than egg cell located on the lower side of the embryo sac

INTRODUCTION

Reproduction is a special biological process essential for the perpetuation of an individual. However, It is not essential for the survival of an individual. The adult organism that reproduces is called parent organism and the young ones produced are called offspring or progenies. Reproduction is a process by which new individuals of the same species are produced by existing parental organisms. The modes of reproduction vary according to individual species and available conditions. It is broadly classified into two categories:

1. **Asexual reproduction:** In this method of reproduction, the offspring is produced from one organism, and hence is exactly identical to its parent.
2. **Sexual reproduction:** In this mode of reproduction, the production of offspring involves two individuals of opposite sexes and the new individual is not exactly identical and shows appreciable distinction from the parents.

Asexual Reproduction

Asexual reproduction is observed generally in lower organisms that are structurally less complex. The lower organisms show different modes of asexual reproduction.

Based on the method followed, asexual reproduction could be of many types. Some of the major methods of asexual reproduction are:

- Fission (binary fission and multiple fission)
- Budding
- Spore formation
- Regeneration
- Fragmentation
- Vegetative reproduction (natural and artificial)

Fission

Fission is classified into two types—binary fission and multiple fission, depending upon the number of offspring produced.

Binary Fission

Binary fission is the splitting up of an organism into two parts that grow independently into new organisms. The genetic material, that is, DNA, is duplicated and distributed among the two daughter cells. The offspring will be exactly identical to the parent organism. Prokaryotes such as archaea (most primitive organisms originated) and bacteria reproduce through binary fission. Unicellular organisms such as *Amoeba* and *Paramoecium* undergo binary fission to produce their offspring.

The process of binary fission in *Amoeba* is described below with the help of following points.

- Bacterium makes a duplicate of its DNA.
- Parent cell gets elongated.
- Nuclear matter divides into two and then cytoplasm undergoes cleavage.
- Thus, two daughter cells are formed.

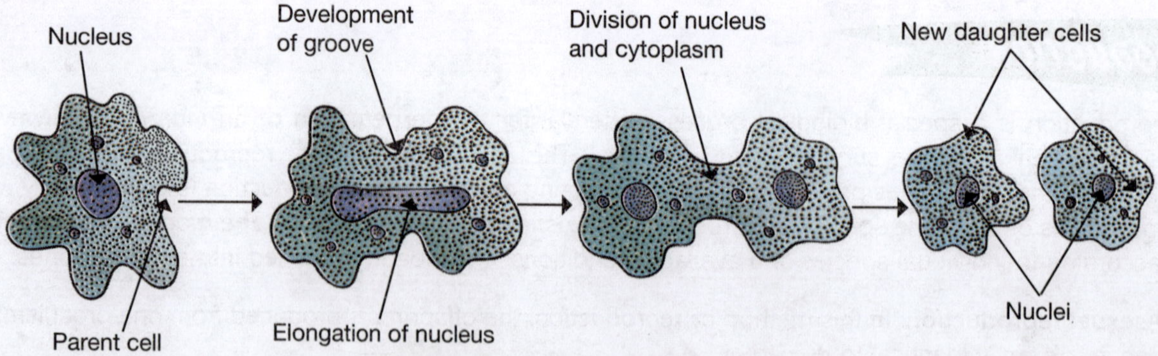

Figure 4.1 Binary fission in *Amoeba*

Multiple Fission

Multiple fission is the splitting up of an organism into multiple parts that grow independently into new organisms. The process of multiple fission in *Plasmodium* is described below with the help of following points:

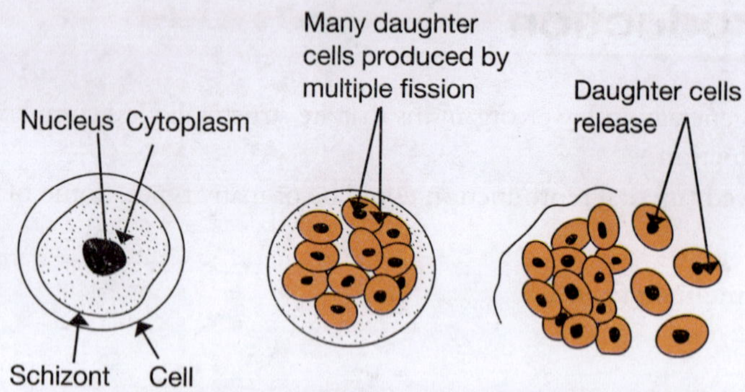

Figure 4.2 Multiple fission in *Plasmodium*

- The nucleus of the cell undergoes divisions repeatedly.
- Each nucleus gets surrounded by a bit of cytoplasm that gets enveloped by plasma membrane.
- Thus, many daughter cells are produced within a protective wall called cyst.
- Under favourable conditions, the cyst bursts and the daughter cells are released, for example, *Plasmodium* (multicellular protozoan).

Budding

Budding is the asexual mode of reproducing new organisms in which a new organism is developed from a small part of the parent's body.

The unicellular fungus, yeast, reproduces through the process of budding. *Hydra,* an organism belonging to phylum Cnidaria, also reproduces by the process of budding. The process of budding is different in fungi and *Hydra*.

Process of Budding in *Hydra*

The process of budding in *Hydra* is described below with the help of following points.

- A small bud develops from the body of parent body.
- The bud is formed through repeated mitotic division.

- The small bud obtains nourishment from the parent *Hydra* body and grows.
- As the bud matures, it starts to develop small tentacles and mouth on its body.
- When the bud attains maturity, it detaches itself from the parent body and lives independently.

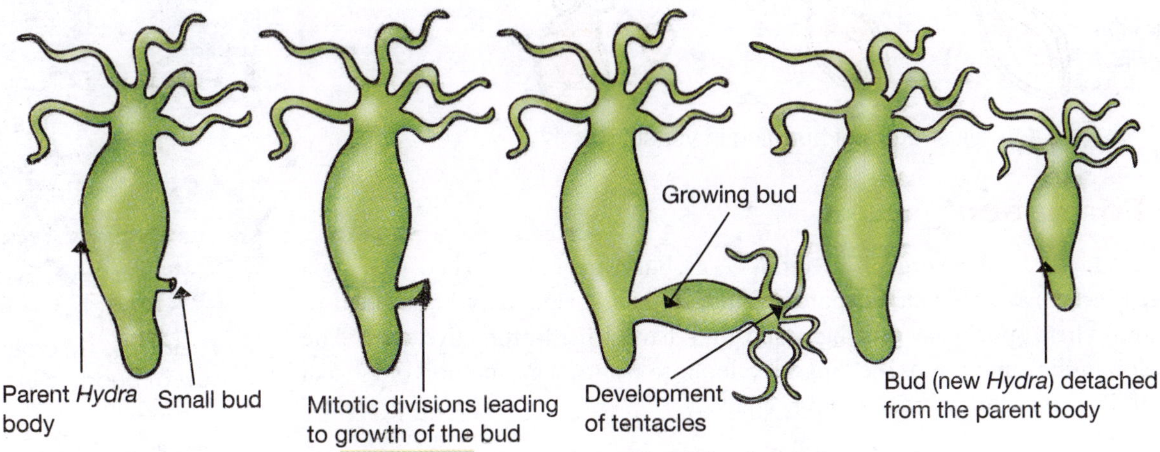

Figure 4.3 Illustration of budding in *Hydra*

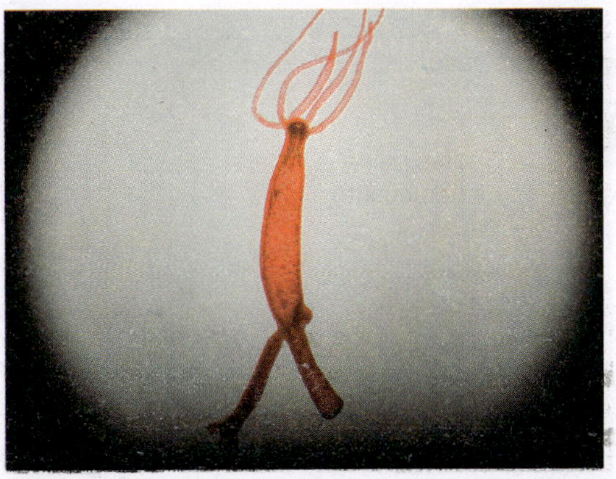

Figure 4.4 Microscopic magnified view of budding in *Hydra*

Info Bytes!

Coral polyps also reproduce through budding, which leads to the formation of vast coral colonies.

Process of Budding in Yeast

The process of budding in yeast is described below with the help of following points.

- A small bud arises as an outgrowth of the parent body.
- Subsequently, the nucleus of the parent cell splits into two daughter nuclei.
- One of the two daughter nuclei migrates to the daughter cell.
- The newly formed bud divides and grows into a new yeast cell.
- Later, the bud disconnects from the parent's body by forming a contraction at the base.

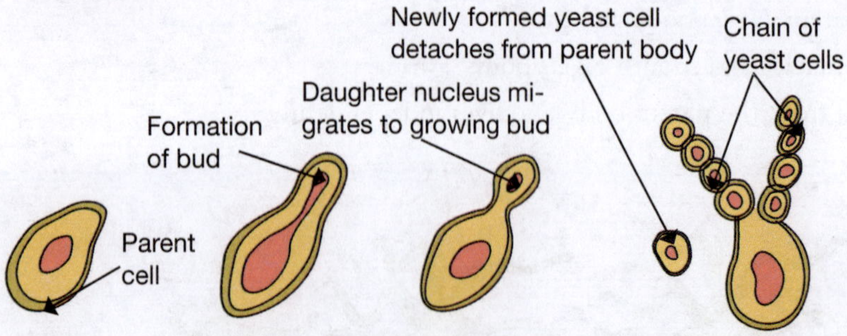

Figure 4.5 Illustration of budding in yeast

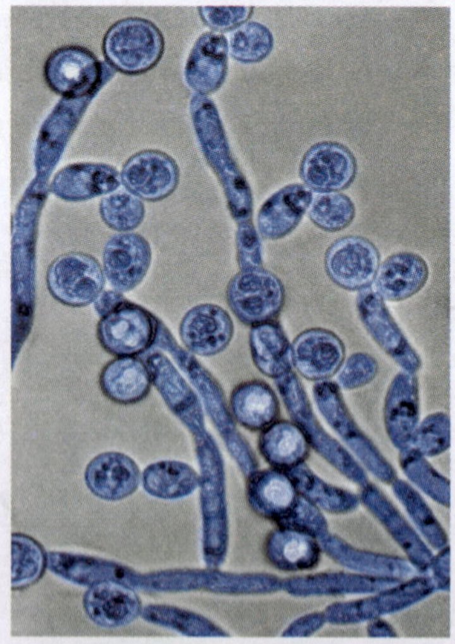

Figure 4.6 Microscopic view of budding in yeast

Spore Formation

In this method, lower plant organisms produce globular structures called sporangia (singular: *sporangium*) which contain spores. When sporangia ripe, they burst open to release spores. These spores are very light and they have a hard protective coat. The spores develop in the same way as seedlings develop into plants. This method of asexual reproduction is seen in fungi, mosses, ferns, etc.

Spore Formation in *Rhizopus*

The process of spore formation in *Rhizopus* is described below with the help of following points.

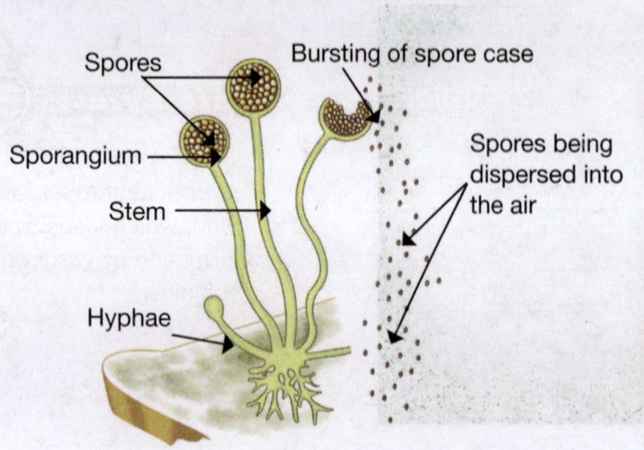

Figure 4.7 Spore formation in Rhizopus

Figure 4.8 Microscopic view of *Rhizopus* with visible sporangia

- *Rhizopus* possesses thread-like projections called hyphae from which small spherical structure, called sporangium, is developed.
- Several reproductive units, called spores, are produced inside the sporangium.
- When the sporangium bursts, spores are released and spread.
- Under favourable conditions, these spores germinate and new organisms are developed.

Regeneration

Regeneration is the mode of asexual reproduction in which there is development of a new organism from a part of the parent organism. It is also considered as the ability of an organism to re-grow its lost parts. For example, flatworm (*Planaria*), *Hydra*, etc.

Regeneration in *Planaria*

The process of regeneration in *Planaria* is described below with the help of following points.

- The parent organism detaches its tail end.
- Each separated half regrows the lost parts.
- New organisms are formed after growth of all body parts.

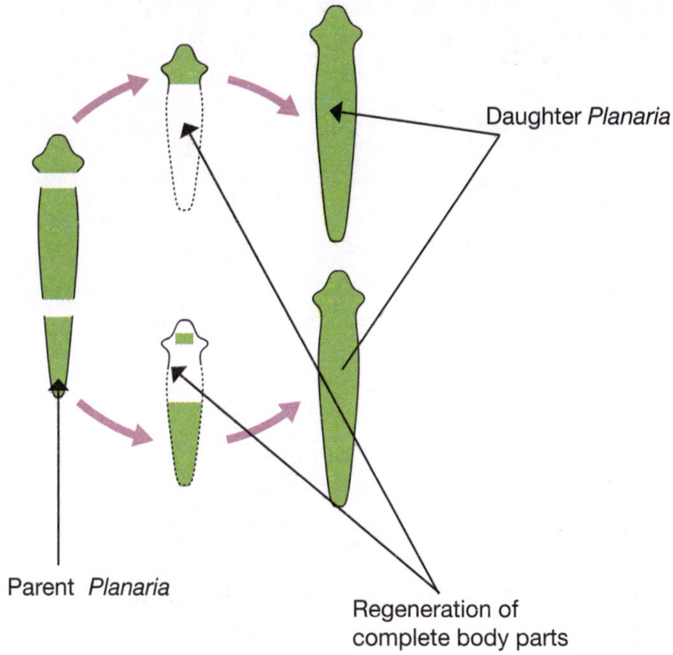

Figure 4.9 Regeneration in *Planaria*

> **Info Bytes!**
> Axolotls, a type of salamander, hold the record for the most complex body parts they can regenerate, including their heart, spine, and a portion of their brain.

Fragmentation

Fragmentation is similar to regeneration, however there is a major difference. Unlike regeneration, fragmentation is characterized by development of complete individual from any divided and separated piece or part. Fragmentation is a common method of reproduction in algae and fungi.

Fragmentation in Algae

When filamentous thallus of algae undergoes accidental breakage, the fragments develop into new organisms.

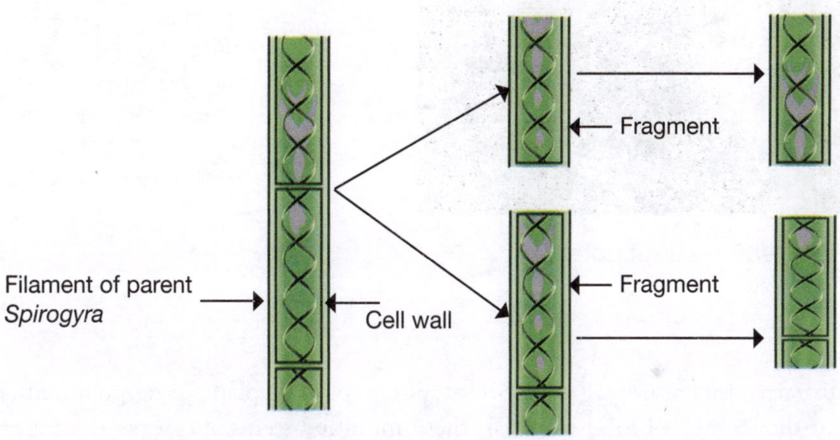

Figure 4.10 Illustration of fragmentation in *Spirogyra*

> **Info Bytes!**
> The largest underwater meadow, formed by fragmentation of the seagrass *Posidonia oceanica* in the Mediterranean Sea, spans over 5 square miles and is thousands of years old.

Vegetative Reproduction

The asexual methods are the main modes of reproduction in lower organisms and lower plants, that is, non-flowering plants called cryptogams. In case of flowering plants called phanerogams, sexual mode of reproduction is the most prominent method due to the presence of specific reproductive organs. In sexual reproduction, seeds are the means of propagation for plant species. Angiosperms are the most advanced and dominating group of flowering plants as they show the most advanced method of sexual reproduction. However, these plants are also capable of reproducing through vegetative reproduction process. Therefore, the vegetative reproduction is also equally important in the flowering plants. In this type of reproduction, non-sexual or vegetative parts of the plant such as root, stem, leaf, or even bud can regenerate to form a new plant. Vegetative reproduction can take place in following two ways:

1. Natural vegetative reproduction
2. Artificial vegetative reproduction

Natural Vegetative Reproduction

The various vegetative parts of the plants go through a certain process of development of new plants on their own without any human intervention. Some of the major vegetative reproduction methods are described as below:

Propagation by Roots

Roots of certain plants become swollen and serve the purpose of food storage. These are called tuberous roots or root tubers. They can also be used for vegetative propagation in addition to food storage.

Root Tubers
Following are the chief features of propagation by root tubers:

- Root tuber can arise from any part of the root or sometimes the entire root can form a tuber.
- There are no nodes and internodes, or scale leaves or axillary buds.
- Only adventitious buds are present.
- Buds develop at the base of the stem and develop into new shoots, for example, sweet potato.

Figure 4.11 Root tuber—sweet potato

Info Bytes!

The largest organism on Earth, the Pando forest in Utah, is a clonal grove of a single quaking aspen tree, spread over 106 acres, all originating from vegetative reproduction.

Propagation by Stems

Stems are the most commonly used vegetative parts for the propagation. Shoot systems of some plants undergo modifications for storage of food material. In addition to the storage of food material, these modified stems also serve the purpose of propagation of new plants. Underground stems and subaerial stems are mainly concerned with the vegetative propagation.

Underground Stems

There are four major types of underground stems that are important as means of vegetative propagation. They are:

1. Rhizome 2. Tuber 3. Corm 4. Bulb

Rhizome

- Rhizome is characterized by the stems with nodes having reduced leaves and short internodes.
- Rhizomes generally store food material in the form of starch and proteins.
- The leaves are reduced to scales.
- The adventitious roots develop from the underside of these stems.
- The stems of rhizomes develop from auxiliary buds and grow horizontally under the soil in contrast to the normal stems.
- At nodes, they give rise to new shoots that grow upward and come above the ground.
- These stems are also called creeping rootstocks or rootstocks, for example, ginger, turmeric, bamboo and sugarcane.

Figure 4.12 Rhizome—turmeric root

Stem Tubers

- These are called stem tubers to distinguish them from root tubers.
- The stem tuber has all the parts of a normal stem, including nodes and internodes.
- The nodes are called eyes, and each has a leaf scar.
- These tubers generally store large amount of starch in them.
- The terminal bud grows away from the stolon.
- The adventitious roots develop from the base of the tuber.
- Once the shoot grows above the soil, it develops leaves and other organs normally, for example, potato, *Dahlia* and *Asparagus*.

Figure 4.13 Stem tuber—potato

Corm

- A corm is a rounded stem with one or more nodes and internodes and at least one growing point.
- It is usually covered by leaves modified into tunics or skin.
- Adventitious roots develop from the base.
- New shoots develop from the buds present on the top, and leaves and flowers arise from these shoots in a normal pattern, for example, *Colocasia*, yam, etc.

Bulbs

Figure 4.14 Corm—*Gladiolus*

- Bulbs are short stems with fleshy leaves as storage organs for food.
- These are covered by dry scaly leaves.
- The adventitious roots develop from the base.
- Apical bud is surrounded by lateral buds.
- New shoots with leaves arise from the lateral buds, and leaves and flower are developed from the apical bud of the bulb, for example, onion, garlic and lily.

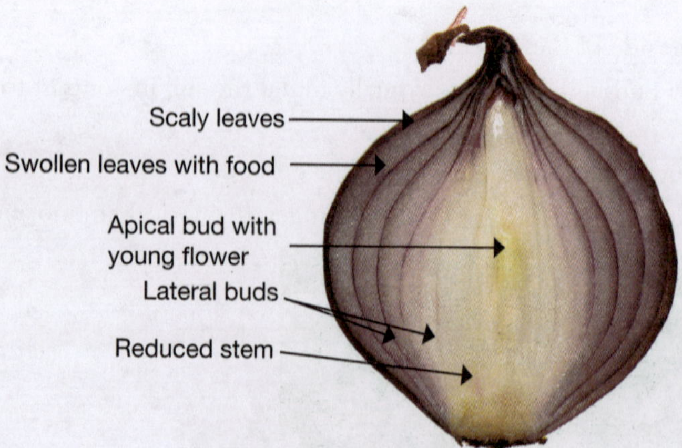

Figure 4.15 Bulb—onion

Subaerial Stem Modifications

In some herbaceous plants, the stems are weak and delicate. In such plants, a part of the stem lies underground and a part of the stem lies just above the ground. Such stems are called subaerial stems. They are basically of two types:

Figure 4.16 Stolon

Stolons

- Stolons are the stems that grow just below the soil surface or just on the surface of the ground.
- Roots are produced from the nodes.
- Buds are developed at the nodes. New shoots arise at the buds that come above the soil surface.
- They develop normal leaves and grow.
- When the stems run horizontally above the ground, stolons are often called runners.
- Once the new stolons are formed, the original stolon dies, for example, *Colocasia*, strawberry, etc.

Offset

- Offsets are short lateral shoots that are capable of developing a root system either naturally, when attached to the parent plant or when separated from the parent plant.
- Offsets often remain attached to the parent plant. Sometimes, they get separated naturally from the parent plant once they develop root system.
- They bear clustered leaves at the tips.
- The offsets appear either on the roots or stems.
- The offsets that are formed on the roots and produce aerial shoots are called suckers, for example, *Pistia, Eichhornia* or water hyacinth (offsets), and banana and pineapple (suckers).

Figure 4.17 Strawberries sending out runners from their plants: long flexible stems with little strawberry plants at the end

Propagation by Leaves

All types of roots and many types of stems are capable of vegetative propagation. But, in few species of plants, leaves show the tendency for propagating new plants. Leaves of some plants possess notches at the leaf margins. Adventitious buds originate on the notches. These buds are called epiphyllous buds. When these buds fall off and placed on the soil, they develop adventitious roots and form new plants, for example, *Bryophyllum*, *Begonia, Kalanchoe* and *Agave*.

Figure 4.18 Offset—*Eichhornia*

Figure 4.19 Propagation through *Bryophyllum* leaf

Figure 4.20 Leaves sprouting out of a parent leaf of *Bryophyllum*

Artificial Methods of Vegetative Reproduction

Vegetative propagation is carried out artificially for the production of economically important and useful plants. The main idea behind propagating plants artificially is to introduce desired characters in the new plants. There are many methods of artificial vegetative propagation. Out of those, three methods are widely followed ones. These are:

1. Cutting 2. Grafting 3. Layering

Cutting

- In this process, a portion of the stem of an existing plant with nodes and internodes is planted in moist soil.
- After plantation, adventitious roots are grown from the part of the stem and subsequently a new plant is developed.
- This method is adopted for the plants such as rose, sugarcane, *Coleus* and *Bougainvillea*.

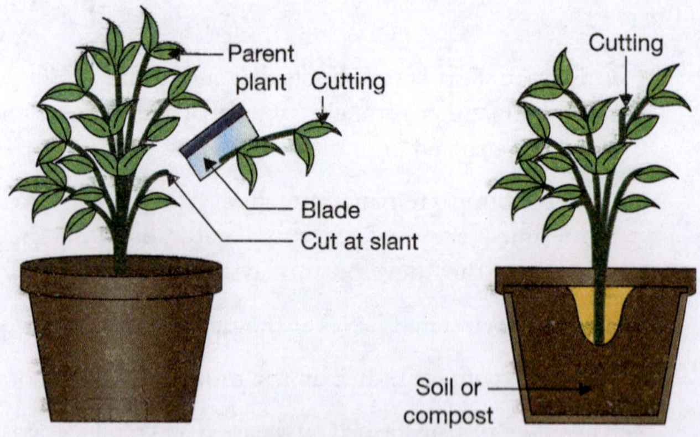

Figure 4.21 Cutting

Grafting

- In this process, the portion of the stem of a plant is cut in a slanting way and this part is called scion. Scion is without root.
- Another part of the plant that is rooted is also cut in the same way and is called stock.
- The exposed surface of scion is attached to that of stock without leaving any gap and bound tightly with a piece of cloth that is covered with a polythene sheet.
- Finally, the stock and scion unite together and grow as one plant.
- Grafting is practiced in guava, mango, rubber, citrus, pear and apple.

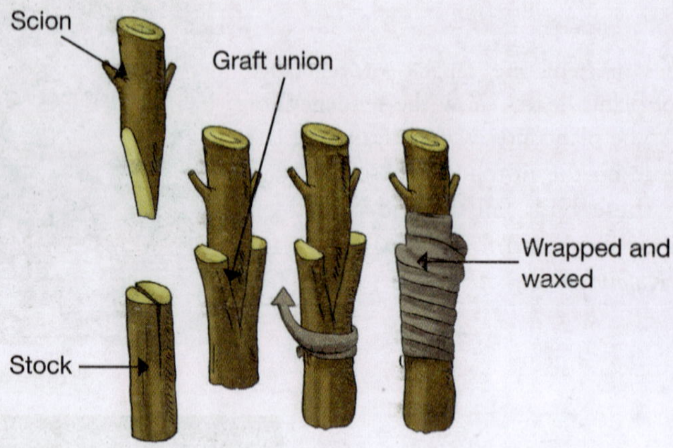

Figure 4.22 Illustration of grafting to grow new varieties of plants

Info Bytes!

Horticulture is the science of growing and cultivating plants.

Layering

- In this method of vegetative propagation, a low-growing and flexible stem is bent.
- A part the stem that touches the ground is covered with soil and the rest of the part remains above the soil.
- Roots grow from the part of the stem that is covered with the soil and a new stem is originated.
- This flexible stem is not detached from the plant.
- Layering process is employed for the plants such as climbing rose, *Forsythia*, *Rhododendron* and honeysuckle.

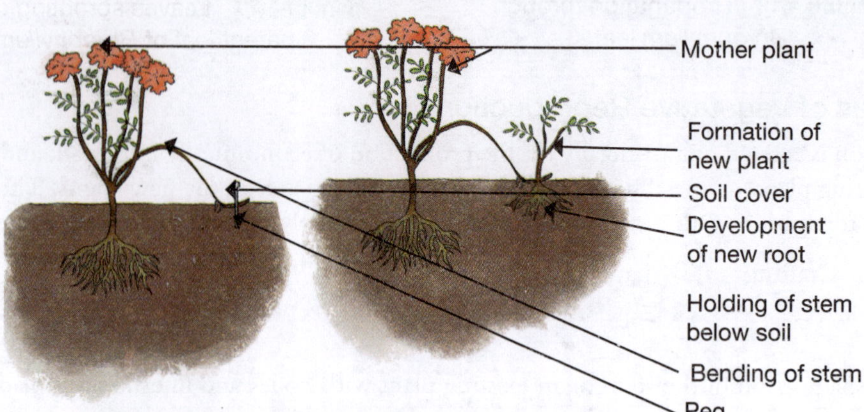

Figure 4.23 Process of layering in a plant

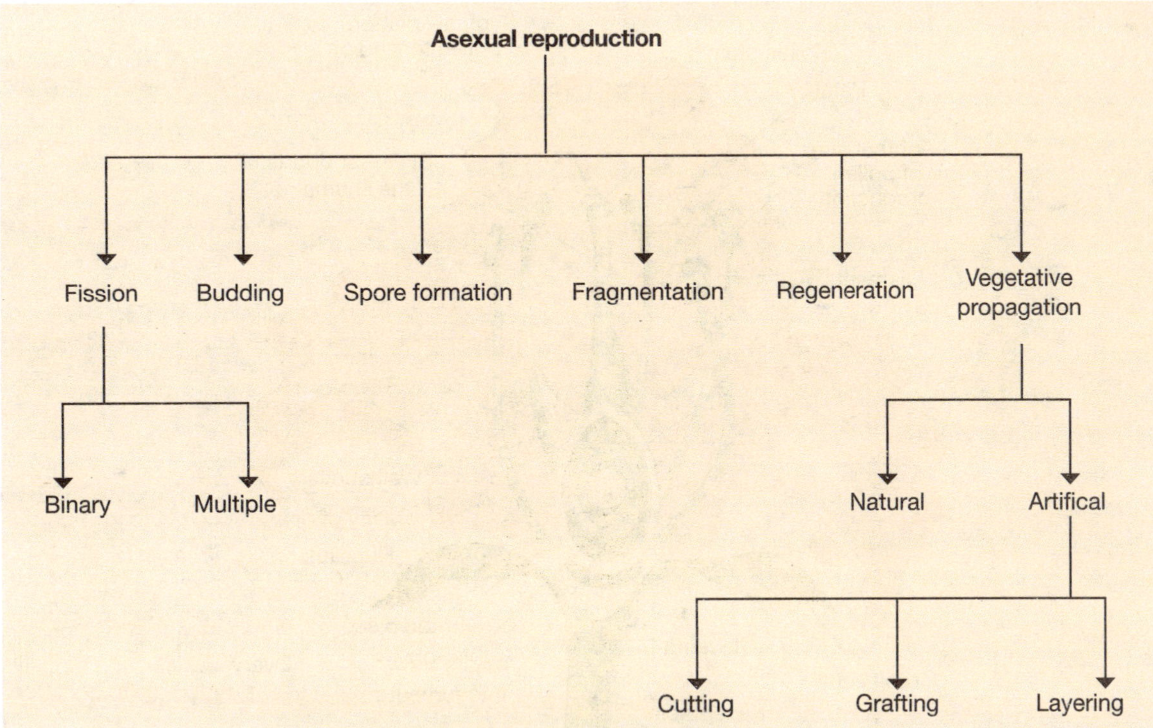

Figure 4.24 Various of modes of asexual reproduction

Sexual Reproduction in Angiosperms

We have understood that reproduction is the most important life process to ensure perpetuation of life. In flowering plants, this process is performed by flowers. The presence of well-developed flower is the characteristic feature of angiosperms. Flower is the reproductive organ in the plant.

Structure of a Typical Flower

The flower is generally attached to the shoot by means of a stalk called pedicel. The flattened portion above the pedicel is called thalamus. The various parts of a flower are arranged on the thalamus as rings known as whorls. Basically, a typical flower comprises two types of floral parts. They are as follows:

1. Non-essential parts
2. Essential parts

Konnect

TISSUE CULTURE

Tissue culture is a method of growing plant or animal cells outside their natural environment, in a controlled and sterile environment. plant tissue culture, which is often used in horticulture and agricultural research.

A healthy plant part (explant) is selected and sterilized to remove contaminants and placed in a growth medium. Using hormones, the explant is encouraged to produce multiple shoots or cells. Another set of hormones might be used to induce root formation. The tiny plants are gradually exposed to the outside environment in a controlled manner.

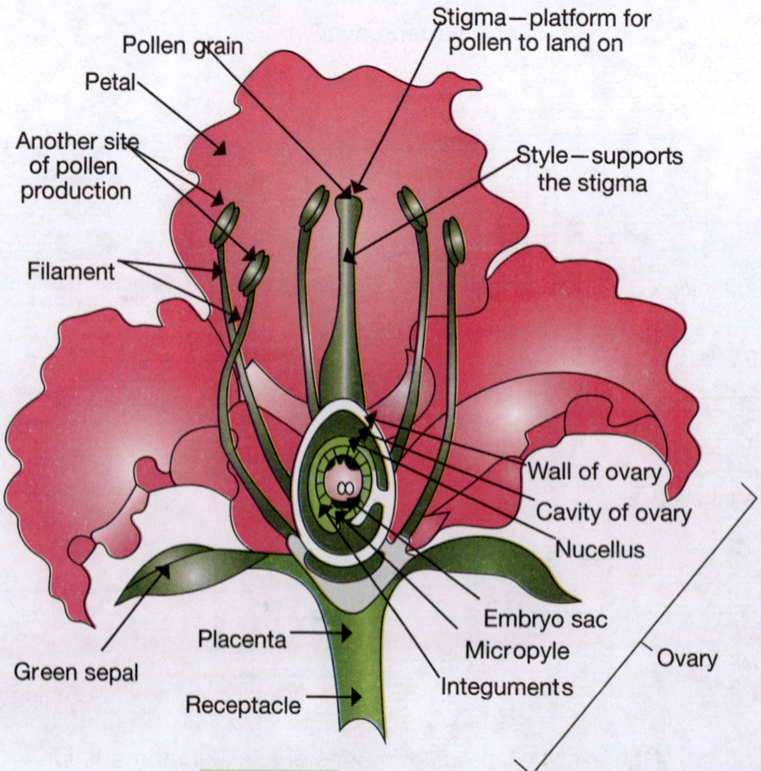

Figure 4.25 Structure of a flower

Non-essential Parts

The non-essential parts of a flower are those which are not directly involved in the process of formation and the fusion of gametes. They play only supportive role. The non-essential parts constitute calyx and corolla. Calyx is the outermost whorl that consists of green leaf-like structures called sepals. The calyx encloses and provides protection to the inner whorls of a flower in bud stage. Corolla is the second whorl of the flower that consists of brightly coloured and scented structures called petals. The corolla performs the function of attracting the insects for pollination.

Essential Parts

The essential parts of a flower are those that are directly involved in the formation and fusion of gametes, which are the most significant events of sexual reproduction. The essential parts constitute male and female reproductive organs listed as follows:

1. Androecium or stamen (male reproductive structure)
2. Gynoecium or pistil (female reproductive structure)

Androecium

- Androecium is the third whorl of the flower.
- It is made up male reproductive units called stamens.
- A stamen is made up of a long, thin, narrow stalk called filament and a small bilobed structure called anther.
- Pollen grains containing male gametes are produced in the anther.

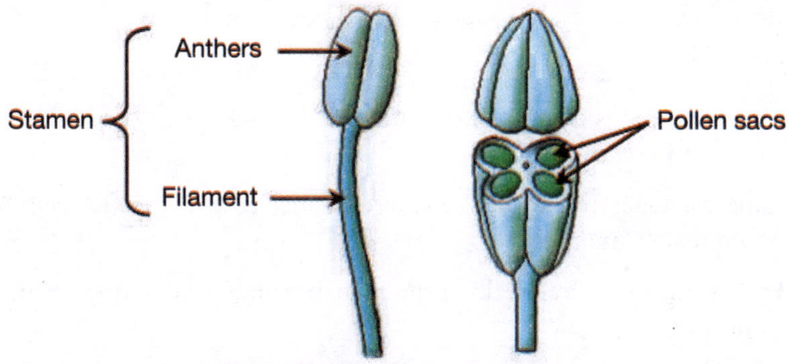

Figure 4.26 Stamen

Info Bytes!

Flowers that lack male and female reproductive organs are called neuter flowers.

Gynoecium

- Gynoecium constitutes the innermost whorl of the flower.
- It is made up of female reproductive units called carpels.
- Each carpel is made up of three parts, namely ovary, style and stigma.
- Stigma is the disc-like structure present at the top of the carpel. It helps in pollination.
- Style is a long narrow tubular structure that acts as a passage for the entry of male gamete into the ovary.
- Ovary is present as a swollen part at the base of the carpel. It contains ovules that produce female gametes.

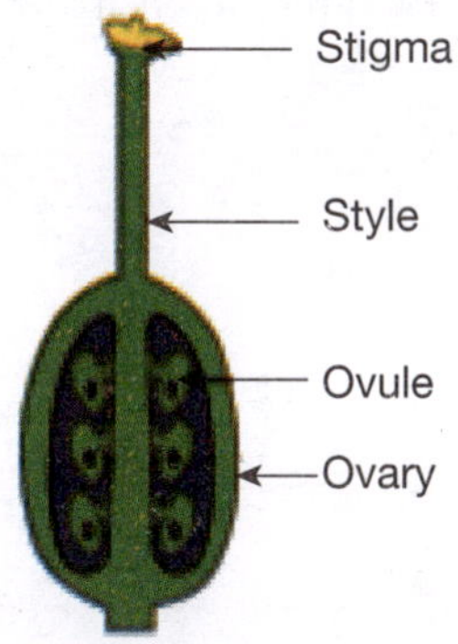

Figure 4.27 Parts of pistil

Process of Sexual Reproduction

The sexual reproduction involves the fusion of male and female gametes, which is known as fertilization. Prior to fertilization, the flower prepares itself for the process. Similarly, after fertilization also, some significant changes take place that are also considered as part of sexual reproduction. Since fertilization is the most significant phase, with respect to this event, the entire process of sexual reproduction can be divided into three significant phases. They are as follows:

1. Pre-fertilization phase
2. Fertilization phase
3. Post-fertilization phase

Pre-fertilization Phase

This phase involves the formation of male and female gametes followed by bringing the male gametes to the site of fertilization. The formation of gametes is called gametogenesis. The transfer of pollen grains containing male gametes to ovary is called pollination.

Formation of Male Gametes

Formation of male gametes can be understood with the help of following points.

- The formation of male gametes takes place in the anther, which is also known as microsporangium.
- In the anther lobe, some of the cells get differentiated into germ cells. These are called microspore mother cells. These are diploid cells.
- These diploid cells undergo meiotic cell division to form haploid cells called microspores. This process is called microsporogenesis.

- The haploid microspores undergo mitotic cell division to produce haploid pollen grains.
- Each pollen grain is a microscopic cell.
- It has two-layered wall. The inner layer is thin and is called intine, whereas the thick outer layer is known as exine. The exine contains some pore-like structures known as germ pores.
- A pollen grain possesses two nuclei, namely a generative nucleus and a tube nucleus or vegetative cell. At this stage, the pollen grain is considered as immature male gametophyte.
- Usually, the pollen grains are released out at this stage by breaking the anther wall. This bursting of anther wall and release of pollen grains is called dehiscence.
- The generative cell is smaller in size and undergoes mitosis to form two male gametes. This process is called male gametogenesis.
- The tube cell elongates to form pollen tube at the time of fertilization.

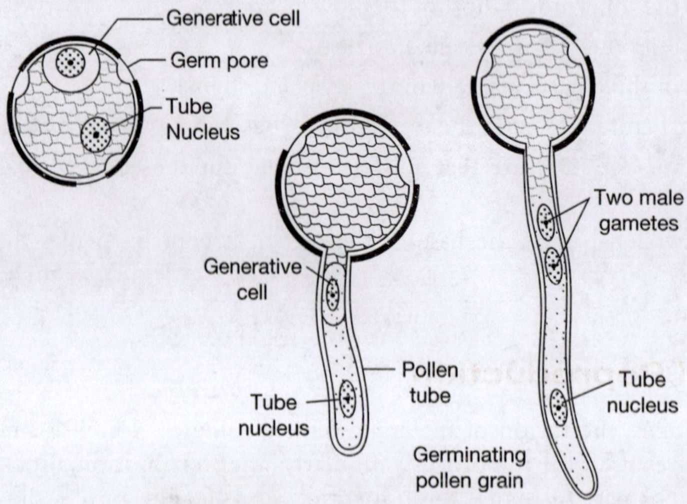

Figure 4.28 Male gametogenesis

Formation of Female Gamete

Formation of female gametes can be understood with the help of following points.

- Small ovules are present inside the ovary that is a part of the carpel.
- Ovules are attached to the wall of the ovary with the help of placenta.
- Placenta holds each ovule with the help of a stalk called funicle.
- The funicle helps in the nourishment of the ovule.
- The ovule is made up of three parts:
  1. Integuments
  2. Nucellus
  3. Embryo sac

Info Bytes!

Placentation is the pattern in which ovules are attached to the wall of ovary.

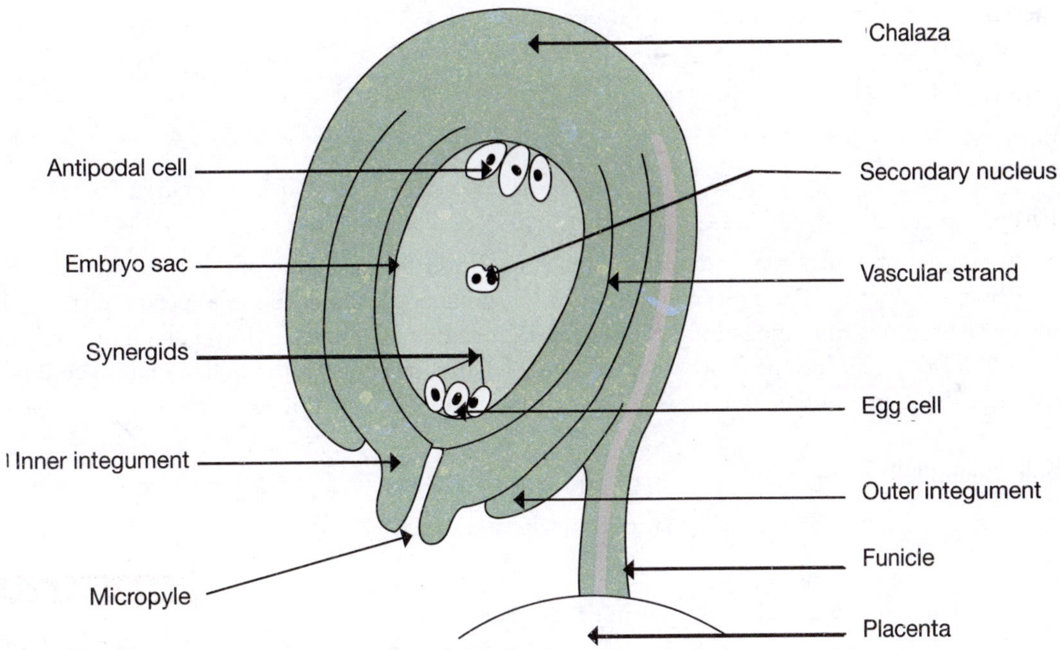

Figure 4.29 Structure of ovule

- Integuments are the two protective coatings surrounding each ovule.
- There is a small opening in the integument that is called micropyle.
- The upper end of the ovule containing the opening, micropyle, is called micropylar end.
- The opposite end of the ovule at the bottom is called chalaza or chalazal end.
- Nucellus is the nutritive tissue present in the ovule.
- In an immature ovule, one cell from the nucellus undergoes differentiation to form a female germ cell called megaspore mother cell.
- At this stage, the ovule is known as megasporangium.
- The megaspore mother cells are diploid and undergo meiotic cell division to form haploid megaspores.
- Of the four haploid megaspores, usually, three degenerate and one functional megaspore develops into embryo sac, which is also called female gametophyte (megagametophyte).
- This embryo sac is present at the micropylar end of the ovule.
- The functional megaspore in the embryo sac undergoes three successive mitotic divisions forming eight haploid cells.
- Of these eight cells, two cells will be lodged in the centre of the embryo sac. These are called polar nuclei. They fuse to form diploid secondary nucleus.
- Three cells are aligned at the chalazal end and are called antipodals.
- The other three cells are aligned at the micropylar end. The central cell is called egg cell or ovum. The other two cells are called synergids.
- The egg cell is the female gamete.
- Nucellus is composed of nutritive tissues and it acts as the source of nutrition of the embryo formed after fertilization.

Pollination

The transfer of pollen grains from the anther of a flower to the surface of the stigma of the same or another flower is known as pollination. Pollination can be of two types as listed below.

1. Self-pollination
2. Cross-pollination

Self-pollination

Self-pollination is the transfer of pollen grains from the anther of a flower to the stigma of the same flower. Self-pollination takes place in some bisexual flowers. The flowers involved in self-pollination should possess specific characteristic features such as homogamy or cleistogamy. In homogamy, the anther and the stigma of a bisexual flower attain maturity together. For example, wheat, rice, *Mirabilis*. Cleistogamy is observed in non-opening flowers since the pollen grain is confined inside the flower and can pollinate the stigma of the same flower. For example, underground flowers of *Commelina benghalensis*.

Advantages of Self-pollination

Following are some of the advantages of self-pollination:

- Parental characteristics are maintained.
- Production of pollen grains in large quantity is not required.
- Flowers need not be attractive as insects are not required to be attracted.
- The production of seeds is ensured. The probability of failure is less.

Info Bytes!

The corpse flower (*Rafflesia arnoldii*) emits a foul odor to attract its pollinators—carrion beetles and flies.

Disadvantages of Self-pollination

Following are some disadvantages of self-pollination:

- Generation of a new variety is not possible.
- Genetic defects are carried forward to the offspring.
- Prolonged self-pollination may result in decrease in vigour and vitality of the particular species.
- Susceptibility to diseases increases.
- Quality of seeds produced may decrease from one generation to the next.

Cross-pollination

The transfer of pollen grains from the anther of a flower to the stigma of another flower of the same plant or different plant of the same species is called cross-pollination. Cross-pollination is inevitable in unisexual flowers. In case of bisexual flowers also, nature favours cross-pollination. Characteristic features of the plants that favour cross-pollination are as follow:

Info Bytes!

Nectar-secreting cells are called nectaries.

- **Unisexuality:** If the flower is unisexual, cross-pollination becomes inevitable. For example, maize, castor, cucumber (unisexual flowers borne on the same plant), and papaya, mulberry, palm (unisexual flowers borne on the separate plants).
- **Self-sterility:** In certain flowers, the pollen grains fail to germinate when they come in contact with the stigma of the same flower. But they germinate on the stigma of the flower of another plant of the same species. Under this situation, cross-pollination becomes obligatory. For example, apple, grape, rye, etc.
- **Dichogomy:** If the stamen and carpel or pistil of a bisexual flower does not attain maturity simultaneously, cross-pollination takes place. This is known as dichogamy. It can be of two types:
  1. **Protogyny**—If the carpel attains maturity earlier than anther, the condition is known as protogyny. For example, peepal, custard apple, etc.
  2. **Protandry**—In this condition, the anther matures earlier than stigma. For example, pea, sunflower, *Salvia*, etc.

- **Herkogamy**: In some flowers, there is a physical obstacle that prevents self-pollination. This condition is called herkogamy. For example, pansy flower, *Gloriosa*. In pansy, a hood over stigma prevents self-pollination. In *Gloriosa*, stamen and carpel are present in opposite direction. Self-pollination is not possible due to this kind of arrangement.
- **Heterostyly**: In some flowers, the stamen is much longer than the style. On the other hand, there are some flowers having a longer style and a short stigma. This condition is called heterostyly that prevents self-pollination and necessitates cross-pollination. For example, *Primrose, Oxalis*, etc.

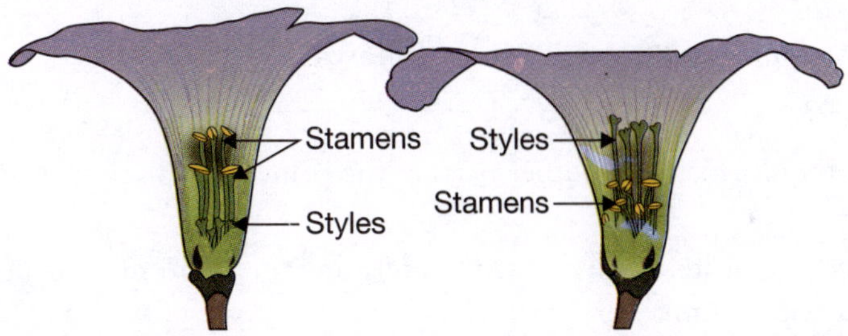

Figure 4.30 Oxalis flowers: Flower with short style and long stamen on left side; and long style and short stamen on right side showing heterostyly

Advantages of Cross-pollination

Following are some advantages of cross-pollination:

- Genetic diversity can be introduced in the various species of plants.
- Seeds with better germinating capacity and greater viability can be produced.
- Offspring can be healthier and disease resistant.

Disadvantages of Cross-pollination

Following are some disadvantages of cross-pollination:

- Dependence on external agencies such as insects and birds. Lack of availability of these agents makes the process difficult.
- Generation of large quantity of pollen grains is required since loss of pollen grains takes place during transfer.
- Flowers should have bright-coloured petals, long stamen and pistils, high fragrance, and should be nectar producing to attract the pollinating agents

Agents of Cross-Pollination

Transference of pollen grains is a vital process involved in cross-pollination. Agents responsible for cross-pollination are classified into two categories:

1. **Biotic agents** (zoophily): These agents are living organisms.
2. **Abiotic agents**: Non-living things that act as agents.

Table 4.1 Various types of cross-pollination agents.

Agent	Pollination
Biotic	Zoophily
Insects	Entomophily
Birds	Ornithophily
Bats	Chiropterophily
Snail	Malacophily
Abiotic	
Wind	Anemophily
Water	Hydrophily

Info Bytes!

Some plants, like the fig tree, have a specialized pollinator. The fig wasp pollinates the fig and in return gets a safe place for its larvae.

Biotic pollination

Biotic pollination is a type of pollination in which transfer of pollen grains takes place by living organisms such as insects, birds, bats and snails.

Entomophily

It is a type of biotic pollination in which insects carry the pollen from the anther of a flower to the stigma of a flower of another plant of same species.

Characteristic features of entomophilous flowers are as follows:

- Large, brightly coloured petals.
- If petals are not prominent, transformation of other parts of the plant takes place to attract the insects. For example, in *Bougainvillea*, bracts are colourful.
- If the flowers are small, they aggregate to form a cluster of flowers called inflorescence and become prominently visible to the insects. For example, sunflower.
- Nectar production and fragrance of the flower. For example, jasmine.
- Some flowers have nectar guides so that the insect can locate the nectaries easily. For example, pansy.
- The pollen grains of entomophilous flowers are sticky or spiny for the purpose of adherence to the insects.
- They are thick-walled for their protection during transfer.

Salvia

Structure and the process of pollination of certain entomophilous flowers are given below.

The characteristic features of structure of *Salvia* are given below.

- The insects responsible for pollination in *Salvia* are bees.
- The corolla is bilabiate (consisting of two lips) and the stamen is epipetalous (fused with corolla).
- The upper lip of the corolla appears like a hood and covers stamen and style.
- Bees land on the lower lip of the corolla.
- The flower is protandrous in nature since anther matures before stigma.
- The short filament of stamen is connected to the anther with the help of a long, curved connective.
- The function of the connective is like a lever.
- The unequal arms of the connective widely separate the two anther lobes.
- The upper lobe is fertile whereas the lower one is sterile since it cannot produce pollen grains.
- The sterile lower lobe blocks the nectary.

Mechanism of the collection of pollen grains in *Salvia* is as described below:

- The bee enters the flower for the nectar and pushes the sterile lower lobe of the anther.
- Then the long connective moves down and helps the stamen bend with a jerk.
- The jerk produced sprinkles the pollen on the back of the bee.

Mechanism of pollination in *Salvia* is described in the following points:

- The flower in which the stigma is matured takes part in pollination.
- The matured stigma protrudes out of the upper lip of the corolla.
- When the bee visits such a flower for collecting nectar, the stigma touches the back of the bee, which carries pollen grain.
- The stigma is sticky in nature and thus, the pollen grains adhere to it.
- Since the connective of the stamen acts as a lever in this process of pollination, it is called lever mechanism.

Sweet Pea (*Lathyrus*)

The characteristic features of structure of a sweet pea flower are as follows:

- The pea plant is a leguminous plant.
- Flowers of pea plant are papilionaceous (butterfly-shaped). They are complete and bisexual.
- A flower of pea plant is zygomorphic (bilaterally symmetrical).
- Calyx of the flower has five pointed sepals that are green in colour.
- In the corolla, there are total five petals that are structurally different and brightly coloured.

Figure 4.31 Saliva flower

- The outermost petal is called standard and it has a prominent vertical groove.
- Below the standard, there is a pair of lateral petals known as wings.
- Because of the presence of these wings, the flower appears like a butterfly.
- Beneath the wings, the rest of the two petals are joined together and form a trough-like structure known as keel petals.
- Keel petals enclose the reproductive organs.
- There are total 10 stamens. Out of which, nine are fused to form a tube-like structure. The tenth one is separated.
- The staminal tube formed by nine fused stamens encloses the ovary as well as the part of the style.
- The pistil or the carpel is constituted of a long, narrow ovary and a long, curved style that is hairy just below the stigma.

Figure 4.32 Sweet pea flower

Mechanism of pollination in sweet pea flower is described in the following points:

- The flower of a sweet pea plant has fragrance, produces nectar and is bright in colour. Thus, it attracts bees. It is a bee-pollinated flower.
- When the bee visits the flower, it lands on the wing petals.
- Due to the body weight of the bee, wing as well as keel petals move down exposing the style and stigma.
- Then the bee finds the nectar that is present at the base of the ovary and the anther comes in contact of the bee.
- Thus, pollen grains adhere to the body of the bee.

Other types of biotic pollinations such as ornithophily, chiropterophily and malacophily take place in very few plants. Some examples are:

- Ornithophily: *Canna, Begonia*
- Chiropterophily: Kadam tree
- Malacophily: *Lemna* and snake plant

Abiotic Pollination

Abiotic pollination is a type of pollination in which transfer of pollen grains takes place by non-living organisms such as wind and air.

Anemophily

Anemophily is a type of abiotic pollination in which pollen grains are carried from the anther of a flower to the stigma of a flower of another plant of the same species by air.

Characteristic features of anemophilous flowers are as follows:

- Flowers are small and inconspicuous.
- Neither they have fragrance, nor do they produce nectar.
- Elongated stamen that protrudes out of the flower for a better exposure to air.
- Large quantities of pollen grains are produced.
- Pollen grains are light in weight and dry for easy transportation by air.
- In some plants such as pine, the pollen grains are associated with wings that facilitate their movement in air.
- Wider, feathery stigma that is sticky in nature and extended outside the flower facilitates the trapping of pollen grains. For example, maize, rice, grasses, sugarcane, pine, etc.

Anemophilous Pollination in Maize

In maize, flowers are small in size and they are clustered. The cluster of flowers is called inflorescence. Male inflorescence is grown at the apex of the plant, whereas female inflorescence is found at the base of the plant in the axil of the leaf. Large quantities of pollen grains are produced in the anther. When the anther matures, it bursts and pollen grains are carried by wind. In the female flower, there is a long style with feathery stigma that traps pollen grains easily from air. Thus, the anemophilous pollination takes place in maize.

Hydrophily

Hydrophily is a type of abiotic pollination in which pollen grains are carried from the anther of a flower to the stigma of a flower of another plant of same species by water. This kind of pollination takes place in aquatic, submerged plants.

Characteristic features of hydrophilous flowers are listed below:

- Flowers are small and inconspicuous. Male and female flowers are grown on different plants. Such kind of plants are called dioecious plants.
- Neither they have fragrance, nor do they produce nectar.
- Large quantity of pollen grains is produced.
- Pollen grains have long, ribbon-like structure, which facilitates their transportation in the current of water. For example, *Vallisneria, Hydrilla,* etc.

Mechanism of pollination in *Vallisneria* flower

- *Vallisneria* is a dioecious, submerged plant.
- The female flower has a long, coiled stalk.
- The stalk of the flower straightens for pollination so that the flower can rise above the surface of water.
- When the male flowers mature, they get separated from the plants and start floating on the surface of water.
- Then male flowers cluster around the female flower.
- Matured anthers of male flowers burst and the pollen grains adhere to the stigma of the female flower. Thus, the hydrophilic pollination takes place in *Vallisneria.*
- After pollination, the stalk of the female flower coils down and the flower becomes submerged.

Figure 4.33 (a) Anemophily, (b) Entomophily; and (c) Hydrophily

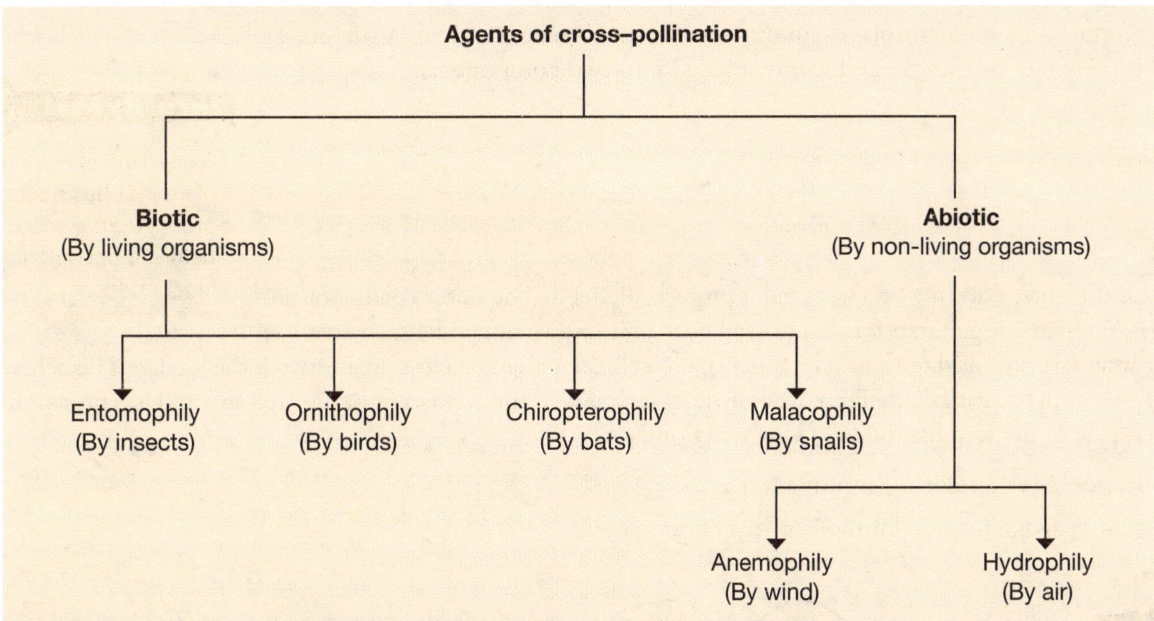

Figure 4.34 Classification of agents of cross-pollination

Fertilization Phase

After pollination, fusion of male and female gametes takes place. Fertilization is the union of male and female reproductive cells or gametes.

Process of Fertilization

When the pollen grains come in contact with the stigma, they swell up by absorbing a sugary substance produced by stigma. Thus, the pollen grain germinates. During this process, the tube nucleus grows and emerges out by rupturing the intine. Then it comes out through the germ pore present in the exine. The pollen tube secretes an enzyme that helps in the dissolution of the tissue of the stigma. The dissolution of stigma facilitates the passage of pollen tube through the style. Finally, the pollen tube reaches the ovary and enters the ovule through the micropyle. Meanwhile, the generative nucleus present in the pollen tube undergoes mitotic division to form two male gametes. When the pollen tube reaches the embryo sac, two processes of fusion take place inside the embryo sac. One of the male gametes fuses with the egg cell and a diploid zygote is formed. The other male gamete fuses with the diploid secondary nucleus formed

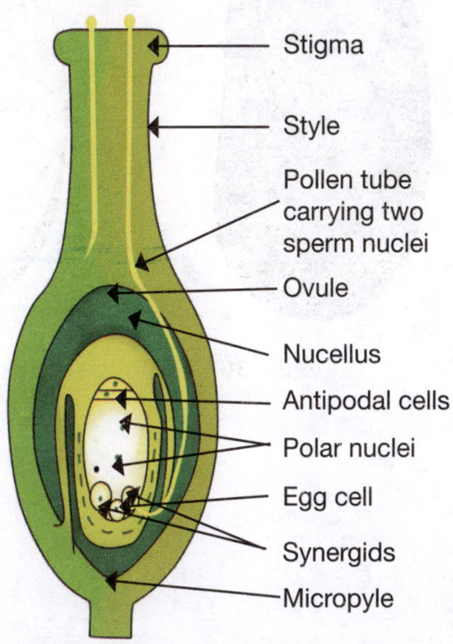

Figure 4.35 Ovule showing the embryo sac

in the embryo sac by the fusion of two polar nuclei. This results in the formation of a triploid primary endosperm nucleus (PEN). This develops as endosperm that acts as nutritive tissue for the growing embryo. Since the fusion of three nuclei takes place in the above process, resulting in the formation of a triploid cell, this process is called triple fusion. Two fertilizations occur in the embryo sac, hence the entire process is known as double fertilization. This is a unique phenomenon found in angiosperms.

Post-fertilization Changes

After fertilization, the parts of the flower other than ovary are shed off. In some plants, sepals are found to exist in the shriveled form, like in tomato, peas, brinjal. Ovary grows in size to form fruit. Ovary wall becomes the fruit wall. The ovule gets converted to seed.

> **Info Bytes!**
> Exalbuminous seeds are non-endospermic seeds, e.g., mango, pea.

Structure of a Seed

The seeds produced by different plants are different in appearance, but basic structure of every seed is the same. A seed can be broadly divided into two components:

1. Seed coat
2. Embryo

> **Info Bytes!**
> A seedling is a young plant that has been grown from a seed before it become fully independent.

Seed Coat

A seed coat is the outer covering of a seed and it protects the seed. The outer coating of the ovary, that is, integument gets transformed to seed coat after fertilization. The seed coat has two layers, outer layer is called testa and the inner one is called tegmen. A scar remains when the seed gets detached from its stalk. The mark of the scar is called hilum. Micropyle of the ovule is found to exist in the seed also and it is present below the hilum. Micropyle of the seed has the following functions:

- Absorption of water during germination
- Providing passage for the diffusion of respiratory gases.

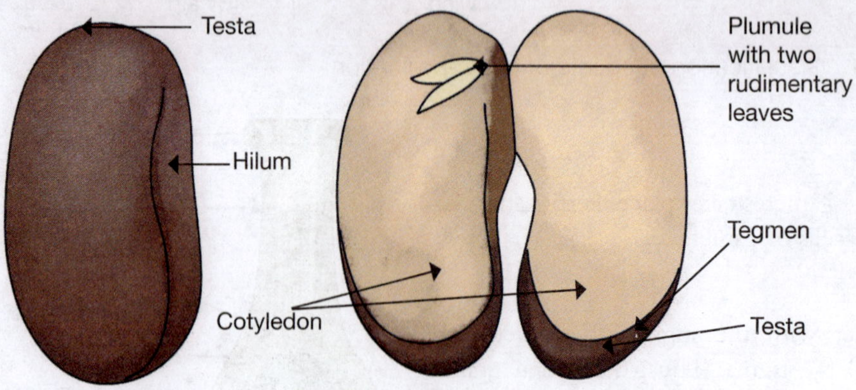

Figure 4.36 Structure of a seed (left: external; right: internal)

> **Info Bytes!**
> The Java cucumber, holds the record for having the smallest known seeds, which are just about 0.3 mm in length.

Embryo

The part of the seed enclosed in the seed coat is called embryo. The embryo forms the new plant in conducive environment. The embryo of a matured seed can be divided into five parts:

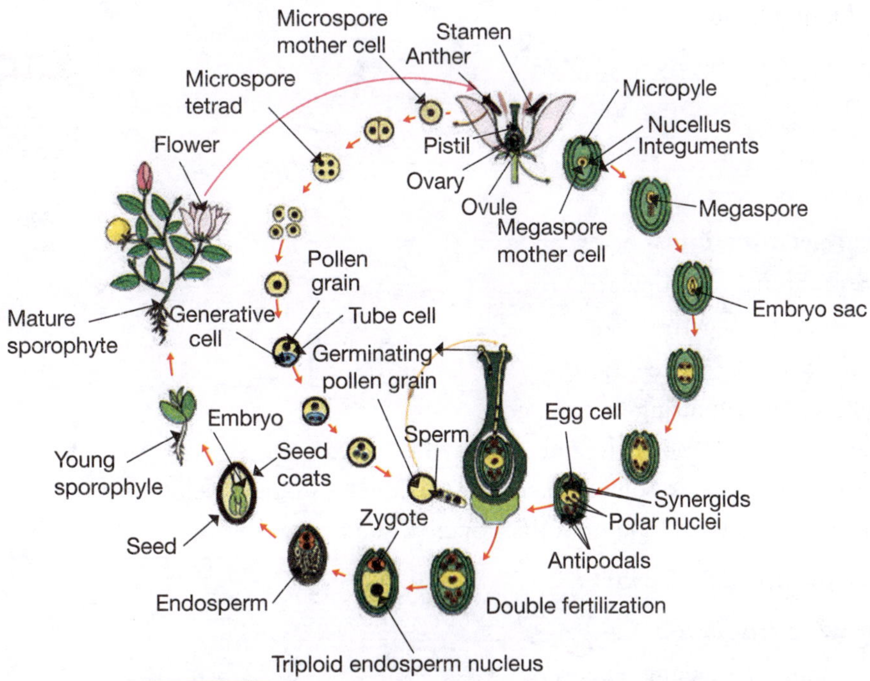

Figure 4.37 Detailed stages of life of an angiospermic plant

1. One or two cotyledons
2. Epicotyl
3. Hypocotyl
4. Plumule
5. Radicle

Cotyledons form the first leaves after germination of seed. Epicotyl is the portion just below the plumule, whereas hypocotyl is the portion just above the radicle. After germination, plumule gives rise to the shoot, whereas radicle forms the root.

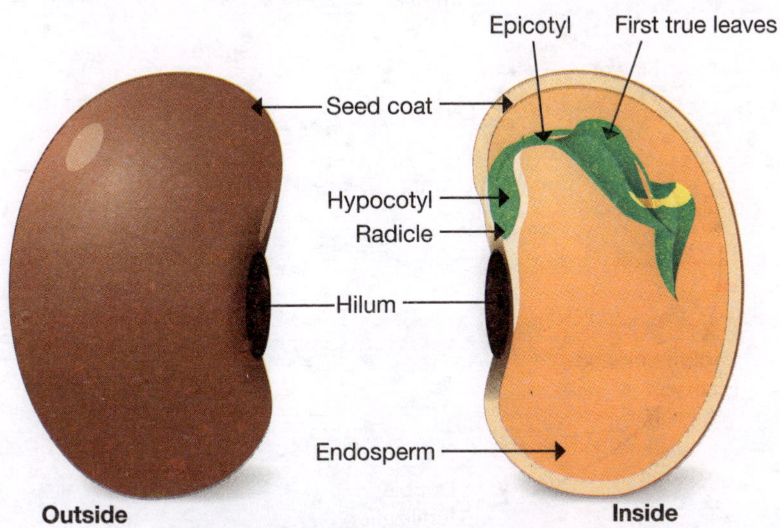

Figure 4.38 Parts of a seed

Germination of a seed

Germination is the process of the development of a new plant from the seed. All the biological processes take place in the seed very slowly. Hence, the seed in the dry state is alive, but remains in the dormant stage.

Conditions necessary for germination

Conditions required for germination are:

- Water
- Air (oxygen)
- Favourable temperature

Info Bytes!

Seeds that are sown too deep in soil fail to germinate due to improper supply of oxygen.

Role of water in seed germination

- Seeds absorb water through micropyle.
- After absorbing water, seeds germinate.
- Water helps in the following processes.
  - Softening followed by rupturing the seed coat.
  - Allowing the plumule and radicle to emerge out of the seed coat.
  - Converting the stored food to soluble material, which helps in the development of the new plant.
  - Transportation of the soluble food from the storage tissue to the developing embryo.

Thus, water accelerates the metabolic activities.

Role of oxygen in seed germination

- The process of germination requires energy.
- Energy is liberated through respiration.
- The rate of respiration in germinating seed increases.
- The process of respiration involves the oxidation of food stored in the seed.
- Oxidation of food material takes place by the usage of aerial oxygen.

Role of temperature in seed germination

- Different biological processes take place during germination. Those processes require the maintenance of an optimum temperature that ranges from 25 to 35°C.

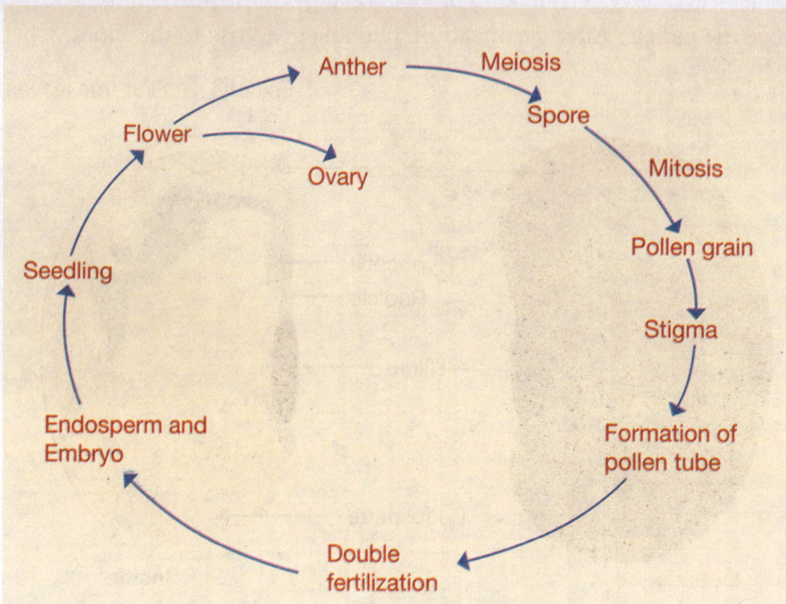

Figure 4.39 Life cyle of an angiosperm

Types of Germination Processes

There are two ways in which seeds germinate—hypogeal and epigeal. Both ways are described below by taking one example from each of the two.

Hypogeal Germination in Pea Seed

The term hypogeal is combination of two words, 'hypo' meaning below and 'geo' meaning Earth. In this type of germination, water is absorbed by the seeds, as a result of which they swell. This leads to softening and bursting of testa. Later, radicle emerges and grows downwards. The plumule grows upwards and forms the shoot of the seedling. Plumule protects the young seeds by forming an arch. Food is supplied to the growing seeds by cotyledons. Eventually, seeds shrink and wither away.

Figure 4.40 Germination of pea sprout in soil

Epigeal Germination in Bean Seed

The term epigeal is combination of two words, 'epi' meaning above and 'geo' meaning Earth. In this type of germination, water is absorbed by the seeds, as a result of which they swell. Radicle grows downwards and forms the root system. Hypocotyl forms an arch and grows above the soil. Later, it straightens and brings the cotyledons above the soil.

Figure 4.41 Bean sprout germination

Quick Recap

✔ **Determine the difference between fission and vegetative reproduction. How do these methods contribute to species diversity or uniformity?**

Fission, which is common in unicellular organisms, involves an organism splitting into parts that develop into new organisms. The formation of a new plant from non-sexual parts is known as vegetative reproduction. Fission contributes to genetic diversity because new organisms can be born with mutations, whereas vegetative reproduction frequently maintains genetic uniformity because the offspring are genetically identical to the parent.

✔ **Describe the vegetative reproduction process and its importance in the artificial propagation of economically important plants.**

Vegetative reproduction is the process of creating a new plant from non-sexual or vegetative parts such as roots, stems, leaves, or buds. It does not necessitate fertilization. This method is important in artificial propagation because it ensures rapid multiplication, preserves genetic uniformity, and aids in the propagation of plants that are difficult to reproduce using seeds.

✔ **Why is pollination such an important part of the reproductive cycle of flowering plants? Explain what happens if pollination does not occur.**

The transfer of pollen grains from an anther to a stigma is referred to as pollination. It ensures that male pollen gametes reach female ovule gametes, resulting in fertilization. If pollination does not occur, fertilization does not occur, preventing seed formation and, as a result, the production of new plants.

✔ **Discuss the importance of a seed coat in germination. Why is it critical for the growth of a new plant from a seed?**

The embryo inside the seed is protected by the seed coat from physical damage, desiccation, and pathogens. During germination, the seed coat absorbs water, triggering metabolic processes that promote embryo growth. Its integrity ensures that the embryo remains viable until germination conditions are met.

✔ **Explain the various stages of sexual reproduction in angiosperms.**

Microsporogenesis is the formation of four haploid microspores from each microspore mother cell by meiotic cell division.

- Formation of male gametes
  - → Microsporogenesis
  - → Male gametogenesis
- Formation of female gametes
  - → Megasporogenesis
  - → Female gametogenesis

Male gametogenesis is the formation of two pollen grains from each microspore by mitosis. Each pollen grain possesses two nuclei. The smaller generative nucleus produces two male gametes by mitotic cell division.

Megasporogenesis is the formation of female gametes. Megaspore mother cell in the ovule undergoes meiotic cell division to form four haploid megaspores. Three of them degenerate. One is functional megaspore that develops into female gametophyte or embryo sac. This undergoes a series of changes to become mature and to be ready for fertilization.

Female gametogenesis involves three successive mitotic divisions of the mature megaspore to form eight haploid nuclei. Two nuclei, called polar nuclei, migrate to the centre and fuse to form a diploid secondary nucleus. Three nuclei migrate to the micropylar end and are called antipodal cells.

Three nuclei migrate to the chalazal end. The middle one is called egg cell and the other two are called synergids. The egg cell is the female gamete.

Fertilization is the process in which one male gamete fuses with the egg cell to form a diploid zygote. One male gamete fuses with the diploid secondary nucleus to form a triploid primary endosperm nucleus. This develops into endosperm to serve as nutritive tissue for the developing embryo.

✔ **Tissue culture in plants is easier than in animals. Give reason.**

In animals, the tissues are more complex and require many proteins, hormones, etc., for their growth, in addition to the nutrients. In plants, the tissues can be made to grow if proper nutrient medium is provided. Moreover, in plants, many cells are totipotent and are capable of cell division and cell differentiation even in adult plant.

In animals, only few kinds of cells are totipotent, which makes the tissue culture a more challenging task.

POINTS TO REMEMBER

- ✔ Reproduction is a special biological process essential for the perpetuation of an individual.
- ✔ The adult organism that reproduces is called parent organism and the young ones produced are called offspring or progenies.
- ✔ Fission is the splitting up of an organism into parts that grow independently into new organisms.
- ✔ In vegetative reproduction, non-sexual or vegetative parts of the plant such as root, stem, leaf, or even bud can regenerate to form a new plant.
- ✔ Vegetative propagation is carried out artificially for the production of economically important and useful plants.
- ✔ Flower is the reproductive organ in the plant.
- ✔ Androecium is the male reproductive structure and gynoecium or pistil is the female reproductive structure in flowering plants.
- ✔ The transfer of pollen grains from the anther of a flower to the surface of the stigma of the same or another flower is known as pollination.
- ✔ A seed consists of a seed coat and an embryo.
- ✔ Germination is the process of development of a new plant from the seed.

PRACTICE QUESTIONS CLASSROOM WING

Very Short Answer Type Questions

Directions for questions from 1 to 10.
Fill in the blanks.

1. Reproduction ensures the __________ of an individual.
2. The __________ is the reproductive organ in plants.
3. Androecium represents the __________ reproductive structure in flowering plants.
4. The process wherein a seed develops into a new plant is called __________.
5. In vegetative reproduction, __________ parts of the plant can regenerate to form a new plant.
6. In plants, __________ is both a process and an organ, responsible for ensuring the continuity of the species.
7. The female reproductive structure in the flower is ________.
8. The pollination with the help of animals is known as ________.
9. ____ provides nutrition for the egg in the embryo sac.
10. After fertilization, ________ gets converted to seed.

Directions for questions from 11 to 32.
For each of the following questions, four choices have been provided. Select the correct alternative.

11. Prokaryotes are associated with which mode of reproduction?
    (a) Binary fission (b) Multiple fission
    (c) Regeneration (d) Fragmentation
12. Identify the mode of reproduction that takes place in protozoans.
    (a) Binary fission (b) Multiple fission
    (c) Regeneration (d) Fragmentation
13. Identify the most common mode of reproduction that takes place in *Hydra*.
    (a) Binary fission (b) Multiple fission
    (c) Regeneration (d) Budding
14. Identify the organisms in which reproduction can take place by the method of regeneration.
    (a) *Planaria* (b) Sporangium
    (c) *Algae* (d) *Amoeba*
15. Which among the following organisms can reproduce by the method of fragmentation?
    (A) Algae (B) Fungi
    (C) Sporangium
    (a) Both A and C (b) Only B
    (c) Only C (d) Both A and B
16. Match the entries of Column 1 with those of Column 2.

Column 1	Column 2
A. Rhizome	(i) *Colocasia*
B. Stem tuber	(ii) Yam
C. Root tuber	(iii) *Dahlia*
D. Corm	(iv) Ginger

    (a) A→ (iv), B→ (iii), C→ (ii), D→ (i)
    (b) A→ (iv), B→ (ii), C→ (iii), D→ (i)
    (c) A→ (iv), B→ (iii), C→ (i), D→ (ii)
    (d) A→ (iii), B→ (iv), C→ (ii), D→ (i)
17. Which of the following methods ensures the production of economically significant plants?
    (a) Germination
    (b) Pollination
    (c) Fission
    (d) Vegetative propagation
18. What does the gynoecium represent in a flowering plant?
    (a) Male reproductive part
    (b) Site of pollination
    (c) Female reproductive part
    (d) Part of germination
19. What results from the transfer of pollen grains from the anther to the stigma?
    (a) Fission
    (b) Germination
    (c) Pollination
    (d) Vegetative reproduction
20. Which process involves the splitting up of an organism into parts that grow as new organisms?
    (a) Germination
    (b) Vegetative reproduction

(c) Fission
(d) Pollination

21. What does a seed primarily consist of?
(a) Anther and stigma
(b) Seed coat and root
(c) Seed coat and embryo
(d) Pollen grain and embryo

22. What could be a potential disadvantage of vegetative propagation for plant species in the wild?
(a) Increased genetic diversity
(b) Faster growth rate
(c) Lack of genetic variation
(d) Enhanced resistance to diseases

23. Why might a plant benefit from ensuring cross-pollination over self-pollination?
(a) Reduced energy expenditure
(b) Genetic consistency
(c) Increased genetic diversity
(d) Faster reproduction rate

24. Identify the biotic agents that are responsible for pollination in *Saliva* flower.
(a) Bees (b) Birds
(c) Snails (d) Bats

25. Which of the following features are the characteristics of hydrophilous flowers?
(i) Brightly coloured petals
(ii) Pollen grains with long ribbon-like structures
(iii) Production of nectar
(iv) Production of large number of pollen grains
(a) (i); (ii) (b) (ii); (iii)
(c) (ii); (iv) (d) (i); (iv)

26. 100 pollen grains are produced from how many microspore mother cells?
(a) 50 (b) 25
(c) 100 (d) 75

27. Which of the following stages in the process of reproduction is associated with the reduction in the number of chromosomes?
(a) Formation of pollen grains from microspores
(b) Formation of megaspores from megaspore mother cells.
(c) Formation of egg cell from megaspores
(d) Formation of PEN

28. Identify the stage of reproduction that involves three successive mitotic divisions.
(a) Formation of pollen grains from microspores
(b) Formation of megaspores from megaspore mother cells
(c) Formation of embryo sac from megaspore
(d) Formation of PEN

29. Which of the following is known as triple fusion?
(a) Fusion of male gamete with female gamete to form zygote
(b) Fusion of secondary nucleus with male gamete
(c) Fusion of polar nuclei to form secondary nucleus
(d) Fusion of generative nucleus with tube nucleus.

30. In which of the following conditions, pollen grains shed from the flower?
(a) Diploid uninucleate condition
(b) Haploid uninucleate condition
(c) Diploid binucleate condition
(d) Haploid binucleate condition

31. Identify the wrongly matched pair with reference to the post-fertilization changes in a flowering plant.
(a) Ovary—fruit
(b) Ovule—seed
(c) Ovary wall—seed coat
(d) Sepals—shriveled

32. Match the entries of Column 1 with those of Column 2.

Column 1	Column 2
A. Anemophily	(i) Snails
B. Chiropterophily	(ii) Birds
C. Ornithophily	(iii) Bats
D. Malacophily	(iv) Wind

(a) A→ (iv), B→ (iii), C→ (ii), D→ (i)
(b) A→ (iv), B→ (ii), C→ (iii), D→ (i)
(c) A→ (iv), B→ (iii), C→ (i), D→ (ii)
(d) A→ (iii), B→ (iv), C→ (ii), D→ (i)

Short Answer Type Questions

33. Define reproduction.

34. Explain the process of reproduction that takes place in bacteria.

35. Distinguish between sexual reproduction and asexual reproduction.

36. Answer the following:

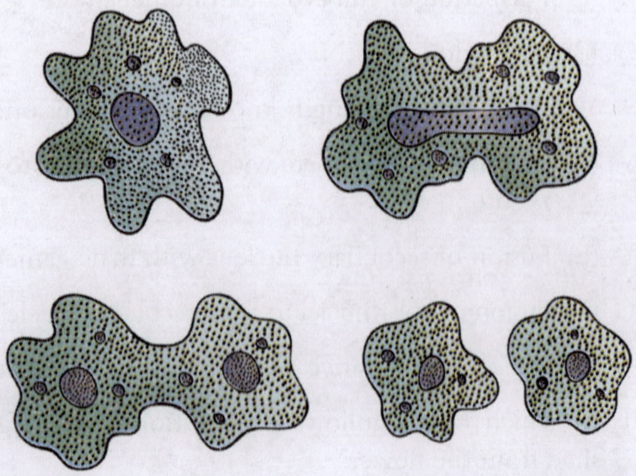

(a) Give an example of an organism that undergoes this type of reproduction.

(b) Name the process of reproduction.

(c) Explain the above process.

37. What could be a long-term ecological implication of the overuse of vegetative propagation in agricultural practices?

38. Why might pollination be a more intricate process in plants compared to the simple act of fission in certain organisms?

39. How might the method of vegetative propagation provide both an advantage and a disadvantage in terms of ecological resilience for a plant species?

40. Why might a plant species that primarily relies on self-pollination still retain mechanisms for cross-pollination?

41. Which method has to be employed to get a single plant with the desired characteristics of two or more plants and making it resistant to diseases? Explain the process.

42. Differentiate regeneration from fragmentation.

43. Identify the process by which the lost part of star fish can be regained in natural course.

44. Draw the following diagrams and label their parts:

(a) Stamen (b) Pistil

45. Define the following:

(a) Pollination (b) Fertilization

46. Explain the formation of the male gamete.

47. Name the different types of pollinations.

48. What are the disadvantages of cross-pollination?

49. Write a brief note on the agents for cross-pollination.

50. Differentiate biotic pollination from abiotic pollination.

51. Mention the characteristics of entomophilous flower.

52. Explain the following:

(a) Herkogamy (b) Heterostyly

53. What do you mean by dichogomy?

54. Why self-pollination is not possible in *Gloriosa*?

55. (a) Identify the pollination that generally takes place in bisexual flowers.

(b) Mention the specific characteristic features of the flowers involved in this type of pollination.

56. Why is cross-pollination not possible in all flowers?

Essay Type Questions

57. Name the flower in which the pollination is carried out by bees. Explain the mechanism of collection of pollen grains in it.

58. Name the flower in which lever mechanism takes place and explain the mechanism.

59. Explain the mechanism of pollination in papilionaceous flower.

60. Explain the formation of eggs in the flower.

61. Why is the fertilization in angiosperms called double fertilization? What is meant by triple fusion?

PRACTICE QUESTIONS COMPETITION WING

Level 1: Apply your Concepts

Directions for questions from 1 to 12.
Fill in the blanks.

1. An essential function of the Androecium and Gynoecium in plants is to facilitate ___________, a key step in sexual reproduction.
2. The presence of both seed coat and embryo are critical as they provide __________ and __________, respectively, during germination.
3. A unique aspect of vegetative reproduction is that the offspring are genetically _________ to the parent plant.
4. Fission, unlike other reproductive methods, is characteristic of organisms that often do not possess __________ reproductive structures.
5. _______ is the process of regrowth of an organism from its lost body part.
6. Flowering plants reproduce by the process _____.
7. _____ of onion can generate into a new plant.
8. _______ is the male reproductive organ in the flower.
9. ___________ is the female reproductive organ in the flower.
10. __________ helps in the nourishment of the ovule.
11. __________ produces female gametes in the flower.
12. __________ pollination can take place in both unisexual and bisexual flowers.

Directions for questions from 13 to 18.
For each of the following questions four choices have been provided. Select the correct alternative.

13. Which among the following organism reproduces by the process of regeneration?
    (a) Flatworm (b) *Rhizopus*
    (c) *Plasmodium* (d) Yeast
14. Name the type of pollination in which the pollen grains are carried from the anther of a flower to the stigma of another plant of same species.
    (a) Anemophilous (b) Anemophily
    (c) Hydrophily (d) Ornithophily
15. In the context of plant reproduction, how does cross-pollination primarily differ from self-pollination?
    (a) Cross-pollination occurs within the same flower.
    (b) Cross-pollination always requires external agents.
    (c) Cross-pollination increases genetic consistency.
    (d) Cross-pollination introduces new genetic combinations.
16. Why might fission be less prevalent as a reproductive strategy in complex multicellular organisms compared to unicellular ones?
    (a) Multicellular organisms have more genetic material.
    (b) Fission provides too much genetic diversity.
    (c) Complex organisms cannot physically split easily.
    (d) Fission requires the presence of pollinators.
17. Which component primarily ensures the protection of the embryonic plant during its initial developmental phase?
    (a) Anther (b) Stigma
    (c) Seed coat (d) Androecium
18. Which reproductive strategy in plants can lead to a potential lack of resilience against diseases or pests due to reduced genetic diversity?
    (a) Fission
    (b) Cross-pollination
    (c) Self-pollination
    (d) Vegetative propagation

Directions for questions from 19 to 22.
Correct the following statements.

19. The process of uniting stock and scion to grow a single plant is known as layering.
20. Budding is a sexual process of reproduction that takes place in *Hydra*.
21. Hydrophily pollination takes place in maize.
22. On fertilization, the ovary gets converted into seed and ovule gets converted into fruit.

Directions for questions from 23 to 26.
Write the missing correlated terms.

23. Archaea : ___________ : : *Rhizopus* : spore formation
24. Sugarcane : cutting : : *Forsythia* : ________
25. Rhizome : ginger : : _____ : potato
26. Self-pollination : rice : : _____________ : maize

Direction for Questions from 27 to 34.
Choose the correct option.

(1) Both A and R are true and R is the correct explanation for A.

(2) Both A and R are true, but R is not the correct explanation for A.

(3) A is true and R is false.

(4) A is false and R is true.

27. Assertion (A): Binary fission results in genetically identical progenies.
Reason (R): Cell division in prokaryotes does not exhibit DNA replication.

28. Assertion (A): The cells in bacteria and parasitic protozoans remain in inactive stage for long periods.
Reason (R): The cells possess cell walls around them.

29. Assertion (A): In custard apple, nature favour cross-pollination.
Reason (R): Custard apple is unisexual plant.

30. Assertion (A): Herkogamy favour cross-pollination.
Reason (R): In sunflower, androecium matures earlier than gynoecium.

31. Assertion (A): Pollen grains are diploid.
Reason (R): Male gametes are produced within the pollen grains.

32. Assertion (A): Endosperm formed after fertilization is triploid.
Reason (R): Angiosperms are characterized by double fertilization.

33. Assertion (A): In mustard seed, there is no endosperm.
Reason (R): Endosperm is the nutritive tissue for the developing embryo.

34. Assertion (A): Flowering plants are heterosporous
Reason (R): Flowering plants produce haploid spores.

Level 2: Review your Concepts

Directions for questions from 35 to 48:
Answer the following questions.

35. Explain the type of pollination observed in *Commelina benghalensis*.

36. Explain the process by which unicellular fungus like yeast reproduces.

37. Observe the figure given below and answer the following questions.

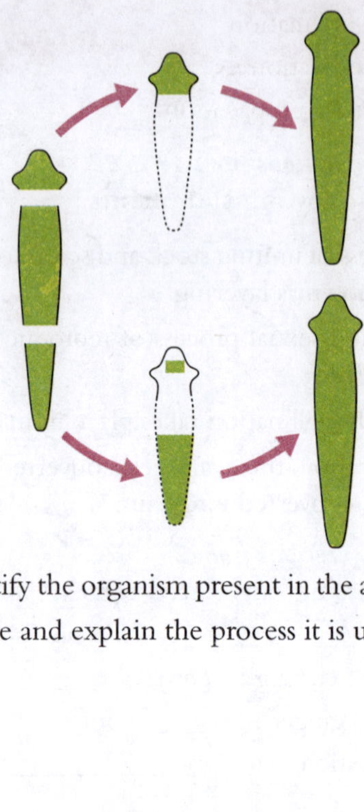

(a) Identify the organism present in the above diagram.

(b) Name and explain the process it is undergoing.

38. Differentiate anemophily from hydrophily.

39. What are the main functions of the layer that is found below the hilum in seed?

40. What is meant by seed dormancy? What are the causes for it?

41. Observe the figure given below and answer the following questions.

Which among the three seeds germinate? Justify.

42. Both spores and seeds go through the process of germination to produce new individuals. How do they differ from each other?

43. Explain the alternation of generations seen in angiosperms.

44. Explain the role of synergids and antipodal cells in the process of sexual reproduction in flowering plants.

45. Identify the ploidy of the cells involved in fertilization in angiosperms.

46. The process of sexual reproduction involves meiotic and mitotic cell divisions at various stages. With respect to the type of cell division associated with various stages, answer the following questions.

   (a) Identify the stages of reproduction associated with meiotic cell division.

   (b) How many pollen grains are formed from four microspore mother cells? How many nuclei do they possess?

   (c) How are eight cells formed from one megaspore mother cell?

47. An angiospermic plant has 32 chromosomes in its somatic cells. Find out the number of chromosomes in each of the following:

   (a) Megaspore mother cell

   (b) Egg cell

   (c) Pollen grain

   (d) Embryo of seed

   (e) Endosperm of seed

   (f) Microspores

   (g) Secondary nucleus

48. Justify that parthenogenesis is different from parthenocarpy.

Level 3: Assess Your Concepts

49. Monocot plants cannot be propagated by means of grafting. Give reason.

50. Usually, Chrysanthemum plants are found to propagate naturally and found spreading in the entire area. Which method of propagation does it depict? Can they be propagated by any other artificial methods?

51. Why do banana plants not produce true seeds? How are they propagated?

52. Tissue culture in plants is easier than in animals. Give reason.

53. Considering the significance of pollination in the reproduction of flowering plants, how might human interventions and environmental changes impact the process, and what could be the long-term consequences for the ecosystem and food security?

54. If a farmer wants to get an economically important plant having useful characters seen in two different plants in a short time, suggest a method to follow for the development of such a new plant.

55. Algae are capable of rapid multiplication in short duration. Why?

AT

PRACTICE QUESTIONS NEET SPECIAL WING

Multiple-Answer Type Questions

1. If the male gamete of an organism with diploid somatic cells contains 36 chromosomes. Identify the correct statement from the following:

(a) The zygote will have 72 autosomes and 2 X chromosomes.
(b) The zygote will have 70 autosomes and 1 X and 1 Y chromosome.
(c) The germ cells have 36 autosomes and 2 X chromosomes.
(d) The germ cells have 35 pairs of autosomes and 1 pair of allosomes.

2. If 40 haploid cells are produced after meiotic and mitotic division of megaspore mother cells, then which of the following statements among the following are true?
(a) 10 eggs are produced by the haploid cells.
(b) 5 eggs are produced from the haploid cells.
(c) 40 cells are produced by division of 5 megaspore mother cell.
(d) 40 cells are produced by division of 10 megaspore mother cells.

3. Which of the following processes are part of female gametogenesis?
(a) Formation of PEN
(b) Development of megagametophyte
(c) Degeneration of 3 megaspores out of 4
(d) Microsporogenesis

4. Which among the following are the characteristic of an anemophilous flower?
(a) Light weight pollen grains.
(b) No fragrance or nectar produced by flowers.
(c) Protruding elongated stamen.
(d) Pollen grains associated with wings.

5. Which of the following feature favours cross pollination?
(a) Protogyny
(b) Dichogomy
(c) Cleistogomy
(d) Herkogamy

Comprehension-Based Questions

A. Read the paragraph given below and answer the questions number 6 to 11:

6. Which of the following plants produces cleistogamous flowers?
(a) Wheat
(b) Mirabilis
(c) *Commelina benghalensis*
(d) All of the above

7. Which of the following plant and pollinator combination is incorrect?
(a) Salvia - bees
(b) Sanke plant - Snail
(c) Sweet pea - birds
(d) Kadam tree - Bats

8. The main advantage of homogamy is:
(a) High amounts of genetic variation
(b) Progeny produced in more vigorous
(c) Zero dependence on pollinators
d) More number of pollen grains need to be produced

9. In a bisexual flower if there is physical obstacle between style and stamen, then such a situation is seen in:
(a) Herkogamy
(b) Heterostyly
(c) Protoandry
(d) Protogyny

10. If a flower is small and inconspicuous and do not produce nectar nor fragrance. The plants are dioecious and the pollen grains are long ribbon like structure which can flow with the current of water, then the type of pollination shown by them is:
(a) Anemophily
(b) Entomophily
(c) Hydrophily
(d) Malacophily

11. Match the column:

Column – A	Column – B
(i) Canna	(a) Anemophily
(ii) Lemna	(b) Hydrophily
(iii) Sugarcane	(c) Ornithophily
(iv) Hydrilla	(d) Entomophily
(v) Pansy	(e) Malacophily

B. Read the paragraph given below and answer the questions number 12 to 17:

In sexually reproducing plants, germline development starts with the differentiation of sporophytic cells into spore mother cells (megaspore mother cell and microspore mother cell). These undergo meiosis to produce four haploid spores. During male gametogenesis, four uniform and equal microspores are produced which then give rise to pollen grains. The pollen grains have two nucleus- the generative nucleus forms two haploid male gametes and the tube nucleus at fertilization produces pollen tube. During female gametogenesis only one of the four megaspores survive which undergo mitosis 3 times to produce 8 nucleated embryo sac. After pollination, one male gamete fuses with the egg to form zygote and the other fuses with the secondary nucleus to form primary endosperm nucleus. This is known as double fertilization and is a unique feature of angiosperms.

12. In a female gametophyte of a plant the 8 nuclei form how many cells?
(a) 5 (b) 6
(c) 7 (d) 8

13. By which process pollen grains are produced from microspores?
(a) Mitosis (b) Meiosis
(c) Dehiscence (d) Both a and b

14. If 20 microspore mother cells are present, then how many male gametes can be produced? Assuming all the male gametes can successfully germinate and undergo fertilization, how many zygotes can be produced?
(a) 80, 160 (b) 160, 320
(c) 320, 160 (c) 160, 80

15. If the plant has 24 chromosomes in its somatic cells, how many chromosomes will be in its primary endosperm nucleus?
(a) 8 chromosomes
(b) 12 chromosomes
(c) 48 chromosomes
(d) 36 chromosomes

16. The female gametophyte of an angiospermic plants after fertilization contains:
I. Haploid
II. Diploid
III. Triploid

(a) I and II only
(b) II and III only
(c) I and III only
(d) I, II and III

17. Match the column:

Column – A	Column – B
(i) Microsporangium	(a) Ovule
(ii) Megasporangium	(b) Anther
(iii) Female gametophyte	(c) Antipodal cells
(iv) Male gametophyte	(d) Pollen grain
(v) Cells at chalazal end	(e) Embryo sac

ANSWER KEYS

Crossword

Across

4. Budding
5. Plumule
9. Heterostyly
11. Chalaza
12. Synergids
13. Androecium
14. Cotyledons
15. Thalamus
16. Chiropterophily

Down

1. Hilum
2. Stolon
3. Nucellus
6. Hyphae
7. Rhizome
8. Fragmentation
10. Cleistogamous
12. Sporangia

Classroom Wing

Very Short Answer Type Questions

1. Perpetuation
2. Flower
3. Male
4. Germination
5. Non-sexual or vegetative
6. Flower
7. Gynoecium or carpel or pistil
8. Zoophily
9. Nucellus
10. Ovule
11. (a)
12. (b)
13. (d)
14. (a)
15. (d)
16. (a)
17. (d)
18. (c)
19. (c)
20. (c)
21. (c)
22. (c)
23. (c)
24. (a)
25. (c)
26. (b)
27. (b)
28. (c)
29. (b)
30. (d)
31. (c)
32. (a)

Competition Wing

Level 1: Apply Your Concepts

1. Pollination
2. Protection, growth potential
3. Identical
4. Specialized
5. Non-sexual or vegetative
6. Flower
7. Bulb
8. Stamen
9. Pistil or carpel
10. Funicle
11. Embryo
12. Cross
13. (a)
14. (c)
15. (d)
16. (c)
17. (c)
18. (d)
23. Binary fission
24. Layering
25. Stem
26. Cross-pollination
27. (c)
28. (b)
29. (c)
30. (b)
31. (d)
32. (a)
33. (a)
34. (b)

NEET Special Wing

Multiple-Answer Type Questions

1. (b, d) **2.** (b, c) **3.** (b, c) **4.** (a, b, c, d) **5.** (a, b, d)

Comprehension-Based Questions

6. (d) **7.** (c) **8.** (c) **9.** (a) **10.** (a)

11. (i) → (c); (ii) → (e); (iii) → (a); (iv) → (b); (v) → (d)

12. (c) **13.** (a) **14.** (d) **15.** (d) **16.** (d)

17. (i) → (b); (ii) → (a); (iii) → (e); (iv) → (d); (v) → (c)

Hints and Explanations

CLASSROOM WING

Short Answer Type Questions

33. Reproduction is a process by which new individuals of the same species are produced by the existing of parental organisms.

34. Bacterium reproduces by the process of binary fission. Following are the steps that take place during the process:

(a) Bacterium makes a duplicate of its DNA.

(b) The parent cell gets elongated.

(c) The nuclear matter divides into two and then cytoplasm undergoes cleavage.

(d) Thus, two daughter cells are formed.

35.

Sexual reproduction	Asexual reproduction
The production of new individual from two individuals of opposite sexes.	The production of new offspring is from one individual organism.
The new individual is genetically distinct from the parents.	The new offspring formed is identical to its parents.

36. (a) This kind of reproduction is observed in fungus called *Rhizopus*.

(b) This type of reproduction is known as spore formation.

(c) *Rhizopus* possesses thread-like projections called hyphae, from which small spherical structure called sporangium is developed.

Several reproductive units called spores are developed inside the sporangium.

When it bursts, spores are released and spread.

37. Overuse of vegetative propagation in agriculture could lead to vast areas of genetically identical plants. This homogeneity makes crops more susceptible to diseases, pests, or environmental changes, potentially leading to widespread crop failures.

38. Pollination often involves multiple steps and factors, from the maturity of the reproductive organs to external agents like wind or pollinators. Fission, on the other hand, is a direct split of the organism, making it simpler in comparison.

39. Vegetative propagation ensures the rapid spread of a plant species with successful genetic traits, which is advantageous in a stable environment. However, since all the offspring are genetically identical, they share the same vulnerabilities. If a disease or pest that can exploit this vulnerability emerges, the entire population could be at risk, reducing ecological resilience.

40. Retaining mechanisms for cross-pollination, even in primarily self-pollinating plants, offer a backup reproductive strategy. In case environmental conditions change or the plant population dwindles, cross-pollination can introduce genetic variability, enhancing adaptability and resilience against diseases and changing conditions.

41. Grafting is the process that is employed to get a single plant by joining two or more plants with desired characteristics along with resistant to diseases.

(a) In this process, a portion of the stem of a plant is cut in a slanting way and this part is called scion. Scion is without root.

(b) Another plant that is rooted is also cut in the same way and is called stock.

(c) The exposed surface of the scion is attached to that of the stock without leaving any gap and bound tightly with a piece of cloth that is covered with a polythene sheet.

(d) Finally, the stock and the scion unite together and grow as one plant.

42.

Regeneration	Fragmentation
Regeneration is the process of regrowth of an organism from its lost body part.	Fragmentation is a common method of reproduction in algae and fungi.
When a body part is separated from the organism, it develops the tissues and finally a new organism is grown from the separated part.	When filamentous thallus of algae and fungi undergoes accidental breakage, the fragments develop into new organisms.

43. Regeneration is the process by which lost part of star fish can be grown back again in the natural course. It is the ability of an organism to regrow the lost part.

44. Refer to the notes sections for diagram.

45. (a) **Pollination:** The transfer of pollen grains from the anther of a flower to the surface of the stigma of the same or another flower is known as pollination.

(b) **Fertilization:** It is the union of the male and female reproductive cells or gametes.

46. Formation of male gamete:

(a) The diploid cells undergo meiotic division and form haploid cells in anther.

(b) Haploid cells undergo division to form microscopic pollen grains.

(c) Each pollen grain has two-layered outer wall.

(d) The inner layer is thin and is called intine and the thick outer layer is known as exine.

(e) Exine contains some pore-like structures known as germ pores.

(f) Pollen grains contain two nuclei:

(i) A generative nucleus—these cells undergo mitosis division to form two male gametes

(ii) A tube nucleus—these cells elongate to form pollen tube.

47. There are two types of pollinations:

(a) Self-pollination

(b) Cross-pollination

48. Major disadvantages of cross-pollination are as follows:

(a) Dependence on the external agencies such as insects and birds. Lack of availability of these agents makes the process difficult.

(b) Generation of large quantity of pollen grains is required since the loss of pollen grains takes place during pollination.

(c) Flowers should have bright-coloured petals, long stamen and pistil, fragrance, or they should produce nectar to attract the pollinating agents.

49. Agents that are responsible for the cross-pollination can be classified into two categories, namely:

(a) **Biotic agents:** These agents are living organism such as insects, birds, bats and snails.

(b) **Abiotic agents:** The non-living things that act as agents such as wind and water.

50.

Biotic Pollination	Abiotic pollination
It is a type of pollination in which transference of pollen grains takes place by living organisms such as insects, birds, bats and snails.	It is a type of pollination in which transference of pollen grains takes place by non-living organisms such as wind and air.

51. The type of pollination in which the insects carry the pollen from the anther of a flower to the stigma of another plant of the same species.

The main characteristic features of entomophilous flowers are as follows:

(a) Large, brightly coloured petals:

(i) If the petals are not prominent, transformation of the other parts of the plant takes place to attract the insects.
For example, *Bougainvillea*

(ii) If the flower is small, they aggregate to form a cluster of flowers called inflorescence and become prominently visible to the insects.
For example, sunflower

(b) Nectar production and fragrance of the flower.

(i) Some flowers have guides so that the insect can locate the nectaries easily.
For example, pansy

(c) The pollen grains of entomophilous flowers are sticky or spiny for the purpose of adherence to the insects. They are thick walled for their protection during transference.

52. (a) Herkogamy: In some flowers, there is a physical obstacle that prevents self-pollination. This condition is known as herkogamy.

(b) Heterostyly: In some flowers, the stamen is much longer than the style and in some flowers the style is longer than stigma. This condition is known as heterostyly.

53. Dichogamy: If the stamen and carpel or pistil of a bisexual flower do not attain maturity simultaneously, cross-pollination takes place. This situation is favourable for the cross-pollination and is known as dichogamy.

54. In *Gloriosa*, the stamen and carpel are present in the opposite direction. Hence, self-pollination is not possible.

55. (a) Self-pollination generally takes place in the bisexual flowers.

(b) The flowers involved in self-pollination should possess specific characteristic features such as homogamy and cleistogamy.

(i) **Homogamy:** The anther and the stigma of a bisexual flower attain maturity together.

(ii) **Cleistogamy:** It is observed in non-opening flowers since the pollen grain is confined inside the flower and can pollinate the stigma of the same flower.

56. Cross-pollination is not possible in all flowers since they need to possess the following characteristic features:
   (a) Unisexuality
   (b) Self-sterility
   (c) Dichogamy
   (d) Herkogamy
   (e) Heterostyly

Essay Type Questions

57. In *Salvia* flowers, the pollination is carried out by bees. Mechanism of collection of pollen grains in *Salvia* is as follows:
   (a) The bee enters the flower for the nectar and pushes the sterile lower lobe of the anther.
   (b) Then long connective moves down and helps the stamen bend with a jerk.
   (c) The jerk produced sprinkles the pollen grains on the back of the bees.

58. The flower in which the lever mechanism takes place is *Salvia*.
   Mechanism of pollination in *Salvia* as follows:
   (a) The flower in which the stigma is matured takes part in pollination.
   (b) The matured stigma protrudes out of the upper lip of the corolla.
   (c) When the bee visits such a flower for collecting nectar, the stigma touches the back of the bee that carries the pollen grains.
   (d) The stigma is sticky in nature and thus the pollen grains adhere to it. Since the connective of the stamen acts as a lever in this process of pollination, it is called lever mechanism.

59. The flowers of sweet pea plant are papilionaceous. They are complete and bisexual.
   (a) The flower of a sweet pea plant has fragrance, produce the nectar, and it is bright in colour.
   (b) Thus, it attracts bees. When the bee visits the flower, it lands on the wing petals.
   (c) Due to the body weight of the bee, wing as well as keel petals move down exposing the style and the stigma.
   (d) Then the bee finds the nectar that is present at the base of the ovary and the anther comes in contact of the bee.
   (e) Thus, pollen grains are adhered to the body of the bee.

60. Formation of eggs or female gametes:
   (a) Ovules are present inside the ovary that is a part of carpel or pistil.
   (b) Ovules are attached to the placenta that holds each ovule with the help of a stalk called funicle.
   (c) An ovule contains two structures inside the integuments called embryo sac and nucleus.
   (d) Embryo sac produces eggs or female gametes.

61. When the pollen tube reaches the embryo sac, two processes of fusion take place inside the embryo sac.

   One of the male gametes fuses with the egg cell and a diploid zygote is formed.

   The other male gamete fuses with the diploid secondary nucleus formed in the embryo sac by the fusion of two polar nuclei.

   This results in the formation of a triploid primary endosperm nucleus (PEN). This develops as endosperm that acts as nutritive tissue for the growing embryo.

   Since the fusion of three nuclei takes place in the above process resulting in the formation of triploid cell, this process is called triple fusion.

   Two fertilizations occur in the embryo sac, and hence, the entire process is known as double fertilization. This is a unique phenomenon found in angiosperms.

COMPETITION WING

Level 1: Apply your Concepts

19. The process of uniting the stock and scion to grow a single plant is known as layering.
20. Budding is an asexual process of reproduction that takes place in hydra.
21. Anemophily pollination takes place in maize.
22. On fertilization, the ovary gets converted into fruit and ovule gets converted into seed.
23. Archaea : binary fission : *Rhizopus* : spore formation
24. Sugarcane: cutting : forsythia : layering
25. Rhizome : ginger : stem : potato
26. Self-pollination : rice : cross-pollination : maize.
27. Binary fission is a method of asexual reproduction. This results in genetically identical progenies because it involves only mitotic cell division that results in the duplication of DNA identical to parent organism.
Hence, the correct option is (c)
28. The cells in bacteria and parasitic protozoans remain in inactive stage for long periods because the daughter cells are surrounded by a cyst till the conditions become favourable. When the conditions become favourable, the cyst breaks open releasing the daughter cells that become active.
Hence, the correct option is (b)
29. Custard apple is a bisexual plant, but cross-pollination is favoured because the gynoecium matures earlier than androecium. This condition is known as protogyny.
Hence, the correct option is (c)
30. In sunflower, androecium matures earlier than gynoecium. This condition is known as protandry. Herkogamy is a condition in which a barrier develops between stamens and pistil.
Hence, the correct option is (b)
31. Pollen grains are haploid. They undergo mitotic division to produce male gametes. Pollen grains are formed from haploid microspores by mitotic division. The microspores are formed from microspore mother cells by meiotic cell division.
Hence, the correct option is (d)
32. Endosperm is formed by the fusion of diploid secondary nucleus with the haploid male gamete. This phenomenon is known as triple fusion. This is a part of double fertilization in angiosperms. This is a unique phenomenon found in angiosperms.
Hence, the correct option is (a)
33. Mustard seed is exalbuminous seed. It has no endosperm because this serves as nutritive tissue for the developing embryo and is used up during the formation of the embryo in the seed.
Hence, the correct option is (a)
34. Flowering plants are said to be heterosporous because the male and female sporangia are different and produce different spores called microspores and megaspores. The spores are haploid. But this is not the reason for the heterosporous condition.
Hence, the correct option is (b)

Level 2: Review your Concepts

35. Cleistogamy self-pollination is observed in *Commelina benghalensis*. This type of pollination is observed in the non opening flowers since the pollen grain is confined inside the flower and can pollinate the stigma of the same flower.
36. Yeast reproduces by the process of budding.
    (a) In this process of reproduction, a small bud-like projection or outgrowth called bud is developed at a particular site.
    (b) This outgrowth is the new organism that remains attached with parent organism.
    (c) When the new organism becomes matured, it gets separated from the parent and leaves a scar tissue. Thus, new yeast is formed.
37. (a) *Planaria* is the organism that is present in the above process.
    (b) The above process is known as regeneration. It is the process of regrowth of an organism from its lost body part. When the body part is separated from the organism, it develops the tissues and finally a new organism grows from the separated part.
38.

Anemophily	Hydrophily
It is abiotic pollination in which the pollen grains are carried from the anther of a flower to the stigma of a flower of another plant of same species by air.	It is abiotic pollination in which the pollen grains are carried from the anther of a flower to the stigma of a flower of another plant of same species by water.

39. Micropyle of the ovule is present below the hilum. The main functions of micropyle are as follows:

(a) Absorption of water during germination.

(b) Providing passage for the diffusion of respiratory gases.

40. The condition in which the seeds do not germinate even when all the suitable conditions are provided is known as seed dormancy. The period of dormancy and the causes of dormancy may be different for different species of plants.

Important causes:

- Seed coat formed at the time of maturation of fruit or seed may be impermeable. This prevents the entry of water and oxygen into the seed.
- Presence of hard seed coat may prevent the embryo from coming out.
- Immature embryos or underdeveloped embryos.
- Presence of some chemical substances in the seed, which inhibit the germination.

41. Seed 'B' germinates whereas 'A' and 'C' do not germinate at all.
A is exposed to oxygen, but not supplied with water.
C is exposed to water but not exposed to oxygen.

42. Spores are usually unicellular and have lesser complexity than seeds. Seeds are multicellular and have greater complexity.
Haploid spores give rise to haploid gametophytes. Seed possesses a diploid zygote or embryo that develops into diploid sporophyte.
Spores are smaller in size and are the agents of asexual reproduction in lower plants. Seeds are larger in size and are produced only in higher plants (gymnosperms and angiosperms) and serve as agents of sexual reproduction.
In higher plants, spores are microscopic, produced internally within the structures called sporangia. Seeds are macroscopic and are found either naked in the reproductive organs (flowers) or enclosed within the fruits.

43. In the life cycle of an angiosperm plant, the adult plant is the diploid sporophyte, which is the main phase.

The flowers possess structures called microsporangia and megasporangia within the male and female reproductive parts. Within these structures, microspores and megaspores are produced.

The microspores produce pollen grains that are the male gametophytes. The megaspores produce ovules with female gametophytes. They produce haploid male and female gametes.

They fuse to form diploid zygote that develops into embryo. This embryo is enclosed in a seed that undergoes germination to give rise to a new plant, which is again a diploid sporophyte.

Hence, the life cycle of an angiosperm shows a unique phenomenon of alternation of generations between the diploid sporophyte and haploid gametophyte. Diploid sporophyte is the dominant phase of the plant life within which the haploid male and female gametophytes interchange. This phase is not conspicuous and short lived and confined to the production of male and female gametes.

44. Antipodals serve the function of providing nutrition to the egg cell and zygote later.

Synergids help the entry of the male gamete into the embryo sac and the fusion of male gamete with the egg.

45. Microspore mother cells—diploid (2n)

Microspores—haploid (n)
Pollen grains—haploid (n)
Male gametes—haploid (n)
Megaspore mother cells—diploid (2n)
Megaspores—Haploid (n)
All cells in embryo sac—haploid(n)
Zygote—diploid (2n)
Secondary nucleus—diploid (2n)
Primary endosperm nucleus—triploid (3n)

46. (a) Meiotic cell division takes place during the following stages. Formation of microspores from microspore mother cells in anther. Formation of megaspores from megaspore mother cell in carpel.

(b) Each microspore mother cell produces four microspores. Four microspore mother cells produce 16 microspores. Each microspore on mitotic cell division forms two pollen grains. That means, 16 microspore mother cells produce 32 pollen grains.

(c) A megaspore mother cell undergoes meiotic cell division to form four megaspores. Of these, three degenerate. The functional megaspore undergoes three successive mitotic divisions forming eight cells.

47. (a) Megaspore mother cell—32
(b) Egg cell—16
(c) Pollen grain—16
(d) Embryo—32
(e) Endosperm of seed—48
(f) Microspores—16
(g) Secondary nucleus—32

48. Parthenogenesis is the production of new organism without fertilization process. This can be seen both in lower animals and all plants.

Parthenocarpy is the development of fruits without fertilization. The ovary directly develops into fruit. These fruits do not possess seeds. This is seen only in flowering plants.

Level 3: Assess Your Concepts

49. The grafting involves the cell division of meristematic tissue of the cork cambium of the two joined parts. This cork cambium is absent in the stems of monocots. Therefore, monocots cannot be propagated by the method of grafting.

50. The method of propagation that is involved in the natural distribution of chrysanthemum is by suckers. They can also be propagated by the method of cutting.

51. Banana plants usually do not produce viable seeds. This is because the spores are triploid with three sets of chromosomes. Therefore, they cannot undergo meiotic cell division to produce gametes.
Banana plants are usually cultivated by the method of suckers. Structures called rhizomes arise from the adult banana plants. These are removed from the mother plant and are replanted. They develop into small baby plants called suckers.

52. In animals, the tissues are more complex and require many proteins, hormones, etc., for their growth in addition to the nutrients. In plants, the tissues can be made to grow if proper nutrient medium is provided.
Moreover, in plants, many cells are totipotent and are capable of cell division and cell differentiation even in adult plant.
In animals, only few kinds of cells are totipotent, which makes the tissue culture a more challenging task.

53. Human interventions, such as habitat destruction, pollution, and the use of pesticides, can negatively impact pollinators like bees, butterflies, and birds. Environmental changes, like global warming, can alter flowering times and pollinator activity. This misalignment can lead to reduced pollination, leading to decreased crop yields, and impacting food security. In the long run, a decline in pollination can disrupt the balance of ecosystems, affecting biodiversity. Proper pollination ensures genetic diversity, which in turn results in robust populations capable of withstanding diseases and changes in environmental conditions. Without effective pollination, the long-term sustainability of many plant species and the animals that rely on them for food could be jeopardized.

54. Usually, all asexual methods produce offsprings having the same characteristics as the parent plant.
However, in the method of grafting, the daughter plant can get the mixed characteristics of two plants. The plants of desirable characteristics are chosen for grafting. When the cut stem of one plant is grafted on another plant, a new plant is produced with new characteristics. Tissue culture is also another method of propagation that helps to raise plants of new desirable characteristics in very short time.

55. The lifespan of algae are short and the life cycle is shortest. Therefore, algae generally propagate by asexual or vegetative methods. During favourable conditions, they reproduce by various asexual methods such as fragmentation, zoospores, aplanospores, and akinetes. The actual method of vegetative propagation depends upon the availability of water.

NEET SPECIAL WING

Multiple-Answer Type Questions

1. If a male gamete has 36 chromosomes, then it has 35 autosomes and 1 Y gamete. When it fuses with the egg, the zygote will have 70 autosomes and 1 X and 1 Y chromosome. The germ cells will also have 35 pairs or 70 autosomes and 1 pair of allosomes.

2. 1 megaspore mother cell produces 8 haploid cells after its various divisions. Thus, 40 haploid cells will be produced by the division of 5 megaspore mother cells. From each haploid cell 1 egg is produced, so from 40 haploid cells 5 eggs are produced.

3. The megaspore mother cells are diploid and undergo meiotic cell division to form haploid megaspores. Of the four haploid megaspores, usually, three degenerate and one functional megaspore develops into embryo sac, which is also called female gametophyte (megagametophyte). The functional megaspore in the embryo sac undergoes three successive mitotic divisions forming eight haploid cells.

4. Anemophily is a type of abiotic pollination in which pollen grains are carried from the anther of a flower to the stigma of a flower of another plant of the same species by air. Flowers are small and inconspicuous. Neither they have fragrance, nor do they produce nectar. Elongated stamen that protrudes out of the flower for a better exposure to air. Large quantities of pollen grains are produced. Pollen grains are light in weight and dry for easy transportation by air.
   In some plants such as pine, the pollen grains are associated with wings that facilitate their movement in air.

5. The flowers involved in self-pollination should possess specific characteristic features such as homogamy or cleistogamy. In homogamy, the anther and the stigma of a bisexual flower attain maturity together.

Comprehension-Based Questions

A.

6. The flowers involved in self-pollination should possess specific characteristic features such as homogamy or cleistogamy. In homogamy, the anther and the stigma of a bisexual flower attain maturity together. For example, wheat, rice, *Mirabilis*. Cleistogamy is observed in non-opening flowers since the pollen grain is confined inside the flower and can pollinate the stigma of the same flower. For example, underground flowers of *Commelina benghalensis*.

7. The flower of a sweet pea plant has fragrance, produces nectar and is bright in colour. Thus, it attracts bees. It is a bee-pollinated flower.

8. Self-pollination is the transfer of pollen grains from the anther of a flower to the stigma of the same flower. Self-pollination takes place in some bisexual flowers. Parental characteristics are maintained. Production of pollen grains in large quantity is not required. Flowers need not be attractive as insects are not required to be attracted for pollination.

9. In some flowers, there is a physical obstacle that prevents self-pollination. This condition is called herkogamy. For example, pansy flower, *Gloriosa*. In pansy, a hood over stigma prevents self-pollination.

10. Hydrophily is a type of abiotic pollination in which pollen grains are carried from the anther of a flower to the stigma of a flower of another plant of same species by water. This kind of pollination takes place in aquatic, submerged plants. Flowers are small and inconspicuous. Male and female flowers are grown on different plants. Such kind of plants are called dioecious plants. Neither they have fragrance, nor do they produce nectar. Large quantity of pollen grains is produced. Pollen grains have long, ribbon-like structure, which facilitates their transportation in the current of water.

11. Match the following:

    Canna is pollinated by birds also called as Ornithophily.
    (i) (c)

    Lemna is pollinated by bats also called as Malacophily.
    (ii) (e)

    Sugarcane plants are pollinated by wind and is called as Anemophily.
    (iii) (a)

    Hydrilla is an aquatic plant and is pollinated by water called as Hydrophily.
    (iv) (b)

    Pansy is pollinated by insects and is known as entomophily.
    (v) (d)

B.

12. In a female gametophyte the 8 nuclei arrange themselves into seven cells- the egg, two synergids, three antipodal cell and one large central cell containing two polar nuclei.

13. During male gametogenesis, the haploid microspores undergo mitotic cell division to produce haploid pollen grains.

14. 20 microspore mother cells by meiosis form 80 microspores or pollen grains. These 80 pollen grains produce 160 male gametes as each pollen grain produces 2 male gametes. In double fertilization 1 of the two male gametes fuses with the egg and the other fuses with the secondary nucleus to produce primary endosperm nucleus. Thus, of the total male gametes produce only half fuse with the eggs to produce zygote and that is 80 zygote.

15. The diploid (2n) somatic cells of the plants have 24 chromosomes. Since the gametes are haploid(n), they will have 12 chromosomes. A primary endosperm nucleus is formed by triple fusion of 3 haploid nuclei, so it is triploid or 3n. Thus, primary endosperm nucleus has 36 chromosomes (3n= 36).

16. A fertilized gametophyte have haploid cells which are the antipodal cells, a diploid cell which is zygote and a triploid cell which is the primary endosperm nucleus.

17. Match the following:

The structure that houses the pollen grains within the plant body is called microsporangium and it is the anther.
(i) (b)

In an immature ovule, one cell from the nucellus undergoes differentiation to form a female germ cell called megaspore mother cell. At this stage, the ovule is known as megasporangium.
(ii) (a)

The megaspore mother cells are diploid and undergo meiotic cell division to form haploid megaspores. Of the four haploid megaspores, usually, three degenerate and one functional megaspore develops into embryo sac, which is also called female gametophyte (megagametophyte).
(iii) (e)

The diploid microspore mother cells undergo meiotic cell division to form haploid cells called microspores. This process is called microsporogenesis. The haploid microspores undergo mitotic cell division to produce haploid pollen grains. Each pollen grain is a microscopic cell and forms the male gamete. So pollen grains are also called as male gametophyte.
(iv) (d)

Three cells are aligned at the chalazal end and are called antipodal cells.
(v) (c)

CHAPTER

5

Life Processes in Human Beings–I

(Digestive and Excretory Systems)

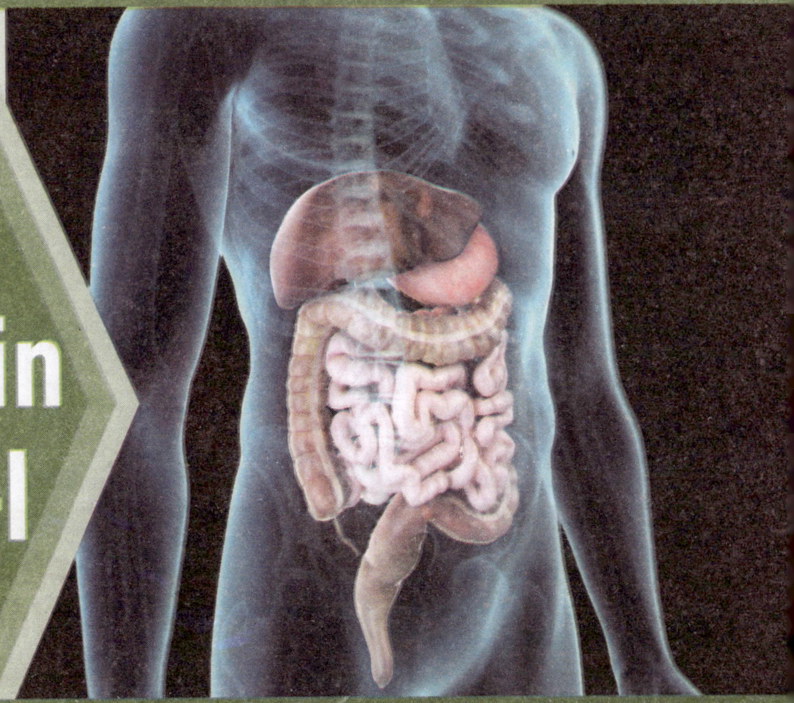

Remember

Before beginning this chapter, you should be able to:

- Recall different parts of the digestive system
- Remember basic structure and function of teeth, tongue, oesophagus, stomach, small intestine, large intestine, liver, etc.
- Recall different parts of human excretory system
- Remember the basic concept of life processes and products generated in them

Key Ideas

After completing this chapter, you should be able to:

- Understand the need of digestive system and role of enzymes
- iscuss the structure and functions of organs and glands associated with digestive system
- Explain the digestion process of different types of food constituents
- List the metabolic wastes produced in human body
- Know the different excretory organs in human body
- Explain the structure and function of urinary system
- Define the process of osmoregulation
- Understand the concept of haemodialysis

A Tribute to Claude Bernard (1813–1878)

Claude Bernard (1813–1878), a renowned French physiologist, is widely regarded as one of the forefathers of modern physiology, having made indelible contributions to the study of the digestive and excretory systems. Bernard's meticulous investigations into the pancreas and liver paved the way for a better understanding of digestion and physiological chemistry. His discovery of the liver's glycogenic function broke new ground, emphasising the organ's critical role in glucose regulation.

Aside from that, Bernard is well-known for coining the term 'homeostasis.' This revolutionary concept emphasised organisms' inherent ability to regulate their internal environment, maintaining stability and equilibrium despite external changes, a concept critical to understanding the intricate life processes in humans.

He emphasised the scientific method's importance in physiological research, advocating for an empirical approach to experimentation and observation. His meticulous research demonstrated the interdependence of various physiological systems.

The international scientific community recognised Bernard's long-term contributions. He received the prestigious Copley Medal, recognising his profound impact on the field of physiology.

FUN TIME

CROSSWORD

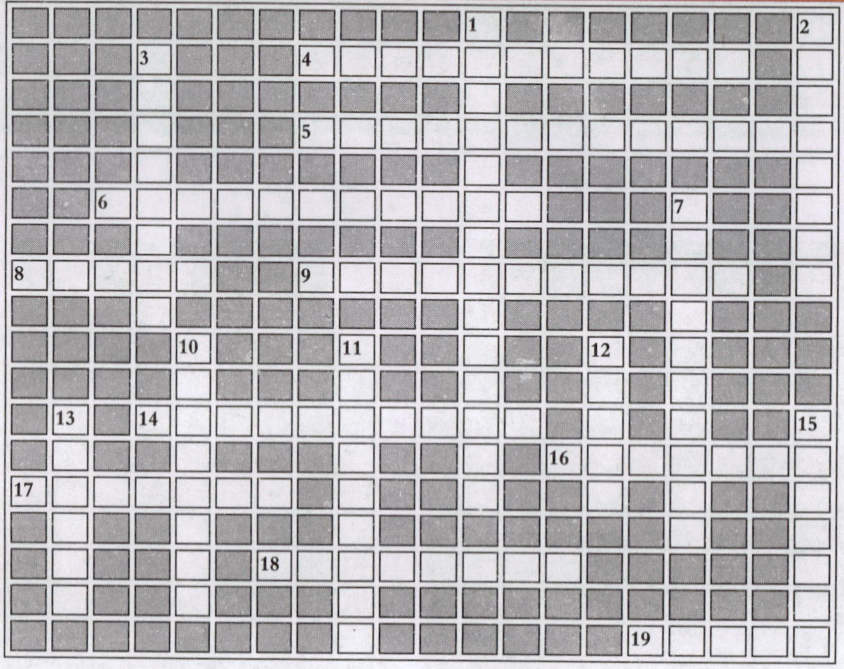

Across

4. The wave like movement in the alimentary canal which pushes the food from one part to the next
5. diverting blood into an external machine, where it's filtered before being returned to the body
6. The organ in which bile juice is stored
8. The longest part of the large intestine
9. The process of expulsion of urine from the urinary system
14. A flap like structure which prevents the entry of food into the respiratory tract
16. The enzyme which is present in saliva and facilitates digestion of starch
17. The sharp pointed teeth helpful for tearing flesh
18. The first part of the small intestine
19. The region of the tooth which is exposed above the gum

Down

1. Maintaining the fluid balance and electrolyte concentration in the blood
2. The expulsion of undigested waste through large intestine
3. The hormone which helps to elevate the glucose level in the blood
7. The bunch of blood capillaries enclosed inside the cup shaped Bowman's capsule
10. The vestigial organ of the digestive system
11. The pigment responsible for the yellow colour of urine
12. The semi-digested food which passes from the stomach to the small intestine
13. The hard coating covering the teeth
15. The anti-coagulant added to the blood for which dialysis is performed

INTRODUCTION

Different life processes take place in the human body throughout the life. The most important life processes are digestion, respiration, blood circulation, excretion, reproduction, etc. Human body has specific organ systems for each of the life processes. Energy is required for carrying out the various life processes. This energy is obtained from the different nutrients such as carbohydrates, proteins and fats. These nutrients are supplied to the body through different kinds of food. Food that is consumed contains complex molecules. These complex molecules should be converted into simpler form and assimilated in the body. This leads to growth and metabolism. The intake of food, simplification of complex food materials followed by their assimilation, altogether constitutes the process of nutrition. Nutrition takes place in the digestive system. After processing of food in the digestive system, the waste materials are left behind. Many waste substances are produced during the metabolic activities in the body. They are thrown out of the body by means of excretory system. The simple food undergoes oxidation to produce energy in the respiratory system. The food materials are transported to various cells of the body by means of circulatory system. Digestive system plays a vital role in the sustenance of human life.

Need for Digestive System

Food that we eat cannot be utilized by our body in its complex form. To be able to reach the cells, the food has to be broken down into simpler molecules. The broken down simple molecules are of such size and characteristics that they can easily get absorbed in the intestine and pass through the cell membranes to reach inside of the cells. Hence, our body has an elaborate system that is involved in making the food available for use.

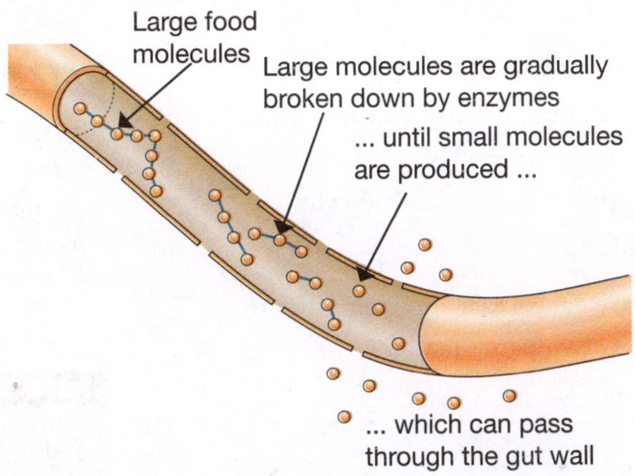

Figure 5.1 Diagram illustrating the need for digestion

Info Bytes!

Six classes of nutrients required by human body are carbohydrates, fats, proteins, minerals, vitamins and water.

To achieve this goal, our digestive system makes use of a number of enzymes which break down the specific nutrient molecules.

Role of Enzymes

Enzymes are biological catalysts which act only on their specific substrate. A substrate is a substance on which an enzyme acts. Chemically, enzymes are protein in nature. They speed up the rate of reactions. Following are some of the important features of enzymes:

- Enzymes get destroyed by heating.
- They only affect the rate of the reactions. They do not get changed in the course of reaction.

- They can be used again and again.
- They work at an optimum pH.
- They act within a narrow range of temperature (optimum temperature).

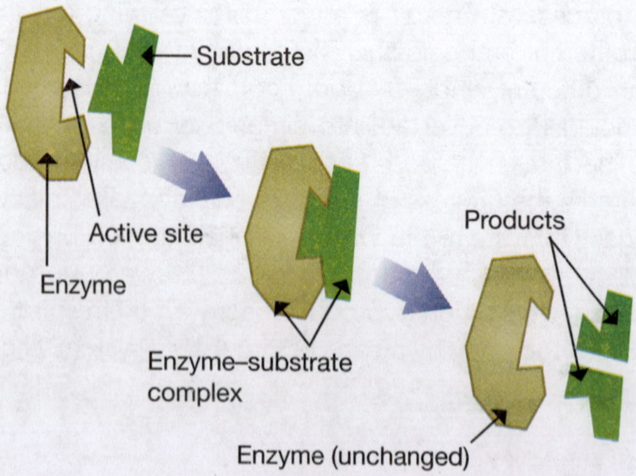

Figure 5.2 Diagram showing an enzyme helping to break up a large molecule

Digestive System

In digestive system, the process of nutrition takes place in the following stages—ingestion, digestion, absorption, assimilation and egestion.

- Ingestion involves the process of intake of food.
- Digestion involves the breaking down of complex food to simpler forms.
- Absorption involves the transportation of simplified forms of food from digestive system into blood.
- Assimilation involves the utilization of transported food by all the cells.
- Egestion involves the removal of undigested food.

Different stages of nutrition mentioned above take place in specific parts of the digestive system. Digestive system broadly comprises two parts, namely

1. Alimentary canal or digestive tract
2. Associated digestive glands

Info Bytes!

All enzymes are protein except ribozymes which are made up of RNA molecules.

Info Bytes!

Your mouth produces about 1 to 2 liters of saliva daily.

Konnect

The stomach's acidic environment is strong enough to dissolve metal, but the lining protects it from self-digestion.

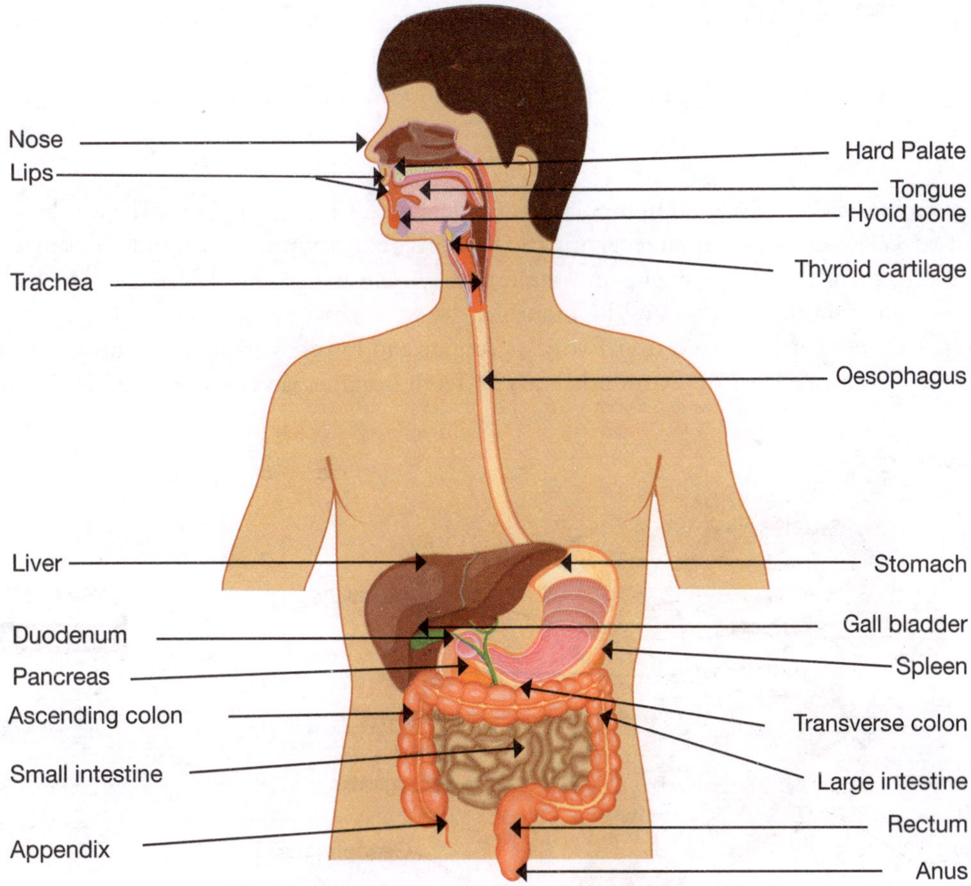

Figure 5.3 Alimentary canal and associated glands

Alimentary Canal or Digestive Tract

In human body, the length of the digestive tract is about 9 m. It has a convoluted, tube-like muscular structure. It is constituted of different organs which are interconnected. Different organs of alimentary canal are as follows:

- Mouth
- Pharynx
- Oesophagus
- Stomach
- Small intestine
- Large intestine

Info Bytes!

You don't need gravity to swallow. People in space can swallow too.

Associated Digestive Glands

The alimentary canal is also associated with three digestive glands as follows.

- Salivary glands
- Pancreas
- Liver

Alimentary Canal

The various organs of the alimentary canal are discussed in detail in the following section.

Mouth

Digestive system starts with mouth. Two soft, muscular lips (upper and lower) are present as the border of the mouth cavity which is also called buccal cavity. Lips help in receiving the food inside the mouth cavity and they are sensitive to heat and cold. Inside the mouth, there are teeth, tongue and three pairs of salivary glands. There is a flat structure called palate which forms the roof of the mouth. It separates the mouth cavity from nasal cavity. Tongue is present on the floor of the cavity. Different types of teeth are arranged over two jaws (upper and lower) which act as support of the mouth cavity. Apart from digestion, the various parts of the mouth, such as, teeth, tongue, jaws and lips are helpful in speech.

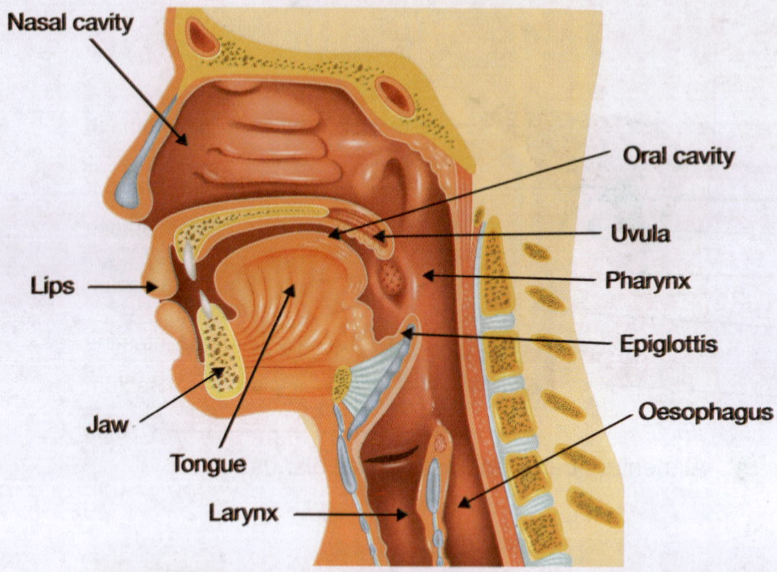

Figure 5.4 Illustration of mouth cavity and its parts

> **Info Bytes!**
> The most times a person can swallow in one minute is 290, set by Michaela M of Germany in 2001.

Human Teeth

The teeth (singular: tooth) have a specialized function in the process of digestion. They cut and break the food into small parts. The breaking down of food by teeth helps in increasing the surface area for the enzymes to act upon it.

The arrangement of teeth in a particular species is called dentition. In human body, the teeth are embedded in sockets just like other mammals. This kind of dentition is called the thecodont dentition. The total number of teeth in an adult human being is 32. Due to the omnivorous feeding habits, the mouth in human body consists of four varieties of teeth, suitable for almost all kind of food. This type of dentition is called heterodont dentition. The four types of teeth are as follows:

1. **Incisors (total eight in number):** Four incisors are arranged at the centre of each jaw.

   They have chisel-like structures and help in cutting and biting the food.
2. **Canines (total four in number):** They are positioned beside the incisor on the upper and lower jaws. They are conical in shape, pointed at the end and used for holding the food and tearing the flesh.
3. **Premolars (total eight in number):** On each side of the two jaws, there are two premolars present just beside the canines.

   Each premolar has two cusps or projections on its surface which help in crushing and chewing.
4. **Molars (total twelve in number):** The last three teeth on each side of both the jaws are molars. Molars have a broader surface than that of premolars and help in grinding the food.

The last molar on each side of both the jaws is called wisdom tooth. There are total four wisdom teeth which grow at the age of around 18.

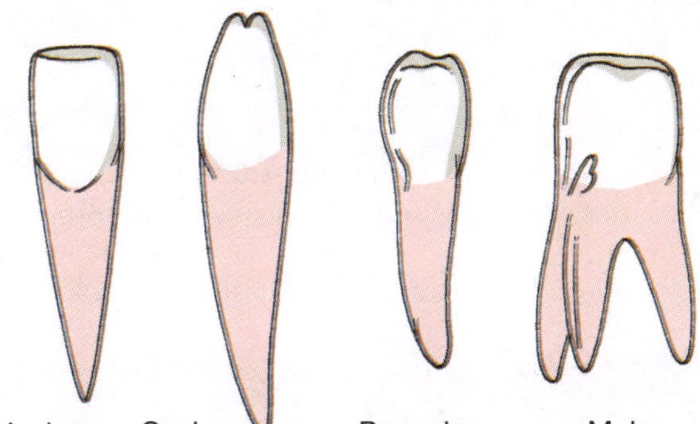

Figure 5.5 Illustration of different types of human teeth

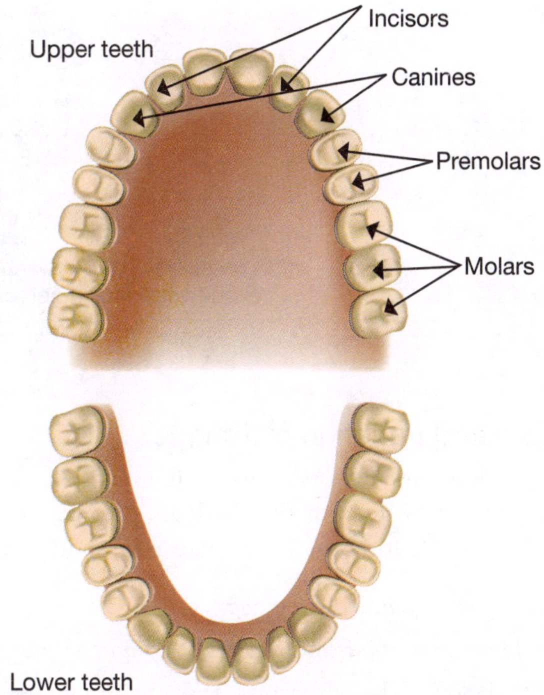

Figure 5.6 Arrangement of permanent teeth in humans

In humans, teeth appear in two sets during their life time. The first set, or milk teeth, comprise 20 teeth (all except molars). Milk teeth start to appear when the child is about 7–9 month old. These teeth are called milk or deciduous teeth. These teeth fall out by about the age of 12 years. Milk teeth are then replaced by permanent teeth.

Dental Formula

Dental formula represents the number of teeth of each type present at one side of the mouth. The type of teeth is represented by the initial letter of their names. The number of teeth in upper and lower jaws is indicated separately in two rows—upper row is for upper jaw and the lower row is for lower jaw. In human beings, both the jaws contain same number of teeth. (i2/2, c1/1, pm2/2, m3/3) × 2 = 32 (total number of teeth)

Dental formula of a child of about 3 years of age $\frac{2,\ 1,\ 0,\ 2}{2,\ 1,\ 0,\ 2}$ Dental formula of a human adult $\frac{2,\ 1,\ 2,\ 3}{2,\ 1,\ 2,\ 3}$

Structure of Human Tooth

Each tooth contains three broad parts—crown, neck and root. Crown is the region that is exposed above the gum. Roots is the part which is embedded in the socket and neck is the constriction present between crown and root.

Crown is covered by enamel which is the hardest material in the body. Below the enamel, there is a hard, bony tissue that makes the bulk of the tooth, called dentin. It has small canals through which cytoplasmic strands of the cells run. Cement covers and fixes the root in its position. Pulp is the soft connective tissue present in the pulp cavity (central space of the tooth). Pulp comprises blood vessels, nerve fibres, lymph vessels, etc.

> **Info Bytes!**
>
> A diphyodont is an animal with two successive sets of teeth. Example, most mammals.

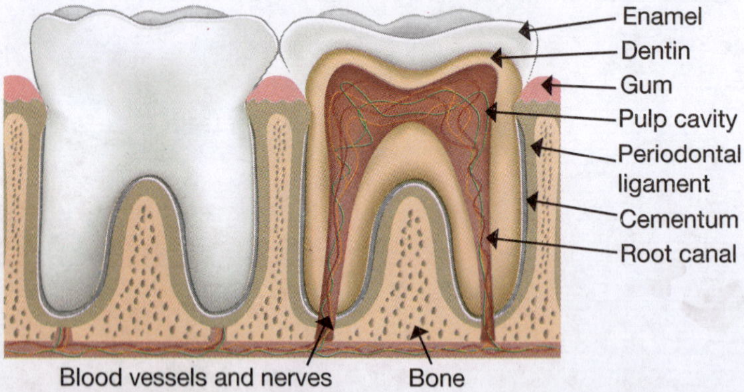

Figure 5.7 Illustration of parts of human tooth

Structure and Function of Tongue

The tongue is a muscular organ inside the mouth cavity. The tongue is covered with a moist tissue called mucosa which is pink in colour. Numerous taste buds are present on the surface of the tongue and they help in tasting the food. Taste buds at different locations on the tongue are responsible for different tastes.

- Tip of the tongue—sweet taste
- Either side of the front part of the tongue—salty taste
- Either side of the posterior part of the tongue—sour taste
- Posterior part of the tongue—bitter taste

Other than tasting, tongue helps in mastication and swallowing of food.

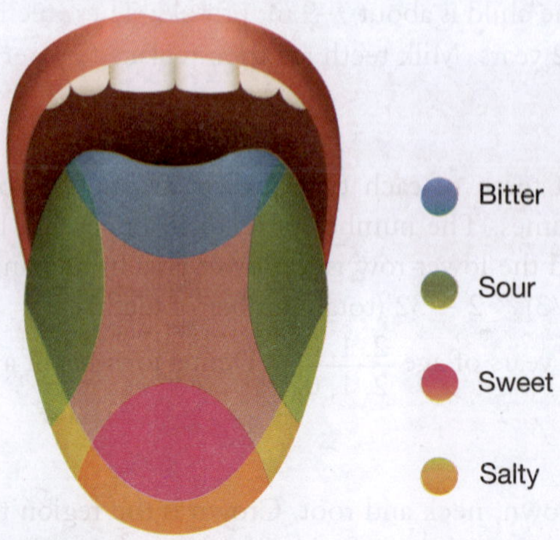

Figure 5.8 Illustration of taste map of human tongue

Pharynx

There is a muscular tube behind the mouth cavity. It is semicircular in shape and is known as pharynx. It connects nasal cavity to the larynx which is a part of the respiratory system. It also connects mouth cavity to oesophagus (food pipe), which is the next part of the digestive tract. There is a muscular flap-like structure at the opening of larynx. It is called epiglottis. It closes the opening of larynx at the time of swallowing of food. Thus, it ensures the entry of food into the food pipe and protects the larynx.

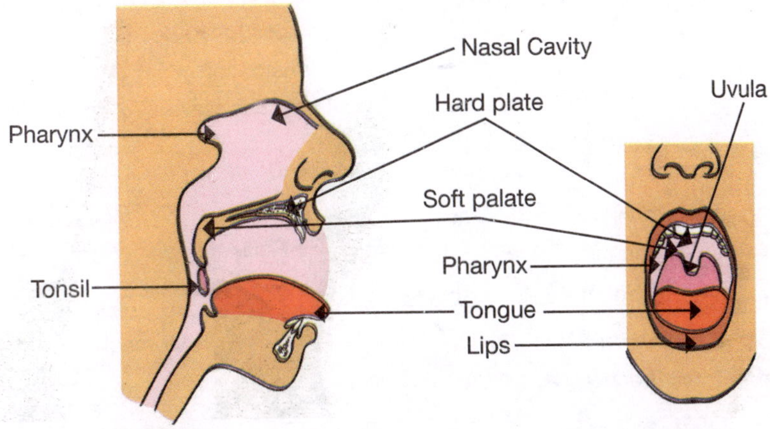

Figure 5.9 Location of pharynx, larynx and epiglottis

Oesophagus

Oesophagus is a straight, muscular tube and about 25-cm long in adults. It provides the connectivity between mouth cavity and the stomach. The wall of the oesophagus contracts to facilitate the transportation of food from mouth cavity into the stomach.

Swallowing and Peristalsis

Swallowing is the process that enables a substance to pass from the mouth, to the pharynx and into the oesophagus, while closing the epiglottis. This process involves many simultaneous activities, three of which are discussed.

1. The tongue is pressed upwards and backwards against the roof of the mouth and this forces the ball of chewed food into the pharynx.
2. Soft palate closes the opening between throat and nasal passage.
3. Larynx (located at the entrance of the wind pipe) is pulled upwards and is brought close to the back of the tongue when epiglottis closes its opening.

Thus, the only passage available to the swallowed food material is the oesophagus.

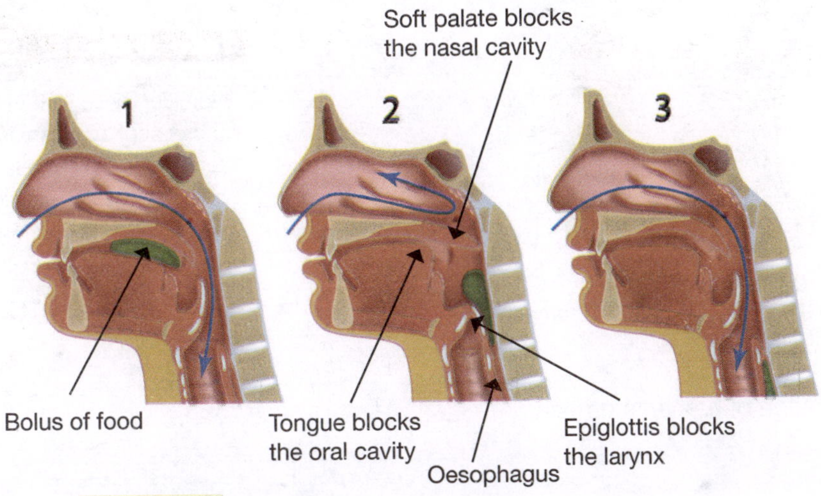

Figure 5.10 Stages involved in the process of swallowing

Info Bytes!

The act or process of swallowing is called deglutition.

Once the swallowed material reaches oesophagus, it is made to pass through the system by progressive wave of contraction and relaxation caused by the muscles of the alimentary canal. Generally, smooth muscles contract which propels and pushes the ball of food along the tract.

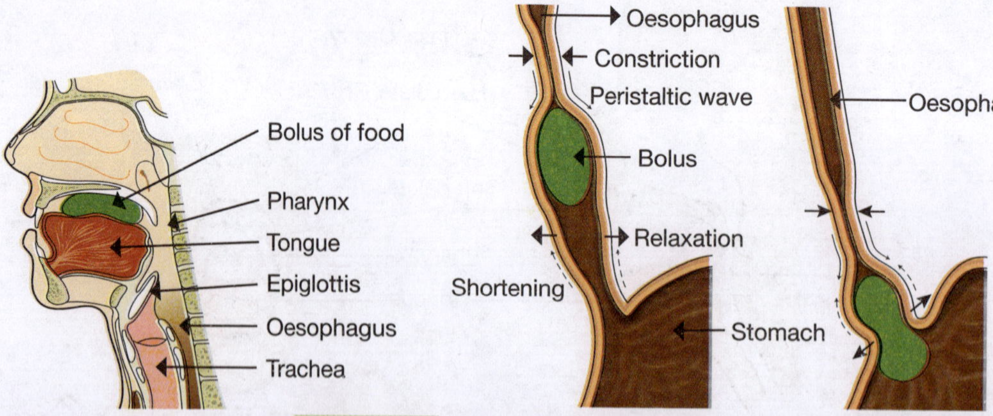

Figure 5.11 Peristalsis movement

Stomach

The stomach is a J-shaped expandable, muscular sac, present in the left side of the upper abdomen. It is located between oesophagus and small intestine. The passage of food from oesophagus to stomach takes place through a valve-like muscle which is known as lower oesophageal sphincter. Several gastric glands are located in the stomach lining which secrete gastric juice.

> **Info Bytes!**
> The opening of stomach into the intestine is called pylorus (Greek: *pylon* meaning gate).

Function

Contraction of stomach muscles churns the food in the stomach. Thus, the food breaks down mechanically in the stomach. The food also gets simplified in the stomach due to the chemical reactions occurring in the presence of gastric juice. Pyrolic sphincter is a ring-like muscular valve which controls the passage of food from the stomach to intestine, the next part of the digestive system. Pyrolic sphincter does not open unless the food is properly churned in the stomach.

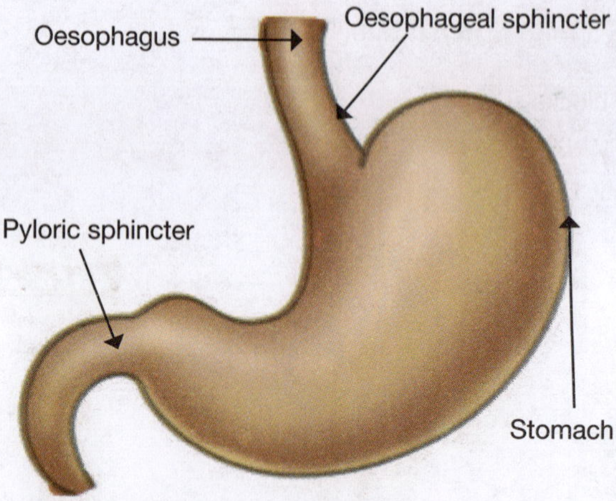

Figure 5.12 Illustration of human stomach

> **Info Bytes!**
> Vomiting occurs when the oesophageal sphincter opens and there is reverse wave of muscular contraction which causes the content to move out from the stomach through mouth.

Small Intestine

Small intestine is a very long and highly convoluted tube located between stomach and large intestine in the digestive system. It is about 6–7 m long and its diameter is about 2.5 cm. It is called small intestine since its diameter is about half the diameter of the large intestine. Numerous tiny finger-like structures are projected inward from the inner lining of the small intestine. These finger-like structures are called villi (singular: villus). The function of villi is to provide a larger surface area to facilitate an effective absorption of nutrients from the small intestine to the blood. Villi are covered by a single layer of epithelial cells. Blood capillaries and small lymph vessels are present in villi. The small intestine us divided into following three regions:

1. Duodenum
2. Jejunum
3. Ileum

Duodenum is the first and the shortest part of the small intestine. It is C-shaped and digestion process gets completed in the duodenum. Jejunum is the middle portion of the small intestine and the primary site for the absorption of the nutrients. Ileum is the last and the longest part of the small intestine where digestion and absorption processes get completed.

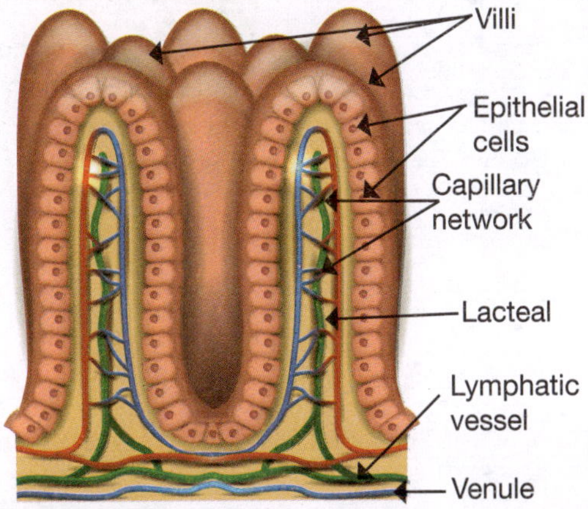

Figure 5.13 Illustration of villi in small intestine.

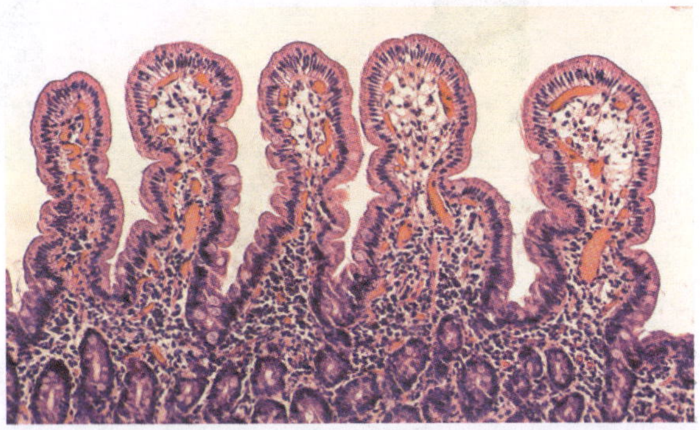

Figure 5.14 Microscopic view of villi

Other than villi, there are digestive glands embedded in the inner lining of the small intestine. These glands secrete digestive enzymes into the intestinal lumen (inside space of a tubular structure) and thus help in the digestion of food.

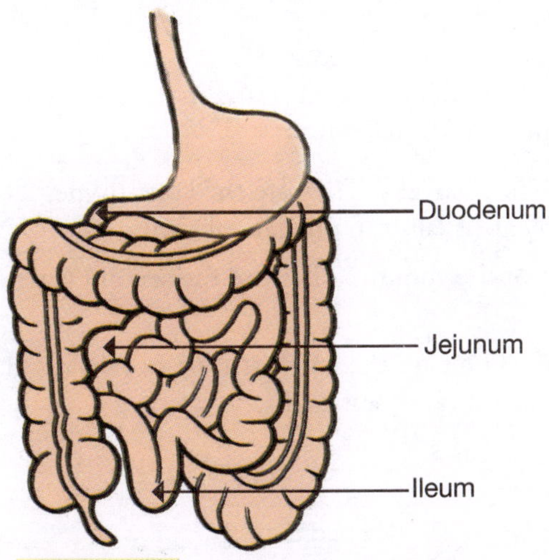

Figure 5.15 Parts of small intestine

Info Bytes!

Most of the digestion occurs in the small intestine rather than stomach.

Large Intestine

The next and the last part of the digestive tract is the large intestine. It is present at the right side of the lower abdomen. It can be divided into three parts which are as follows.

1. **Caecum:** It is a pouch-like structure at the beginning of the large intestine. It is the portion where ileum is connected to large intestine. A finger-like structure called vermiform appendix is protruded from this part of the large intestine. Vermiform appendix is a vestigial organ in human beings.

2. **Colon:** It is the longest part of the large intestine between caecum and rectum. Water is absorbed and undigested residue of the food is processed in this part of the large intestine.
3. **Rectum:** The final segment of large intestine is rectum. Rectum connects colon to anus, the external opening of rectum. A flat, ring-like muscular structure, called anal sphincter, controls the bowel movement.

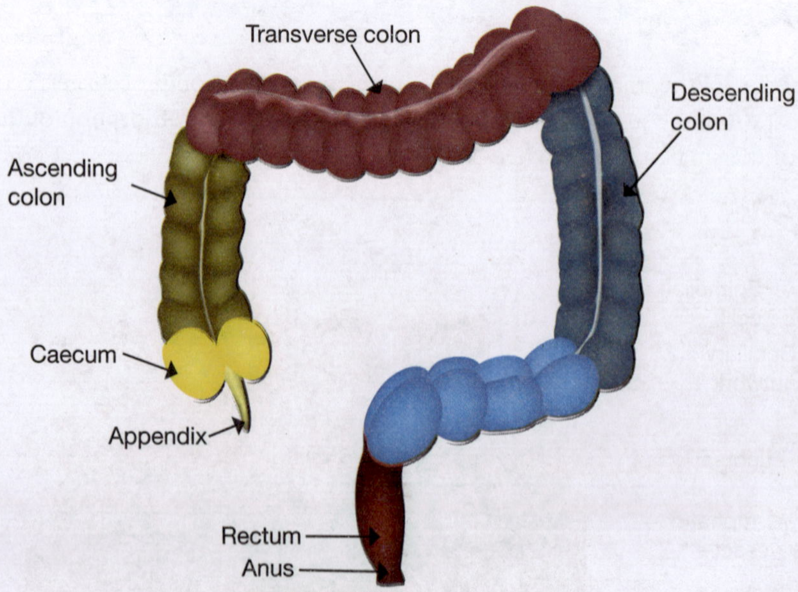

Figure 5.16 Large intestine

> **Info Bytes!**
> Vestigial organs are the organs which have lost their original functions through evolution.

Associated Digestive Glands

The associated digested glands of the digestive system are discussed as follows.

Salivary Glands

Salivary glands are primarily responsible for producing saliva. They are exocrine in nature. That means they secrete their secretions through ducts. There are three pairs of salivary glands, namely

1. **Parotid glands:** They are located within each of our cheeks. They are the largest type of the salivary glands. They facilitate chewing and account for up to 20 per cent of saliva in our buccal cavity.
2. **Submandibular glands:** They lie on the floor of the mouth. They are the second largest salivary glands and account for up to 60 per cent of the saliva.
3. **Sublingual glands:** They lie below the tongue. They are the smallest type of salivary glands and mostly secrete mucus. They produce about only 5 per cent of the saliva in oral cavity.

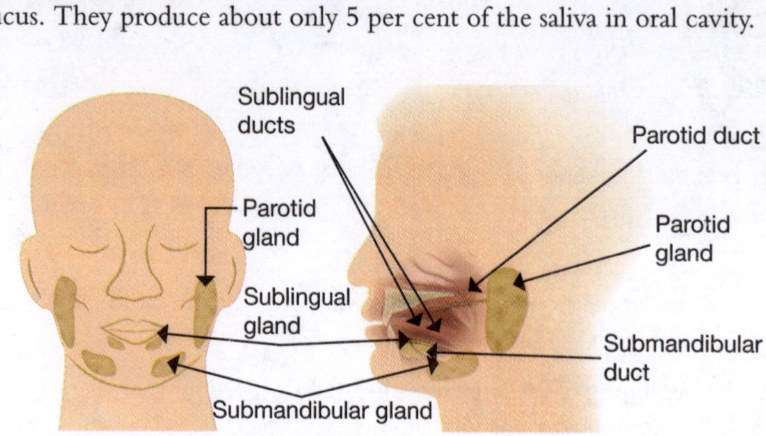

Figure 5.17 Salivary glands

> **Info Bytes!**
> We produce about 1000–1500 mL of saliva everyday.

Saliva

Have you ever noticed that just the sight or taste of our favourite food can cause increased flow of saliva in mouth, also known as watering of the mouth? Saliva is produced by salivary glands located in our mouth. It is slightly acidic in nature with pH value of 6.8. It contains about 99 per cent water. Rest of the substances present in saliva are salt, mucus and enzyme salivary amylase. Functions of saliva are

- Lubricates the inner lining of buccal cavity and tongue to facilitate swallowing.
- Moistens food for easy and comfortable swallowing.
- Helps in digesting starch (a type of carbohydrate) with the help of salivary amylase.
- Helps in formation of bolus.

Info Bytes!

Our saliva contains an enzyme called lysozyme which fights against bacteria.

Pancreas

Pancreas is a lobed and elongated gland. It is located in the left side of upper abdomen and between duodenum and stomach. The main function of pancreas is the secretion of pancreatic juice. Pancreatic juice contains three enzymes which are as follows:

1. **Lypase:** Helps in digestion of fats
2. **Trypsin:** Helps in digestion of proteins
3. **Amylase:** Helps in digestion of starch

Pancreas is connected to the duodenum, the first part of small intestine through a duct, called common bile duct.

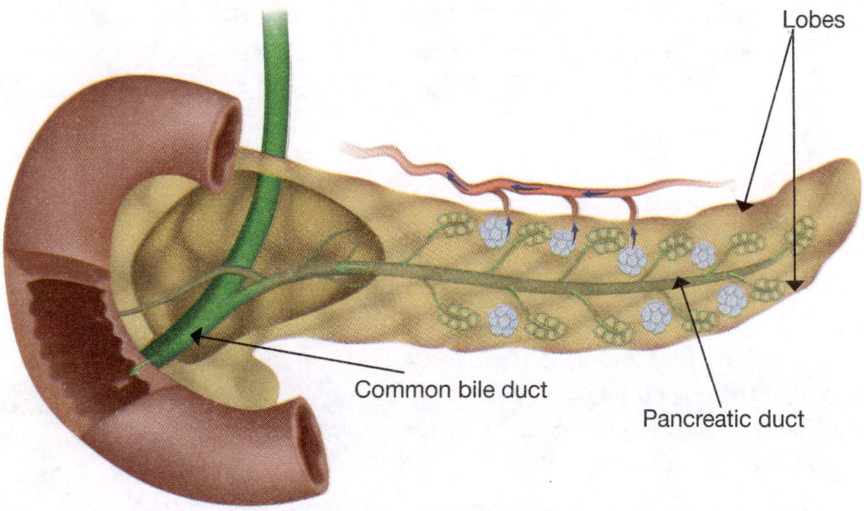

Figure 5.18 Pancreas

Pancreas also secretes hormones such as insulin and glucagon. Insulin helps in the metabolism of carbohydrates and thus, controls the glucose level in blood. Glucagon elevates the glucose level in blood. Since the effects of glucagon and insulin are opposite, they work in partnership to optimize the glucose level in blood.

Info Bytes!

The process by which large fat molecules are broken down into small, tiny droplets is known as emulsification, which increases the surface area of fats to facilitate the process of digestion.

Liver

Liver is located in the right part of the upper abdomen. It is the largest gland in the human body, reddish-brown in colour and triangular in shape. Structurally, the liver can be divided into two portions, the left lobe and the right lobe. Gall bladder is a small pouch-like structure located just below the liver. Liver produces bile, a yellowish-brown fluid which gets stored in gall bladder. Bile is released in duodenum through common bile duct.

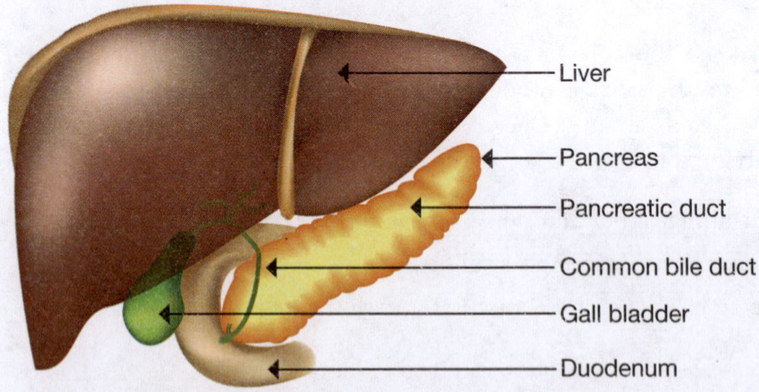

Figure 5.19 Liver–Gall bladder–Pancreas

Functions of Liver

Following are the major functions of liver:

- **Formation of bile:** Bile salts present in bile help in emulsification and absorption of fat in the small intestine.

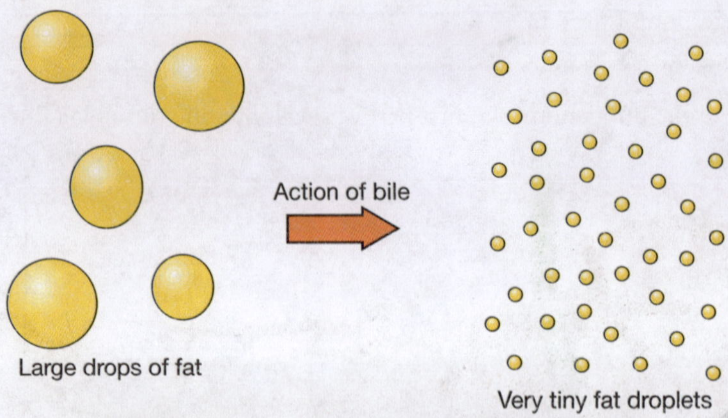

Figure 5.20 Emulsification: Action of bile on fats

- **Regulation of blood sugar:** Liver stores glucose in the form of glycogen after the intake of food. When there is no intake of food in human body, liver supplies glucose in the blood by hydrolyzing glycogen. Thus, glucose level in the blood is maintained throughout the day in our body.
- **Storage of iron:** Numerous red blood cells get disintegrated in liver every day.

  Red blood cells contain haemoglobin, and iron is an essential component. During the decomposition of red blood cells, iron content of haemoglobin gets stored in liver.

  The stored iron in liver can replenish the iron requirement of our body.
- **Deamination:** Excess amino acids (simplified forms of proteins) in our body undergo decomposition to form toxic substances. Liver converts these toxic substances to a relatively less harmful product called urea. Urea is then excreted by kidney. The process of conversion of excess amino acids to urea by liver is called deamination.
- **Manufacture of fibrinogen:** Fibrinogen is a blood protein which is required for clotting of blood. Liver produces fibrinogen and releases it into the blood.
- **Detoxication:** Liver separates toxic substances and waste material from blood, converts them into less harmful products. Finally, they are excreted through urine.
- **Storage of vitamins:** Liver can store fat-soluble vitamins like A, D, E, K and supply them when our body needs.

Info Bytes!

Stomach growling (or) borborygmic is the result of peristalsis in. the stomach and small intestines, and happens all the time, but it is just louder when your stomach is empty because there is no food to muffle it.

- **Production of heparin:** Liver produces heparin, an anticoagulant which prevents coagulation of blood.
- **Role of liver in maintaining body temperature:** Liver is the site for different metabolic activities which release heat energy. This heat energy is circulated all over the body and thus, the body temperature is maintained.

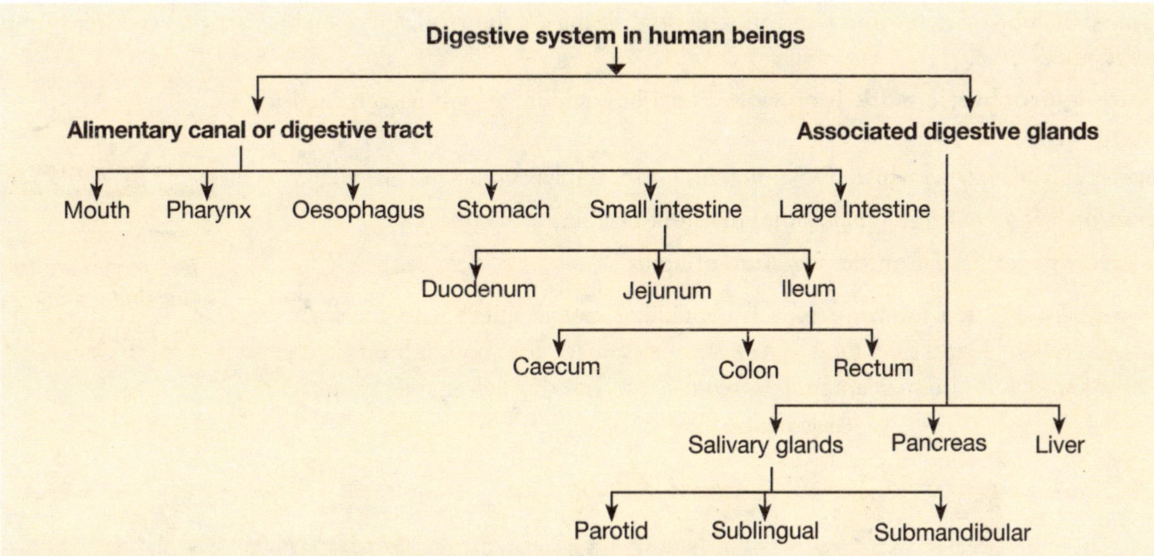

Figure 5.21 Parts of human digestive system

Process of Digestion

Digestion of food takes place in different parts of the digestive system like mouth, stomach and small intestine. Enzymes secreted from different digestive glands play an important role in digestion. Enzymes are natural, proteinaceous chemical compounds produced in the cells of living organisms and act as biocatalysts to enhance the rate of biochemical reactions without themselves undergoing any change. Enzymes are nutrient specific. A particular enzyme acts on a specific type of nutrient. Enzymes act effectively in a particular range of temperature (35–40°C) as well as in a particular degree of acidity or alkalinity.

Digestion in Mouth

After the intake of food inside the mouth, it is masticated with help of teeth. Mastication of food increases the surface area of food particles. Salivary glands secrete saliva which mixes with the masticated food. Saliva contains the enzyme, amylase which converts complex carbohydrates present in the food into simpler disaccharide molecules, called maltose. Saliva also moistens the food so that the chewed and ground food particles get the shape of a ball which can roll down. This ball-like mixture of food and saliva is called bolus. Bolus enters oesophagus through pharynx with the help of tongue. During swallowing, epiglottis closes the passage of the larynx (a part of respiratory system) to prevent the entry of food into the respiratory tract. Successive contraction and relaxation of the muscular wall of oesophagus transport the food into the stomach through lower oesophageal sphincter. This process of involuntary movement of muscles of digestive tract for the transportation of food is called peristalsis.

> **Info Bytes!**
> Cows have stomach with four compartments.

$$\text{Starch} \xrightarrow[\text{pH 6.8}]{\text{Salivary amylase}} \text{Maltose}$$

Figure 5.22 Action of salivary amylase on starch

Digestion in Stomach

After the entry of food in stomach, the gastric juice secreted by stomach mixes with the food. Muscular movement of stomach helps in further churning of food. It ensures thorough mixing of gastric juice and the food. The food along with gastric juice forms a creamy fluid. Gastric juice contains the following:

- **Mucus:** It lubricates the food and protects the lining of the stomach from the action of other components of gastric juice.
- **Dilute hydrochloric acid:** It provides an acidic medium which is congenial for the enzymes to be activated.
- **Pepsin:** It is an enzyme which breaks proteins into a simpler substance, called peptone.
- **Rennin:** It is an enzyme which simplifies milk protein.
- **Gastric lipase:** It helps in the digestion of lipids.

Info Bytes!

Inactive forms of pepsin and rennin are called pepsinogen and prorennin, respectively.

The partially digested food in stomach containing gastric juices is in the form of semi-fluid pulp called chyme. The food remains in the stomach for about 3 hours and gets transported to duodenum in small amounts at regular intervals through pyrolic sphincter.

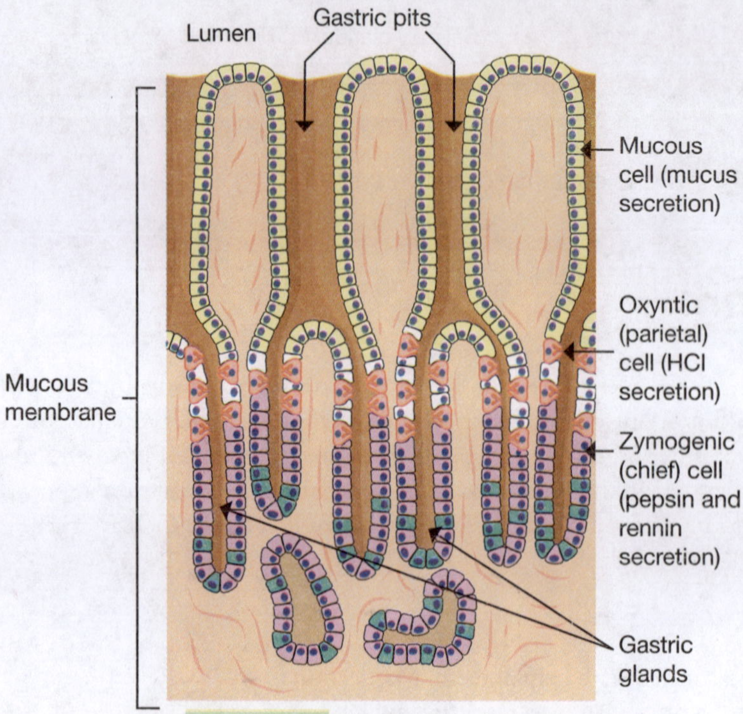

Figure 5.23 Illustration of gastric glands

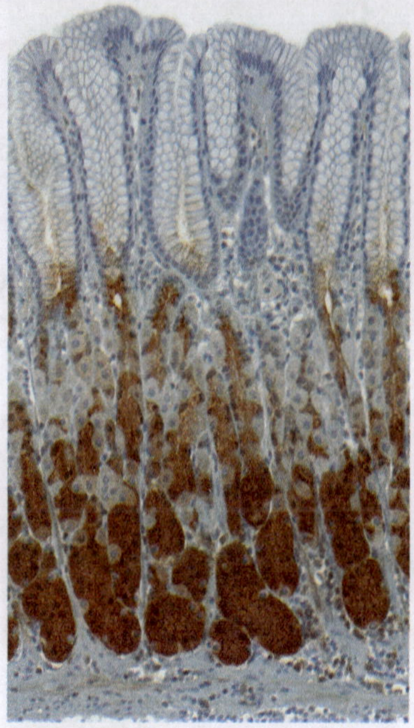

Figure 5.24 Microscopic view of gastric glands showing pepsinogen (brown)

(1) Pepsinogen $\xrightarrow{\text{HCl}}$ Pepsin

Proteins $\xrightarrow{\text{Pepsin}}$ Peptides

(2) Prorennin $\xrightarrow{\text{HCl}}$ Rennin

Milk protein $\xrightarrow{\text{Rennin}}$ Paracasein

Figure 5.25 Action of enzymes present in gastric juice

Digestion in Small Intestine

The partially digested food in the form of chyme moves into duodenum which is the first part of the small intestine. The chyme is acidic in nature. When the food enters duodenum, it mixes with two types of juices. One is bile juice secreted by liver and the other one is pancreatic juice secreted by pancreas. These juices enter duodenum through common bile duct. Gall bladder stores bile juice and releases it into duodenum.

Info Bytes!
Rennin is absent from the stomach of adult humans.

Table 5.1 Activity of bile and pancreatic juices

Components of Bile Juice	Action
Sodium salts	• Reduction in acidity of chyme (creamy fluid of food formed in stomach) • Providing an alkaline medium congenial for the activity of enzymes • Emulsification of fats; providing a larger surface area for easy digestion
Bile pigments (biliverdin and bilirubin)	• Yellow colour of bile pigments imparts colour to bile juice, intestinal content and faeces. • They are waste products obtained from haemoglobin of disintegrated red blood cells. • They have no physiological role.
Components of Pancreatic Juice	**Action**
Trypsin (an enzyme)	• Converts proteins to peptones • Also converts peptones to peptides and amino acids
Amylase (an enzyme)	• Converts complex carbohydrates to simpler molecules, maltose
Lipase (an enzyme)	• Converts fats into fatty acid and glycerol

Digestion in duodenum takes place in alkaline medium. In duodenum, alkaline medium is obtained due to secretion of succus entericus. The intestinal juice secreted from the digestive glands embedded in the lining of small intestine is called succus entericus. It contains water, bicarbonate ions and enzymes which are effective in alkaline medium. The bicarbonate ions convert the food from acidic to alkaline medium.

Table 5.2 Enzymes present in succus entericus and their functions

Enzymes	Functions
Erepsin	Peptones to amino acids
Maltase	Maltose to glucose (the simplest sugar)
Sucrase	Sucrose to glucose and fructose
Lactase	Lactose to glucose and galactose
Lipase	Fats to fatty acids and glycerol

Thus, the digestion starts in mouth, continues in stomach and gets completed in small intestine. Digested food is then absorbed from the intestine into the blood.

Absorption of Food

Absorption is the process by which the products of digestion are taken into the blood stream. Jejunum is the site for most of the process of absorption. In jejunum, the absorption of amino acids, glucose, vitamins, carbohydrates, etc., takes place. Then the food passes into the last part of the small intestine, that is, ileum. The products of digestion which were not absorbed in the jejunum are absorbed into the blood in ileum. Ileum is mainly responsible for the absorption of vitamin B_{12} and bile salts. The presence of villi, finger-like projections on the inner lining of small intestine makes the process of absorption very effective by providing a larger surface area. The digested food present in the intestinal lumen passes over villi and the nutrients diffuse through the epithelial cells and finally enter the bloodstream through the blood vessels. Glucose, amino acids, vitamins and minerals reach the liver by absorption followed by transportation through hepatic portal vein, a part of circulatory system. Fatty acids and glycerol are absorbed by lacteals and finally reach the blood stream. Lacteals are the lymph vessels (part of circulatory system) of the small intestine and they absorb digested fats. After the absorption of different nutrients in the small intestine, the remaining undigested food moves into large intestine. No enzymes are secreted in large intestine.

The functions of large intestine are absorption of water, storage of undigested food in the rectum and egesting it through the anus.

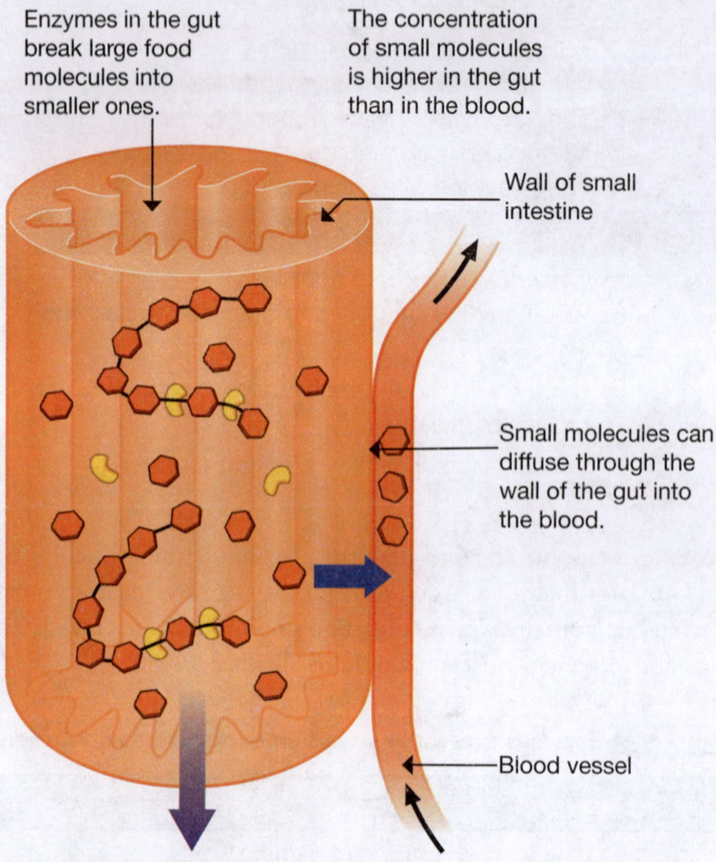

Figure 5.26 Diagram showing how food molecules diffuse from gut into blood

Assimilation of Food

The absorbed food reaches different parts of the body by the bloodstream and becomes the integral component of protoplasm of the body cells. The nutrients are used for growth, repair of damaged tissues and the production of energy. This process is called assimilation of food.

Assimilation of Carbohydrates

Simple sugars are utilized for the generation of energy which is required for different life processes. Excess simple sugar molecules get stored in the liver and in muscle cells in the form of a complex carbohydrate called glycogen. If there is deficiency of glucose in blood, glycogen gets converted to glucose and replenishes it.

Proteins

Amino acids, the basic units of proteins are utilized for the synthesis of different types of proteins. These proteins are used for growth and repair of damaged tissues.

Fats

Fatty acids and glycerol get converted to fats which are stored in adipose tissues. Fats are readily available as the source of energy in our body.

Egestion

The digested food is assimilated in the body after digestion. The undigested food is eliminated from the body by the process of egestion.

The undigested matter of the ingested food is called faeces. It is thrown out from the rectum though anus. This process is called defaecation. The formation of faeces from waste material and expulsion of it from the body is known as egestion. It is the last stage of the process of nutrition.

Info Bytes!

Bacterial action in faeces is responsible for their odour.

Table 5.3 Summary of digestion in various parts of digestive system

Location	Secretion	Enzyme	Substrate	Product/Result
Mouth	Saliva	Salivary amylase	Starch	Maltose
Oesophagus	–	–	–	–
Stomach	Gastric juice	Pepsin	Proteins	Large polypeptides
		Rennin	Milk protein	Curdling of milk
Duodenum	Bile	–	Fats	Emulsification of fats, alkalinity to food
	Pancreatic juice	Amylopsin	Starch	Maltose
		Trypsin + Chymotrypsin + carboxypeptidase	Large polypeptides	Small polypeptides
		Lipase	Emulsified fats	Fatty acids and glycerol
Ileum	Intestinal juice	Erepsin	Peptides	Amino acids
		Maltase	Maltose	Glucose
		Sucrase	Sucrose	Glucose and fructose
		Lactase	Lactose	Glucose and galactose
		Lipase	Fats	Fatty acids and glycerol
Colon	–	–	–	Absorbs water
Rectum	–	–	–	Temporarily stores undigested food

Quick Recap

✔ **Explain the stages of the nutritional process in the digestive system. How does each of these stages ensure that food is efficiently broken down and assimilated into our bodies?**

Ingestion (taking in food), digestion (breaking down food into simpler substances), absorption (transport of digested nutrients into the blood), assimilation (cell utilization of absorbed nutrients), and egestion are the stages of nutrition in the digestive system (expelling undigested wastes). Each stage is significant. Ingestion allows food to be consumed, digestion breaks down complex food materials, absorption transports nutrients to the blood, assimilation uses them for growth and energy, and egestion prevents waste accumulation.

✔ **Explain the function of the alimentary canal and its associated digestive glands. How do they work together to aid digestion?**

The alimentary canal, also known as the digestive tract, is the pathway through which food travels while being digested. Digestive juices are produced by associated digestive glands such as the salivary glands, liver, and pancreas. The salivary glands produce saliva, which begins carbohydrate digestion, the liver produces bile, which emulsifies fats, and the pancreas produces digestive enzymes. The canal and glands work together to ensure efficient nutrient breakdown and absorption.

✔ **What does it mean when the small intestine is described as 'long and highly convoluted'? What role does this anatomical feature play in digestion and absorption?**

Because it is an elongated, winding tube, the small intestine is referred to as 'long and highly convoluted.' This design increases the surface area of the product, which improves nutrient absorption. Villi and microvilli on its walls increase absorption even further. As a result, its structure ensures that the maximum amount of nutrients are absorbed from the food we consume.

Excretory System in Humans

During digestion and other life processes, many biochemical reactions take place. These biochemical reactions generate a lot of substances. Some of the products are not useful to our body and a few of them are toxic in nature. Moreover, water content and the concentration of ions in our body also vary in each of the processes. Our digestive system, respiratory system, skin and excretory system play significant roles to maintain an ionic balance and right proportion of water in our body and also remove the toxic substances from the body.

Wastes Generated in Human Body

Different waste products generated in human body are as follows:

- **Carbon dioxide and water**: During respiration, carbon dioxide and water are formed due to oxidation of glucose. The excess water and carbon dioxide are released from our body through **lungs, a part of respiratory system**.
- **Nitrogenous wastes**: The excess amino acid which cannot be stored in our body undergoes decomposition. Decomposition of amino acids generates different nitrogenous wastes like ammonia, urea and uric acid. Among them, the toxicity of ammonia is the maximum. As soon as ammonia is produced, liver converts it into urea which is less harmful. Urea and uric acid are removed from the body through kidneys, part of excretory system.
- **Bile pigments**: Decomposition of haemoglobin, present in red blood cells generates bile pigments in liver and the cells of the liver release bile pigments into bile juice. Bile pigments are removed from our body through faeces and urine.

- **Excess salts and vitamins**: Excess salts and vitamins are released from the body through kidneys. Excess salts and water also get excreted through skin. Sweat glands are present in the skin and secrete excess salts, water and urea which are not required by our body.

Thus, the main excretory organs in human beings are:

1. Lungs
2. Skin
3. Kidneys
4. Liver

Info Bytes!

Osmoregulation is the maintenance of constant osmotic pressure in the fluids of an organism by regulating the concentrations of water and salt.

The major part of excretion of harmful substances (nitrogenous wastes) takes place with the help of kidneys. The nitrogenous waste products generated in different parts of the body are carried by blood. Then the blood gets purified by a pair of kidneys and is expelled out in the form of urine. The formation of urine in the kidneys is a complicated multistep process. Hence, the system associated with the formation of urine in the kidneys is more appropriately called urinary system. Excretion and osmoregulation are the two major functions of excretory system. The process of expelling the toxic and unwanted wastes from the body of an organism is called excretion.

Excretory Organs in Humans

As discussed, excretion in humans is carried out with the help of kidneys, lungs, skin and liver. Let us study each of them in detail.

Lungs

The exchange of substances between an organism and its surroundings eventually occurs at the cellular level. The inputs/resources that an animal cell requires, such as O_2, enter the cytoplasm by crossing the cell membrane and metabolic by-product, CO_2 exit the cell by crossing the same. We rely on specialized system, respiratory system that carries out the exchange of these gases. Lungs are the respiratory organs which act as the surface that is responsible for providing oxygen to the bloodstream and taking in carbon dioxide from the blood stream. Hence, they are involved in excreting CO_2 out of our body.

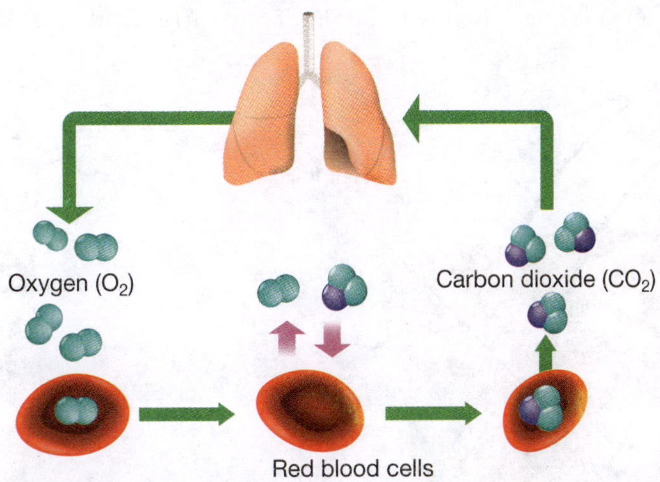

Figure 5.27 Both oxygen and carbon dioxide are transported around the body in the blood—from the lungs to the organs and again to the lungs.

Gaseous Exchange in the Alveolus of the Lungs

The lungs eliminate carbon dioxide, a byproduct of cellular metabolism, from the body. In the lungs, the primary site for gaseous exchange is the alveolus (plural: alveoli). These are tiny, balloon-like structures that provide a large surface area for gases to diffuse across. The tiny alveoli in the lungs are sites where O_2 from the inhaled air diffuses into the bloodstream. Simultaneously, CO_2 from the bloodstream diffuses into the alveoli to be exhaled. Factors such as the thinness of the alveolar and capillary walls, the extensive surface area of the alveoli, and their rich blood supply ensure efficient gaseous exchange.

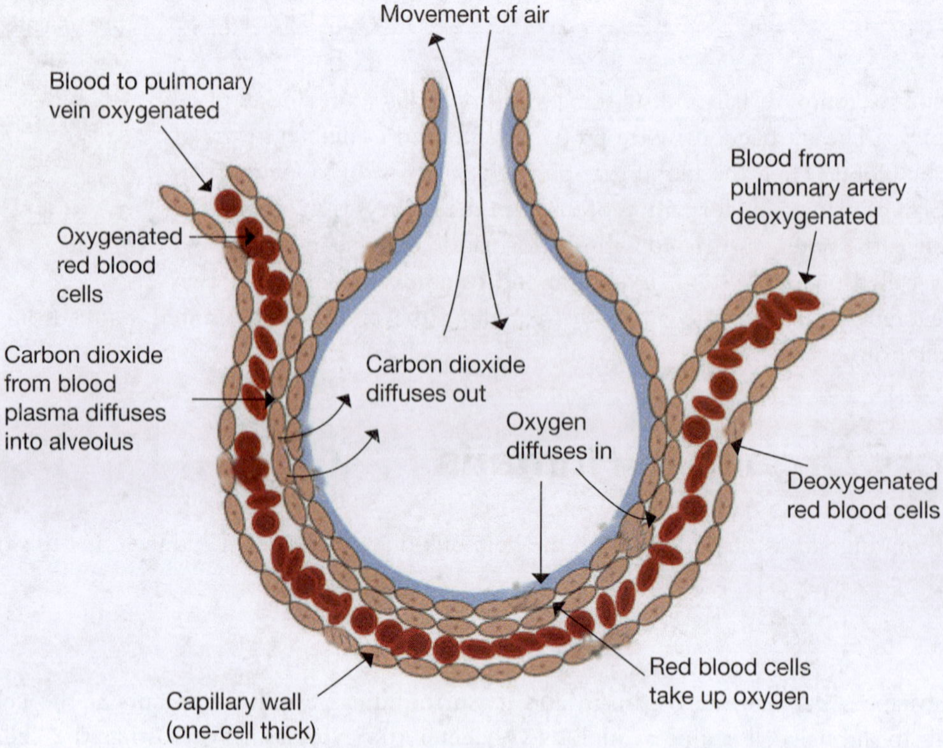

Figure 5.28 Gaseous exchange in alveolus of the lungs

Skin

The sweat (also called sudoriferous) glands are small tubular glands situated within and under the skin. They discharge sweat by minute openings on the surface of the skin. Sweat glands are primarily responsible for regulating body temperature. The sweat is a transparent colourless fluid with odour. It also carries with it small amounts of nitrogenous wastes, excess salts and water.

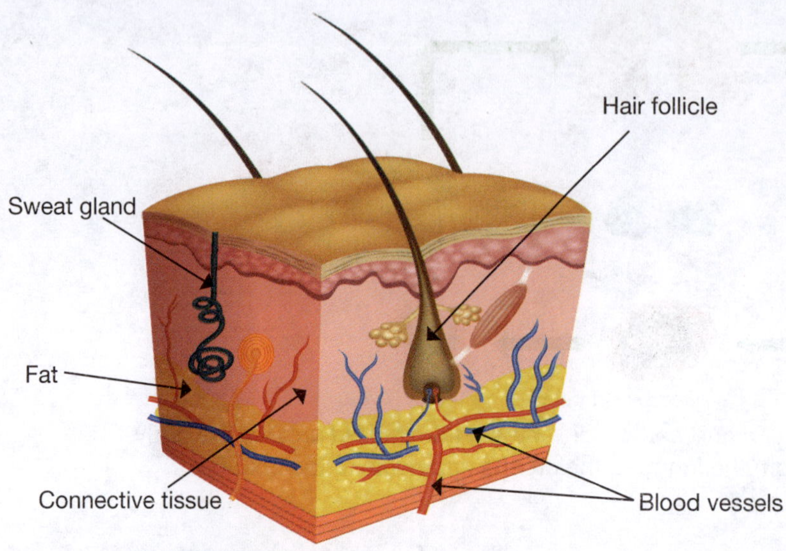

Figure 5.29 Illustration of layer of skin with sweat gland

Info Bytes!

The skin is an excretory organ and can release up to 3 gallons of sweat in hot weather.

Liver

Liver changes the disintegrated haemoglobin of the aged red blood cells into bile pigments, biliverdin and bilirubin. These pigments are passed into the alimentary canal with the bile for elimination in the faeces. Liver also excretes cholesterol and certain drugs through the bile. Urea (nitrogenous waste) is formed in the liver by a cyclic process called urea cycle. The amino acids that are not needed in the body are deaminated by an enzyme producing ammonia (highly toxic) which is converted to urea.

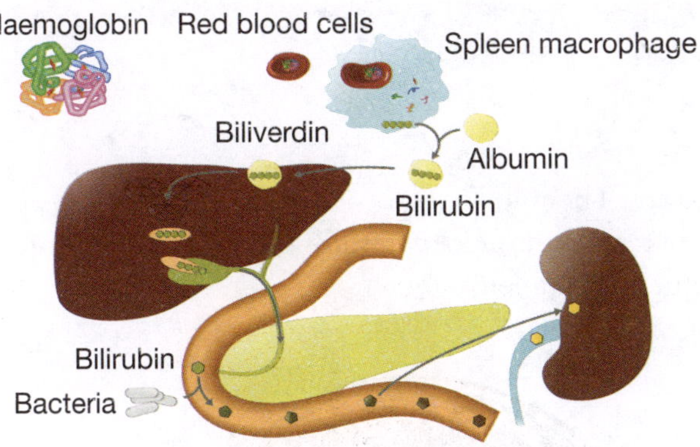

Figure 5.30 Metabolism of bilirubin

> **Info Bytes!**
> Jaundice is caused as a result of high bilirubin levels in body. High bilirubin levels in adults generally means that there may be a problem involving the red blood cells, liver or gallbladder.

Kidneys

The major function of the pair of kidneys is the separation of waste from bloodstream in the form of urine. Kidneys are in fact part of the urinary system which comprises other organs, such as ureters, urinary bladder and urethra.

- **Ureters:** There is a pair of ureters which connect kidneys to urinary bladder. Each ureter is attached to one kidney and carries urine from the kidney to urinary bladder.
- **Urinary bladder:** It receives urine through ureters and acts as a temporary storage organ for urine.
- **Urethra:** A urethra is a tube-like structure which originates from urinary bladder. It carries urine from urinary bladder and expels it outside the body. There are two muscles, called urethral sphincters which control the expulsion of urine from urinary bladder to the urethra.

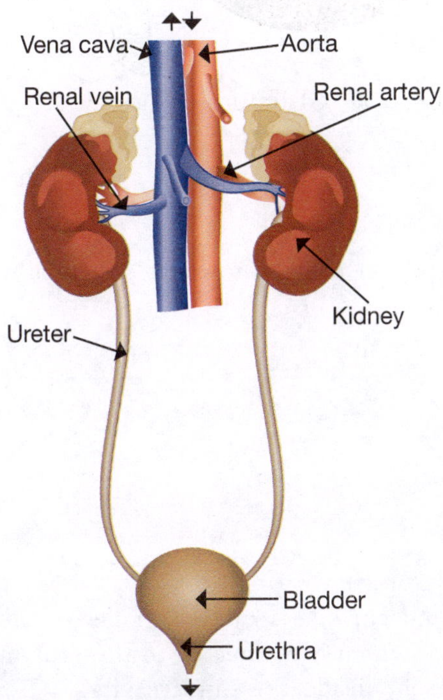

Figure 5.31 Urinary system

> **Info Bytes!**
> The urinary system removes the wastes in blood and excretes urine as a result.
> The excretory system comprises the urinary system and other excretory organs such as the lungs, skin and liver.

Location and Structure of Kidneys

Kidneys are bean-shaped organs which are reddish brown in colour. They are located in the upper abdominal cavity on the either side of the backbone. These are protected by ribs. The position of the left kidney is slightly higher than that of the right kidney. This is due to the presence of large liver on the right side. The length of each kidney is 10 cm and the width is 3.5 cm.

Each kidney has an intricate inner structure and it can be divided into following three main regions.

1. Cortex, the outer region
2. Medulla, the middle region
3. Renal pelvis, the innermost region

Cortex, the outermost region has granular texture. The middle region, medulla is composed of cone-shaped structures called renal pyramids. The broader bases of the pyramids are aligned towards the cortex. The structural and functional unit of a kidney is a nephron. Each kidney is constituted of numerous nephrons.

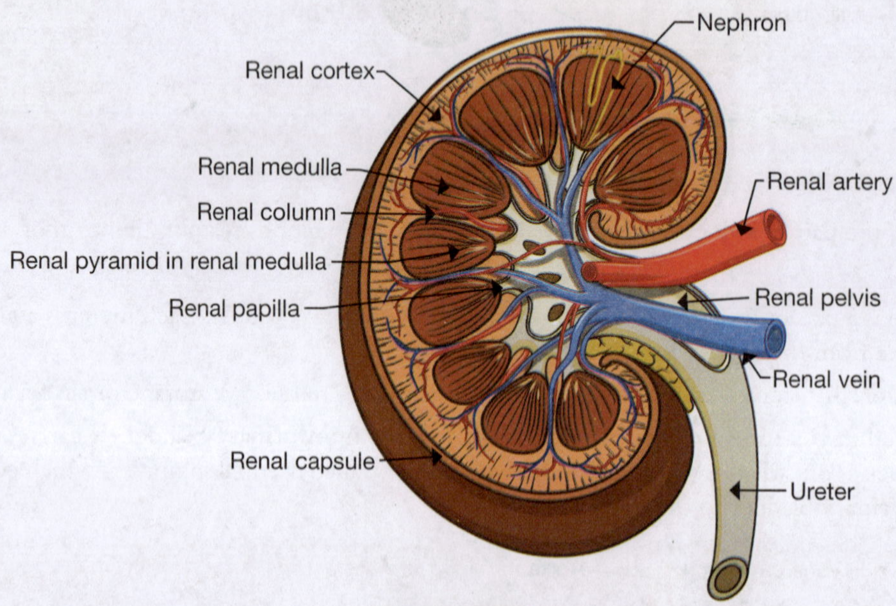

Figure 5.32 Structure of kidney

Nephron

Each kidney contains more than one million nephrons. A nephron is the microscopic, structural and functional unit of the kidney. Each nephron consists of four regions.

1. Bowman's capsule
2. Proximal convoluted tubule
3. Loop of Henle
4. Distal convoluted tubule

Bowman's Capsule

Bowman's capsule is a thin-walled (one-cell thick) round cup-like structure. It lies in the cortex region of the kidney. Inside Bowman's capsule, there is a hollow space which is connected to the proximal convoluted tube. A network of blood capillaries, called glomerulus is present inside the outer cavity of Bowman's capsule. Both

Bowman's capsule and glomerulus together are called Malpighian capsule. The next part of the nephron is proximal convoluted tubule.

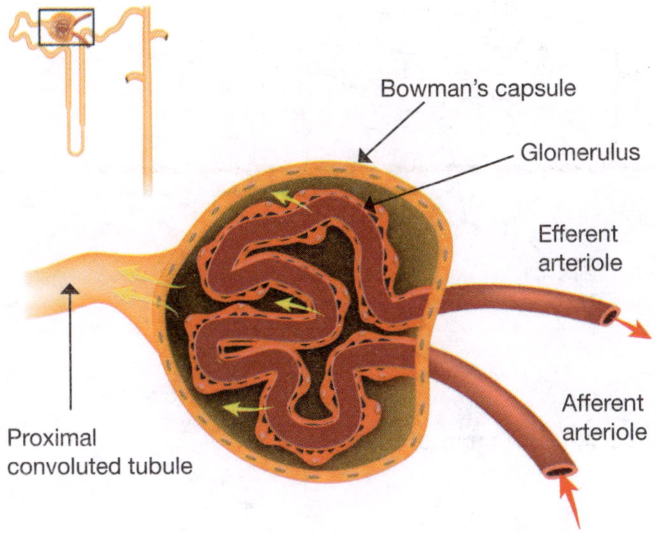

Figure 5.33 Magnified illustration of a Malpighian capsule

Info Bytes!

The Bowman's capsule was identified by Sir William Bowman in 1842. Hence, it is named after him.

Proximal Convoluted Tubule

Other than Malpighian capsule, the rest of the part of the nephron is called renal tubule. Proximal convoluted tubule is the first part of the renal tubule. Cortex region appears dotted internally due to the presence of this part of the nephron. Proximal convoluted tubule can be divided into two parts based on their functions.

1. **Pars convoluta**: It is the first segment and it receives the urine from glomerulus.
2. **Pars recta**: It is the rest of the part of proximal tubule.

Proximal tubule passes the urine to the next part of renal tubule, which is Loop of Henle.

Loop of Henle

It is U-shaped and constitutes the middle part of the renal tubule. Loop of Henle is the connectivity between the proximal and distal convoluted tubules. This portion of renal tubule passes through the medulla and then turns back to the cortex region again. Loop of Henle continues to distal convoluted tubule.

Distal Convoluted Tubule

It is the last part of the renal tubule as well as the nephron. The lining of distal tubule is constituted of simple cuboidal cells which are shorter than those which constitute the lining of proximal tubule. Hence, the lumen in distal convoluted tubule appears wider than that in proximal convoluted tubule. Distal tubule touches glomerulus through a thickened area called macula densa. Distal convoluted tubules of many nephrons combine to form the collecting duct. The urine collected in collecting duct transports urine to renal pelvis via medulla.

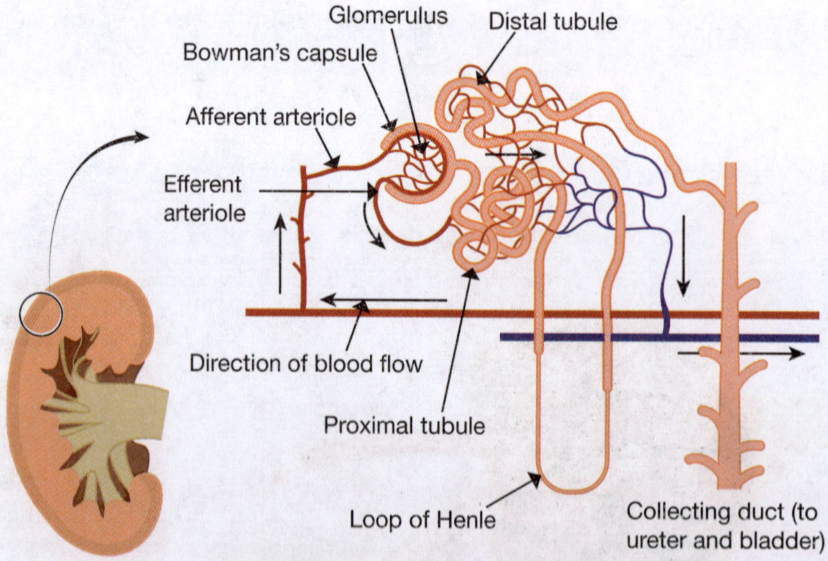

Figure 5.34 Structure of nephron

Blood Supply to the Kidney Through Nephrons

Blood supply to the network of nephrons in the kidneys can be explained with help of following points.

- Renal artery, a part of circulatory system, supplies blood to the kidney through nephrons.
- The renal artery undergoes divisions and subdivisions to form afferent arteriole.
- From afferent arteriole, a bunch of blood capillaries, called glomerulus is evolved.
- Glomerulus is present in the outer cavity of Bowman's capsule and the blood capillaries of glomerulus rejoin to form efferent arteriole.
- Inflow of blood takes place from the afferent arteriole to glomerulus and outflow of blood from glomerulus takes place through efferent arteriole.
- Efferent arteriole is again divided into branches which surround renal tubule for the exchange of water, different ions and waste material.
- These branches of blood vessels reunite to form a vein.
- During the flow of blood through afferent arteriole, efferent arteriole, glomerulus and the network of blood vessels surrounding the renal tubule, exchange of water, nitrogenous waste, salts, etc., takes place. Thus, the urine is formed in kidney.

Formation of Urine

Primary function of nephrons is to form urine. Urine is a liquid by-product of metabolism in our body. It flows from the kidneys through the ureters to the urinary bladder. Urine contains about 95 per cent water. Other constituents of urine include urea, ions, such as chloride, sodium, potassium, creatinine and other inorganic and organic compounds. Formation of urine can be described in three stages. These are:

1. **Ultrafiltration:** Occurs in glomerulus
2. **Selective reabsorption:** Occurs in proximal convoluted tube
3. **Tubular secretion:** Occurs in distal convoluted tube

Info Bytes!

Yellow colour of urine is due to presence of pigment, urochrome in it.

Ultrafiltration

The process of ultrafiltration involves the filtration of body solutes and fluids from the blood. This stage can described in the following points.

- The diameter of efferent arteriole is smaller than that of afferent arteriole, and hence, the bloodstream inside glomerulus is under pressure.
- Due to this pressure, water and solutes pass through a membrane and enters Bowman's capsule.
- Blood cells, protein and fat molecules remain in the bloodstream.
- These are carried forward into the blood circulation through efferent arteriole.
- Thus, the blood passing through efferent arteriole is more concentrated.
- The fluid that comes out of Bowman's capsule and entering renal tubule is called glomerular filtrate.
- The glomerular filtrate is an extremely dilute solution containing a lot of useful materials such as glucose, amino acids, etc., along with urea which is a waste material.

Selective Reabsorption

The process of selective reabsorption involves the absorption of certain components of the glomerular filtrate back into the blood as the filtrate flows through the nephrons of the kidney.

This stage can described in the following points:

- Selective reabsorption takes place when filtrate generated from glomerulus passes through proximal convoluted tubule, the next part of the nephron.
- This filtrate contains many useful materials like different ions, glucose, amino acids along with waste material.
- Reabsorption of the useful material takes place from the filtrate in proximal tubule to the bloodstream in the surrounding blood vessels.
- Major part of the water is reabsorbed by the process of osmosis.
- Some ions like sodium and chloride, glucose and amino acids which are required by our body, are reabsorbed by active transport system. Energy is required for such type of transportation.
- The next step of urine formation takes place in distal convoluted tubule.

Info Bytes!

Approximately 180 L of glomerular filtrate is formed by both kidneys but about 99% of it is reabsorbed and the remaining 1% becomes urine.

Tubular Secretion

The process of tubular secretion involves addition of certain material to the tubular fluid by removing excessive quantities of certain dissolved substances from the body. This stage can described in the following points:

- In this step of urine formation, the unwanted ions and nitrogenous waste materials like uric acid, ammonia, urea, creatinine, etc., are passed from the blood vessels to renal tubule.
- Some substances like potassium ions and any foreign chemicals, such as medicines, are passed into the urine, in this step.
- The passage of these substances involves the activity of the cells of the tubular wall. Hence, this process is called tubular secretion.
- Then the urine so formed passes through distal convoluted tube and reaches the collecting duct.
- In normal adults, the volume of urine formed every minute is approximately 120 mL.

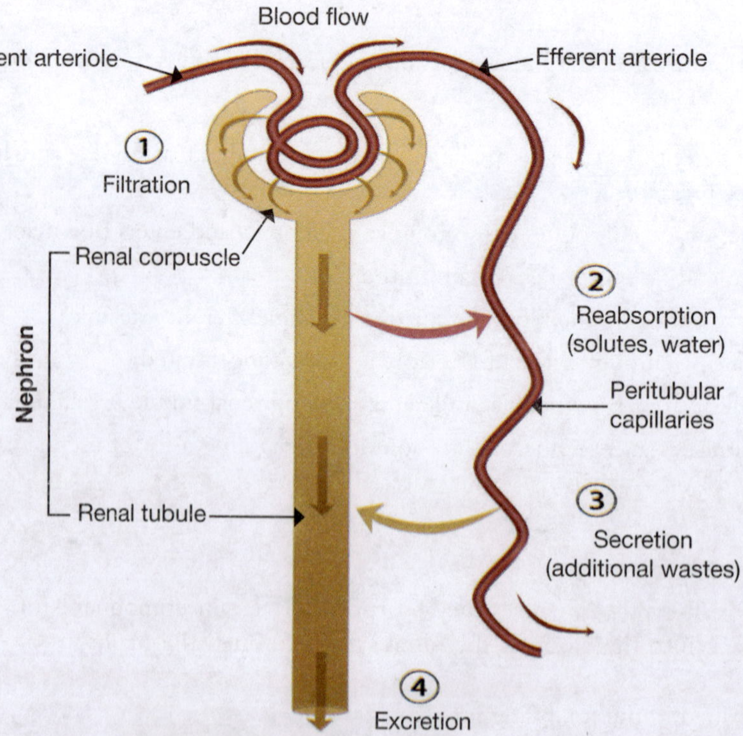

Figure 5.35 Basic steps in urine formation

Expulsion of Urine

Renal pelvis, the innermost region of kidney receives urine from collecting duct. From renal pelvis, the urine enters urinary bladder through ureter. The urine gets stored in urinary bladder temporarily and is passed through urethra at certain intervals. The expulsion of urine from the urinary bladder through the urethra takes place by the relaxation of sphincter muscle under the impulse from the brain. This process of regulated expulsion of urine from the urinary bladder through the urethra is known as micturition.

> **Info Bytes!**
>
> Kidney stones are hard deposits made of minerals and salts that are formed inside the kidneys.

Composition of Urine

The urine of a healthy human being contains 95 per cent of water. The distribution of 5 per cent of solid wastes is given below:

Table 5.4 Distribution of solid wastes in urine

Constituent	Composition
Sodium chloride	9 g/L
Ammonium phosphate	16.5 g/L
Urea	2.3 g/L
Potassium chloride	2.5 g/L
Creatinine	1.5 g/mL
Other nitrogenous substances	2 g/L

The composition of urine varies based on the intake of food. Protein-rich diet increases the content of urea in urine. Intake of salty food increases the salt content in urine. The urine sample of patients suffering from diabetes mellitus may contain glucose.

Table 5.5 Physical properties of urine

Property	Characteristic feature
Colour	Pale yellow
Odour	Pungent smell like ammonia
pH (acidity/alkalinity)	Slightly acidic

Osmoregulation

Apart from the function of excretion, kidneys also perform another major function of osmoregulation. Osmoregulation is the process in which water and salt balance is maintained in the body by means of osmosis. By the process of osmoregulation, the water content and concentration of ions in the cells are maintained. The transfer of water from the body cells to the bloodstream and vice versa in governed by the process of osmosis. If the percentage of water as a solvent is higher in body cells than that in bloodstream, water molecules move from the body cells to the bloodstream. When the percentage of water is in reverse order, the movement of water molecules takes place in reverse direction. Reabsorption is the process that occurs in proximal convoluted tubule of nephron which helps in osmoregulation. Thus, the role of kidney is vital for osmoregulation. In summer, we need to increase the intake of water for osmoregulation. This is because we perspire more in summer to maintain our body temperature and thus, the body cells lose water. The water molecules then move from bloodstream to the body cells. But the kidney needs adequate water for the removal of waste material from the body and thus, the requirement of water in our body increases in summer.

Info Bytes!

Variation in intake of food influences the physical properties of urine.

Haemodialysis

Any abruption in the normal functioning of kidney that does not result in excretion of waste products and maintenance of salt and water balance may lead to renal or kidney failure. It can happen either due to an infection or injury to kidneys. In such condition, urea level in blood rises. If level of urea is increased to an alarming level, it might lead to death. Hence, the patient is required to get rid of the nitrogenous waste substances using artificial kidney. The process by which the blood of a kidney patient is purified is called dialysis. Haemodialysis is the type of dialysis in which needles are used to take the blood out in tubes.

Info Bytes!

Antidiuretic hormone (or vasopressin) controls the water balance and maintains the blood pressure.

Process of Haemodialysis

The procedure of haemodialysis involves following steps.

- Blood is taken out from the main artery.
- The taken-out blood is cooled to 0°C and mixed with heparin.
- Blood is pumped into artificial kidney which is an apparatus wherein blood flows through tubes having semi-permeable membranes.
- Tubes are kept in a special type of fluid called dialysis fluid. Waste material like urea, creatinine, etc., diffuse into the dialysis fluid.
- The blood is thus purified and comes out of the artificial kidney.
- Blood is then warmed to body temperature and mixed with anti-heparin.
- Blood is injected back to a vein of the patient.

Info Bytes!

Heparin is an anti-coagulant which prevents the blood taken out of the patient from clotting.

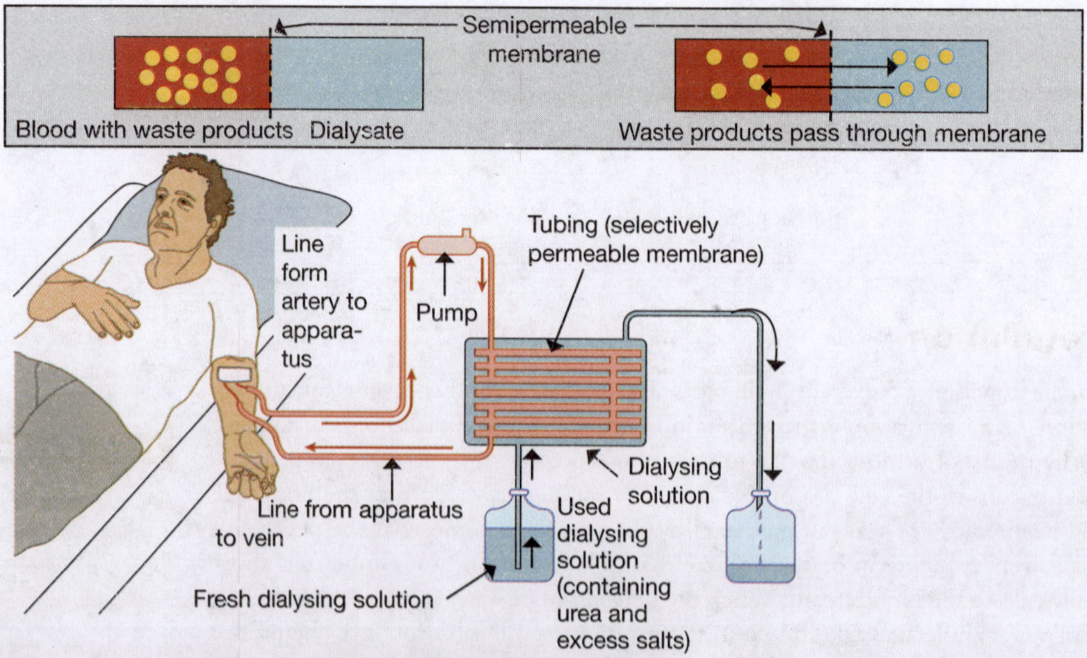

Figure 5.36 Procedure of haemodialysis

Quick Recap

✔ **The human body's water and salt balance is critical. How do the excretory and digestive systems collaborate to keep this balance?**

Osmoregulation is critical for maintaining our body's water and salt balance. The excretory system, particularly the kidneys, filters blood, retaining necessary salts while excreting excess. The digestive system absorbs water and essential salts from food at the same time. The large intestine contributes to this process by absorbing excess water from undigested food. Both systems work together to keep the body's water and salt levels balanced.

✔ **Define the role of each nephron component in ensuring the kidney's effective filtration and reabsorption processes.**

A nephron is the kidney's functional unit. Bowman's capsule, proximal convoluted tubule, Loop of Henle, and distal convoluted tubule make up its structure. Bowman's capsule purifies blood by filtering out waste products. The proximal convoluted tubule returns water, salts, and nutrients to the bloodstream. The Loop of Henle also contributes to reabsorption and maintains a salt gradient in the kidney. The distal convoluted tubule regulates sodium concentrations and connects to collecting ducts, which collect urine for excretion.

✔ **Make a distinction between excretion and osmoregulation. How do these processes maintain the human body's overall health and homeostasis?**

The process of removing toxic wastes and unwanted substances from the body is known as excretion. Osmoregulation, on the other hand, is the maintenance of the body's water and salt balance. While excretion keeps toxins from accumulating in the body, osmoregulation keeps cells from shrinking or swelling due to water imbalance. Both processes are critical for ensuring optimal cell function and overall health by maintaining the internal environment, or homeostasis.

POINTS TO REMEMBER

- ✔ The most important life processes are digestion, respiration, blood circulation, excretion, reproduction, etc.
- ✔ The intake of food, simplification of complex food materials followed by their assimilation, altogether constitutes the process of nutrition which takes place in the digestive system.
- ✔ In digestive system, the process of nutrition takes place in the following stages — ingestion, digestion, absorption, assimilation and egestion.
- ✔ Enzymes are biological catalysts which act only on their specific substrate.
- ✔ Digestive system broadly comprises two parts: alimentary canal or digestive tract and associated digestive glands.
- ✔ Digestive system starts with mouth. The wall of the oesophagus contracts to facilitate the transportation of food from mouth cavity into the stomach.
- ✔ The stomach is the expandable, muscular sac, J-shaped organ which is present on the left side of the upper abdomen.
- ✔ Small intestine is a very long and highly convoluted tube located between stomach and large intestine in the digestive system.
- ✔ Water is absorbed and undigested residue of the food is processed in the large intestine.
- ✔ Salivary glands, liver and pancreas are associated glands of the digestive system.
- ✔ Our digestive system, respiratory system, skin and excretory system play significant roles to maintain an ionic balance and right proportion of water in our body, and also remove the toxic substances from our body.
- ✔ Waste products generated by human body are carbon dioxide, nitrogenous wastes, bile pigments, excess salts and vitamins.
- ✔ The main excretory organs in human beings are: lungs, skin, kidneys and liver.
- ✔ Excretion and osmoregulation are the two major functions of excretory system.
- ✔ The process of expelling the toxic and unwanted wastes from the body of an organism is called excretion.
- ✔ The major function of the pair of kidneys is the separation of waste from bloodstream in the form of urine.
- ✔ A nephron is the microscopic structural and functional unit of the kidney.
- ✔ Each nephron consists of four regions: Bowman's capsule, proximal convoluted tubule, Loop of Henle and distal convoluted tubule.
- ✔ Osmoregulation is the process in which water and salt balance is maintained in the body by means of osmosis.
- ✔ The process by which the blood of a kidney patient is purified is called dialysis.

PRACTICE QUESTIONS CLASSROOM WING

Very Short Answer Type Questions

Directions for questions from 1 to 10.
Fill in the blanks.

1. The main life processes that support the functioning of living organisms are _______, _______, and _______.
2. Enzymes are considered _______ that act specifically on a certain _______.
3. The digestive system starts with the _______ and ends with the _______.
4. The pair of _______ in humans primarily separates waste from the bloodstream to produce _______.
5. The process of maintaining water and salt balance in the body using osmosis is called _______.
6. The process of _______ not only involves taking in food but also the simplification of complex food materials, eventually leading to their utilization by the body.
7. Kidneys are ______ shaped and reddish brown in colour.
8. Kidney on the ______ side is slightly higher than the kidney on the ______ side.
9. Each kidney is constituted of numerous ______, which are the functional units of excretory system.
10. A network of blood capillaries present inside the outer cavity of Bowman's capsule is known as ______.

Directions for questions from 11 to 26.
For each of the following questions, four choices have been provided. Select the correct alternatives.

11. Which of the following waste products is NOT generated by the human body?
    (a) Carbon dioxide
    (b) Nitrogenous wastes
    (c) Bile pigments
    (d) Lactic acid
12. What is the process called where a kidney patient's blood is purified externally?
    (a) Transfusion
    (b) Osmosis
    (c) Dialysis
    (d) Filtration
13. Which of the following best explains the role of the liver in the context of the digestive system?
    (a) Producing digestive enzymes
    (b) Absorption of nutrients
    (c) Synthesis of bile to aid fat digestion
    (d) Storage of undigested food
14. Why is the small intestine described as 'highly convoluted'?
    (a) To increase the area for absorption
    (b) To slow down food passage
    (c) To aid in the movement of food
    (d) To protect against pathogens
15. Which of the following systems plays the most significant role in maintaining the body's pH balance?
    (a) Digestive system
    (b) Respiratory system
    (c) Excretory system
    (d) Circulatory system
16. In the context of enzymatic action, what does substrate specificity mean?
    (a) Enzymes can act on any substrate.
    (b) Enzymes need a specific pH to act.
    (c) Each enzyme acts on a specific substrate.
    (d) Enzymes act faster at higher temperatures.
17. Identify the teeth which have chisel-like structures and help in cutting and biting the food.
    (a) Canines (b) Incisors
    (c) Premolars (d) Molars
18. In which part of the tongue, the bitter taste is perceived?
    (a) Tip of the tongue
    (b) Either side of the front part of the tongue
    (c) Either side of the posterior part of the tongue
    (d) Posterior part of the tongue.
19. Identify the name given to the partially digested food entering duodenum from stomach.
    (a) Bolus (b) Succus entericus
    (c) Chyme (d) Faeces

20. Match the entries of Column 1 with those of Column 2.

Column 1	Column 2
A. Small intestine	(i) Gall bladder
B. Large intestine	(ii) Amylase
C. Pancreas	(iii) Colon
D. Liver	(iv) Duodenum

	A	B	C	D
(a)	(iv)	(iii)	(ii)	(i)
(b)	(iii)	(ii)	(i)	(iv)
(c)	(i)	(ii)	(iii)	(iv)
(d)	(iv)	(iii)	(i)	(ii)

21. Which organ in the excretory system expels the urine out from the body?
(a) Kidneys (b) Ureters
(c) Urinary bladder (d) Urethra

22. Which organ helps in the separation of waste from blood stream in the form urine?
(a) Kidneys (b) Ureters
(c) Urinary bladder (d) Urethra

23. Which region of the kidney is composed of cone-shaped structures called renal pyramids?
(a) Cortex (b) Bowman's capsule
(c) Medulla (d) Renal pelvis

24. Which two regions together constitute Malpighian capsule?
(a) Loop of Henle and Bowman's capsule.
(b) Bowman's capsule and glomerulus
(c) Proximal convoluted tubule and glomerulus
(d) Distal convoluted tubule and proximal convoluted tubule.

25. Consumption of which of the following diets increases the content of urea in the urine.
(a) Rice (b) Ghee
(c) Peanuts (d) Vegetables

26. Match Column 1 with Column 2.

Column 1	Column 2
A. Bowman's capsule	(i) Pars recta
B. Proximal convoluted tubule	(ii) Macula densa
C. Renal pelvis	(iii) Glomerulus
D. Distal convoluted tubule	(iv) Inner most region.

	A	B	C	D
(a)	(iii)	(i)	(iv)	(ii)
(b)	(iii)	(ii)	(i)	(iv)
(c)	(i)	(ii)	(iii)	(iv)
(d)	(iv)	(iii)	(i)	(ii)

Short Answer Type Questions

27. Mention the different organs that are part of alimentary canal.

28. Name the different glands that are associated with the digestive system.

29. Complete the following table.

Type of Teeth	Number in each jaw	Location	Function
Incisors			
		Last part of jaw	
			Tearing the flesh
			Crushing and chewing

30. What do you mean by dental formula? Explain the dental formula in humans.

31. How many enzymes are present in pancreatic juice? Name and mention their role in digestion.

32. What do you mean by emulsification? Mention its significance.

33. Explain the process of digestion in small intestine.

34. Identify and explain the structure and function of the gland which secretes the enzyme amylase.

35. Explain the anatomy and function of tongue.

36. Explain the significance of the 'highly convoluted' structure of the small intestine in relation to its primary function.

37. What is the significance of osmoregulation in the human body, and how does the excretory system facilitate this process?

38. Explain the assimilation of fats during the process of digestion.

39. Define the following:

(a) Excretion
(b) Osmoregulation

40. Name the different organs associated with excretory system.

Essay Type Questions

41. On the basis of the diagram given, answer the following questions.

(a) Identify A, B, C

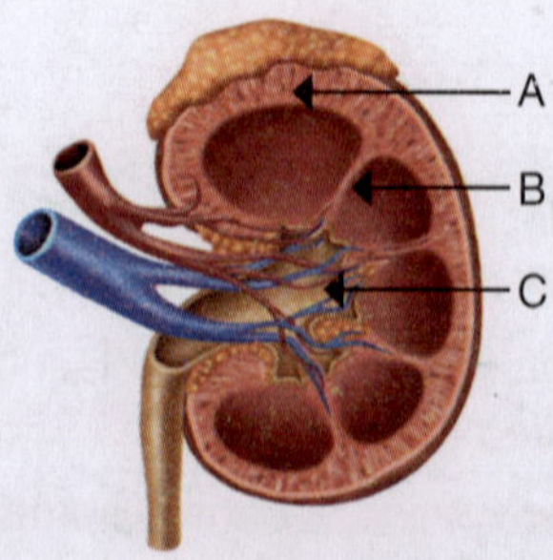

(b) What is the structural and function unit of the organ given in the diagram.

(c) Name the parts of the above structural and functional unit.

42. Name and explain the process that takes place in the network of blood capillaries present outside the Bowman's capsule during the formation of urine.

43. Drawing from the principle that form follows function, explain how the J-shaped structure of the stomach contributes to its digestive role.

44. Enzymes are often termed 'biological catalysts'. Expound on this terminology by emphasizing the specificity and efficiency of enzymatic action in the digestive process.

PRACTICE QUESTIONS COMPETITION WING

Level 1: Apply your Concepts

Directions for questions from 1 to 12.

Fill in the blanks.

1. While the _______ helps in the initial mechanical breakdown of food, it is in the _______ where the major chemical breakdown happens using acid and enzymes.
2. The _______ is pivotal in maintaining an ionic balance in the body, while the _______ primarily focuses on expelling gaseous wastes.
3. _______ act as biological accelerators, ensuring that reactions occur at rates feasible for life, without altering themselves in the process.
4. A patient suffering from kidney failure might require _______, a process mimicking the kidney's filtration mechanism externally.
5. The tongue is covered with the moist tissue called _________.
6. The organs which lost their original function through evolution are known as ________.
7. The final segment of the large intestine is________.
8. The bowel movement is controlled by ________.
9. The undigested matter of the ingested food is called __________.
10. The faeces is thrown out from the rectum through anus. This process is called ________.
11. ________ process takes place in proximal convoluted tubule of nephrons.
12. ________ region of kidney receives urine from the collecting duct.

Direction for Questions from 13 to 21.

Choose the correct option.

(a) Both A and R are true and R is the correct explanation for A.

(b) Both A and R are true but R is not the correct explanation for A.

(c) A is true and R is false.

(d) A is false and R is true.

13. **Assertion (A):** Dentition in an animal depends on the mode of feeding.

    Reason (R): All herbivorous animals have similar dentition.

14. **Assertion (A):** Both pepsin and rennin can simplify milk protein.

    Reason (R): Pepsin and rennin are protein-digesting enzymes.

15. **Assertion (A):** Digestion does not take place in large intestine.

    Reason (R): Undigested food gets converted to faeces in large intestine.

16. **Assertion (A):** Bile juice helps in digestion of food in small intestine.

    Reason (R): Bile juice contains sodium salts.

17. **Assertion (A)**: The process taking place in proximal convoluted tubule is called selective reabsorption.

    Reason (R): Along with waste material, some nutrients also remain in the filtrate.

18. **Assertion (A)**: Osmoregulation is one of the functions of kidney.

    Reason (R): Nutrients are transported to the bloodstream from the renal tubule by the process of osmosis.

19. **Assertion (A)**: The urine passed by a person is thicker in summer than in winter.

    Reason (R): Perspiration is more in summer than in winter.

20. **Assertion (A)**: Perspiration helps to maintain our body temperature.

    Reason (R):Perspiration expels nitrogenous wastes from our body.

21. **Assertion (A)**: Malpighian capsule completely separates the waste material from the nutrients present in the bloodstream.

    Reason (R): Selective reabsorption, secretion and transportation of urine are the functions of renal tubule.

Direction for Questions from 22 to 26.

For each of the following questions four choices have been provided. Select the correct alternatives.

22. How do lungs contribute to the excretory system?
(a) By filtering blood
(b) By expelling undigested food
(c) By eliminating carbon dioxide
(d) By producing enzymes

23. Given the processes involved in digestion, which sequence correctly represents the journey of food in the digestive system?
(a) Digestion, Ingestion, Absorption, Assimilation, Egestion
(b) Ingestion, Digestion, Absorption, Assimilation, Egestion
(c) Ingestion, Digestion, Assimilation, Absorption, Egestion
(d) Absorption, Ingestion, Digestion, Egestion, Assimilation

24. The specificity of enzymes is often compared to a lock and key mechanism. This implies that:
(a) Any enzyme can act on any substrate.
(b) Enzymes change their structure to fit the substrate.
(c) Each enzyme is specific to a particular substrate.
(d) Enzymes can only function in high-temperature conditions.

25. If a person's nephrons are not functioning correctly, which process would be most directly affected?
(a) Digestion of food
(b) Regulation of blood pH
(c) Filtration and reabsorption in the kidneys
(d) Production of saliva

26. Considering the importance of osmoregulation in the human body, which organ system primarily oversees the maintenance of water and salt balance?
(a) Respiratory system
(b) Digestive system
(c) Excretory system
(d) Circulatory system

Direction for Questions from 27 to 30.

Correct the following statements.

27. The undigested residue of the food is processed in rectum.

28. Gall bladder produces bile, a yellow-brown fluid.

29. Fibrinogen does not help in clotting the blood.

30. The voluntary movement of muscles of digestive tract for the transportation of food is called peristalsis.

Direction for Questions from 31 to 34.

Write the missing correlated terms.

31. Rennin: Milk protein: : Gastric lipase : ________.

32. Lipase: Fat :: ______ : starches.

33. Sublingual: Salivary glands :: liver : ___________.

34. Loop of Henle : ______:: Cortex : Kidney.

Level 2: Review your Concepts

35. Lactose intolerance is a common health problem in elderly people. Give reason.

36. How does the process of dialysis mimic the function of a human kidney, and why is it essential for certain individuals?

37. Different areas of tongue are responsible for different tastes. Explain.

38. Although appendix is considered a vestigial organ in human being, it plays certain role. Explain.

39. How do bile salts emulsify fats?

40. Explain the role of liver in maintaining glucose level in blood throughout the day.

41. Why do enzymes act in a particular range of temperature?

42. Enzymes are substrate (the molecule on which an enzyme acts) specific. Give the reason.

43. HCl is secreted in stomach to promote the activity of enzymes. Why does this HCl does not corrode the lining of the stomach?

44. When we chew a piece of bread for some time, we feel sweet taste in our mouth. Give reason.

45. The diameter of efferent arteriole is less than that of afferent arteriole. Give reason.

46. Why is the process taking place in proximal convoluted tubule called reabsorption? What is the significance of this process?

47. How does the formation of stones take place in kidney?

Direction for Questions from 48 to 51:

Answer the following questions.

48. What do you mean by absorption of food? Explain.

49. Name the valve which controls the passage of food from the stomach to the intestine.

50. Complete the following table:

Enzymes	Functions
Erepsin	
	Maltose to glucose (simplest sugar)
Sucrase	
	Lactose to glucose and galactose
Lipase	

51. What are the different steps involved in formation of urine?

Level 3: Assess Your Concepts

52. Liver is the main detoxifying organ in the body. Justify.

53. Why are patients suffering from kidney diseases advised to take low sodium salts?

54. A disease, gout indicates the malfunction of kidney. Give reason.

55. Hyperglycemia increases the frequency of urination. Explain.

56. The concentration of creatinine in the blood is measured to examine the condition of kidney. Give reason.

AT

PRACTICE QUESTIONS NEET SPECIAL WING

Multiple-Answer Type Questions

Questions number 1 to 5 are multiple-choice questions. Each question has FOUR options (a), (b), (c), and (d). ONE OR MORE THAN ONE of these four option(s) is/are the correct answer(s).

1. Which of the following are reactions carried out by intestinal juices?
   (a) Converts carbohydrates to small molecules like maltose
   (b) Converts fats into fatty acids and glycerol
   (c) Converts proteins to storable fat
   (d) Both b and c

2. Sodium salts in the bile juice helps with:
   (a) Providing larger surface area for digestion
   (b) Providing acidic medium for the action of enzymes
   (c) Imparting colour to bile
   (d) Converts fats to fatty acids

3. Which of the following statements is/are correct for haemodialysis?
   (a) Blood is taken out of the body from a main vein
   (b) The blood is cooled to 0^0 C and also mixed with heparin
   (c) Waste products diffuse into the dialysing fluid
   (d) Purified blood is injected back into the vein of the patient

4. Identify the functions of liver form the following:
   (a) Storage of iron (b) Deamination
   (c) Detoxification (d) Storage of water

5. Which among the following are part of the large intestine?
   (a) Caecum (b) Colon
   (c) Rectum (d) Ileum

Comprehension-Based Questions

A. Read the paragraph given below and answer the questions number 6 to 11:

The digestive system helps us to convert the food that we eat into simpler forms like sugars, amino acids and fatty acids. This broken-down food is then absorbed in the blood from the small intestine and the nutrients are carried to each and every cell in the body. The alimentary canal starts at the mouth and end in anus. Different organs of the digestive system include mouth, pharynx, oesophagus, stomach, small intestine and large intestine. The three major glands of the digestive system include salivary glands, pancreas and liver. Every step of digestion is helped by biological catalysts called enzymes lime the enzyme salivary amylase begins the digestion process in the mouth itself. All the enzymes are substrate specific and the reactions take place in a narrow temperature range.

6. If a disease of small intestine causes loss in the number of intestinal villi and the animal becomes weak with loss of weight, this is most likely due to
   (a) Slowdown in digestion of proteins
   (b) Loss of peristaltic movement
   (c) Loss of trypsin enzyme action
   (d) Decreased rate of nutrient absorption

7. Why do humans in advance age find it difficult to digest milk and experience flatulence and diarrhoea?
   (a) They are sucrose intolerant
   (b) Their intestinal walls become weak
   (c) Lactase production is low
   (d) Both a and b

8. Which of the following salivary glands are present below the tongue?
   (a) Parotid gland
   (b) Submandibular glands
   (c) Sublingual glands
   (d) Both a and b

9. Which pancreatic hormone controls the blood sugar level?
   (a) Insulin
   (b) Glucagon
   (c) Somatostatin
   (d) Adrenaline

10. Which function of liver helps in the blood clotting process?
(a) Regulation of blood sugar
(b) Storage of vitamin
(c) Storage of iron
(d) Manufacture of fibrinogen

11. Match the column:

Column – A (Enzyme)	Column – B (Product formed)
(i) Erepsin	(a) Glucose and galactose
(ii) Lactase	(b) Maltose
(iii) Sucrase	(c) Fatty acids and glycerol
(iv) Amylopsin	(d) Glucose and fructose
(v) Lipase	(e) Amino acids

B. Read the paragraph given below and answer the questions number 12 to 17:

Excretion is the process of removal of wastes from the body. One of the organs involved in excretion is kidneys. The physiological parts of excretory system in humans include renal artery, renal veins, a pair of kidneys, ureters, bladder and ureter. Nephron is the functional unit of kidneys. It consists of four main regions- Bowman's capsule, proximal convoluted tubule, loop of Henle and Distal convoluted tubule. Mechanism of urine formation takes place in three main stages include- ultrafiltration, selective reabsorption and tubular secretion. The composition of urine varies greatly based on the intake of food. If kidney functioning is disrupted then haemodialysis is carried out to remove the nitrogenous waste from the blood.

12. Excreting urea is a major disadvantage for certain animals because:
(a) It requires lots of water to be eliminated
(b) It requires lots of energy expenditure
(c) It is an important chemical for the body
(d) Urea is very toxic to the body

13. What will happen if Proximal convoluted tubule is removed from the nephron?
(a) The urine formed will be highly concentrated
(b) Highly diluted urine will be formed
(c) Urine will not be formed
(d) Urine will be formed normally

14. What happens if the diameter of efferent and afferent arteriole is the same?
(a) Ultrafiltration will become faster
(b) Ultrafiltration will become slow
(c) No ultrafiltration takes place
(d) It becomes impermeable to water

15. Which substance from the following are not selectively reabsorbed in the nephron?
(a) Creatinine
(b) Ions
(c) Glucose
(d) Amino acids

16. Active absorption of sodium ions takes place through the:
(a) Glomerulus
(b) Proximal convoluted tubule
(c) Loop of Henle
(d) Distal convoluted tubule

17. Match the column:

Column – A	Column – B
(i) Ureter	(a) Storage of urine
(ii) Urethra	(b) Expulsion of urine
(iii) Urinary bladder	(c) Supply blood from heart to kidneys
(iv) Renal artery	(d) Transports urine
(v) Renal vein	(e) Carries blood from kidneys to heart

ANSWER KEYS

Crossword

Across

4. Peristalsis 5. Haemodialysis 6. Gallbladder 8. Colon 9. Micturition
14. Epiglottis 16. Amylase 17. Canines 18. Duodenum 19. Crown

Down

1. Osmoregulation 2. Egestion 3. Glucagone 7. Glomerulus 10. Appendix
11. Urochrome 12. Chyme 13. Enamel 15. Heparin

Classroom Wing

Very Short Answer Type Questions

1. Digestion, respiration, blood circulation 2. Biological catalysts, substrate
3. Mouth, large intestine 4. Kidneys, urine 5. Osmoregulation 6. Nutrition
7. Bean-shaped 8. Left, Right 9. Nephrons 10. Glomerulus 11. (d)
12. (c) 13. (c) 14. (a) 15. (c) 16. (c)
17. (b) 18. (d) 19. (c) 20. (a) 21. (d)
22. (a) 23. (c) 24. (b) 25. (c) 26. (a)

Competition Wing

Level 1: Apply Your Concepts

1. Mouth, stomach 2. Excretory system, respiratory system 3. Enzymes 4. Dialysis
5. Mucosa 6. Vestigial organs 7. Rectum 8. Anal sphincter 9. Faeces
10. Defaecation 11. Reabsorption 12. Renal pelvis 13. (c) 14. (d)
15. (b) 16. (a) 17. (a) 18. (c) 19. (a)
20. (b) 21. (d) 22. (c) 23. (b) 24. (c)
25. (c) 26. (c)
31. lipids 32. Amylase 33. Associated digestive glands 34. Nephron

NEET Special Wing

Multiple-Answer Type Questions

1. (a, b) 2. (a, b) 3. (b, c, d) 4. (a, b, c) 5. (a, b, c)

Comprehension-Based Questions

6. (d) 7. (c) 8. (c) 9. (a) 10. (d)
11. (i) → (e); (ii) → (a); (iii) → (d); (iv) → (b); (v) → (c)
12. (a) 13. (b) 14. (c) 15. (a) 16. (b)
17. (i) → (d); (ii) → (b); (iii) → (a); (iv) → (c); (v) → (e)

Hints and Explanations

CLASSROOM WING

Short Answer Type Questions

27. Alimentary canal is constituted of different organs which are interconnected. Different organs are:

(a) Mouth (b) Pharynx
(c) Oesophagus (d) Stomach
(e) Small intestine (f) Large intestine

28. There are three digestive glands that are associated with the alimentary canal. These are:

(a) Salivary gland
(b) Pancreas
(c) Liver

29.

Type of Teeth	Number in each jaw	Location	Function
Incisors	4	Centre of jaw	Biting
Molars	6	Last part of jaw	Grinding food
Canine	2	Beside incisors	Tearing the flesh
Premolars	4	Between molars and canines	Crushing and chewing

30. Dental formula represents the number of teeth of each type present at one side of the mouth. The type of the teeth is represented by the initial letter of their name. The number of teeth in upper and lower is indicated separately in two rows where upper row indicates the upper jaw and the lower row indicates the lower jaw.

The dental formula in humans is ($i2/2$, $c1/1$, $pm2/2$, $m3/3$) × 2 = 32 (total number of teeth)

31. Pancreatic juice contains three enzymes which are as follows:

(a) Lipase: It helps in digestion of fats.
(b) Trypsin: It helps in digestion of proteins
(c) Amylase: It helps in digestion of starches

32. Emulsification is the process by which the large fat globules are converted to small tiny droplets. This helps in increasing the surface area of fats to facilitate the action of enzymes for the process of digestion.

33. When the food enters duodenum, it mixes with two types of juices.

One is bile juice secreted by liver and the other one is pancreatic juice secreted by pancreas. These juices enter the duodenum through common bile duct. Digestion takes place in alkaline medium, which is obtained due to secretion of bicarbonate ions from the wall of duodenum.

Ileum is the last and the longest part of the small intestine. The movement of food in the small intestine takes place by the process of peristalsis. The completion of the process of digestion takes place in ileum. The intestinal juice secreted from the digestive glands embedded in the lining of the small intestine is called succus entericus. This contains the enzymes which are effective in the alkaline medium.

34. Saliva contains an enzyme called amylase which helps in the digestion of the starch. It lubricates the food and helps in swallowing the food. Saliva is secreted by the salivary glands named parotid, submaxillary and sublingual.

35. Tongue is a muscular organ inside the mouth cavity. It is covered with a moist tissue called mucosa which is pink in colour. Numerous taste buds are present on the surface of the tongue which help taste different types of food.

Taste buds at different locations are responsible for different tastes.

(a) Tip of the tongue—Sweet taste
(b) Either side of the front part of the tongue—Salty taste
(a) Either side of the posterior part of the tongue—Sour taste
(b) Posterior part of the tongue—Bitter taste

36. The small intestine's 'highly convoluted' structure, characterized by numerous folds and villi, greatly increases its surface area. This enhanced surface area is crucial for its primary function of nutrient absorption. A larger surface area allows for a more efficient exchange and absorption of digested nutrients into the bloodstream.

37. Osmoregulation refers to the process of maintaining a balance between water and salt concentrations in the body. It's essential for ensuring that cells neither shrink nor swell excessively, both of which could be detrimental. The excretory system, especially the kidneys, plays a key role in osmoregulation. Kidneys filter the blood, reabsorbing necessary water and salts while expelling excess amounts, thus ensuring an optimal balance is maintained.

38. Fatty acids and glycerol get converted to fats and stored in adipose tissues.

Fats are readily available as the source of energy in our body.

39. (a) Excretion: The process of expelling the toxic and unwanted wastes from the body of an organism is called excretion.

(b) Osmoregulation: The process of maintaining the right amount of water and proper ionic balance is called osmoregulation.

40. Following are the different organs that are associated with the excretory system:

- A pair of kidneys
- Ureters
- Urinary bladder
- Urethra

Essay Type Questions

41. (a) (A) Cortex—The outer region

(B) Medulla—The middle region

(C) Renal pelvis—The innermost region

(b) The structural and functional unit of kidney is a nephron.

(c) (a) Bowman's capsule

(b) Proximal convoluted tubule

(c) Loop of Henle

(d) Distal convoluted tubule

(e) Glomerulus

42. Ultrafiltration is the process that takes place in the network of blood capillaries called glomerulus present outside the Bowman's capsule during the formation of urine. Following are the steps that take place during ultrafiltration process:

- The diameter of efferent arteriole is smaller than that of afferent arteriole, and hence, the blood stream inside the glomerulus is under high pressure. Due to this pressure, water and solutes pass through a membrane and enter Bowman's capsule.
- Blood cells, proteins and fat molecules remain in the blood stream.
- Thus, the blood passes through efferent arteriole is more concentrated.
- In normal adults, the volume of the urine formed every minute is approximately 120 mL.

43. The stomach's J-shaped design isn't just an anatomical curiosity; it's a testament to evolution's principle that form follows function. This unique shape provides a strategic advantage in digestion. First, the curvature creates a larger storage area, allowing the stomach to accommodate varying quantities of food. As food enters, the stomach expands, ensuring there's enough time for enzymes and acids to act upon the ingested material. The J-shape also facilitates the mechanical churning and mixing of food, ensuring it's well combined with gastric juices. This promotes the effective breakdown of proteins and the conversion of food into a semi-liquid state known as chyme, preparing it for further digestion in the small intestine.

44. Referring to enzymes as 'biological catalysts' provides insight into their fundamental role in life processes. In chemistry, a catalyst is a substance that accelerates a reaction without being consumed or undergoing permanent change. Similarly, enzymes speed up biological reactions crucial for life, but they remain unchanged after the reaction. Their true marvel lies in their specificity. Each enzyme has an active site, a region that binds to a particular substrate (or reactant) like a lock and key. This ensures that each digestive enzyme acts only on specific nutrients: lipase for fats, protease for proteins, and amylase for carbohydrates. By doing so, they ensure that multiple nutrients in our varied diet are broken down simultaneously and efficiently, optimizing nutrient absorption and overall health.

COMPETITION WING

Level 1: Apply your Concepts

13. Dentition depends on the food habit of an animal. Although all the herbivorous animals feed on plants, but they depend on different types of plants. Thus, dentition is specific and all herbivorous animals do not have similar dentition.
Hence, the correct option is (c)

14. Although pepsin and rennin are both protein-digesting enzyme, but every enzyme is substrate specific. Pepsin cannot digest milk protein. Rennin can digest it.
Hence, the correct option is (d)

15. Digestion does not take place in large intestine since enzymes are not secreted here. In large intestine, undigested food gets converted to faeces.
Hence, the correct option is (b)

16. Enzymes secreted in small intestine get activated in alkaline medium. Bile juice contains sodium salts which provide an alkaline medium in small intestine.
Hence, the correct option is (a)

17. Only nutrients are reabsorbed from the proximal convoluted tubule, not the waste material. Hence, the process is called selective reabsorption.
Hence, the correct option is (a)

18. Osmoregulation is the maintenance of water content and ionic balance. The process by which the movement of water from the region of low concentration of solute to the region of high concentration of solute takes place is called osmosis.
Hence, the correct option is (c)

19. Due to increased perspiration, a person loses more amount of water in summer. In order to maintain the quantity of water in the tissues, the kidneys have to reabsorb more amount of water from the urine making it thicker and more concentrated.
Hence, the correct option is (a)

20. Perspiration helps maintain our body temperature because loss of heat takes place from our body during perspiration. Perspiration also releases nitrogenous waste like urea from our body.
Hence, the correct option is (b)

21. Some amount of nutrients also pass into Bowman's capsule from glomerulus along with waste material. These nutrients are reabsorbed into the bloodstream from proximal convoluted tube. Selective reabsorption, secretion and transportation of urine to the collecting duct are the functions of renal tubule.
Hence, the correct option is (d)

27. The undigested residue of the food is processed in colon.

28. Liver produces bile, a yellow-brown fluid.

29. Fibrinogen helps in clotting the blood.

30. The involuntary movement of muscles of digestive tract for the transportation of food is called peristalsis.

31. Rennin: Milk protein: : Gastric lipase : lipids.

32. Lipase: Fat :: Amylase : starches.

33. Sublingual: Salivary glands :: liver : Associated digestive glands

34. Loop of Henle :Nephron :: Cortex : Kidney.

Level 2: Review your Concepts

35. Lactose intolerance is a condition in which dairy products do not get digested. It occurs when the cells of the small intestine do not produce enough lactase, the enzyme that digests the milk sugar, lactose. Lactose intolerance increases with age. Hence, it is a common health issue in elderly people.

36. Dialysis is a medical procedure that replicates the kidney's filtration function. It involves circulating a patient's blood through a machine that removes waste products and excess substances, essentially 'cleaning' the blood. This mimics the kidneys' role in filtering blood and producing urine to expel wastes. Dialysis is vital for individuals with kidney failure or severe impairment, as their kidneys can't perform their natural functions adequately, risking waste accumulation and subsequent health complications.

37. Different taste receptors are present in different areas of tongue. A particular taste receptor is concentrated more in a specific area of tongue. Different organic compounds and inorganic salts present in the food activate specific taste receptors and thus, surface of the tongue can be divided into different zones which are responsible for specific tastes.

38. Our digestive system contains many harmless bacteria which help in digestion of food.
These friendly bacteria are flushed out when a person suffers from dysentery or cholera.
Appendix has a stock of good bacteria which help in proper functioning of digestive system under this condition.

39. Fluid in the digestive tract is water based. The fats consumed by us forms large globules since they do not mix with water-based fluid. Bile juice produced by liver contains bile salts. The molecules of bile salts have one hydrophobic end and one hydrophilic end. Hydrophobic end mixes with fats while hydrophilic end mixes with water-based fluid. Thus, the large fat globules mix with water-based digestive fluid. This process is called emulsification of fats.

40. Glucose gets stored in the liver in the form of glycogen. Glycogen can be synthesized from glucose or broken down according to the needs of our body. Insulin hormone helps in synthesis of glycogen and glucagon helps in breaking down glycogen. Thus, homeostasis of glucose is maintained.

41. The reactivity of any substance decreases at lower temperature since the interaction between the reactant molecules decreases with the decrease in temperature. This is due to the decrease in kinetic energy of the reactant molecules.

Enzymes are protein molecules. All sorts of protein molecules start breaking down above 40°C. Hence, enzymes act well in a very narrow range of temperature which is around our body temperature.

42. Enzymes are complex protein molecules. The shape of each enzyme is specific. The shape of an enzyme should match the shape of the molecule of the nutrient. The part of the enzyme molecule that matches the substrate is called active site. Hence, enzymes are nutrient specific.

43. The secretive glands embedded in the lining of stomach secrete large quantity of mucus which protects the lining of stomach from the attack of HCl.

Moreover, bicarbonate ions are trapped inside the layer of mucus. They are basic in nature. If HCl penetrates the mucus, bicarbonate ions neutralize it.

44. Bread contains carbohydrates. Saliva secreted in our mouth contains amylase which converts complex carbohydrates to simple sugar molecules. Hence, we feel sweet taste in our mouth.

45. Efferent arteriole carries blood away from the glomerulus. Since it is narrower than afferent arteriole, it creates some resistance to blood flow. Thus, high pressure is created in the blood flowing through the glomerulus. This high pressure ensures the elimination of all the waste products from the blood.

46. The absorption of minerals, nutrients and water into the bloodstream takes place in small intestine for the first time. This process then gets repeated in proximal convoluted tubule of nephrons. Hence, the process of absorption in nephrons is called reabsorption.

Reabsorption in proximal tubule helps to maintain the right levels of the salts and water, essential for the normal functions of the tissues.

Reabsorption takes place in two steps. At first, water and required solutes move out of the tubular wall. Then these substances are transported to bloodstream through capillary walls.

47. In kidney, the stone formation takes place due to the crystallization of soluble salts like calcium oxalate. Soluble salts crystallize if their concentration is high in urine. There are certain substances which prevent crystallization of soluble salts. Citrate is a substance which can be taken through our diet that prevents crystallization. There are some proteins which are synthesized in our body which also help in the same process. Less intake of water and the change in pH of urine are responsible for stone formation. Lack of water content in urine hastens the process of crystallization.

48. Absorption is the process by which the products of the digestion are taken into the blood stream.
Ileum is the portion where most of absorption take place. Villi makes the process of absorption more effective providing the larger surface area. The digested food present in the intestinal lumen passes over villi and the nutrients diffuse through the epithelial cells and finally enter the blood stream in the blood vessels. Fatty acids and glycerol are absorbed by lacteals and finally reach the blood stream.

49. Pyrolic sphincter is a ring-like valve which controls the passage of the food from the stomach to the intestine. It does not open unless the food is properly churned in the stomach.

50.

Enzymes	Functions
Erepsin	Peptones to amino acids
Maltase	Maltose to glucose (simplest sugar)
Sucrase	Sucrose to glucose and fructose
Lactase	Lactose to glucose and galactose
Lipase	Fats to fatty acids and glycerol

51. Different steps that are involved in the formation of urine are as follows:

(a) Ultrafiltration: Occurs in glomerulus

(b) Selective reabsorption: Occurs in proximal convoluted tube

(c) Tubular secretion: Occurs in distal convoluted tube

Level 3: Assess Your Concepts

52. Decomposition of amino acid takes place by the cells of liver leading to the formation of ammonia which is extremely toxic. Liver is the organ which quickly converts ammonia to urea before it gets transported to kidney. Urea is excreted through urine and it is much less toxic than ammonia.

53. The major role of the kidneys is to remove waste products and purify blood. It also maintains the water content in the tissue and concentration of electrolytes like sodium, potassium, calcium, bicarbonate ions.

    If the kidneys of a person malfunction, water content and concentration of electrolyte get imbalanced. Hence, normal intake of sodium salt may disturb the fluid and electrolytic balance. To reduce the burden on the kidney with impaired function and to avoid disturbances in fluid and electrolytic balance, patients are advised to consume low sodium salt.

54. Gout is a disease in which uric acid crystallizes at the joints of the body and causes pain. Uric acid is the normal waste product present in the blood stream. Increase in the concentration of uric acid in the blood causes deposition of it at the skeletal joints. Concentration of uric acid increases in the blood if kidney cannot extract it properly from the bloodstream. Hence, gout indicates malfunction of kidney.

55. In a healthy person, glucose is completely filtered from the blood in the glomerulus and then reabsorbed from proximal convoluted tubule. The bloodstream of a patient suffering from hyperglycemia has more glucose in the blood than normal persons. The filtered glucose cannot be completely reabsorbed by the renal tubule. Due to the higher concentration of glucose in the urine, more water is drawn by osmosis. Hence, frequency of urination increases.

56. Creatinine is a metabolic product which is excreted through urine. Creatinine is filtered from the bloodstream through glomerulus. If the capacity of filtering of glomerulus decreases, the concentration of creatinine in the bloodstream increases. Thus, kidney function can be assessed based on the creatinine concentration in the blood.

NEET SPECIAL WING

Multiple-Answer Type Questions

1. In the large intestine, the pancreatic juices like Trypsin converts proteins into peptones and further to peptides and amino acids. An enzyme called amylase converts complex carbohydrates to simple sugars like maltose.
2. Sodium salts in the bile juice help in the following way in digestion-reduces acidity of chyme, provides alkaline medium for action of enzymes and emulsifies fats.
3. The procedure of haemodialysis involves following steps.
   - Blood is taken out from the main artery.
   - The taken-out blood is cooled to 0°C and mixed with heparin.
   - Blood is pumped into artificial kidney which is an apparatus wherein blood flows through tubes having semi-permeable membranes.
   - Tubes are kept in a special type of fluid called dialysis fluid. Waste material like urea, creatinine, etc., diffuse into the dialysis fluid.
   - The blood is thus purified and comes out of the artificial kidney.
   - Blood is then warmed to body temperature and mixed with anti-heparin.
   - Blood is injected back to a vein of the patient.
4. The functions of the liver include storage of iron obtained from the haemoglobin of disintegrated blood cells, conversion of amino acids to urea and removal of toxic substances from blood.
5. The large intestine consists of caecum- the first swollen portion, colon which is the longest part and rectum which is final part connected to the anal orifice.

Comprehension-Based Questions

A.

6. The presence of villi, finger-like projections on the inner lining of small intestine makes the process of absorption of nutrients very effective by providing a larger surface area. The digested food present in the intestinal lumen passes over villi and the nutrients diffuse through the epithelial cells and finally enter the bloodstream through the blood vessels.
7. In old age humans cannot digest the lactose present in milk as with advancing age lactase production becomes low. As a result of this lactose remains undigested and becomes fermented producing gas and acid leading to diarrhoea and flatulence.
8. Sublingual glands lie below the tongue. They are the smallest type of salivary glands and mostly secrete mucus. They produce about only 5 per cent of the saliva in oral cavity.
9. Pancreas also secretes hormones such as insulin and glucagon. Insulin helps in the metabolism of carbohydrates and thus, controls the glucose level in blood.
10. Liver helps in the manufacture of fibrinogen. Fibrinogen is a blood protein which is required for clotting of blood.
11. Match the following:

    Erepsin - Amino acids
    (i) (e)

    Lactase - Glucose and galactose
    (ii) (a)

    Sucrase - Glucose and fructose
    (iii) (d)

    Amylopsin - Maltose
    (iv) (b)

    Lipase - Fatty acids and glycerol
    (v) (c)

B.

12. Urea requires lots of water for elimination from the body, so the high requirements of water creates a disadvantage.
13. If proximal convoluted tubule is removed from the nephron, then selective reabsorption will be affected and hence urine formed will be very dilute.
14. If there is no difference in diameter of efferent and afferent arterioles then no pressure is created and ultrafiltration is not possible.
15. Selective reabsorption takes place when filtrate generated from glomerulus passes through proximal convoluted tubule, the next part of the nephron. This filtrate contains many useful materials like different ions, glucose, amino acids along with waste material. Creatinine is removed from the body via tubular secretion.
16. Active reabsorption of sodium ions takes place through the proximal convoluted tubule. Some ions like sodium and chloride, glucose and amino acids which

are required by our body, are reabsorbed by active transport system. Energy is required for such type of transportation.

17. Match the following:

Ureters connect kidneys to urinary bladder. Each ureter is attached to one kidney and carries urine from the kidney to urinary bladder.
(i) (d)

A urethra is a tube-like structure which originates from urinary bladder. It carries urine from urinary bladder and expels it outside the body.
(ii) (b)

Urinary bladder receives urine through ureters and acts as a temporary storage organ for urine.
(iii) (a)

Renal artery supplies oxygenated blood from the heart to the kidneys where it undergoes filtration and waste substances are removed from the blood.
(iv) (c)

Renal vein transports deoxygenated blood from the kidneys back to the heart for oxygenation.
(v) (e)

CHAPTER

6

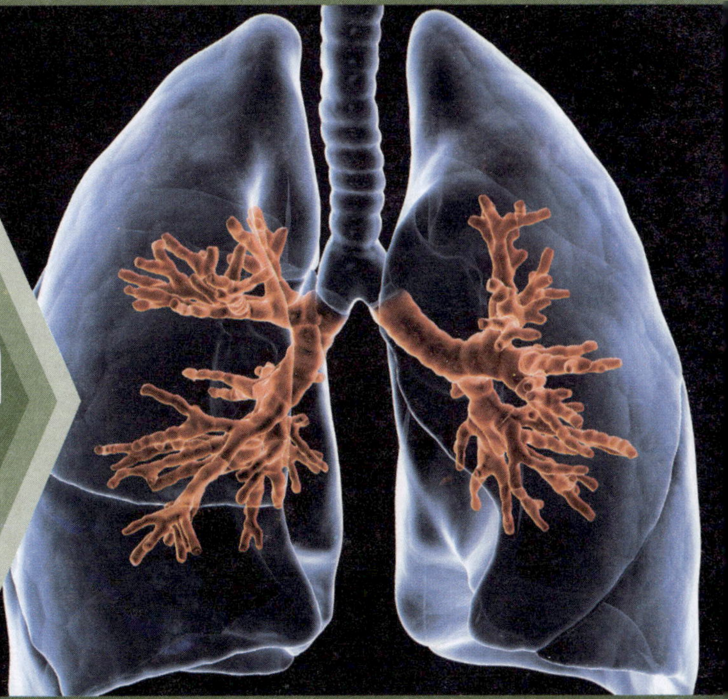

Life Processes in Human Beings–II (Respiratory and Circulatory Systems)

Remember

Before beginning this chapter, you should be able to:

- Recall different parts of human respiratory system
- Remember aerobic and anaerobic modes of respiration
- Recall different parts of the circulatory system
- Remember the primary functions of heart, blood and vessels
- Understand the basic mechanism of circulation of blood

Key Ideas

After completing this chapter, you should be able to:

- Understand the need for respiratory system
- Explain the structure and function of human respiratory system
- Discuss respiratory disorders
- Understand the need of circulatory system
- Explain structure and functions of different components of the circulatory system
- Discuss the major functions of blood, blood vessels and heart
- Explain the role of lymphatic system

A Tribute to Archibald Vivian Hill (1886–1977)

Archibald Vivian Hill (1886–1977) was a pioneering British physiologist whose work continues to shape our understanding of life processes, particularly those involving the respiratory and circulatory systems. Hill pursued the complexities of muscle physiology and respiration with unwavering dedication, providing profound insights into how muscles receive and utilise energy.

His pioneering research resulted in the development of the 'Hill Equation,' a seminal contribution that reshaped scientific perspectives on muscle contractions and oxygen consumption. This equation clarified the complex relationship between oxygen intake and energy production in muscles, bridging knowledge gaps in muscular activities and respiratory systems.

Hill received the Nobel Prize in Physiology or Medicine in 1922 in recognition of his pioneering contributions. His seminal research shaped our current understanding of the interactions between the respiratory and circulatory systems, providing a richer, more nuanced perspective on the mechanisms governing human life processes.

FUN TIME

CROSSWORD

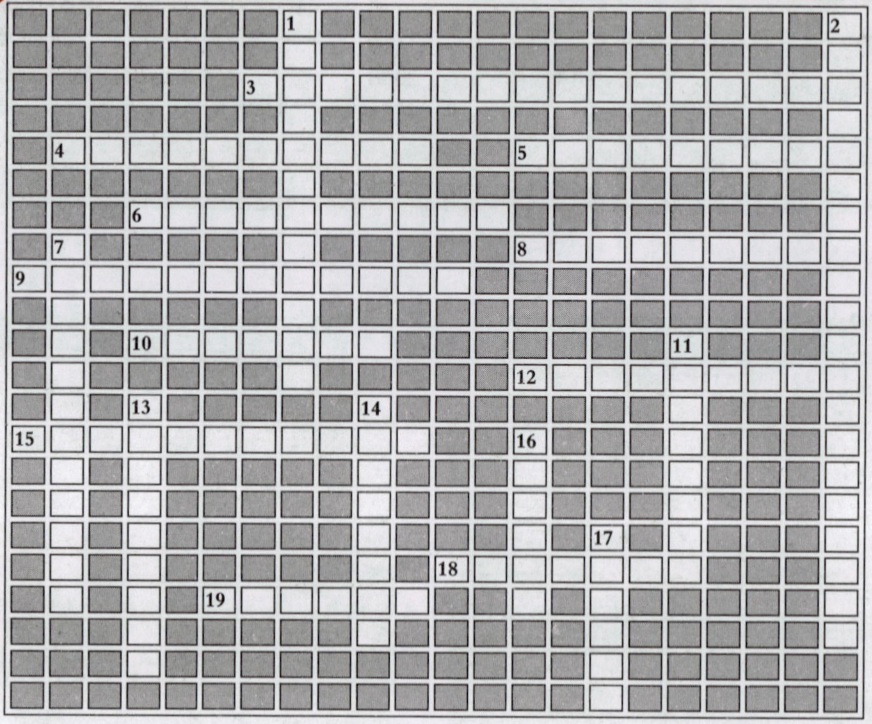

Across

3. The instrument used for measuring blood pressure
4. The process of cellular respiration common in both aerobic and anaerobic respiration
5. Breathing difficulty faced by a person due to the damage of alveoli
6. The protein in the blood responsible for clotting of blood
8. chemical that transmits the messages from one area of the brain to another and also helps with mood, sleep, digestion, etc.
9. Engulfing of foreign particles by the concerned cells as a part of the defence mechanism
10. The small bulb like structures at the end of bronchioles in the lungs
12. The shape of the erythrocytes
15. Type of leucocytes that respond to allergies
18. The blood capillaries which unite to form veins
19. The largest lymph organ in the human body

Down

1. The severe oxygen deficiency resulting in complete blockage of respiratory tract by some
2. The form in which carbon dioxide is transported through the blood plasma
7. The other name for platelets
11. Proteins that produce antibodies
13. An elastic muscular sheet which separates the thoracic cavity and the abdominal cavity
14. The form in which the unused glucose is stored in the hepatocytes
16. The organ of the respiratory system which aids in producing voice
17. The membranes covering the lungs

INTRODUCTION

Respiration is an indispensable process in all living organisms. It is essential for sustenance for a human being in a number of ways. This system works closely with the circulatory system to provide oxygen and to remove the carbon dioxide from cells of human body. In this chapter, we shall learn various aspects related to the process of respiration in human body, such as the raw materials used, end products, etc.

Respiratory System

Need for Respiration

If someone tries to hold their breath, how long can he/she do it? A typical human cannot survive without breathing for more than 3 mins. This is because every cell in our body needs to run the process of cellular respiration, the process by which energy is produced. For this to occur, oxygen is utilized as an input material and carbon dioxide is released as a metabolic product, which needs to be removed out of the cell.

Respiration is the chemical process in which energy is released in a cell by breaking down the glucose. This energy is required to carry out all the life activities in human body.

The chemical reaction for this process is as mentioned below.

$$\underset{\text{Glucose}}{C_6H_{12}O_6} + \underset{\text{Oxygen}}{6O_2} \rightarrow \underset{\text{Carbon dioxide}}{6CO_2} + 6H_2O + \text{Energy}$$

Let us understand some principal key points related to this process with the help of following points.

- The step of the respiration process that involves generation of energy happens inside the cell, hence, it is called cellular process.
- The breakdown of glucose occurs in a multi-step process. Some of these steps happen in the cytoplasm and some happen inside the mitochondria.
- The energy generated is in the form of chemical energy (ATP—Adenosine triphosphate) and some of it is in the form of heat.
- Each step in the process of cellular respiration involves action of enzymes.

Energy Needs in Organisms

Animals need more energy than plants. This can be explained with the help of the fact that animals do physical work hence, consume more energy. For example, they have to move around to obtain food, to run to escape rivals, chew their food to break it into absorbable material, look after their young ones, etc.

However, birds and mammals from animal kingdom require more energy than other animals. This is because they produce heat to keep their bodies warm. In winters, when the outside temperature is low, our body loses heat to the outside air and to compensate this loss, it has to produce more heat.

Info Bytes!

Shivering is an activity of the muscles that produces extra heat in case one feels very cold.

Role of Glucose

The energy produced in the process of cellular process comes from the breakdown of glucose (a simple carbohydrate). Glucose has no replacement for respiration. If glucose is not accessible to the cells, cells may break fats or proteins to produce glucose.

Figure 6.1 Glucose being used up as a reactant in cellular respiration

For organisms who eat flesh, the main constituent of their diet is proteins and little carbohydrates. The breakdown of proteins through the process of digestion involves generation of amino acids. These amino acids are broken down in the liver to form glucose. The glucose thus produced, may either be utilized for meeting energy needs or get stored as glycogen in the liver cells (called hepatocytes) for future requirements.

Types of Respiration

On the basis of need for oxygen, the respiration process is of two types:

1. Aerobic respiration
2. Anaerobic respiration

Aerobic Respiration

Aerobic respiration occurs in the presence of oxygen. The overall chemical change is represented below.

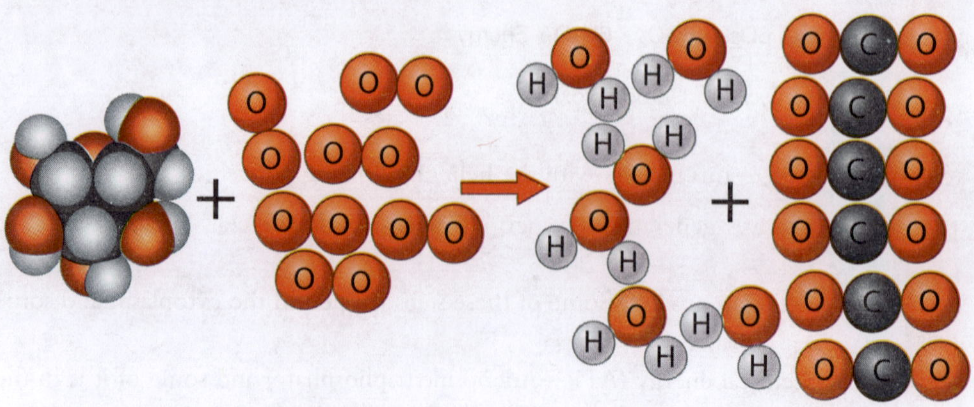

Glucose + Oxygen ⟶ Water + Carbon dioxide (+ energy released)

$C_6H_{12}O_6$ + $6O_2$ ⟶ $6H_2O$ + $6CO_2$

Figure 6.2 Diagram showing aerobic respiration

Info Bytes!

Humans exhale up to 17.5 milliliters of water per hour.

The equation described above, takes into account the chemical change in moles. If 180 g of glucose is oxidized, the energy released is 686 kcal.

Info Bytes!

One mole of ATP needs 7 kcal, hence, 266 kcal are needed to produce 38 moles of ATP. Rest of the energy (686-266) is released as heat

Anaerobic Respiration

Anaerobic respiration occurs in the absence of oxygen. It may occur in our skeletal muscles during physical exercise. In this scenario, enough oxygen is not available to fast-working muscles. Hence, to provide extra energy, anaerobic respiration happens that leads to formation of lactic acid.

Glucose ⟶ Lactic acid + Energy

Figure 6.3 Equation of anaerobic respiration

No CO_2 is produced in anaerobic respiration.

Table 6.1 Difference between aerobic and anaerobic respiration

Parameter	Aerobic respiration	Anaerobic respiration
Oxygen	Present	Absent
Energy released	High	Less
CO_2	Produced	Not all Anaerobic pathways produce CO_2

Real-Life Applications of Aerobic and Anaerobic Respiration:

- **Baking and Brewing**
  Anaerobic Respiration: Yeast undergoes alcoholic fermentation, producing CO_2 that makes bread rise and ethanol for alcoholic beverages.
- **Energy Production**
  Aerobic Respiration: Our body cells use aerobic respiration for efficient energy production, allowing us to perform daily activities.
  Anaerobic Respiration: During short, intense activities (like sprinting), muscles may resort to anaerobic respiration for quick energy.
- **Waste Treatment**
  Anaerobic Respiration: Anaerobic digesters in wastewater treatment plants break down organic matter, reducing waste volume and producing methane, which can be harnessed as a renewable energy source.
- **Food Preservation**
  Anaerobic Respiration: Lactic acid fermentation by certain bacteria preserves foods, leading to products like yogurt, pickles, and sauerkraut.
- **Sports Training**
  Anaerobic Respiration: High-intensity interval training (HIIT) relies on brief, intense bursts of activity, tapping into anaerobic pathways. Understanding lactic acid production aids in sports science and athlete training.
- **Biogas Production**
  Anaerobic Respiration: Decomposition of organic waste by specific bacteria in the absence of oxygen produces methane-rich biogas, a renewable energy source.
- **Medical Treatments**
  Anaerobic Respiration: Knowledge of anaerobic bacteria helps in treating infections they cause. Oxygen therapies can be used to counteract their growth.

Parts of Respiratory System

During respiration, oxygen is inhaled and carbon dioxide is exhaled. The respiratory system in human beings includes a series of organs by which oxygen is taken in and carbon dioxide is expelled out. The organs involved in respiratory system are as follows:

- Nose and nostrils
- Nasal passage
- Pharynx
- Larynx
- Trachea
- Bronchi
- Bronchioles and alveoli
- Lungs

Info Bytes!

Another role of nose is to smell. Sensory cells of smell are located in the nasal chamber.

Nose and Nostrils

There are two nostrils at the external end of the nose. They are separated by a cartilaginous wall called septum. Tiny hair-like structures called cilia are present in the nostril. The intake of atmospheric air happens through the nostrils. Cilia prevent the entry of dust particles into the respiratory tract.

Nasal Passage

The inner layer of nasal passage is lined with glands that secrete mucus. Mucus helps in purifying air by entrapping solid, unwanted particles and keeps the nasal passage moist. The inhaled air becomes warm and humid while passing through the nasal passage. The mucous inner lining of nasal passage performs various functions some of which are:

- Adding moisture to the air,
- Warming the air,
- Entrapping the dust particles present in the inhaled air.

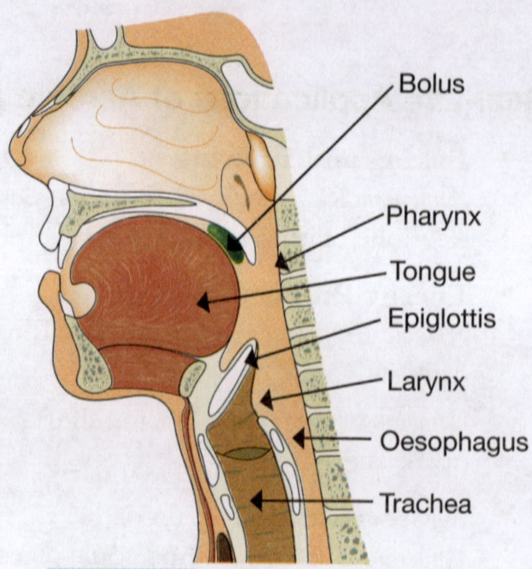

Figure 6.4 Illustration of pharynx, epiglottis and related organs

Pharynx

The nasal passage opens into the pharynx. Food and air enter the digestive and respiratory tracts, respectively through a common cavity called pharynx. A slit-like passage through which air enters the respiratory tract from the pharynx is called glottis. When we swallow food, a leaf-like cartilaginous flap covers the glottis to prevent the entry of food particles in the respiratory tract. This is called epiglottis.

Larynx

In the respiratory tract, larynx is positioned between the pharynx and trachea. It is a cartilaginous cavity which contains twin ligamentous fold-like structures called vocal cords. Vibration of vocal cords generates sound by forcibly expelling air and thus it helps in speaking. Hence, larynx is also called voice box. Larynx is the part which rises and falls during swallowing. Vocal cords are two ligamentous folds which forcibly expel air which produces sound. A range of sounds can be produced by adjusting the distance between the cords with the help of attached muscles.

Info Bytes!

Cough is caused due to incomplete closure of epiglottis during swal-lowing.

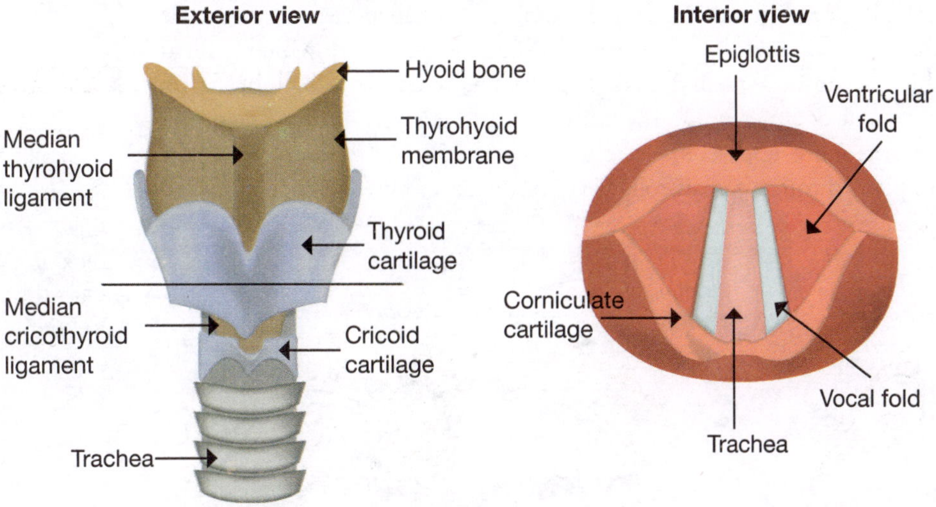

Figure 6.5 Illustration of larynx showing vocal cords

Trachea

Larynx opens into a tube-like structure called trachea. Trachea provides the passage of air from the larynx to the lungs. There are horseshoe-shaped cartilaginous rings around the trachea. These rings act as a support of trachea and provide flexibility as well as strength to the trachea. Trachea never collapses because of these structures. Two branches are formed from trachea for the passage of air into both the lungs.

Bronchi and Bronchioles

Bronchi are the two branches generated from trachea and each of them enters the lungs from their respective side. Each bronchus (singular) gets divided into small branches, called bronchioles and is present inside the lungs. There are small balloon-like thin-walled air sacs at the end of each bronchiole. They are called alveoli.

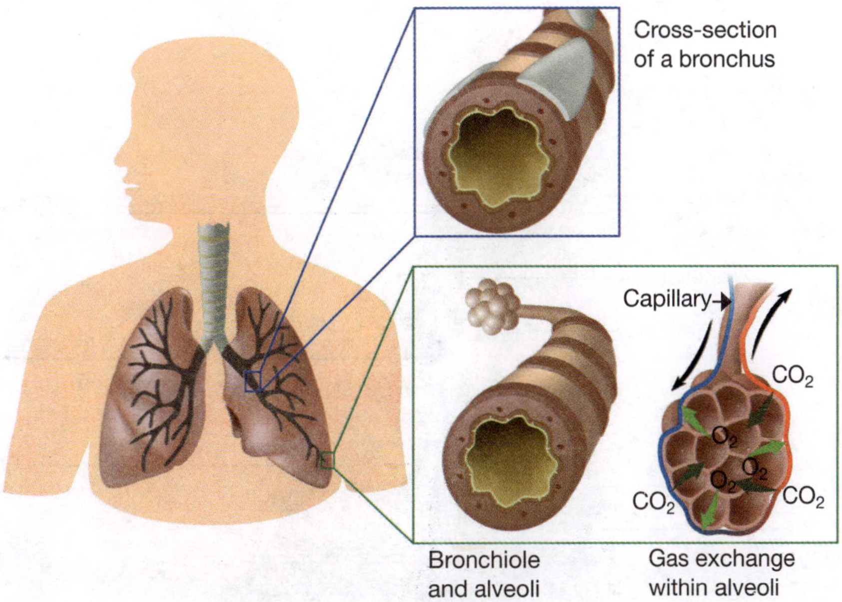

Figure 6.6 Illustration of bronchus and bronchiole

Lungs

A pair of lungs is present in the thoracic cavity. Right lung is slightly bigger than the left lung since heart is also present slightly towards the left side of the thoracic cavity. Each lung is enclosed in a double-layered membrane called pleura. The inner membrane is called visceral pleura and outer membrane is called parietal pleura. In between inner and outer membranes, there is a cavity called pleural cavity which is filled with watery fluid, which is known as pleural fluid. This fluid helps in providing lubrication for easy and free movement of lungs while they contract and expand during breathing. Alveoli present inside the lung appear like a cluster of grapes and the exchange of respiratory gases takes place through the alveoli. Very thin walls of alveoli are surrounded by blood vessels.

Info Bytes!

Although oxygen is a vital need for our cells, it effects the build up of carbon dioxide that principally drives our need to breathe.

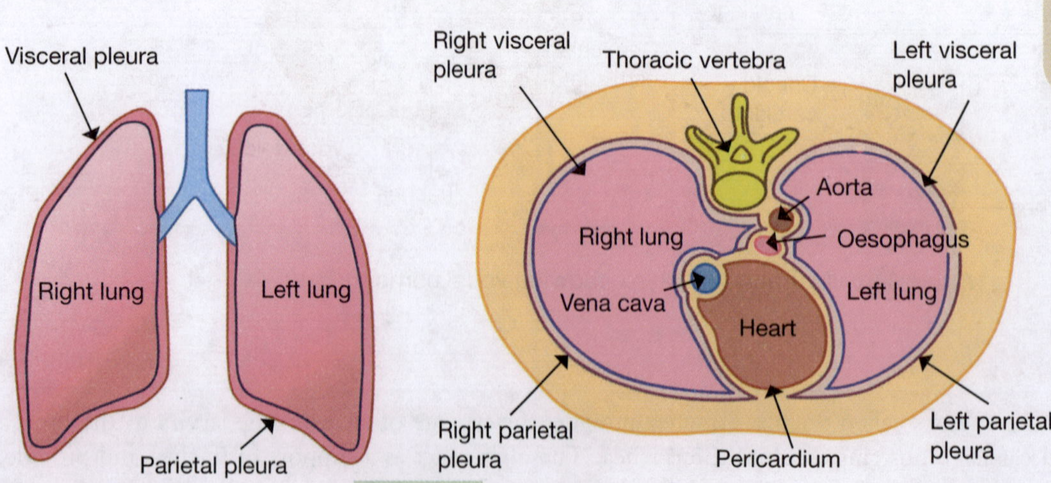

Figure 6.7 Illustration of pleura

Oxygen from the alveoli is transported to the bloodstream by the process of diffusion after inhalation. Similarly, carbon dioxide diffuses from the bloodstream to alveoli and is exhaled. Haemoglobin present in the red blood cells transports oxygen as well as carbon dioxide.

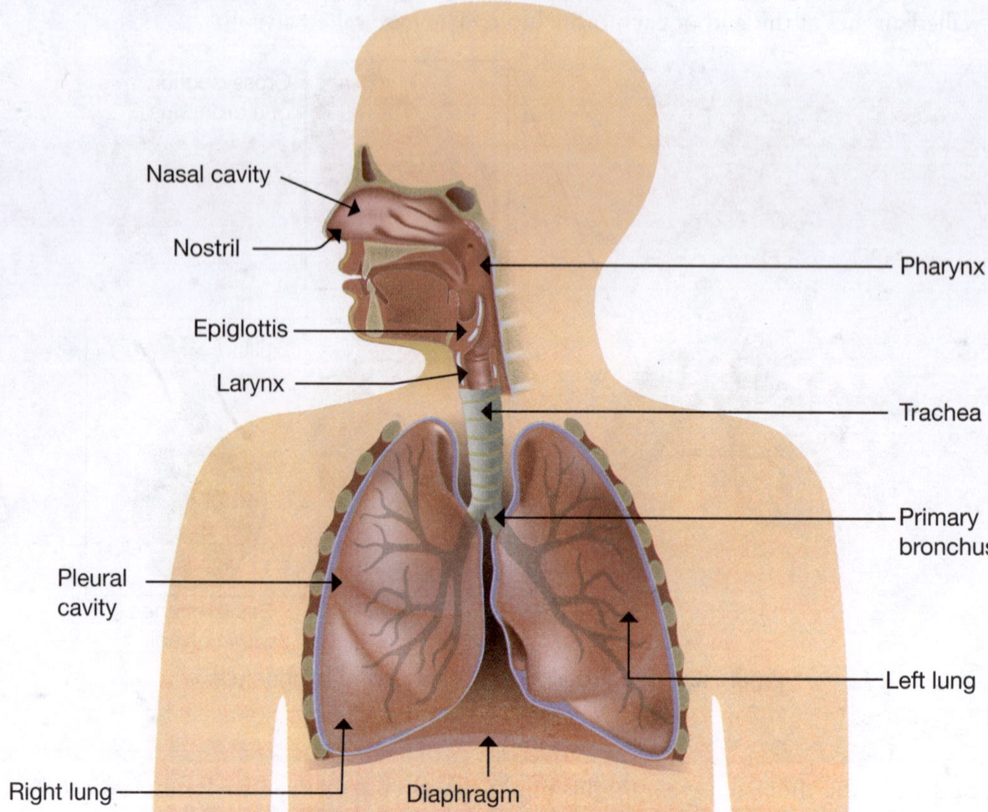

Figure 6.8 Human Respiratory System

Process of Respiration

Respiration involves major four processes. They are discussed below:

1. Breathing
2. Gaseous transport
3. Tissue respiration
4. Cellular respiration

Breathing

The mechanical process by which oxygen is inhaled or inspired and carbon dioxide is exhaled or expired is called breathing. Actually, we inhale air (not just oxygen) which contains more oxygen and less carbon dioxide, and we exhale air that contains more carbon dioxide and less oxygen.

Info Bytes!

Inflammation of pleura is called Pleurisy.

Gaseous Transport

Oxygen gas is transported from the lungs to the bloodstream in the form of oxyhaemoglobin. Thus, oxygen reaches the tissues all over the body. Carbon dioxide is transported in two different ways.

- Carbon dioxide gas dissolves in blood plasma forming bicarbonate ions and gets transported to lungs. Major portion of carbon dioxide is transported in this way.
- About 20% of the carbon dioxide binds with haemoglobin with the help of amino acid forming carbaminohaemoglobin.

Thus, it gets transported by red blood cells or erythrocytes.

Info Bytes!

Each of our lungs contains approximately 300 million alveoli.

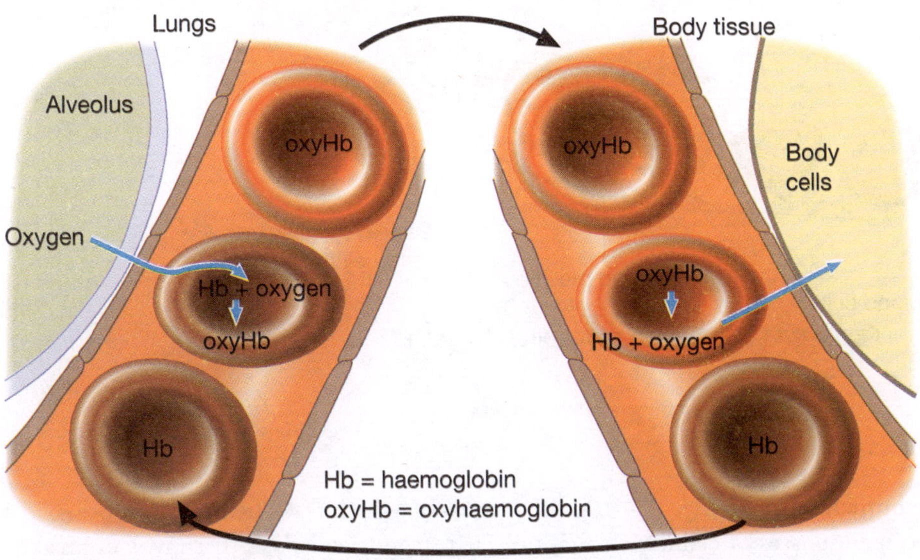

Figure 6.9 Formation of oxyhaemoglobin

Info Bytes!

Affinity of haemoglobin to combine with carbon monoxide is 200 times its affinity to combine with oxygen.

Tissue Respiration

Tissue respiration is the metabolic process by which oxygen reaches the body cells and carbon dioxide is released from them. Oxygen enters the cells through the thin walls of the blood capillaries by the process of diffusion and carbon dioxide is released in the same way. Diffusion of oxygen takes place due to the higher concentration of oxygen in the blood than that in the cells.

Similarly, diffusion of carbon dioxide (formed due to cellular respiration) takes place due its higher concentration in cells than that in the blood.

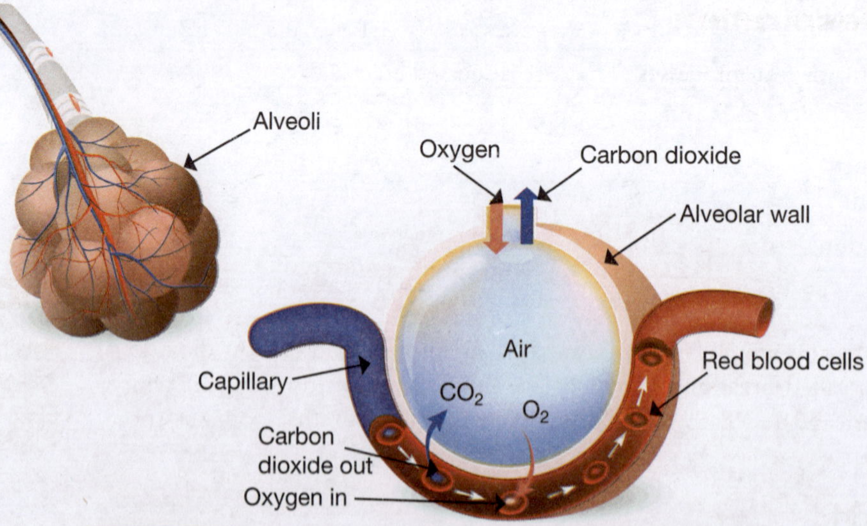

Figure 6.10 Illustration of alveoli and capillaries in lungs

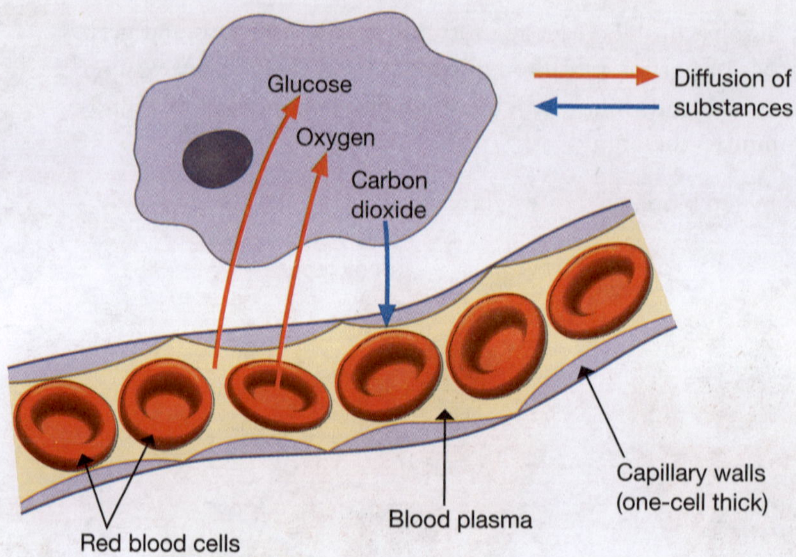

Figure 6.11 Diffusion of respiratory gases

Cellular Respiration

Cellular respiration takes place in the mitochondria of the cells. It is the process by which the glucose undergoes oxidation and energy is released. There are two main phases of cellular respiration. First stage is glycolysis that involves breakdown of glucose, second stage is a process known as Krebs cycle.

1. **Glycolysis:** It occurs in the cytoplasm (outside the mitochondria) and involves breaking down of glucose to a substance known as pyruvic acid.
2. **Krebs Cycle:** It occurs inside the mitochondria. This process requires oxygen. It involves step-by-step breakdown of pyruvic acid to produce ATP and carbon dioxide.

Info Bytes!

Lungs can float on water.

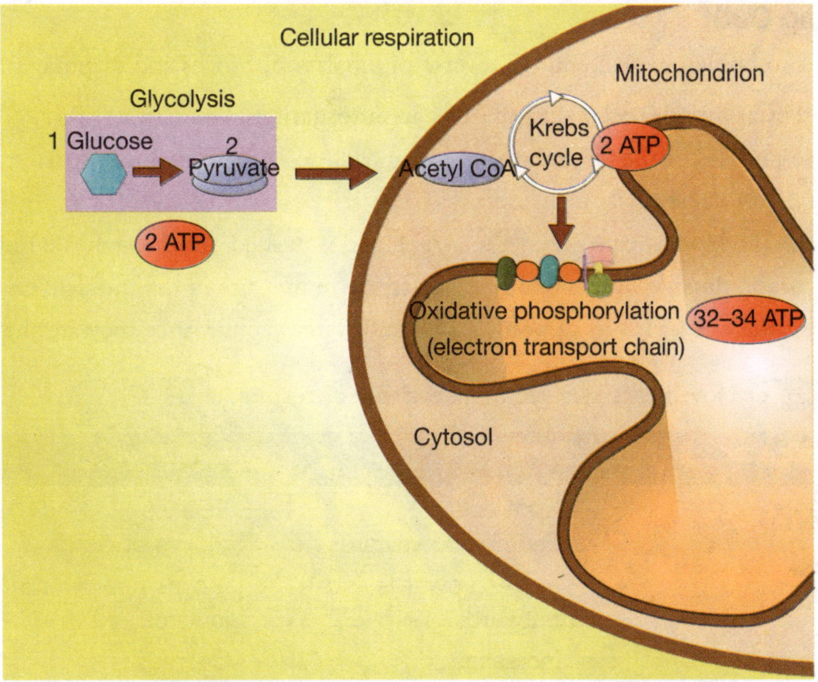

Figure 6.12 Illustration of cellular respiration

Mechanism of Respiration

Lungs are the elastic bag-like structures which do not have any muscles. Hence, they themselves cannot contract or relax. A muscular, elastic sheet, called diaphragm, is extended across the bottom of thoracic cavity. Diaphragm separates thoracic cavity from the abdominal cavity. The movement of diaphragm and muscles of the ribs facilitates the contraction and relaxation of lungs during breathing. The mechanism of respiration can be broadly understood by the processes of inhalation and exhalation as discussed below.

Inhalation (Breathing in)

The process of inhalation is the result of combined activity of diaphragm and ribs which results in increase in size of the thoracic cavity. This stage is described as:

- During inhalation or inspiration, the muscles of the ribs and the diaphragm contract.
- Thus, the diaphragm moves downwards and the volume of the thoracic cavity increases.
- Due to increase in volume, the air pressure in the thoracic cavity decreases.
- Under this situation, the air pressure outside the body is higher and hence, air from the environment enters the lungs through the respiratory tract.
- Thus, air reaches alveoli and oxygen diffuses to the bloodstream through the thin walls of alveoli.
- Then, the blood flows to the heart through the pulmonary vein and the heart pumps the blood to the tissues, all over the body.
- Thus, oxygen required for respiration is transported.
- Carbon dioxide generated during respiration in the cells is transported back to the heart through the bloodstream.
- From heart, it goes to the lungs through the pulmonary artery.

Exhalation (Breathing Out)

Exhalation is the result of combined movements (in reverse of inhalation) of ribs and diaphragm.

- The internal intercostal muscles relax and there is an automatic movement of ribs.
- Diaphragm and the muscles of the ribs relax and move back to the original position.
- Thus, the space in the thoracic cavity decreases.
- Carbon dioxide from the bloodstream enters the alveoli and is pushed out through the respiratory tract.
- The expulsion of carbon dioxide occurs due to the increase in pressure in the thoracic cavity.
- Thus, the air we breathe out is rich in carbon dioxide and water vapour since they are the products of respiration.

Table 6.2 Movements involved in mechanism of respiration

Part/Parameter	Inhalation	Exhalation
Diaphragm	Contracts Flattens downwards	Relaxes Moves upwards
Rib cage	Moves upwards and outwards	Moves downwards and inwards
Thoracic cavity	Increases	Decreases
Air pressure of thorax and lungs	Decreases	Increases
Internal intercostal muscles	Relax	Contract

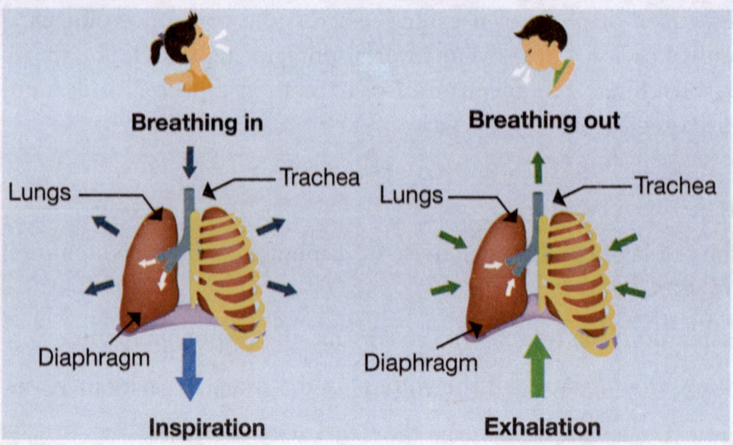

Figure 6.13 Movement of ribs and diaphragm during inhalation and exhalation

Control of Respiration

Breathing movements are majorly under the control of respiratory centre located in the medulla oblongata of the hindbrain. Medulla oblongata is stimulated by the carbon dioxide amount in the blood. Breathing is faster when the carbon dioxide content is high in the blood. Generally, breathing movements are involuntary but at times one can increase or decrease the rate of breathing. However, we cannot hold our breathe beyond a point, as a stage would come when it could not be held any longer.

Capacities of the Lungs

Capacity of the lung or the respiratory volumes are the quantities of air inhaled, exhaled and stored within the lungs at any given time.

Tidal Volume

About 500 mL of air is inhaled by a person in normal breathing. This is called tidal volume. The rate of respiration in terms of volume of air breathed in per minute is called the rate of ventilation. Therefore, the rate of ventilation = tidal volume × frequency of respiration. In an adult human being, the frequency of respiration is 12 breathings per minute.

Vital Capacity

Vital capacity is the volume of air that a normal human being can exhale after the inhalation with the maximum effort. The vital capacity of an adult is 4500 mL. The volume of air that cannot be expelled from the lungs even with the maximum effort is called residual air or residual volume. In a normal human being, residual air is 1500 mL.

Inspiratory and Expiratory Reserve Volumes

- Inspiratory reserve volume (IRV) is the excess volume of air that can be inhaled by the deepest breathe on top of the tidal volume.
- Expiratory reserve volume (ERV) is the additional volume of air that can be exhaled with the maximum effort after the normal expiration.
- In a normal adult, the inspiratory and expiratory reserve volumes are 3000 and 1000 mL, respectively.
- Therefore, vital capacity = tidal volume + IRV + ERV = 500 mL + 3000 mL + 1000 mL = 4500 mL
- Thus, total lung capacity (amount of air that can be held anytime in the two lungs) = vital capacity + residual air = 4500 mL + 1500 mL = 6000 mL

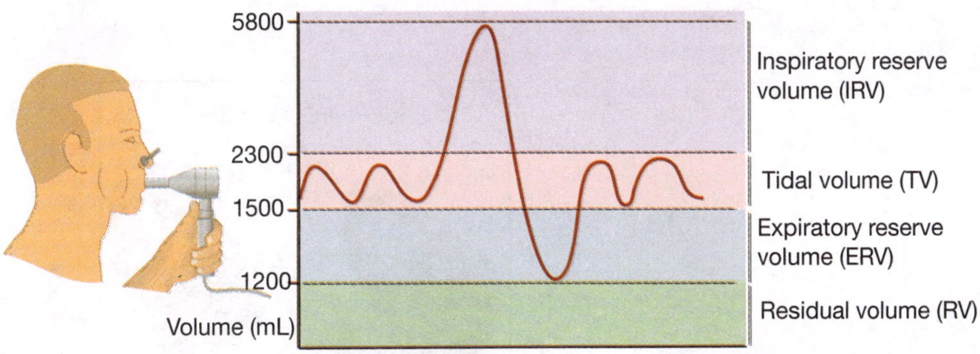

Male	Female
3000	1900
500	500
1100	700
1200	1100
5800 mL	4200 mL

Figure 6.14 Illustration of capacities of the lungs

Effect of Altitude on Breathing

With the increase in the altitude, the pressure of the air as well as percentage of oxygen in air decreases. Hence, symptoms such as headache, breathlessness, dizziness, nausea, loss of hearing capacity and lack of muscular coordination develop at the higher altitude. This negative health effect due to high altitude is called mountain sickness or altitude sickness.

Respiratory Disorders

Following are some of the major disorders that may occur when any part of the respiratory system is disturbed or there is lack of oxygen supply in our body.

Emphysema

In this disease, the lung tissue involved in exchange of respiratory gases gets impaired and the walls separating alveoli break. Hence, the available surface area of alveoli for the exchange of respiratory gases gets reduced. Thus, the person suffering from emphysema faces difficulty in breathing.

Info Bytes!

Smoking aggravates emphysema.

Hypoxia

This disease occurs when the tissues of a region of a body or the whole body do not receive adequate oxygen. Lack of haemoglobin and reduction of blood flow could be the causes of this disease.

Asphyxiation

Severely deficient-oxygen supply in the body due to the partial or complete blockage of respiratory tract by some object causes this problem. Under this condition, accumulation of carbon dioxide takes place in the blood and it can be fatal.

Chronic Obstructive Pulmonary Disease (COPD)

Chronic obstructive pulmonary disease is caused by long-term exposure to harmful gases or particulate matter present in polluted air. People suffering with COPD are at increased risk of developing heart disease. Emphysema is one of the most common conditions that cause COPD.

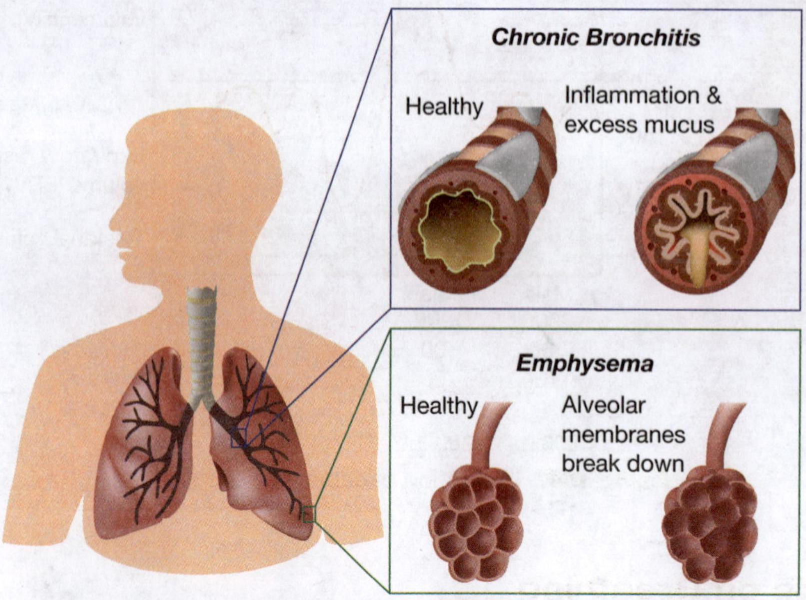

Figure 6.15 Condition of lungs in Chronic obstructive pulmonary disease and Emphysema

Quick Recap

✔ **How are pulmonary circuit and respiratory process related?**

During inhalation, air is taken in through the respiratory tract. Diffusion of oxygen takes place from the alveoli to the blood capillaries. Then oxygenated blood is transported to the left auricle of the heart through the pulmonary vein. Bloodstream transports oxygen from the left ventricle to all parts the body.

Cellular respiration takes place in mitochondria and carbon dioxide is formed in this process. This carbon dioxide is transported through the bloodstream to the right auricle of the heart from different parts of the body. Deoxygenated blood flows to the right ventricle from the right auricle. From the right ventricle, deoxygenated blood reaches the lungs through the pulmonary artery. Carbon dioxide gas diffuses from the blood capillaries to the alveoli and is finally exhaled.

✔ **Distinguish between the functions of arteries, veins, and capillaries in the circulatory system. What is the relationship between their structure and their specific functions?**

Arteries, veins, and capillaries all serve different functions in the circulatory system. Arteries carry oxygenated blood from the heart to body tissues and have thick, muscular walls to withstand high pressure. Veins have thinner walls and valves to prevent the backflow of deoxygenated blood back to the heart. Capillaries, the smallest of the blood vessels, allow for the exchange of gases, nutrients, and wastes between blood and tissues; their walls are only one cell thick, allowing for easy diffusion.

✔ **Explain the significance of fibrinogen presence in plasma. How does it help the body's defence mechanism?**

Fibrinogen is a protein that is soluble in plasma. When a blood vessel is damaged, fibrinogen converts to fibrin threads, which form a mesh-like structure. This structure traps red blood cells and platelets, resulting in the formation of a blood clot. This clotting mechanism prevents excessive bleeding and keeps infections from entering the body through the wound.

Circulatory System

The organ systems in human body are highly organized. Digestive, circulatory, respiratory, excretory and nervous systems are the different organ systems in human body. Each system is involved in performing specific functions. The digestive system is broadly involved in digestion and absorption of food. The absorbed food needs to be assimilated in the cells of different parts of the body. Hence, transportation of food from the digestive tract is essential. Circulatory system carries out the function of transportation of food. The food needs to be converted into energy, which takes place in the presence of oxygen in the respiratory system. The respiratory system is involved in the above process. The circulatory system also transports oxygenated blood from the lungs to different parts of the body and transports back deoxygenated blood from the whole body to the lungs for purification. The circulatory system is also involved in the transportation of waste materials generated during the metabolism of the body. The waste materials are then expelled out through the excretory system.

In this part of the chapter, we will learn about the major components of circulatory system and their functions.

Need for Circulatory System

Circulatory system in our body essentially performs distributing and collecting functions. These processes are required to occur for the sustenance of every organ in our body. Following are some of the major reasons why we need to have an elaborate circulatory system.

Transport of nutrients: Our digestive system digests and absorbs food particles so that they are easily absorbable by the cells. Circulatory system is required to transport these nutrients to each and every cell of the body.

Transport of gases: We have learnt that our cells generate energy in mitochondria with the help of oxygen and in this process, carbon dioxide is generated which needs to be removed out from the cells. Circulatory system is responsible for transport of oxygen to all the cells and also for the transport of carbon dioxide outside the cells. Circulatory system works in close association with respiratory system for exchange of gases.

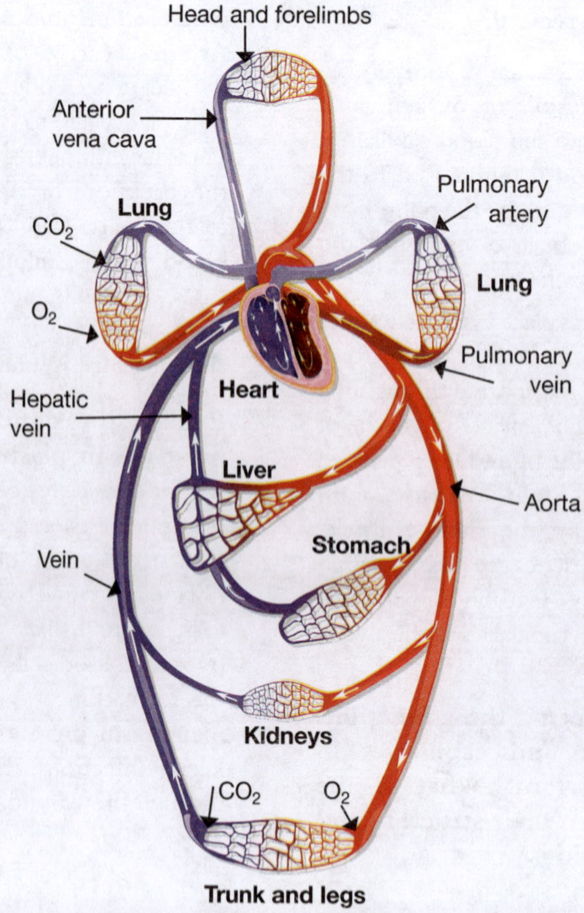

Figure 6.16 Transportation of food, gases and waste material via circulatory system

> **Info Bytes!**
> If all the blood vessels in your body were laid end to end, they'd measure over 60,000 miles long.

Removal of waste: Various metabolic activities takes place inside every cell in our body. As a result, there is formation of a lot of products, some of which are waste material and/or toxic to the cells. Hence, there is a necessary requirement for these substances to be removed out of the cell and taken to excretory system. Circulatory system does so by transporting waste material from different parts of the body to excretory organs.

Transport of hormones: In our body, there is an endocrine system which is responsible for secreting hormones (chemicals responsible for regulation of various activities in human cells). These chemicals are required to be carried to specific locations where their action is needed. Circulatory system assists in the transport of these hormones to parts of our body, where necessary.

Components of Circulatory System

For the reasons mentioned above, our circulatory system is designed such that we have fluids in our body that fulfill the need of collecting and distributing materials. There are two types of body fluids that circulate in the body for the transportation of useful and unwanted materials separately, they are blood and lymph. The types of fluids and their characteristics are presented below.

Blood

Blood is a connective tissue that exists in the form of liquid in our body. It is present in heart and blood vessels. Arteries, veins and blood capillaries are three different blood vessels that play major role in circulating blood. Blood is circulated from the heart to the arteries and then circulated back to the heart through veins. The total volume of the blood is about

5–6 L in an adult human being. The weight of the blood is 7–8% of the total body weight. Blood in human body is salty in taste and slightly alkaline in nature (pH is 7.3–7.45). It is composed of three different types of cells that are present in a liquid matrix called plasma. These blood cells are also called corpuscles and are generated by stem cells present in the bone marrow. The various components and functions of blood will be discussed in the later sections of this chapter.

Tissue Fluid

When blood passes through the capillaries surrounding different tissues, certain fluid comes out from the blood vessels. This fluid occupies the interstitial spaces between the cells of the tissue. The tissue fluid contains water and some small solute particles.

Lymph

Tissue fluid that is collected in lymphatic vessels is called lymph. Lymph vessels form the secondary circulatory system in our body and are spread throughout our body. It is light yellow in colour. Other than transportation of food material and gases involved in respiration, lymph also helps to defend our body against the microorganisms.

Info Bytes!

Plasma without fibrinogen is called serum.

Composition of Blood

The two main components of blood are plasma and blood cells.

Plasma

It is a pale yellow-coloured liquid. It is alkaline in nature and occupies 55 per cent of the total blood volume. The content of water in plasma is 90-92%. The solid components of plasma include inorganic and organic substances. Inorganic substances are different positive and negative ions such as Na^+, Ca^{++}, Mg^{++}, Cl-, HCO^-_3, etc. Organic substances are glucose, amino acids, lipids, etc. Plasma also contains a protein, called fibrinogen that is responsible for blood coagulation.

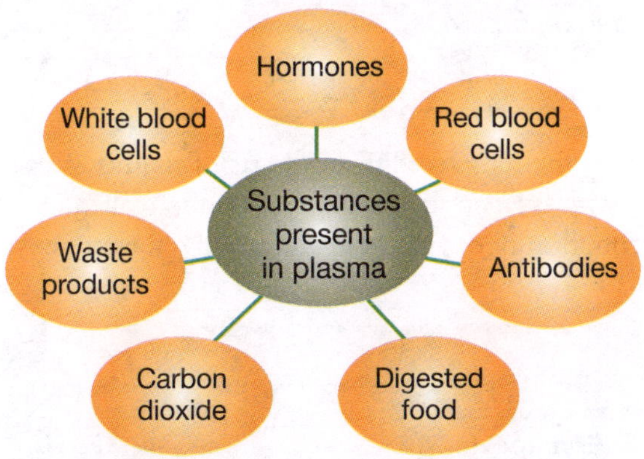

Figure 6.17 Substances present in plasma

Info Bytes!

Proteins present in plasma are made in the liver.

Cellular Components

Cellular components of the blood are also called formed elements as they have recognizable structures that can be seen under microscope.

Forty five per cent of the total volume of blood is occupied by blood cells. These are of following three types:

1. Red blood cells or erythrocytes (RBCs)
2. White blood cells or leucocytes (WBCs)
3. Platelets or thrombocytes

Red blood cells

Red blood cells (RBCs) are also called erythrocytes (Greek erythros: red; cyte: cell). They are the most common type of blood cell and primary means of delivering oxygen to the body tissues. There are 5.5 million RBCs in one cubic millimetre of blood.

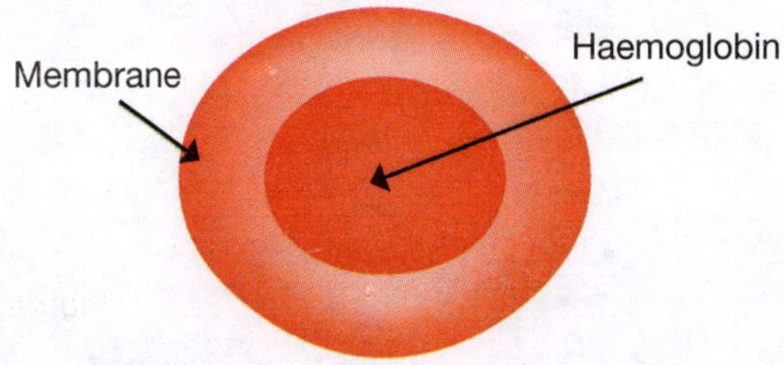

Figure 6.18 RBC with haemoglobin

Structure

- They have biconcave, and disc-like structure.
- They do not have any nucleus in them.
- A red pigment, haemoglobin is present in their cytoplasm.
- Haemoglobin imparts red colour to the blood.
- Haeme means iron and globin means protein.
- Thus, haemoglobin is an iron-containing protein.

Info Bytes!

The only place where your blood isn't red is in the corneas of your eyes.

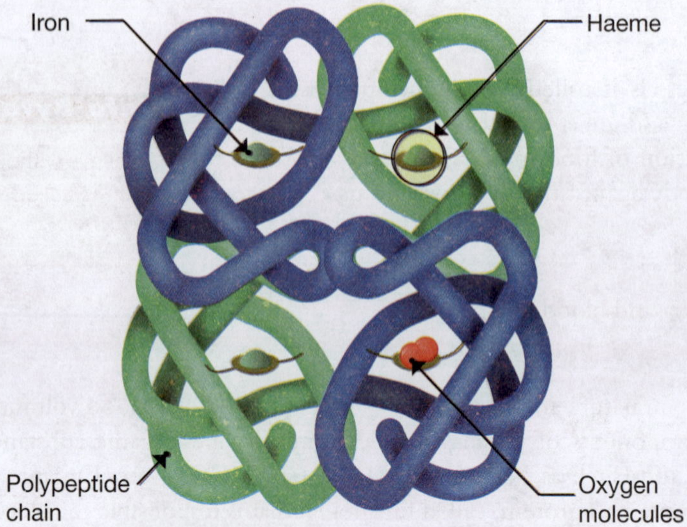

Figure 6.19 Structure of haemoglobin

Info Bytes!

An RBC can survive about 120 days and then it undergoes disintegration in liver or spleen.

Functions

The main function of RBCs is to transport oxygen from the lungs to different parts of the body and carbon dioxide from different tissues to the lungs. Haemoglobin combines with oxygen forming a compound, called oxy-haemoglobin. When oxy-haemoglobin reaches the region where the concentration of oxygen is low, it readily liberates oxygen.

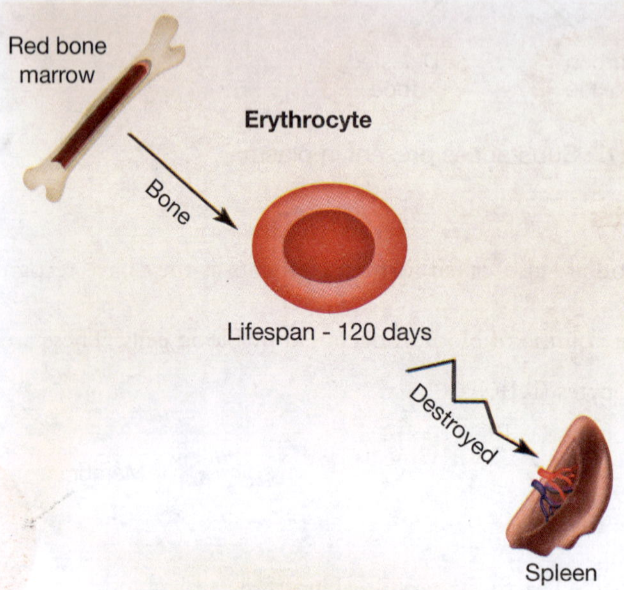

Figure 6.20 Life cycle of a red blood cell

White Blood Cells

White blood cells (WBCs) are also called leucocytes (Greek leukos: white; cyte: cell). They form major part of the immune system and are involved in protecting the body against foreign invaders. They are much less in number than RBCs. In one cubic millimetre of blood, the number of WBCs is 5000–10,000.

White blood cells are larger in size than red blood cells and contain nucleus. The number of white blood cells in blood is much less than red blood cells. WBCs can be broadly classified into two categories based on their structure and function, which are granulocytes and agranulocytes.

Granulocytes

Granulocytes have granular cytoplasm and lobed nucleus. Granulocytes can be further classified into three categories of cells based on their structure as well as function, which are eosinophils, basophils and neutrophils.

Eosinophils

- Eosinophils have bi-lobed nucleus and both the lobes are connected with a thin strand.
- They make up only about 2–5% of WBC.
- One millilitre of blood contains about 60–300 eosinophils.
- Cytoplasmic granules of eosinophils turn orange-red in response to the acid dye (eosin).
- The main function of eosinophils is to destroy pathogens, particularly parasitic worms and also responding to allergic reactions.
- Eosinophilia is a condition in which the number of eosinophils in per unit volume of blood increases due to some parasitic infection.

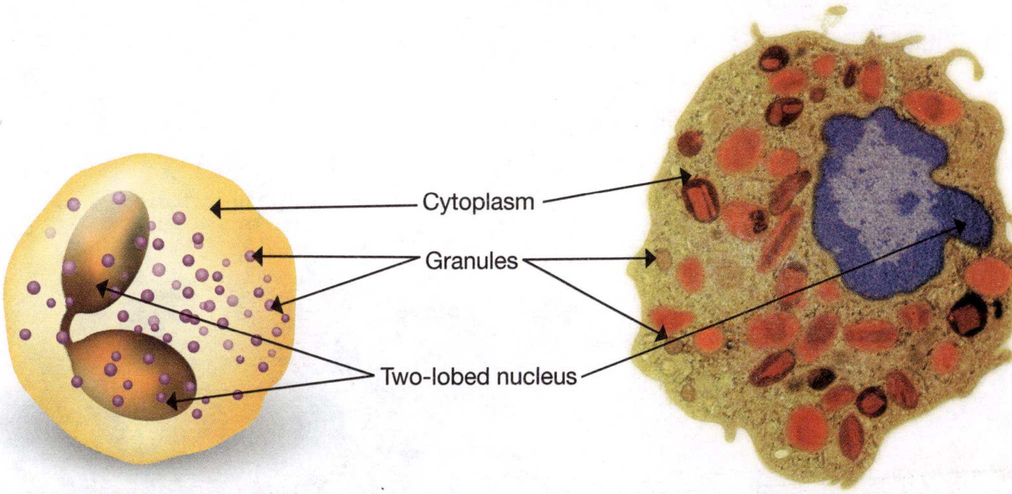

Figure 6.21 Illustration of an eosinophil

Figure 6.22 Electron microscope image of a human eosinophil

Basophils

- The nucleus in basophils has two or more lobes.
- About 1 per cent of the leucocytes are basophills.
- One millilitre of the blood contains 35–100 basophils.
- They are mostly found in skin and mucosal tissues.
- Basophils turn blue–black in response to basic dyes.
- They secrete chemicals such as histamine, heparin and serotonin.
- Histamine produces an allergic reaction when an unwanted substance tries to enter our body.

- It also makes the blood vessels permeable so that other leucocytes can act against the pathogens.
- Heparin prevents clotting of blood.
- Serotonin is a chemical that transmits the messages from one area of the brain to another.

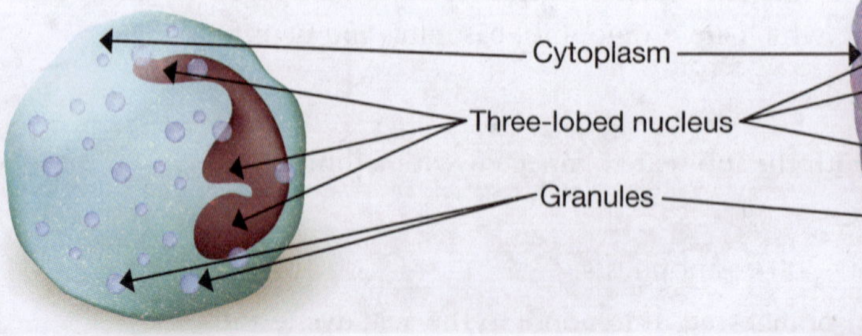

Figure 6.23 Illustration of a basophil

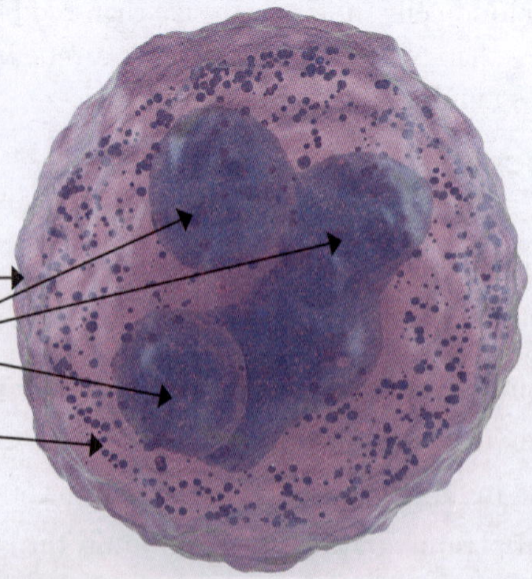

Figure 6.24 Microscopic view of a basophil granulocyte

Neutrophils

- The nucleus of neutrophils has 3–5 lobes.
- Neutrophils get stained in response to neutral dyes.
- About 70 per cent of the total WBC count is neutrophils.
- One millilitre of blood contains 4000–5000 neutrophils.
- Neutrophils engulf the pathogens invaded in our body by the process of phagocytosis.
- They act as body's natural antibiotics.

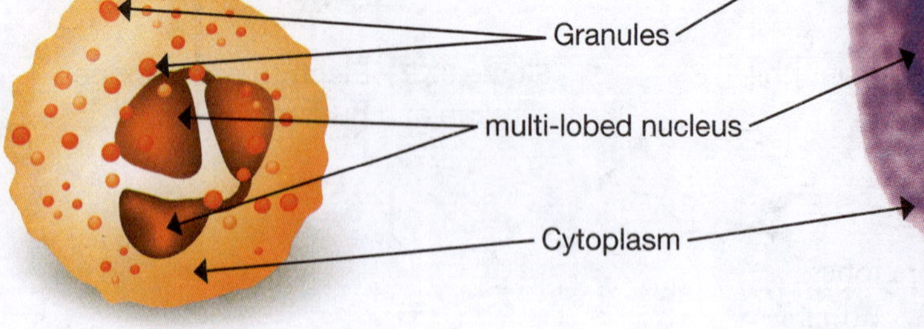

Figure 6.25 Illustration of a neutrophil

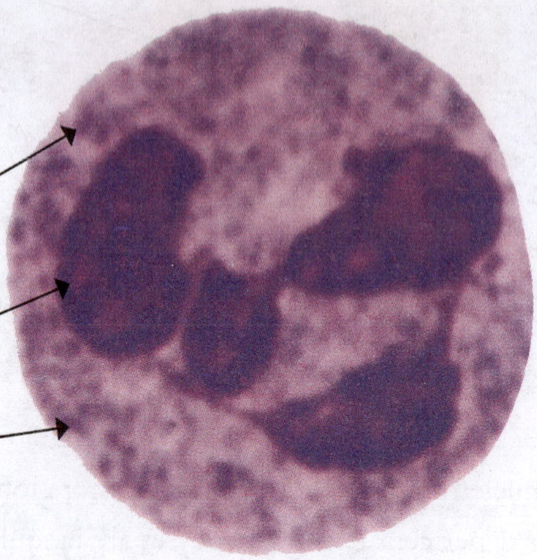

Figure 6.26 Microscopic view of a neutrophil

Agranulocytes

The cytoplasm of agranulocytes is not granular. Thirty five percent of total WBC count is a granulocytes. They can be classified into two categories based on their structure and function, which are lymphocytes and monocytes.

Lymphocytes

- They have large mono-lobed nucleus.
- One millilitre of blood contains 1800–3000 lymphocytes.
- About 30–32% of total WBC count is lymphocytes.
- The main function of lymphocytes is the production of antibodies and thus, they provide immunity to our body.

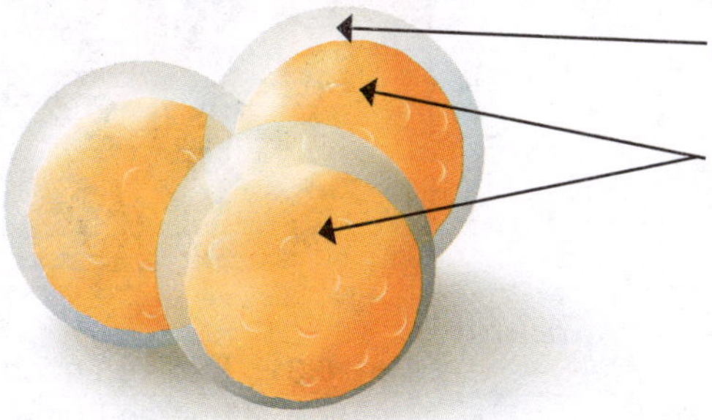

Figure 6.27 Illustration of lymphocytes

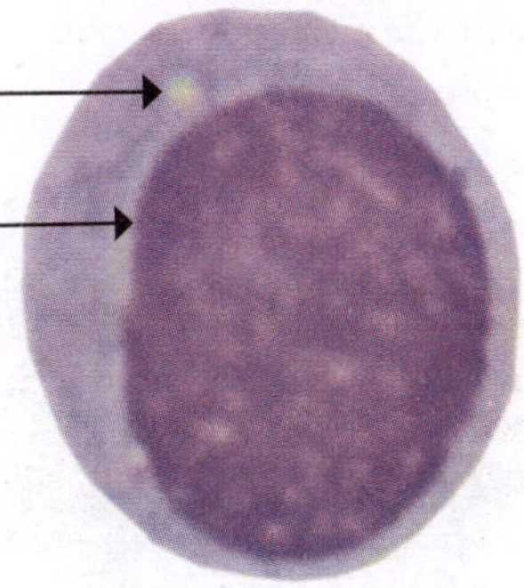

Figure 6.28 A microscopic and magnified view of a lymphocyte

Monocytes

- They have a large cytoplasm and kidney-shaped nucleus.
- One millilitre of blood contains 200–700 monocytes.
- About 2–3% of total WBC count is monocytes.
- They ingest microorganisms that intrude our body and also act as scavengers by removing the dead cells.
- The total WBC count of a person who is suffering from a type of blood cancer, leukaemia, increases.

This in turn results in decrease in the production of RBCs and platelets.

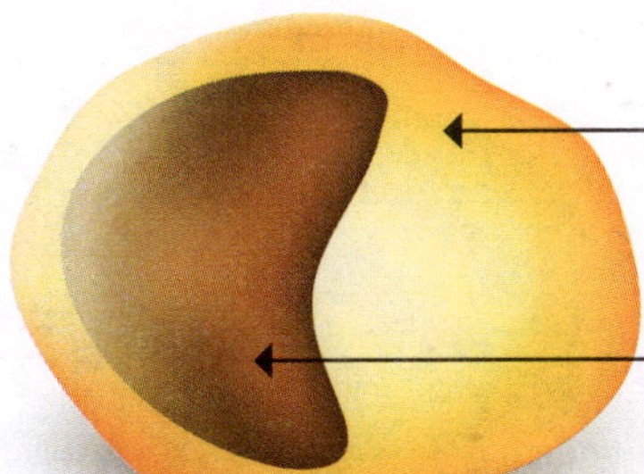

Figure 6.29 Illustration of a monocyte

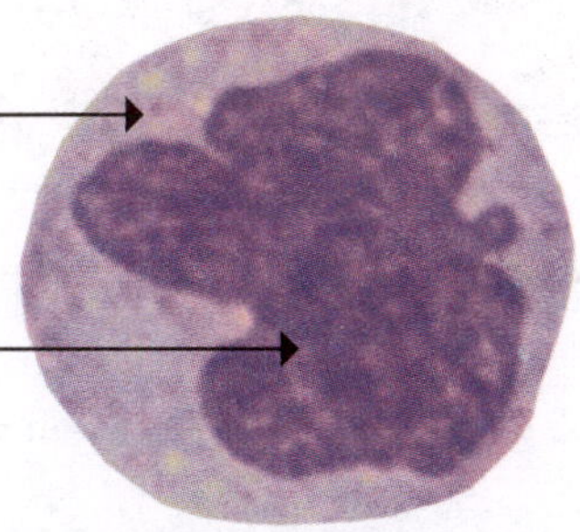

Figure 6.30 A microscopic and magnified view of a Monocyte

Platelets

Platelets are also called thrombocytes (Greek thrómbos: lump; cyte: cell).

Platelets are not true cells; rather they are the fragments of cells. They are colourless and irregular in shape. The cell fragments do not contain nucleus and their cytoplasm does not have granules. Their lifespan is very short. They survive for 3–5 days and then disintegrate in the spleen. The main function of platelets is facilitating blood clotting.

Blood Clotting

Whenever there is a cut introduced to a blood vessel, blood comes out of it. However, after sometime, the blood stops to flow out of the vessel and we observe that there is a formation of lump or mass around the wound (region where the cut is made). This process of change of liquid form of blood to a gel-like clump or clot is called blood clotting or blood coagulation. This process can be described the following stages.

- The platelets inside the injured cells release a protein called thromboplastin.
- Thromboplastin, in the presence of calcium ions, converts a substance, prothrombin to thrombin.
- Thrombin, in the presence of calcium ions, converts fibrinogen present in the plasma to fibrin.

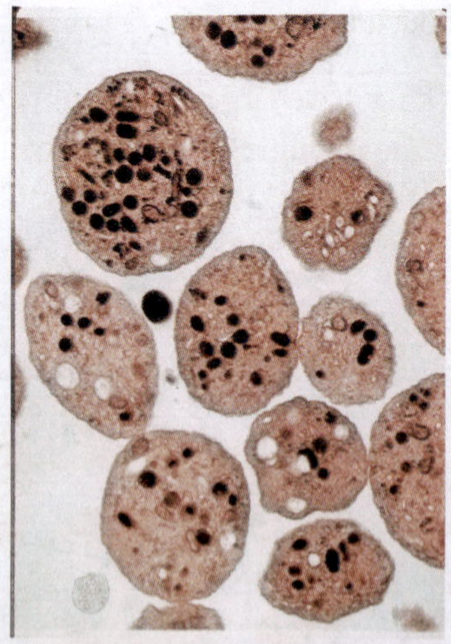

Figure 6.31 Electron microscope image of human platelets

Info Bytes!

Fibrinogen is soluble and fibrin is insoluble in plasma.

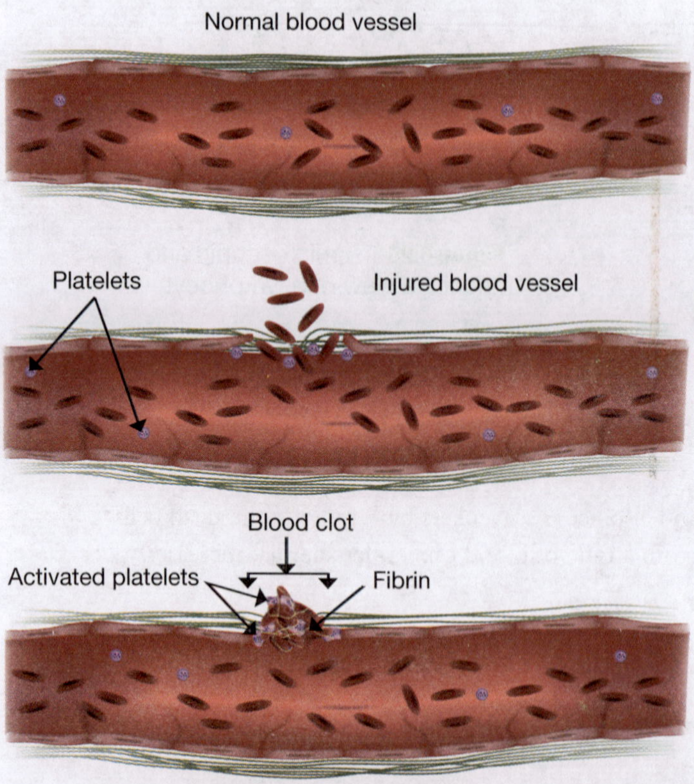

Figure 6.32 Steps involved in clotting of blood

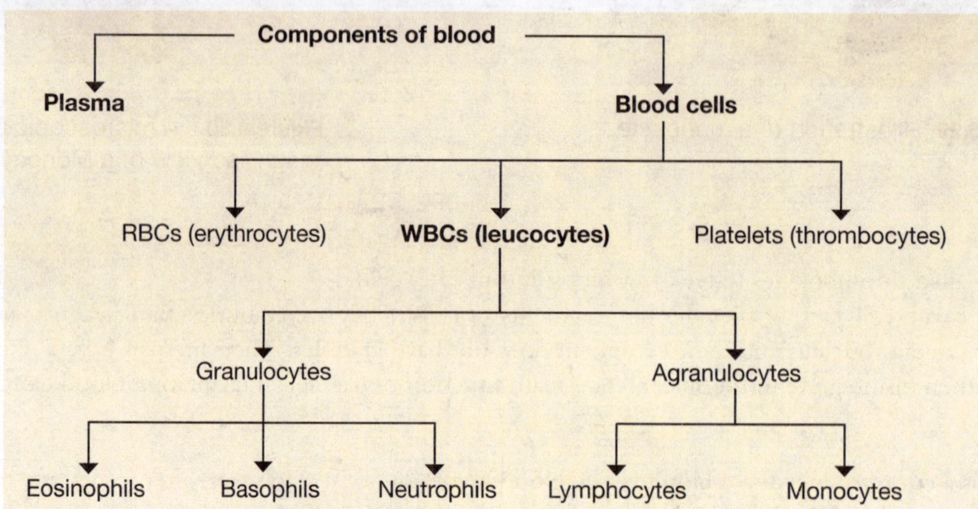

Figure 6.33 Components of blood

- Fibrin threads form a mesh-like network around the wound.
- Fibrin network traps the blood cells and later squeezes out the serum.
- The semi-solid mass that is left behind is the clot.

Functions of Blood

The major functions of blood can be broadly divided under two categories: (1) Transport and (2) Protection

1. **Transport**
   - Blood transports digested food from the alimentary canal to the cells of the body. Digested food material includes simple carbohydrates, amino acids, vitamins, etc.
   - Blood transports oxygen from the lungs to the tissues. It also transports carbon dioxide from the tissues to the lungs.
   - It transports waste material from the tissues to excretory organs such as liver and kidney.
   - It transports hormones from endocrine glands to the location where they are required.
   - It also supports in maintaining constant temperature in body by distributing heat.
2. **Protection**
   - At the time of injury, there is formation of blood clot which prevents entry of foreign invaders through the wound.
   - Basophils secrete histamine that is involved in inflammatory and allergic responses.
   - Phagocytosis: Neutrophils engulf the foreign particles such as bacteria as a defensive mechanism against invaders.
   - Inflammation: It happens as a response of tissues to either an injury or invasion by foreign particles. Inflammatory reaction is characterized by heat and swelling of the affected area, pain, etc. Lymphocytes migrate to the inflamed region by diapedesis. Here, they attack the damaged cells by phagocytosis.

Info Bytes!

Diapedesis is the passage of blood cells inside the capillaries, commonly accompanying inflammation.

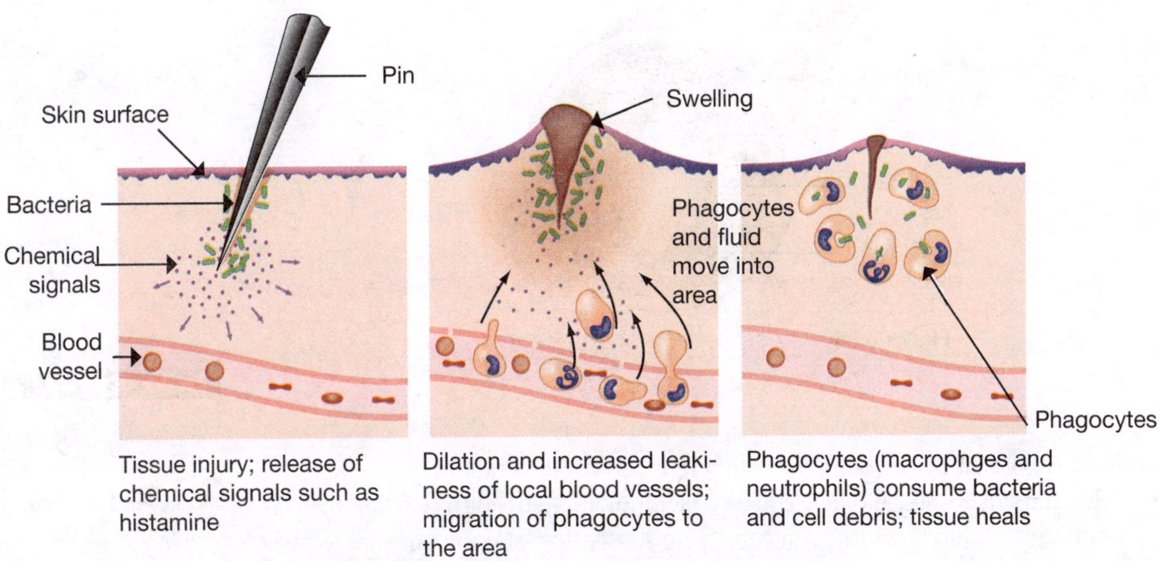

Figure 6.34 Illustration of inflammation process

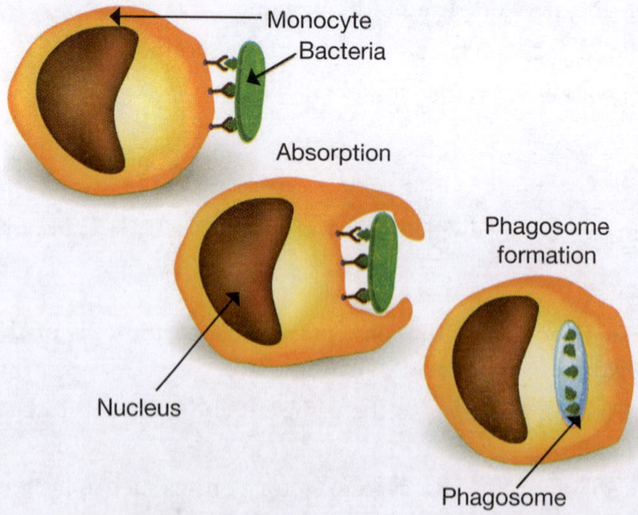

Figure 6.35 Phagocytosis by a monocyte

Blood Vessels

Blood in human body flows through the network of tube-like structures called blood vessels. Following are the three types of blood vessels:

1. Arteries 2. Veins 3. Capillaries

Arteries

An artery is a blood vessel that carries blood away from the heart and transports it to different parts of the body. Arteries have thick muscular wall and their lumen is narrow; therefore, arteries never collapse. Blood passes through the arteries under high pressure with jerks. They do not have any valves. All arteries carry oxygenated blood, except pulmonary artery which carries deoxygenated blood from heart to lungs. Branches originating from the arteries are called arterioles.

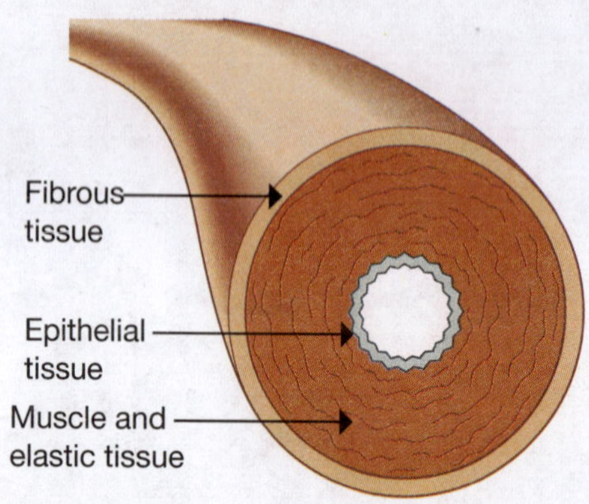

Figure 6.36 Cross-section of an artery

Veins

A vein is a blood vessel that carries blood from different parts of the body to the heart. They have thin and less muscular walls, and hence have wider lumen. Veins collapse when they are empty or cut through. Blood flows through veins with steady flow and the pressure is lower than that of arteries. Valves are present in veins to prevent the back flow of blood. Veins carry deoxygenated blood, except pulmonary vein which carries oxygenated blood from lungs to heart. Small blood vessels that carry blood to veins are called venules.

Info Bytes!

Blood is always red in colour, however our veins appear blue because of difference in wavelength of light penetrating at different degrees.

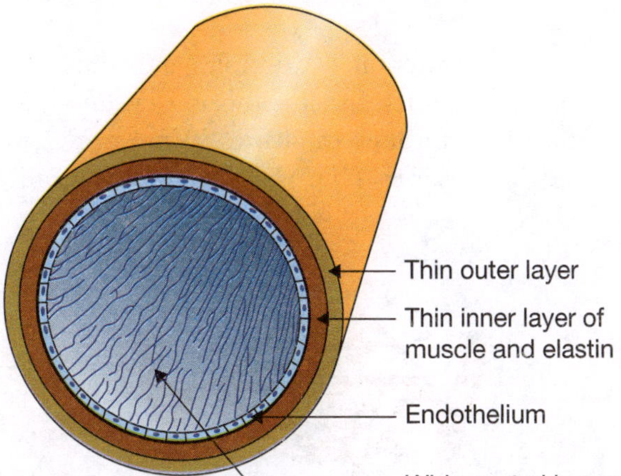

Figure 6.37 Cross-section of vein

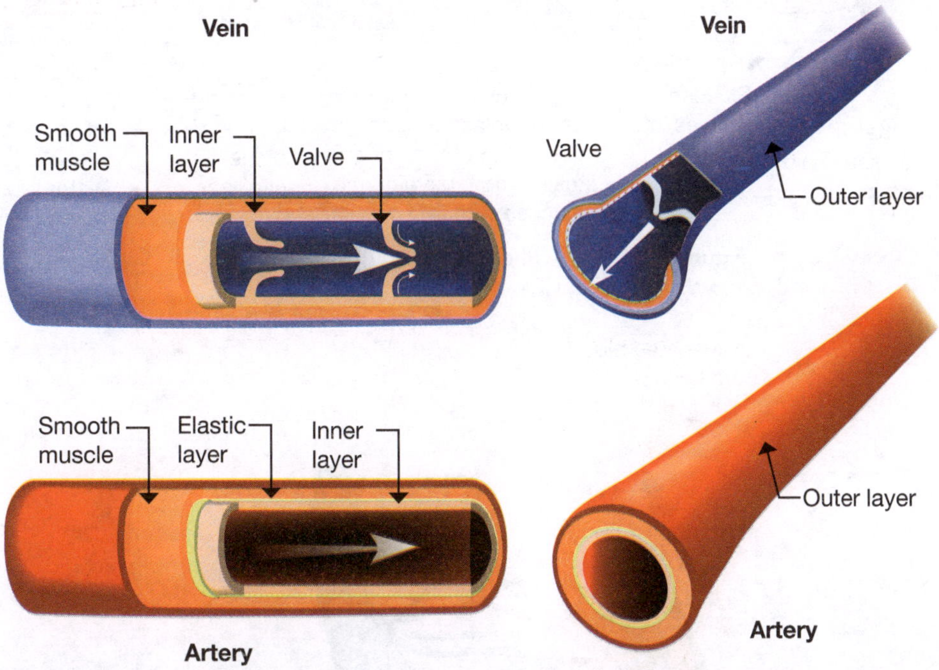

Figure 6.38 Detailed illustration of an artery and a vein

Table 6.3 Differences between artery and vein

Parameter	Arteries	Veins
Function	Carry blood away from the heart	Carry blood towards the heart
Type of blood	Carry oxygenated blood; except pulmonary artery	Carry deoxygenated blood; except pulmonary vein
Blood flow	With jerks	Continuous flow
Pressure	Blood flows under high pressure	Blood flows under little pressure
Wall	Elastic	Non-elastic
Branching	Branch progressively	Unite progressively
Lumen	Narrow	Wide

Capillaries

Capillaries are thin-walled microscopic vessels that connect arterioles and venules. The diameter of capillaries is about eight micron. The wall of capillaries is one-celled thick and it comprises squamous epithelial cells. Nutrients and oxygen gas are transported to the tissues from the blood through capillaries. Waste materials and carbon dioxide gas are carried from the body tissues to the blood through capillaries Thin walls of capillaries provide the passage of leucocytes from capillaries to tissue fluid.

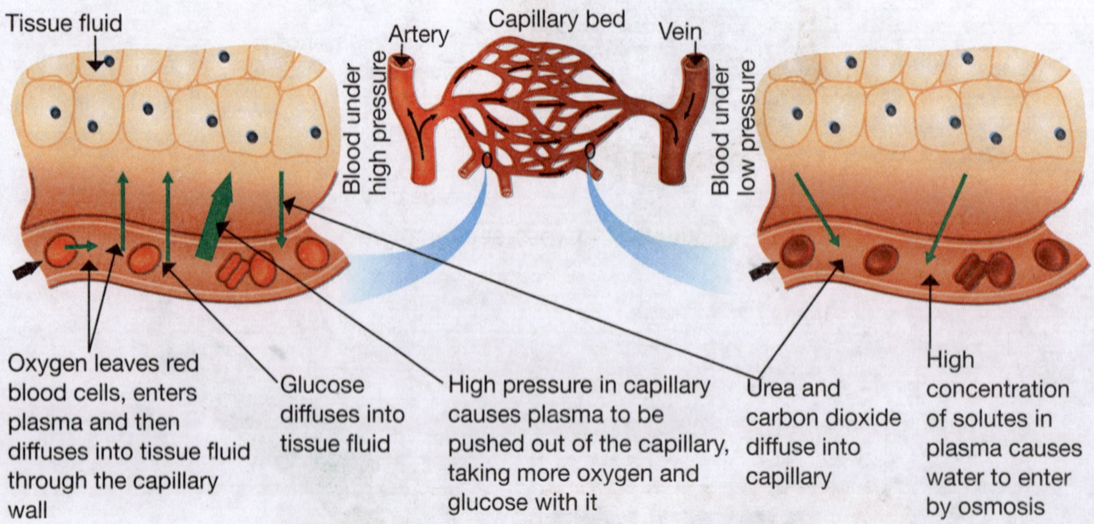

Figure 6.39 Blood flow through capillaries

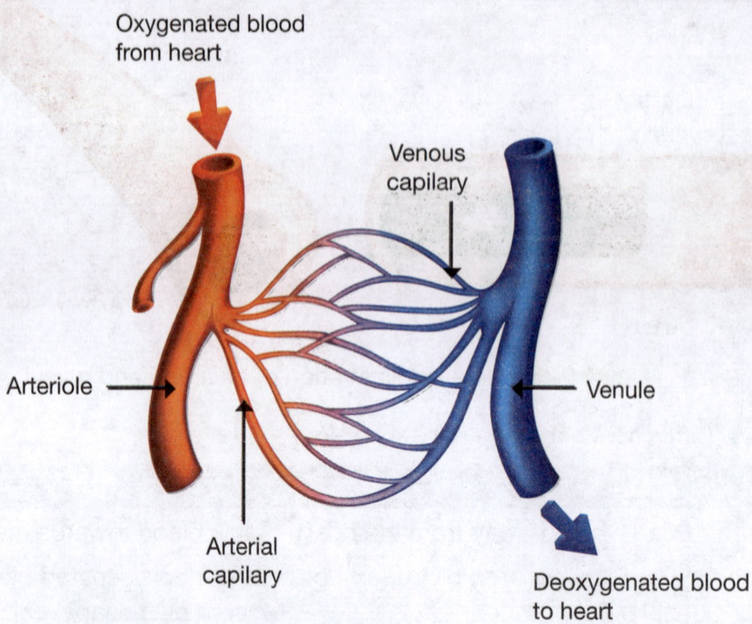

Figure 6.40 Illustration of blood through arteriole and venule

Heart

The heart is the controlling organ of the circulatory system. It controls the flow of blood through the rest of the circulatory system. The heart is a muscular organ and the muscle cells that constitute the heart are called cardiac muscle fibres. In an adult human body, the heart is about the size of a closed fist. The heart is located at the chest cavity slightly tilted towards the left. The heart is present in a fluid-filled cavity, called pericardial cavity. Pericardial cavity is enclosed by a double-walled membrane, called pericardium. The heart contains four chambers listed as follows.

1. Left atrium, the upper left chamber
2. Right atrium, the upper right chamber
3. Left ventricle, the lower left chamber
4. Right ventricle, the lower right chamber

The left atrium (plural: atria) and the left ventricle are completely separated from the right atrium and the right ventricle. The atria receive the blood while the ventricles pump the blood outside the heart. Hence, the ventricles are stronger and larger than the atria. The atria are connected to veins and the ventricles are connected to arteries. Veins transport the blood to the heart while arteries carry the blood out of the heart. The chambers on the left side of the heart are slightly larger than the chambers of the right side due to specific functions. There are two apertures within the heart that control the blood flow from the atrium to the respective ventricle. The aperture that allows the blood to enter left ventricle from left atrium is called left auriculo—ventricular aperture. Similarly, right auriculo–ventricular aperture allows the blood to flow from right atrium to right ventricle.

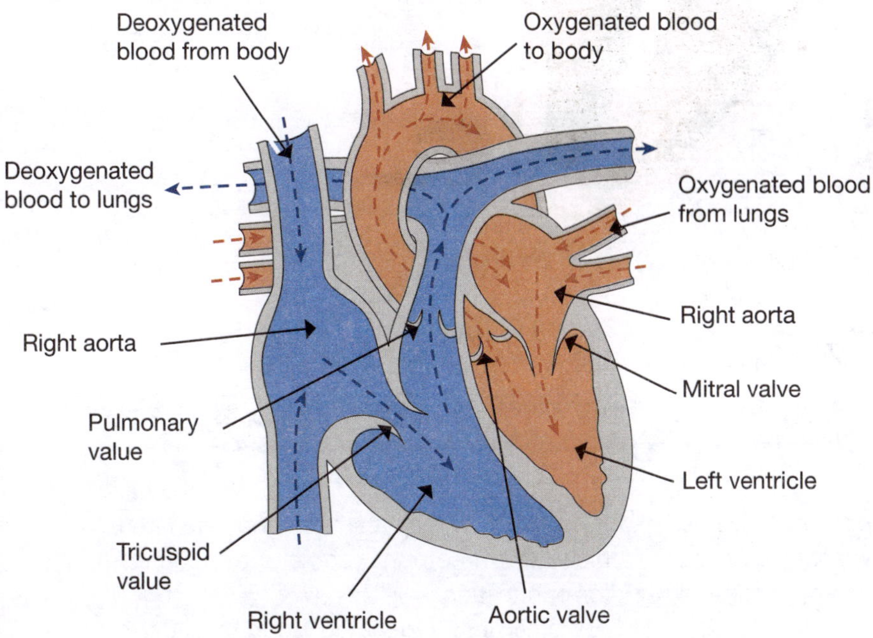

Figure 6.41 Illustration of human heart

Info Bytes!

Auricle is a flap on the wall on the anterior surface of the left atrium of heart.

Info Bytes!

The heart beats about 100,000 times a day, pumping around 7,500 liters (2,000 gallons) of blood daily.

Valves in the Heart

The function of heart in circulatory system is like a pump. The flow of a liquid through any pump is directed by a valve. Similarly, heart being a pump-like organ has valves that make the blood flow uni-directional. The heart has following two types of valves:

1. Atrioventricular valves or cuspid valves are present between atria and respective ventricles.
   - The valve between left atrium and left ventricle is called left atrioventricular valve or bicuspid valve or mitral valve.
   - The valve between right atrium and right ventricle is called right atrioventricular valve or tricuspid valve.
   - These bicuspid and tricuspid valves are attached to the heart muscles with string-like tendons called chordae tendineae.

2. Semilunar valves are located between the ventricles and the opening of large blood vessels originating from the ventricles.

- The valve between the left ventricle and the aorta is called aortic semilunar valve. These are three in numbers.
- The valve between the right ventricle and the pulmonary artery is called pulmonary semilunar valve. These are also three in numbers.

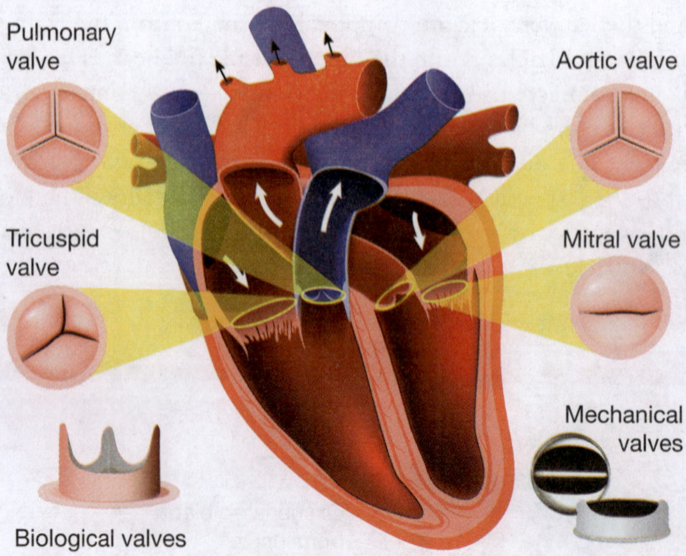

Figure 6.42 Valves of the heart

Table 6.4 Major blood vessels involved in inflow and outflow of blood into or from heart

Blood Vessel Entering	Blood Vessels Leaving
The Heart	
• Superior vena cava or anterior vena cava or precaval vein carries deoxygenated blood from the upper part of body (head, chest and arms) to the right atrium. • Inferior vena cava or posterior vena cava or postcaval vein carries deoxygenated blood from the lower part of body (legs and abdomen) to the right atrium.	• Pulmonary artery carries deoxygenated blood from the right ventricle to the lungs for purification. • Aorta carries oxygenated blood to all parts of the body. • There are two coronary arteries (left and right) that originate from the base of aorta and supply blood to the heart muscle.
The Liver	
• Hepatic artery supplies oxygenated blood to the liver from the aorta. • Hepatic portal vein transports blood from the spleen and gastrointestinal tract to the liver.	• Hepatic vein transports blood from the liver to posterior vena cava for its purification.
The Kidney	
• Renal arteries transport blood from the aorta to the kidney.	• Renal veins transport blood from the kidney to the posterior vena cava for its purification.

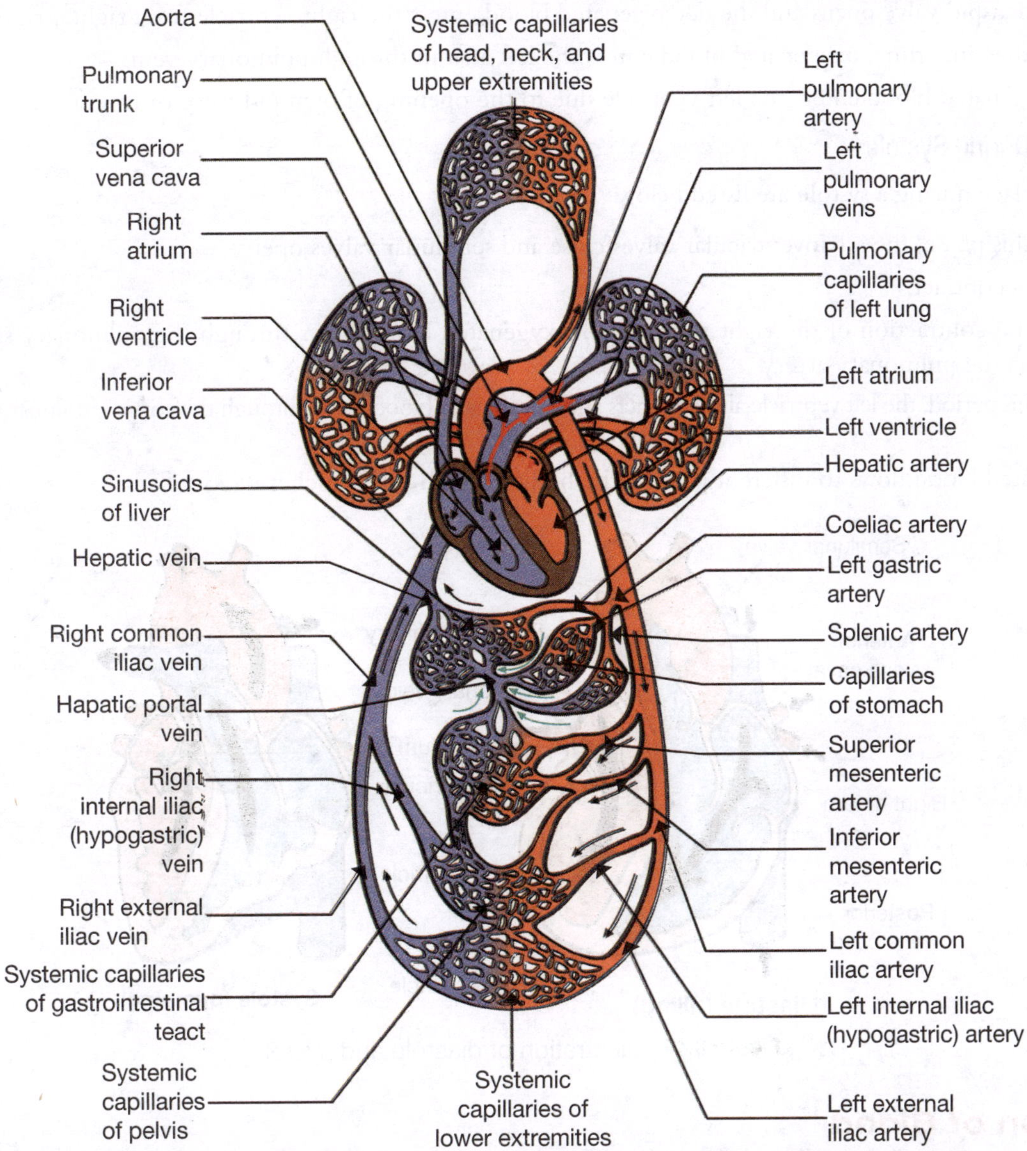

Figure 6.43 Arteries and veins entering and leaving the heart, liver and kidneys

Cardiac Cycle

A cardiac cycle comprises repetitive sequence of events that occur in the heart. There are two phases of cardiac cycle—diastole phase and systole phase. In the diastole phase, the heart gets filled with the blood and then ventricles relax. In the systole phase, the ventricles contract and the outflow of blood takes place from the heart to the arteries. Thus, one cardiac cycle gets completed, and one contraction (systole) and one relaxation (diastole) cause one heartbeat. Heartbeats occur due to this rhythmic contraction and relaxation of the heart muscle. Normal heartbeat in a healthy human body is about 70–72 per minute.

> **Info Bytes!**
>
> Pacemaker is the part of heart that starts the heart beat by producing impulse. In human heart, pacemaker is the sino-atrial node located in the walls of right atrium.

Flow of Blood During Diastole

Events taking place during a diastole are listed below.

- In this phase, the atria and ventricles are relaxed due to the inflow of blood to the heart and atrioventricular valves remain open.
- Deoxygenated blood from different parts of the body enters right atrium through superior and inferior vena cava.

- Then, tricuspid valve opens and the deoxygenated blood enters the right ventricle from right atrium.
- During the same time, oxygenated blood enters the left atrium through pulmonary vein.
- The oxygenated blood enters the left ventricle due to the opening of bicuspid valve or mistral valve.

Flow of Blood During Systole

Events taking place during a systole are listed below.

- During this phase, the artrioventricular valves close and semilunar valves open.
- Ventricles contract.
- Due to the contraction of the right ventricle, deoxygenated blood flows through the pulmonary semilunar valve and enters the pulmonary artery.
- During this period, the left ventricle also contracts and oxygenated blood flows through the aortic semilunar valve and enters the aorta.
- Oxygenated blood flows to different parts of the body through the branches of aorta.

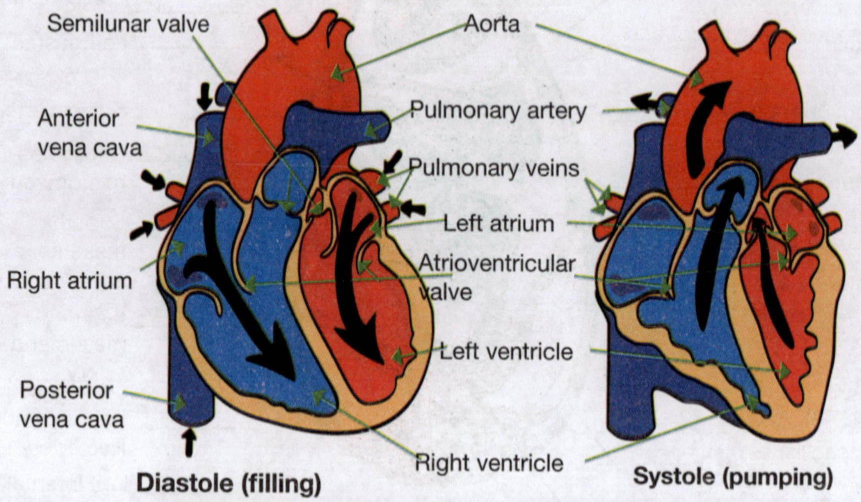

Figure 6.44 Illustration of diastole and systole

Circulation of Blood

Blood is circulated by the heart through two different pathways. The deoxygenated blood from various body parts comes to the heart. It is taken to the lungs for purification and brought back to the heart. This oxygenated blood is pumped to the various parts of the body. Since the blood goes to the heart twice during the circulation, it is known as double circulation. The two pathways are called systemic circuit or systemic circulation, and pulmonary circuit or pulmonary circulation.

Pulmonary Circuit

Movements happening during pulmonary circulation are listed below.

- Pulmonary circuit includes the passage of deoxygenated blood from the right ventricle to the lungs through pulmonary artery for the purification of blood.
- It also includes the flow of oxygenated blood from the lungs to the left atrium through the pulmonary vein. Hence, the pulmonary circuit involves blood flow through the pulmonary vein and pulmonary artery.

Systemic Circuit

Movements happening during systemic circulation are listed below.

- Systemic circuit includes the flow of oxygenated blood from the left ventricle to the aorta.
- Then, oxygenated blood flows through different arteries and capillaries, and reaches tissues of different parts of the body.

- Systemic circuit also includes the flow of deoxygenated blood from different parts of the body through veins to the right atrium via superior and inferior vena cava.

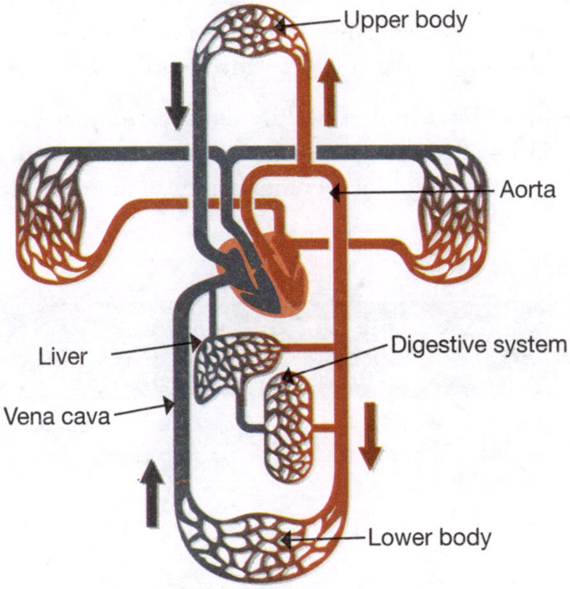

Figure 6.45 Systemic circulation

> **Info Bytes!**
> The heart sounds are called lub-dub which are produced at the beginning of ventricular systole (lub) and at the beginning of ventricular diastole (dub).

Blood Pressure

The pressure exerted by the blood on the walls of blood vessels due to the pumping of the blood from the heart is called blood pressure. The two types of blood pressure are systolic blood pressure and diastolic blood pressure.

> **Info Bytes!**
> The instrument by which blood pressure is measured is called sphygmomanometer.

Systolic Blood Pressure

The pressure of the blood when the heart contracts is called systolic blood pressure. The blood is pumped to the whole body due to systolic blood pressure. In human beings, systolic blood pressure is about 120 mmHg.

Diastolic Blood Pressure

The pressure of the blood when the heart relaxes due to the entrance of blood into different chambers of the heart is called diastolic blood pressure. In human beings, diastolic blood pressure is about 80 mmHg.

Blood Groups

WBCs produce antibodies which are special proteins that help fight against the foreign substances. Antigens are the proteins that are responsible for production of antibodies. Specific antigen evokes the generation of specific antibody.

Table 6.5 Blood grouping system

Blood group	Antigen on the surface of RBC	Antibody in plasma
A	Antigen A	Antibody B
B	Antigen B	Antibody A
AB	Antigen A and B	None
O	None	Antibodies A and B

Based on the combination of antibody present in the plasma and antigens present on the surface of RBCs, human blood can be classified into different groups as given in the table below.

Rh blood grouping: This is another system of blood grouping. People who have factor (protein) Rh (Rhesus) on the surface of RBCs are Rh-positive and those without this are Rh negative. If an Rh-negative person receives blood from Rh positive, his/her body will develop antibodies against Rh. This can lead to adverse medical effects.

Blood transfusion: It is a medical procedure in which blood from a healthy donor is transferred to a person who is in need of blood. The person who donates the blood is called donor and the person who receives the blood is called recipient. The blood of donor and recipient must be compatible. Blood compatibility of different blood groups is listed below.

Table 6.6 Blood transfer compatibility

Blood group of the donor	Blood group of the recipient			
	A	B	AB (universal recipient)	O
A	✓	×	✓	×
B	×	✓	✓	×
AB	×	×	✓	×
O (universal donor)	✓	✓	✓	✓

Hepatic Portal System

Liver is an organ that acts as a digestive gland as well as an excretory organ. Blood does not directly flow from the digestive tract to the inferior vena cava. It is transported to the heart via liver through a system of veins called hepatic portal system. Deoxygenated blood passes through the hepatic portal veins and transports blood from the digestive tract and spleen to the liver.

Info Bytes!

14 June is celebrated as World Blood Donor Day.

Digested food is absorbed from the intestine to the blood. This blood is transported to the liver through the hepatic portal veins and undergoes processing before it reaches the heart. Hepatic portal system starts from the capillaries in the gastrointestinal tract and ends at the capillaries in the liver. Since the blood flows in this system from one capillary to another capillary through veins, it is called portal system.

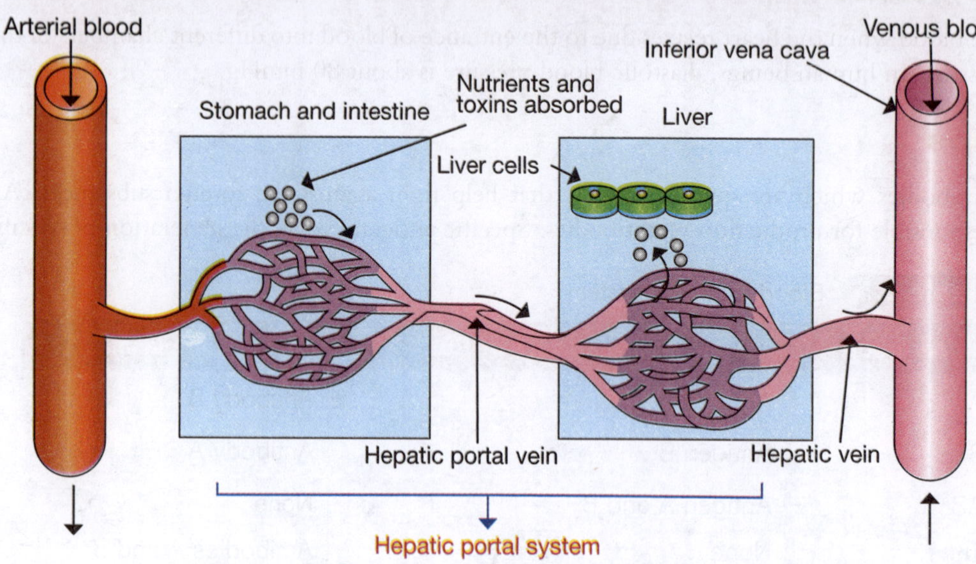

Figure 6.46 Schematic representation of hepatic portal

Lymphatic system

The lymphatic system is also a part of the circulatory system since the lymph also takes part in transportation of food material and waste substances. Some amount of plasma, proteins and blood cells are expelled through the pores of the wall of the capillaries and they occupy the inter-cellular spaces in the tissues. This is called tissue fluid. Lymphatic system comprises lymph vessels and lymph nodes. Tissue fluid that drains into lymphatic vessels from the intercellular spaces is called lymph. Lymph contains 94 per cent of water. Other than water, it contains various substances such as proteins, nitrogenous substances such as urea, carbohydrates, creatinine, chloride and enzymes. The only blood cells present in lymph are lymphocytes. Unlike circulatory system, lymphatic system is not a totally closed system. Lymph vessels transport lymph towards the heart and enable the fluid to enter vena cava which opens into the right atrium. Lymph passes through the lymph vessels due to the skeletal muscular contraction. It also helps in the maintenance of the composition of tissue fluid.

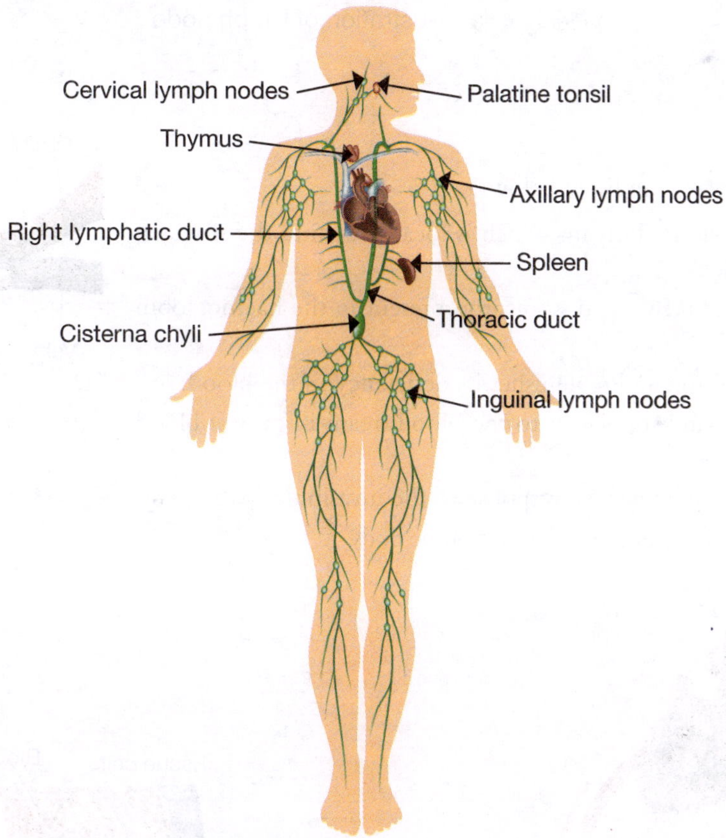

Figure 6.47 Lymphatic System

Lymph Nodes

Structure and functions of lymph nodes are listed below.

- Lymph nodes are present throughout the body.
- The main function of lymph nodes is fighting infection.
- Lymph in the lymph nodes contains lymphocytes which produce antibodies.
- Thus, lymph nodes provide immunity to our body to fight against diseases.
- Other than lymph nodes, there are some lymph organs that also defend our body against the invasion of pathogens.
- Spleen is the largest lymph organ in human body. Tonsils are also important lymph organs present at the back of the pharynx.

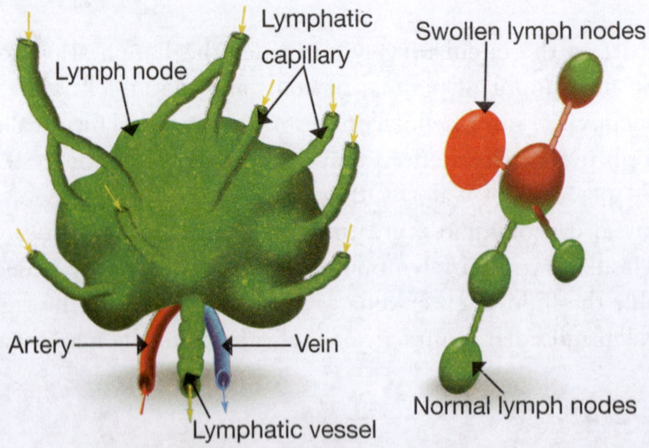

Figure 6.48 Illustration of lymph node

Spleen

Structure and functions of spleen are listed below.

- Spleen is a dark red-coloured organ, which is located behind the stomach and above the left kidney.
- Spleen disintegrates old RBCs and stores iron present in the haemoglobin of the RBCs.
- It acts as a reservoir of iron and replenishes its deficiency in the blood.
- It can also store blood and supplies it to the bloodstream in case of blood loss.
- Spleen can generate lymphocytes in response to the invasion of pathogens.
- Thus, it plays a role in the defence mechanism of the body.

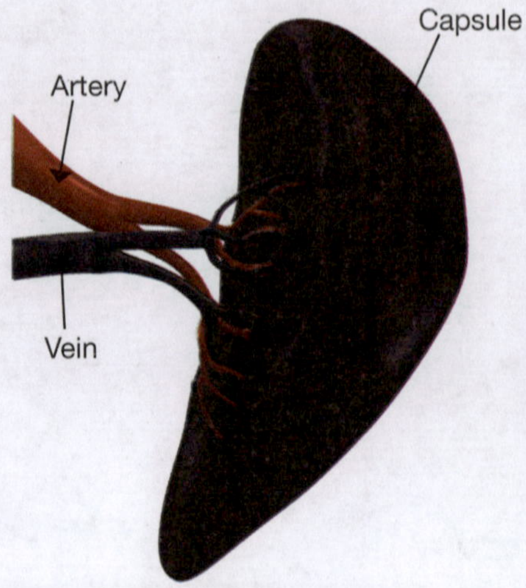

Figure 6.49 Spleen

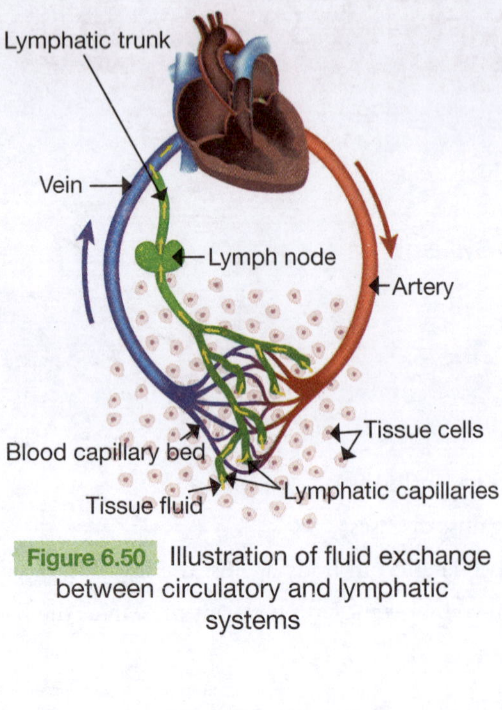

Figure 6.50 Illustration of fluid exchange between circulatory and lymphatic systems

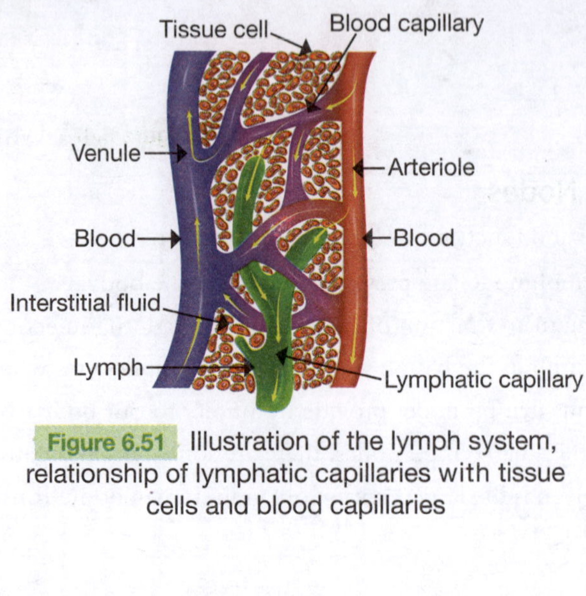

Figure 6.51 Illustration of the lymph system, relationship of lymphatic capillaries with tissue cells and blood capillaries

Quick Recap

✔ **Describe the role of haemoglobin in gas transport in the blood. Why is it so important for red blood cells to contain haemoglobin?**

The protein haemoglobin is found in red blood cells. It has a high affinity for oxygen, allowing it to bind to and transport oxygen molecules from the lungs to body tissues. Haemoglobin also aids in the collection of waste product carbon dioxide from tissues and transporting it to the lungs for exhalation. RBCs would not be able to transport these gases efficiently without haemoglobin, resulting in decreased oxygen delivery to tissues and inefficient carbon dioxide removal.

✔ **What effect does the heart's position in the thoracic cavity have on the size of the right and left lungs? What is the significance of this anatomical arrangement?**

Because the heart is positioned slightly to the left side of the thoracic cavity, the left lung is slightly smaller than the right lung. This anatomical arrangement ensures that the heart, a vital organ, is protected and has enough space to function properly. It also allows both lungs to take up the most space in the thoracic cavity, increasing respiratory capacity.

✔ **How do white blood cells differ from red blood cells in structure and function? Why is the presence of a nucleus in white blood cells significant?**

In the body, white blood cells (WBCs) and red blood cells (RBCs) serve different functions. RBCs, which lack a nucleus, are primarily responsible for the transport of oxygen and carbon dioxide. Their biconcave shape expands the surface area available for gas exchange. WBCs, on the other hand, play an important role in the immune response of the body. WBCs have a nucleus, which allows them to carry genetic information and perform a variety of functions such as producing antibodies, engulfing pathogens, and signalling other immune cells.

✔ **Explain the role of lymph vessels in the secondary circulatory system of the body. How does this system work in conjunction with the primary circulatory system?**

The lymphatic system is made up of lymph vessels that are responsible for returning interstitial fluid (fluid between cells) to the bloodstream. They also transport fats from the digestive tract to the bloodstream and serve as a filter, removing bacteria and other pathogens. This secondary circulatory system works in tandem with the primary circulatory system to maintain fluid balance, aid in fat absorption, and function as an important component of the immune system, filtering harmful substances and producing lymphocytes.

✔ **How does the presence of haemoglobin affect the blood's red colour? What role does it play in carbon dioxide transport?**

Haemoglobin, found in RBCs, binds to oxygen to form oxyhaemoglobin, which gives blood its bright red colour. Deoxyhaemoglobin, a darker shade of red, is formed when oxygen levels are low—furthermore, haemoglobin aids in the transport of carbon dioxide. Carbon dioxide in the blood binds to haemoglobin, forming carbaminohaemoglobin, which is transported back to the lungs for exhalation.

POINTS TO REMEMBER

- ✔ Circulatory system in our body essentially performs distributing and collecting functions.
- ✔ Blood is a connective tissue that exists in the form of liquid in our body.
- ✔ Arteries, veins and blood capillaries are major blood vessels of the circulatory system.
- ✔ Blood is composed of three different types of cells that are present in a liquid matrix called plasma.
- ✔ Lymph vessels form the secondary circulatory system in our body and are spread throughout our body.
- ✔ Plasma contains a protein, called fibrinogen that is responsible for blood coagulation.
- ✔ Haemoglobin imparts red colour to the blood.
- ✔ A red blood cell can survive about 120 days and then it undergoes disintegration in liver or spleen.
- ✔ White blood cells are larger in size than red blood cells and contain nucleus.
- ✔ The heart is a muscular organ that controls the flow of blood through the rest of the circulatory system.
- ✔ Respiration is the chemical process in which energy is released in a cell by breaking down the glucose.
- ✔ The energy produced in the process of cellular process comes from the breakdown of glucose.
- ✔ Aerobic respiration occurs in the presence of oxygen.
- ✔ Anaerobic respiration occurs in the absence of oxygen.
- ✔ Breathing is a physical process that involves taking in of oxygen and releasing out carbon dioxide.
- ✔ The oxygen is absorbed by the blood in lungs and is carried by the RBCs throughout the body.
- ✔ Carbon dioxide from the tissues is transported to lungs by means of veins.
- ✔ Cellular respiration involves chemical reactions which occur inside the cell that involve breakdown of glucose to liberate energy.
- ✔ Right lung is slightly bigger than the left lung since the heart is also present slightly towards the left side of the thoracic cavity.
- ✔ Haemoglobin present in the red blood cells transports oxygen as well as carbon dioxide.

DW

PRACTICE QUESTIONS CLASSROOM WING

Very Short Answer Type Questions

Directions for questions from 1 to 9.
Fill in the blanks.

1. The circulatory system in our body is essentially responsible for ________ and ________ functions.
2. ________ is the liquid matrix in which three different types of blood cells float.
3. The ________ system, which includes lymph vessels, forms a secondary circulation network in the body.
4. The lifespan of a red blood cell is approximately ________ days.
5. Cellular respiration is a process that releases energy by breaking down ________.
6. The two nostrils are separated by a cartilaginous wall called ________.
7. The tiny hair-like structures present in the nostril are called ________.
8. ________ is known as the voice box.
9. In human beings, a pair of lungs is present in the ________.

Directions for questions from 10 to 21.
For each of the following questions, four choices have been provided. Select the correct alternatives.

10. Which component in plasma plays a crucial role in blood coagulation?
    (a) Haemoglobin (b) Oxygen
    (c) Fibrinogen (d) Carbon Dioxide
11. What differentiates aerobic from anaerobic respiration?
    (a) Presence of glucose
    (b) Absence of glucose
    (c) Presence of oxygen
    (d) Absence of carbon dioxide
12. Which cells are responsible for transporting oxygen as well as carbon dioxide?
    (a) White blood cells
    (b) Plasma cells
    (c) Red blood cells
    (d) Blood capillaries
13. Breathing can be best described as:
    (a) A chemical process
    (b) A process where energy is released
    (c) The breakdown of glucose
    (d) A physical process
14. Match the entries of Column 1 with those of Column 2.

Column 1	Column 2
A. Bicuspid valve	(i) Valve between the right atrium and right ventricle
B. Aortic semilunar valve	(ii) Valve between the right ventricle and pulmonary artery
C. Tricuspid valve	(iii) Valve between the left atrium and ventricle
D. Pulmonary semilunar valve	(iv) Valve between the left ventricle and the aorta

    (a) A → (iii), B → (iv), C → (i), D → (ii)
    (b) A → (ii), B → (iv), C → (i), D → (iii)
    (c) A → (iii), B → (i), C → (iv), D → (ii)
    (d) A → (iv), B → (iii), C → (i), D → (ii)
15. Why is the right lung slightly larger than the left lung?
    (a) To accommodate more blood vessels
    (b) Due to evolutionary reasons
    (c) To provide space for the heart on the left side
    (d) To filter more oxygen
16. Given the critical role of plasma in blood coagulation, which scenario is most likely after a significant loss of plasma?
    (a) Increased glucose breakdown
    (b) Increased oxygen transportation
    (c) Decreased clotting capability
    (d) Balanced pH levels

17. What are the ligamentous fold-like structures inside the larynx?
(a) Trachea
(b) Vocal cords
(c) Bronchi
(d) Bronchioles

18. Which component present in blood helps in the transport of oxygen as well as carbon dioxide?
(a) Haemoglobin
(b) Plasma
(c) Cytoplasm
(d) Heparin

19. Where is larynx positioned in the respiratory tract?
(a) Between pharynx and trachea
(b) Between bronchi and alveoli
(c) Between trachea and bronchi
(d) Between pharynx and alveoli

20. What is the form in which oxygen gas is transported from lungs to the bloodstream?
(a) Carboamino–haemoglobin
(b) Bicarbonate ions
(c) Oxyhaemoglobin
(d) Glucose

21. Match the entries of Column 1 with those of Column 2.

Column 1	Column 2
1. Nostril	(A) Carbo amino – haemoglobin
2. Bronchiole	(B) Pleura
3. Lung	(C) Alveoli
4. Carbon dioxide	(D) Cilia

(a) A → (iv), B → (iii), C → (ii), D → (i)
(b) A → (i), B → (ii), C → (iii), D → (i)
(c) A → (ii), B → (iii), C → (iv), D → (i)
(d) A → (ii), B → (iv), C → (iii), D → (i)

Short Answer Type Questions

22. What is the significance of haemoglobin in the transportation of gases in the body?
23. Differentiate between respiration and breathing.
24. How does the structure of arteries differ from that of veins, and why is this difference significant?
25. Explain the structure and function of platelets.
26. What are granulocytes and how are they classified?
27. How are agranulocytes classified?
28. What are the chemicals that are secreted by basophils?
29. What is the main function of eosinophils?
30. Mention some of the general functions of blood.
31. Name the two types of valves that are present in the heart.

Essay Type Questions

32. Write a brief note on the structure of heart.
33. Draw the structure of heart and label it.
34. Identify and explain about the pale yellow-coloured component of the blood.
35. Identify and explain about the type of granulocytes that destroy the parasitic worms.
36. Explain about the type of agranulocytes that possess cells with mono-lobed nucleus.
37. Explain about the blood vessel that carries blood away from the heart and transports to the other parts of the body?
38. Explain about the blood vessel that carries blood from different parts of the body to the heart with the help of a diagram.
39. Explain about the function of the blood vessels that connect arterioles and venules.
40. Explain about the different valves that help in the flow of blood in human pump.
41. Name and explain the cardiac cycle in which the atria and ventricles are relaxed during the inflow of blood.
42. Explain the flow of blood in the cardiac phase where contraction of the blood vessels take place.

43. Explain about the different pathways by which blood is circulated by the heart.

44. Complete the table for the arteries and veins through inflow and outflow of blood from heart, kidneys and liver.

Function of the blood vessels	Entering/leaving blood vessels
It carries blood from the upper part of the body.	
It carries oxygenated blood to all the parts of the body	
It supplies oxygenated blood to the liver from the aorta	
It transports the blood from the kidney to the posterior vena cava for its purification	
It carries the deoxygenated blood from the right ventricle to the lungs for purification	

45. Mention the organs that are involved in the respiratory system.

46. Write briefly about the pharynx.

47. What is the frequency of respiration in human beings?

48. (i) Name the basic processes that are involved in respiration.
(ii) Define breathing.
(iii) What is meant by tidal volume?
(iv) Define the rate of ventilation.

49. Draw the structure of lungs and label the following parts in it.
(a) Nasal cavity
(b) Epiglottis
(c) Lungs
(d) Larynx and vocal cords
(e) Trachea
(f) Diaphragm
(g) Bronchus
(h) Alveoli

50. (i) Identify the type of respiration in which the glucose undergoes oxidation and also mention where it takes place.
(ii) Why food does not enter the respiratory tract when there is a common cavity for both food and air?

51. (a) Identify and explain about the part of the respiratory system that consists of the cluster of structures that resemble grapes for the exchange of gases.
(b) What do you mean by vital capacity and residual capacity?

PRACTICE QUESTIONS COMPETITION WING

Level 1: Apply your Concepts

Directions for questions from 1 to 11.
Fill in the blanks.

1. Blood, being a connective tissue, serves as a medium, linking the cellular components to the ________, ensuring overall homeostasis.
2. While the ________ and ________ typically carry oxygenated and deoxygenated blood respectively, there's an exception in the human body concerning a specific pair of these vessels.
3. Lymph vessels, unlike blood vessels, lack a ________, making their flow unidirectional.
4. Cellular respiration's end goal is the production of ATP, a molecule that stores and releases energy by breaking its bond with ________.
5. The process by which oxygen moves from alveoli in the lungs into the blood is called ________.
6. White blood cells are classified into ______ and ______.
7. ______ is secreted by basophils that help in preventing blood clotting.
8. Neutrophils engulf the pathogens invaded in our body by the process of ________.
9. The main function of lymphocytes is the production of antibodies and thus they provide ________ to our body.
10. The plasma without fibrinogen is called ________.
11. The double-layered membrane that encloses each lung is called ________.

Directions for questions from 12 to 18.
For each of the following questions four choices have been provided. Select the correct alternatives.

12. Why do cells switch to anaerobic respiration even though it's less efficient than aerobic respiration?
    (a) Anaerobic respiration produces more glucose.
    (b) Oxygen levels are sufficiently high.
    (c) The cell requires rapid energy.
    (d) The cell is trying to conserve oxygen.
13. Which component in the blood primarily deals with foreign invaders?
    (a) Plasma (b) Red blood cells
    (c) Platelets (d) White blood cells
14. Considering the difference in sizes of the lungs, which statement is most accurate?
    (a) The right lung has two lobes, while the left has three.
    (b) Both lungs are of equal size to maintain symmetry.
    (c) The left lung is smaller due to the position of the heart.
    (d) The right lung filters more oxygen.
15. Why is haemoglobin crucial for the body's pH balance?
    (a) It neutralizes stomach acid.
    (b) It releases carbon dioxide in the lungs.
    (c) It binds with excess hydrogen ions.
    (d) It increases oxygen in the blood.
16. Which statement best describes the relationship between the respiratory and circulatory systems?
    (a) The respiratory system provides oxygen to the circulatory system, which then transports carbon dioxide to be expelled.
    (b) The circulatory system provides oxygen to the respiratory system, which then expels carbon dioxide.
    (c) The respiratory system and circulatory system function independently with no interaction.
    (d) The circulatory system produces oxygen, and the respiratory system pumps it to the rest of the body.
17. Name the blood vessels that carry blood to the veins.
    (a) Venules (b) Capillaries
    (c) Arterioles (d) Both (a) and (b)
18. Which substance undergoes oxidation during cellular respiration?
    (a) Oxygen
    (b) Carbaminohaemoglobin
    (c) Glucose
    (d) Bicarbonate ions

Directions for questions from 19 to 22.
Correct the following statements.

19. During the process of inhalation, the muscles of the ribs and the diaphragm expand.

20. The space in the thoracic cavity increases during the exhalation process.

21. In systole phase, the ventricles expand and the inflow of blood takes place from the heart to the arteries.

22. Veins carry blood from heart to different parts of the body.

Directions for questions from 23 to 26:
Write the missing correlated terms.

23. ________ : Granulocytes :: Blood : ________.

24. Neutrophils: _________ :: Lymphocytes : ________.

25. Diastole phase:_______ :: Pulmonary circuit : Systematic circuit.

26. Larynx : vocal cords :: bronchioles : _________.

Direction for Questions from 27 to 62:
Choose the correct option.

(1) Both A and R are true and R is the correct explanation for A.
(2) Both A and R are true, but R is not the correct explanation for A.
(3) A is true and R is false.
(4) A is false and R is true.

27. Assertion(A): The heart in human beings is present in a fluid-filled pericardial cavity.
Reason (R): Pericardial fluid transports nutrients to the heart.

28. Assertion(A): The left atrium and the left ventricle are completely separated from the right atrium and the right ventricle.
Reason (R): Oxygenated and deoxygenated blood never mix with each other inside the heart.

29. Assertion(A): Arteries always carry oxygenated blood.
Reason (R): Arteries transport blood from the heart to different parts of the body.

30. Assertion(A): Arteries do not collapse, but veins collapse when they are cut through.

Reason (R): Arteries do not have valves whereas veins have valves.

31. Assertion (A): Lack of muscular coordination takes place in the higher altitude.

Reason (R): Proper muscular coordination requires supply of right proportion of oxygen in the muscular tissues.

32. Assertion (A): During inhalation or inspiration, the muscles of the ribs and the diaphragm expand.

Reason (R): Expansion of diaphragm reduces the space in thoracic cavity.

33. Assertion (A): The expulsion of carbon dioxide occurs due to the increase in pressure in the thoracic cavity.

Reason (R): Exhaled air contains higher percentage of carbon dioxide than normal air.

34. Assertion (A): Oxygen enters the cells in the tissues through the thin walls of the blood capillaries by the process of diffusion.

Reason (R): Diffusion occurs from the region of lower concentration to the region of higher concentration.

35. Assertion (A): Systolic pressure is higher than the diastolic pressure.

Reason (R): During diastole, cuspid valves open while during systole semilunar valves open.

Level 2: Review your Concepts

36. RBCs have biconcave, disc-like structure and they are tiny and flexible. Give reason.

37. What is the role of liver in iron homeostasis?

38. Why does spleen enlarge in a patient suffering from infections due to invasion of pathogens?

39. What is eosinophilia? How does it occur?

40. Why do eosinophils turn orange-red in response to eosin, an acidic dye?

41. Thrombosis is treated with heparin. Give reason.

42. Neutrophils act as body's natural antibiotics. Give reason.

43. What is lymphocytosis? What does this condition generally indicate?

44. Why monocytes are called scavenger cells?

45. How does platelets prevent bleeding?

46. What are myocardium and myocardial infarction?

47. Why blood from gastrointestinal tract is not directly transported to the heart?

48. A person with swollen lymph nodes is generally treated with antibiotics. Give reason.

49. How does carbon monoxide poisoning occur?

50. What is pleurisy?

51. Write a short note on the organ that disintegrates the old red blood cells.

52. Explain briefly about the mechanism of respiration.

53. Explain about tissue respiration.

Level 3: Assess Your Concepts

54. Explain how the positions of the heart and the lungs facilitate efficient oxygenation and circulation of blood in the body.

55. We should avoid talking while eating. Give reason.

56. Why does asthma cause breathlessness?

57. Why is smoking related to emphysema?

58. Why does our finger nail turn bluish in cold weather?

AT

PRACTICE QUESTIONS NEET SPECIAL WING

Multiple-Answer Type Questions

Questions number 1 to 5 are multiple-choice questions. Each question has FOUR options (a), (b), (c), and (d). ONE OR MORE THAN ONE of these four option(s) is/are the correct answer(s).

1. Which of the following are characteristics of eosinophils?
   (a) They are granulocytes
   (b) They respond during allergic reactions
   (c) They secrete histamine, heparin and serotonin
   (d) They fight against parasitic infection

2. Which of the following events occur during inflammation?
   (a) Tissue injury causes release of heparin
   (b) Dilation of blood vessels occur
   (c) Leakiness results in migration of phagocytes to the area
   (d) Phagocytes consume bacteria and cell debris

3. Arteries differ from veins in that:
   (a) Thick muscular wall
   (b) Narrow lumen
   (c) Valves are present
   (d) They collapse when empty

4. Sprinters undergo which kind of respiration and what product is produced?
   (a) Aerobic respiration
   (b) Anaerobic respiration
   (c) Lactic acid
   (d) Ethanol

5. From the following identify the blood vessels which carry oxygenated blood.
   (a) Pulmonary vein
   (b) Pulmonary artery
   (c) Superior vena cava
   (d) Aorta

Comprehension-Based Questions

A. Read the paragraph given below and answer the questions number 6 to 11:

Protein is one of the major nutrients present in a balanced diet. Since proteins cannot be stored in the body, they are broken down by the process of 'A' to produce amino acids. The excess amino acids which contain the nitrogen components are converted into a nitrogenous waste component 'B' which is excreted through urine. The non nitrogenous components are converted to 'C' which is then used up during cellular respiration in the presence of oxygen to produce carbon di oxide, energy and water. In cellular respiration two important processes takes place. In the first ('D') process 'C' is broken down to produce pyruvic acid. In the second process 'E' pyruvic acid is broken down to produce ATP, carbon dioxide and water.

6. What is the process of A and in which organ it takes place?
   (a) Deamination- Liver
   (b) Detoxification- Pancreas
   (c) Deamination- Small intestine
   (d) Detoxification- Kidneys

7. Which nitrogen containing compound (B) is produced as a result of A?
   (a) Creatinine
   (b) Urine
   (c) Urea
   (d) Uric acid

8. Which chemical compound is 'C'?
   (a) Sucrose
   (b) Glucose
   (c) Maltose
   (d) Polypeptide

9. Which is the first process 'D' of cellular respiration?
   (a) Urea cycle
   (b) Kreb's cycle
   (c) Carbaminohaemoglobin
   (d) Glycolysis

10. Name the process 'E'.
   (a) Urea cycle
   (b) Kreb's cycle
   (c) Carbaminohaemoglobin
   (d) Glycolysis

11. Match the column:

In the following table match the correct values with the different lung capacities.

Column – A	Column – B
(i) Inspiratory reserve volume	(a) 4500 mL
(ii) Tidal volume	(b) 1000 mL
(iii) Vital capacity	(c) 3000 mL
(iv) Total lung capacity	(d) 6000 mL
(v) Expiratory reserve volume	(e) 500 mL

B. Read the paragraph given below and answer the questions number 12 to 17:

The human heart is the main organ which pumps blood in the human body. Blood is the main transporting fluid in the body. The blood consists of the fluid part which is plasma and the cells are of two types- agranulocytes and granulocytes. Agranulocytes do not have any cytoplasmic granules like Lymphocytes and Monocytes. Granulocytes have cytoplasmic granules which react with various dyes and get stained namely- Basophils, eosinophils and neutrophils. The blood is transported through blood vessels like arteries, veins and capillaries. Arteries can withstand the highest amount of pressure; veins contain valves and capillaries are only one cell thick. Circulation through the heart is double circulation consisting of pulmonary circuit and systemic circuit. In pulmonary circuit the circulation is between the lungs and the heart whereas in the systemic circuit the circulation is between the body tissues and the heart.

12. The heart produces 'lub-dub' sound. The first heart sound 'lub' is produced due to:
(a) Closing of atrioventricular valves
(b) Closing of semilunar valves
(c) Closing of all the valves at the same time
(d) Opening of semi lunar valves

13. Which of the following blood artery carries deoxygenated blood?
(a) Hepatic
(b) Cardiac
(c) Pulmonary
(d) Renal

14. Identify the correct order of the blood vessels for the amount of pressure in them from highest to lowest.
(a) Capillary> arteriole> Venule> artery> vein> aorta
(b) Capillary> vein> Venule> arteriole> artery> aorta
(c) Aorta > artery> arteriole> capillary> Venule> vein
(d) Aorta> arteriole>Venule> artery> vein> capillary

15. The blood vessels of the heart can help in retention of heat in the body by:
(a) Vasodilation
(b) Vasoconstriction
(c) Decreasing heart contraction
(d) Both a and b

16. Oxygenated blood enters the left ventricle due to:
(a) Opening of Bicuspid valve
(b) Closing of Mitral valve
(c) Opening of Tricuspid valve
(d) Both a and b

17. Match the column:

Column – A (Blood cells)	Column – B (Characteristics)
(i) Eosinophils	(a) Secretes histamine
(ii) Basophils	(b) Natural antibiotics
(iii) Neutrophils	(c) Antibodies
(iv) Lymphocytes	(d) Bilobed nucleus
(v) Monocytes	(e) Scavengers

ANSWER KEYS

Crossword

Across

3. Sphygmomanometer 4. Glycolysis 5. Emphysema 6. Fibrinogen
8. Serotonin 9. Phagocytosis 10. Alveoli 12. Biconcave 15. Eosinophils
18. Venules 19. Spleen

Down

1. Asphyxiation 2. Carbaminohemoglobin 7. Thrombocytes 11. Antigens
13. Diaphragm 14. Glycogen 16. Larynx 17. Pleura

Classroom Wing

Very Short Answer Type Questions

1. Distributing, collecting 2. Plasma 3. Lymph 4. 120
5. Glucose 6. Septum 7. Cilia 8. Larynx 9. Thoracic cavity
10. (a) 11. (c) 12. (a) 13. (d) 14. (a)
15. (c) 16. (b) 17. (d) 18. (a) 19. (a)
20. (c) 21. (a)

Competition Wing

Level 1: Apply Your Concepts

1. Extracellular matrix 2. Arteries, veins 3. Central pump 4. Phosphate 5. Diffusion
6. Granulocytes, Agranulocytes 7. Heparin 8. Phagocytosis 9. Immunity
10. Serum 11. Pleura 12. (c) 13. (c) 14. (c)
15. (c) 16. (a) 17. (a) 18. (c)
23. White blood cells, Plasma 24. Granulocytes, Agranulocytes 25. Systole phase
26. alveoli 27. (c) 28. (a) 29. (d) 30. (b)
31. (a) 32. (d) 33. (b) 34. (c) 35. (b)

NEET Special Wing

Multiple-Answer Type Questions

1. (a, b, d) 2. (b, c, d) 3. (a, b) 4. (b, c) 5. (a, d)

Comprehension-Based Questions

6. (a) 7. (c) 8. (b) 9. (d) 10. (b)
11. (i) → (c); (ii) → (e); (iii) → (a); (iv) → (d); (v) → (b)
12. (a) 13. (c) 14. (c) 15. (b) 16. (a)
17. (i) → (d); (ii) → (a); (iii) → (b); (iv) → (c); (v) → (e)

Hints and Explanations

CLASSROOM WING

Short Answer Type Questions

22. Haemoglobin, present in red blood cells, binds with oxygen to transport it to various body tissues. It also binds with a small portion of carbon dioxide, facilitating its removal from tissues and eventual exhalation from the lungs.

23. Respiration is a chemical process where energy is released by breaking down glucose, either in the presence (aerobic) or absence (anaerobic) of oxygen. Breathing, on the other hand, is a physical process involving the inhalation of oxygen and the exhalation of carbon dioxide.

24. Arteries have thicker walls than veins due to the presence of more muscle and elastic tissues. This structure allows arteries to withstand and maintain the higher pressures of blood pumped directly from the heart. Veins, with their thinner walls and valves, facilitate the return of blood to the heart against gravity.

25. Structure and function of platelets:
    - Platelets are not true cells, rather they are the fragments of cells.
    - They are colourless and irregular in shape.
    - The cell fragments do not contain nucleus and cytoplasm does not have granules.
    - Their lifespan is very short, as they survive for 3–5 days and disintegrate in the spleen.
    - The main function of platelets is facilitating blood clotting.

26. Granulocytes are one of the categories of leucocytes. They have granular cytoplasm and lobed nucleus.

    Granulocytes are further classified into three categories of cells based on their structure and function. These are:

    (a) Eosinophils

    (b) Basophils

    (c) Neutrophils

27. Agranulocytes are another category of leucocytes apart from granulocytes. The cytoplasm of agranulocytes is not granular. Thirty five per cent of the total WBC count is agranulocytes. They are classified into two categories based on their structure and function. These are:

    (a) Lymphocytes

    (b) Monocytes

28. Basophils secrete chemicals like

    (a) Histamine

    (b) Heparin

    (c) Serotonin

29. The main function of eosinophil is to destroy the pathogens, particularly parasitic worms. They also respond to the allergic reactions.

30. General functions of blood:
    - Transportation of respiratory gases.
    - Transportation of digested food to different parts of the body and waste material from different parts of the body to the excretory organs.
    - Distribution of hormones and enzymes.
    - Clotting of blood and providing immunity to the body to fight against diseases.
    - Maintaining the temperature of body by distributing heat evenly all over the body.

31. The heart has two types of valves:

    (a) Atrioventricular valves or cuspid valves

    (b) Semilunar valves

Essay Type Questions

32. **Structure of heart:**

    The heart is the controlling organ of the circulatory system. It controls the blood flow through the rest of the circulatory system. Heart is a muscular organ and the muscle cells that constitute the heart are called cardiac muscle fibres. It is located at the chest cavity slightly towards the left. It is present in a fluid-filled cavity called pericardial cavity. Pericardial cavity is enclosed by a double-walled membrane called pericardium. The heart contains four chambers. Left atrium-the upper left chamber. Right atrium, the upper right chamber, Left ventricle-the lower left chamber, Right ventricle-the lower right chamber. The left atrium and ventricle are completely separated from the right atrium and the right ventricle. The atria receive the blood while the ventricles pump the blood outside the heart. Ventricles are stronger and larger than the atria. The atria are connected to the veins and the ventricles are connected to the arteries. The left side chamber is slightly larger than the right side chamber due to specific functions. There are two apertures within the heart that control the blood flow from the atrium to the respective ventricle.

33.

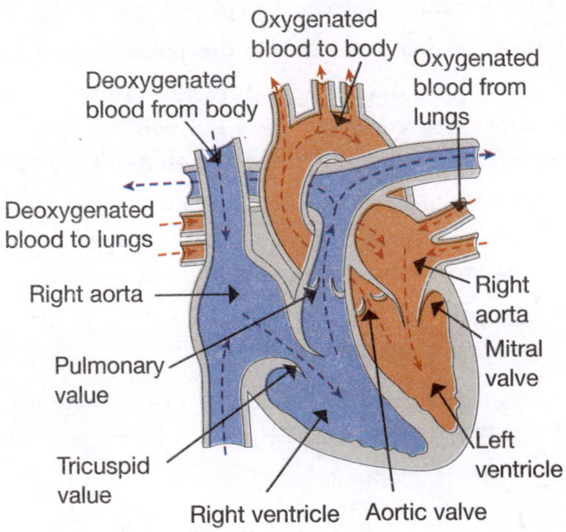

34. Plasma is the pale yellow-coloured liquid component of the blood apart from the blood cells.

It is alkaline in nature and occupies 55 per cent of the total blood volume. The content of the water in plasma is 90–92% in blood. The solid component of plasma includes inorganic and organic substances. Inorganic substances are different than organic substances. They are positive and negative ions such as Na^+, Ca^{++}, Mg^{++}, Cl^-, HCO_3, etc. Organic substances are glucose, amino acids, lipids, etc. Plasma also contains a protein called fibrinogen which is responsible for blood coagulation. Plasma without fibrinogen is called serum.

35. Eosinophils is one of the type of granulocytes that destroys the parasitic worms.

- Eosinophils have bilobed nucleus and both the lobes are connected with a thin strand.
- They make up only about 2–5% of the white cells.
- One milliliter of blood contains about 60–300 eosinophils.
- The number of eosinophils in unit volume of blood increases due to some parasitic infection and this condition is called eosinophilia.
- Cytoplasmic granules of eosinophil turn orange-red in response to the acid dye (eosin).
- The main function of eosinophils is to destroy the pathogens.

36. Lymphocytes are the agranulocytes that have monolobed nucleus.

- About 30–32% of the total WBC count is lymphocytes.
- The main function of lymphocytes is the production of antibodies and thus they provide immunity to our body.
- They have a large cytoplasm and kidney-shaped nucleus.
- They ingest microorganisms that intrude our body and also act as scavengers by removing the dead cells.
- The total WBC count of a person suffering with leukaemia increases and that of RBC decreases.

37. An artery is a blood vessel that carries blood from the heart and transports it to different parts of the body.

- They have a thick muscular wall and lumen is narrow. Hence, the arteries never collapse.
- Blood passes through the arteries under high pressure with jerks. They do not have any valves.
- All arteries carry oxygenated blood, except pulmonary artery. Branches originating from the arteries are called arterioles.

38. A vein is a blood vessel that carries blood from the different parts of the body to the heart.

Veins have thin and less muscular walls, and hence a wider lumen. Veins collapse when they are empty or cut through. Blood has a steady flow through the veins and the pressure is lower than that of arteries. Valves are present in veins to prevent the back flow of blood. Small blood vessels that carry blood to veins are called venules. Veins carry deoxygenated blood, except the pulmonary vein.

39. Capillaries are thin-walled microscopic vessels that connect arterioles and venules.

The diameter of capillaries is about 8 microns. The wall of the capillaries is one cell thick and it constitutes of squamous epithelial cells. Nutrients and oxygen gas are transported to the tissues from the blood through capillaries. Waste material and carbon dioxide gas are carried from the body tissue to the blood through capillaries. Thin wall of capillaries provide the passage of leucocytes from capillaries to tissue fluid.

40. There are two types of valves in the heart:

(a) Atrioventricular valve or cuspid valve: They are present between the atria and respective ventricles.

- Left artrioventricular valve or bicuspid valve: The valve between the left atrium and left ventricle.
- Right artrioventricular valve or tricuspid valve: The valve between the right atrium and right ventricle.
- Chordae tendineae: These are the string-like tendons that attach bicuspid and tricuspid valves to the muscle of the heart.

(b) Semilunar valves: They are located between the ventricles and the opening of large blood vessels originating from the ventricles.

- Aortic semilunar valve: The valve between the left ventricle and aorta. They are three in number.
- Pulmonary semilunar valve: The valve between the right ventricle and the pulmonary artery. They are three in number.

41. Diastole is the cardiac phase in which the atria and ventricles are relaxed due to the inflow of the blood to the heart and atrioventricular valves remain open.

- Deoxygenated blood from different parts of the body enters the right atrium through the superior and inferior vena cava.
- Then the tricuspid valve opens and thus deoxygenated blood enters the right ventricle from the right atrium.
- During the same time, oxygenated blood enters the left atrium through the pulmonary vein. Then this oxygenated blood enters the left ventricle due to the opening of the bicuspid valve.

42. Systole is the cardiac phase where contraction of the blood vessels takes place.

- During this phase, the artrioventricular valves and the semilunar valves open.
- Ventricles contract during this phase.
- Due to the contraction of the right ventricle, deoxygenated blood flows through the pulmonary semilunar valve and enters the pulmonary artery.
- During this period, the left ventricle also contracts and the oxygenated blood flows through the aortic semilunar valve and enters the aorta.
- Oxygenated blood flows to different parts of the body through the branches of aorta.

43. Blood is circulated by the heart in two different pathways. The two pathways are:

(a) Systematic circuit

(b) Pulmonary circuit

44.

Function of the blood vessels	Entering/leaving blood vessels
It carries blood from the upper part of the body.	Superior vena cava or anterior vena cava or precaval
It carries oxygenated blood to all the parts of the body	Aorta
It supplies oxygenated blood to the liver from the aorta	Hepatic artery
It transports the blood from the kidney to the posterior vena cava for its purification	Renal veins
It carries the deoxygenated blood from the right ventricle to the lungs for purification	Pulmonary artery

45. The organs involved in the respiratory system are:

(a) Nose and nostrils

(b) Nasal passage

(c) Pharynx

(d) Larynx

(e) Trachea

(f) Bronchi

(g) Bronchioles and alveoli

(h) Lungs

46. The nasal passage opens into the pharynx. The food and air enter the digestive tract and respiratory tract respectively, through the common cavity, pharynx. A silt-like passage through which air enters into the respiratory tract from the pharynx is called glottis.

47. There are four basic processes that are involved in respiration. They are:

(a) Breathing

(b) Gaseous transport

(c) Tissue respiration

(d) Cellular respiration

48. (i) The frequency of respiration in human being is 12 breathings per minute.

(ii) The mechanical process by which oxygen is inhaled or inspired and carbon dioxide is exhaled or expired is called breathing.

(iii) A person can inhale about 500 mL of air in normal breathing. This is called tidal volume.

(iv) The rate of respiration in terms of volume of air breathed in per minute is called rate of ventilation.

Rate of ventilation = tidal volume × frequency of respiration.

49.

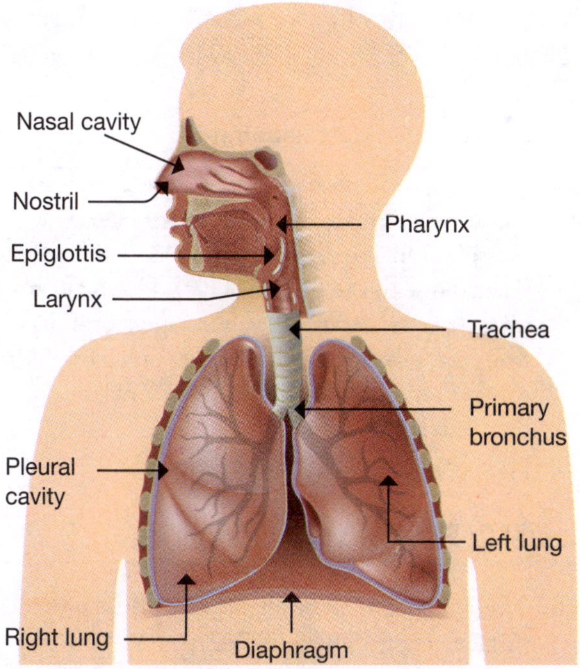

50. (i) Cellular respiration takes place in the mitochondria present in the cells. Glucose undergoes oxidation and releases energy in this process.

(ii) A slit-like passage through which the air enters the respiratory tract from the pharynx is called glottis. When we swallow food, a leaf-like cartilaginous flap covers the glottis to prevent the entry of food particles into the respiratory tract.

51. (a) Lungs are the main part of the respiratory system that are present in the thoracic cavity.

(i) Right lung is slightly bigger than the left lung since the heart is also present slightly towards the left side of the thoracic cavity.

(ii) Each lung is enclosed in a double-layered membrane called pleura.

(iii) Alveoli present in the lung appear like a cluster of grapes and the exchange of respiratory gases takes place through the alveoli.

(iv) Very thin walls of alveoli are surrounded by blood vessels. Oxygen from the alveoli is transported to the bloodstream by the process of diffusion after inhalation.

(v) And carbon dioxide diffuses from the bloodstream to alveoli and is exhaled out.

(vi) Haemoglobin present in the RBC transports the oxygen as well as carbon dioxide.

(b) Vital capacity is the volume of air that a normal human being can exhale after the inhalation with the maximum effort. The vital capacity of an adult is 4500 mL.

The volume of air that cannot be expelled from the lungs even with the maximum effort is called residual air or residual volume. In a normal human being, residual air is 1500 mL.

COMPETITION WING

Level 1: Apply your Concepts

19. During inhalation, the muscles of the ribs and the diaphragm contract.

20. The space in the thoracic cavity decreases during the exhalation process.

21. In systole phase, the ventricles contract and the outflow of blood takes place from the heart to the arteries.

22. Veins carry blood from different parts of the body to the heart.

23. White blood cells: Granulocytes :: Blood : Plasma.

24. Neutrophils: Granulocytes :: Lymphocytes : Agranulocytes.

25. Diastole phase : Systole phase :: Pulmonary circuit : Systematic circuit.

26. Larynx : vocal cords :: bronchioles : alveoli.

27. Pericardial fluid surrounds the heart and is enclosed by the pericardial membrane. Pericardial fluid facilitates the friction-free contraction and expansion of heart.

Hence, the correct option is (c)

28. Oxygenated blood enters the left atrium and then flows to the left ventricle. Deoxygenated blood enters the right atrium and then flows to the right ventricle. The separation of the left atrium and left ventricle from right atrium and right ventricle prevents intermixing of oxygenated and deoxygenated blood.

Hence, the correct option is (a)

29. Only pulmonary artery carries deoxygenated blood. Oxygenated blood is carried to different parts of the body by arteries from the heart.

Hence, the correct option is (d)

30. Arteries have thick, elastic walls but veins have thin non-elastic walls. Hence, arteries never collapse whereas veins collapse when they are empty or cut through. Blood flows through the arteries with high pressure, hence back flow of blood is not possible. But blood flows through veins at a low pressure. So, valves are present in veins to prevent back flow of blood.

Hence, the correct option is (b)

31. At higher altitudes, the density of air as well as percentage of oxygen in air is less. Hence, our muscle cells do not get the right proportion of oxygen and cannot function properly.

Hence, the correct option is (a)

32. During inhalation, contraction of diaphragm takes place to increase space in the thoracic cavity. This leads to decrease in pressure in lungs.

Hence, the correct option is (d)

33. During expiration, diaphragm expands and volume of thoracic cavity decreases. Thus, the pressure in the lungs increases and exhalation takes place. Exhaled air contains higher percentage of oxygen.

Hence, the correct option is (b)

34. The concentration of oxygen is higher in oxygenated blood than that in the surrounding tissues. Thus, diffusion of oxygen takes place from the bloodstream to the tissues.

Hence, the correct option is (c)

35. During systole phase, left and right ventricles contracts and blood is pumped through the arteries with a high pressure. During diastole phase, atria and ventricles are relaxed due to the inflow of blood to the heart. During diastole phase, cuspid valves open and blood flows from the atria to the respective ventricles. During systole phase, semilunar valves open and blood flows from the ventricles to arteries.

Hence, the correct option is (b)

Level 2: Review your Concepts

36. The biconcave, disc shape of RBCs provides larger surface area for efficient absorption of oxygen.

They are tiny and flexible. Hence, they can squeeze through the narrowest blood capillaries to deliver oxygen.

37. A significant portion of the excess iron in our body gets stored in specific type of cell in liver. This type of cells ingests old RBCs and liberates iron by breaking down haemoglobin. The iron ions thus generated get stored in a specific type of protein molecules called ferritin. Ferritin molecules release iron when there is a deficiency of iron in our bloodstream. This is the role of liver in iron homeostasis.

38. The functions of spleen include clearance of pathogens invading the bloodstream with the production followed by circulation of antibodies. Hence, the blood flow in the spleen increases when a person suffers from such kind of infections and thus the spleen enlarges.

39. Eosinophilia is a condition of body in which the eosinophil count increases in the bloodstream.

Eosinophils are a type of white blood cells that play an important role in the body's response to allergic reactons, asthma and parasitic infections. They provide protective immunity against parasitic infections and also contribute to the inflammation that occurs in allergic disorders. Hence, the number of eosinophils increases due to parasitic infection and allergic reaction.

40. Eosinophils are transparent. The granules in cytoplasm of eosinophils contain many basic proteins. Eosin is an acidic dye and they neutralize each other and thus eosinophils appear orange-red.

41. Thrombosis is a condition in which an abnormal clotting of blood takes place in an artery or a vein. Heparin is a blood thinner or anticoagulant. Hence, it is used to treat thrombosis. Basophils secrete heparin which acts as a natural blood thinner in our body.

42. Innate immune system is inherited by human beings as soon as they are born. Neutrophils are white blood cells that play some very important roles in our innate immune system. They circulate around our body in the bloodstream. They engulf the pathogens invading our body by the phagocytosis process. Thus, they act as body's natural antibiotics.

43. Lymphocytosis is a condition in which the number of lymphocytes in blood increases.

Lymphocytes produce antibodies and thus provide immunity to our body.

If a person suffers continuously from infections, continuous development of antibodies is required. Hence, a person suffering from chronic infections generally has lymphocytosis.

44. Monocytes engulf disease-causing pathogens and even infected cells and thus boost our immune system. Hence, they are called scavenger cells.

45. When an injury occurs, blood vessels rupture. The platelets get activated and arrive at the injured areas. They change their shape from round to spiny and stick to the broken blood vessels. They also interact with blood proteins and form fibrin.

Fibrin strands form a net that entraps blood cells and forms a clot. Thus platelets prevent bleeding.

46. Myocardium is the muscular middle layer of the wall of the heart. It is composed of spontaneously contracting cardiac muscle fibres which allow the heart to contract.

The heart requires its own constant supply of oxygen and nutrients, like any muscle in the body. Coronary arteries deliver oxygenated blood to the heart muscle. If one of these arteries or branches becomes blocked, blood flow to the heart decreases or stops causing damage to the heart muscle. Hence, the patient feels pain in the chest or discomfort. This condition is called myocardial infarction or commonly called heart attack.

47. Blood is not transported directly to the heart from the gastrointestinal tract. It is transported to the liver through the hepatic portal system and then from the liver to the heart through hepatic vein. Nutrients are absorbed by the blood from the gastrointestinal tract. Then the blood rich in nutrients flows to the liver for storage of nutrients. Liver is the storehouse of our body. It plays very important role in blood glucose homeostasis. Moreover, many important metabolic reactions involving carbohydrate, fat and protein are related to the functions of liver. To accomplish that blood has to pass through liver. Apart from these, specific cells in liver engulf foreign organisms that enter the bloodstream from the gastrointestinal tract. Thus the transportation of foreign organisms through general circulation is prevented. Liver also has the ability to detoxify the toxic substances and thus the toxic substances cannot reach other tissues or organs through bloodstream.

48. When a person suffers from some infection due to the invasion of pathogens, lymph nodes of that region swell. Lymph in the lymph nodes contains lymphocytes that generate antibodies in response to the activity of the pathogens. Hence, swelling of lymph nodes usually indicates intense infection. Sometimes it is associated with fever. Under this condition, sometimes administration of antibiotics becomes necessary. Antibiotics act against the pathogens, particularly bacteria.

49. Haemoglobin in red blood cells carries oxygen from the lungs to tissues all over the body via heart.

If the inhaled air contains carbon monoxide, it combines with haemoglobin instead of oxygen because the affinity of haemoglobin to combine with carbon monoxide is 200 times the affinity to combine with oxygen. As a result, the body starves of oxygen. Also, this can and it can be fatal if the concentration of CO is high.

50. Each lung is enclosed in a double-layered membrane called pleura. An inflammation in the tissues of pleura is known as pleurisy. Fluid gets accumulated between the layers of pleura due to inflammation. This disease occurs when viral infection of lungs spreads to pleura.

51. Spleen is the red-coloured organ located behind the stomach and above the left kidney.
    - It disintegrates the old RBC and stores the iron present in the haemoglobin of the red blood cells.
    - It acts as a reservoir of iron and replenishes its deficiency in the blood.
    - It can also store blood and supply it to the bloodstream in case of blood loss.
    - Spleen can generate lymphocytes in response to the invasion of pathogens. Thus, it plays a role in the defence of the body.

52. Lungs are the elastic bag-like structures and do not have any muscle. Hence, they themselves cannot contract or relax. A muscular, elastic sheet called diaphragm is extended across the bottom of thoracic cavity. Diaphragm separates the thoracic cavity from the abdominal cavity. The movement of diaphragm and muscles of the ribs facilitate the contraction and relaxation of lungs during breathing.

53. Tissue respiration:
    - It is a metabolic process by which oxygen reaches the body cells and carbon dioxide is released from them. Oxygen enters the cells through the process of diffusion.
    - Diffusion of oxygen takes place due to the higher concentration of oxygen in the blood than that in the cells.
    - Diffusion of carbon dioxide (formed due to the cellular respiration) takes place due to its higher concentration in the cells than that in the blood.

Level 3: Assess Your Concepts

54. The heart and lungs are strategically positioned in the thoracic cavity. The lungs facilitate the exchange of gases: taking in oxygen and expelling carbon dioxide. The heart, situated centrally between the lungs, pumps the oxygenated blood from the lungs to the rest of the body and pumps the deoxygenated blood back to the lungs. This close proximity allows for quick oxygenation of the blood and efficient circulation throughout the body.

55. Both oesophagus and trachea open at the pharynx. Food goes into the oesophagus while air goes into the trachea. We need to breathe when we speak. This causes the larynx to move down, opening the way for the trachea, so that air can pass through. If food is there inside the mouth, it may enter the trachea through the glottis present in the pharynx since epiglottis may not function properly due to the passage of air. This produces a violent coughing so as to force the food out. If the food particle does not come out, it obstructs the entry of air. As a result of it, choking of respiratory tract and difficulty in breathing occurs.

56. Normally when we breathe in, air enters the lungs through the nose, trachea and bronchioles. When we breathe out, air is expelled through the same tract in the opposite direction. The disease asthma causes swelling of the respiratory tract and the tract gets filled with mucus. Hence, the passage of air becomes narrower and people suffer from shortness of breath.

57. Smoke generated from cigarette contains many toxic chemicals such as nicotine, tar, carbon monoxide, etc. When we inhale cigarette smoke, it bypasses the filtering action of the nose and damages the tissues of the lungs. It leads to overproduction of mucus. Tobacco smoke also damages the air sacs in the lungs. Over a period of time, this leads to progressive loss of lung function and a condition known as emphysema. One sign of emphysema is shortness of breath. As the disease progresses, breathing becomes a major effort and may require supplementary oxygen.

58. Blue fingernails are caused by a lack or low level of circulating oxygen in red blood cells. This condition is known as cyanosis. The skin or membrane below the fingernail turns purplish-blue. In cold weather, blood vessels constrict to maintain the body temperature. The constriction of blood vessels reduces the dissipation of heat from the body. The right amount of oxygen-rich blood cannot reach our nails due to the narrow pathways of the blood vessels. Normal nail colour can be revived by massaging our hands. Massaging increases the temperature and reduces the constriction of the blood vessels.

NEET SPECIAL WING

Multiple-Answer Type Questions

1. The following are the characteristics of eosinophils- Cytoplasmic granules of eosinophils turn orange-red in response to the acid dye (eosin). The main function of eosinophils is to destroy pathogens, particularly parasitic worms and also responding to allergic reactions.

2. The steps that occur during inflammation are as follows- Tissue injury causes release of histamine, dilation of blood vessels occur, leakiness results in migration of phagocytes to the area, lastly phagocytes consume bacteria and cell debris and tissue heals.

3. An artery is a blood vessel that carries blood away from the heart and transports it to different parts of the body. Arteries have thick muscular wall and their lumen is narrow; therefore, arteries never collapse. Blood passes through the arteries under high pressure with jerks. They do not have any valves.

4. Sprinters require lots of energy quickly and hence derive energy from anaerobic respiration . The byproduct of anaerobic respiration in muscles is lactic acid.

5. Pulmonary vein transports oxygenated blood from lungs to the heart and Aorta carries oxygenated blood from heart to each and every tissue of the body.

Comprehension-Based Questions

A.

6. The process of deamination takes place in liver. Excess amino acids (simplified forms of proteins) in our body undergo decomposition to form toxic substances. Liver converts these toxic substances to a relatively less harmful product called urea. Urea is then excreted by kidney. The process of conversion of excess amino acids to urea by liver is called deamination.

7. As a result of deamination urea- a nitrogen containing waste product is produced which is excreted out of the body via urine.

8. The non nitrogenous compounds formed as a result of deamination process is converted into simple sugar which is glucose.

9. Cellular respiration takes place in the mitochondria of the cells. It is the process by which the glucose undergoes oxidation and energy is released. There are two main phases of cellular respiration. First stage is glycolysis that involves breakdown of glucose to a substance known as pyruvic acid.

10. There are two main phases of cellular respiration. First stage is glycolysis that involves breakdown of glucose, second stage is a process known as Krebs cycle. Krebs Cycle: It occurs inside the mitochondria. This process requires oxygen. It involves step-by-step breakdown of pyruvic acid to produce ATP and carbon dioxide.

11. Match the following:

    Inspiratory reserve volume (IRV) is the excess volume of air that can be inhaled by the deepest breath on top of the tidal volume which is 3000 mL
    (i) (c)

    About 500 mL of air is inhaled by a person in normal breathing. This is called tidal volume.
    (ii) (e)

    Vital capacity = TV + IRV + ERV = 500 mL + 3000 mL + 1000 mL = 4500 mL
    (iii) (a)

    Total lung capacity (amount of air that can be held anytime in the two lungs) = vital capacity + residual air = 4500 mL + 1500 mL = 6000 mL
    (iv) (d)

    Expiratory reserve volume (ERV) is the additional volume of air that can be exhaled with the maximum effort after the normal expiration which is 1000 mL.
    (v) (b)

B.

12. The heart produces the 'lub' sound due to the closing of atrio ventricular valves. The second sound 'dup' is produced when semi lunar valves also close.

13. Pulmonary artery carries deoxygenated blood from the right ventricles to the lungs for oxygenation. Since this blood is to be carried against gravity, it is carried by great force via an artery.

14. Blood pressure is highest at the origin of aorta. The pressure keeps on reducing as blood flows through smaller arterioles and capillaries. Blood pressure decreases considerably in Venules and veins so as to allow gaseous exchange.
15. The blood vessels constrict and restrict the blood flow to the extremities of the body namely palms and soles and prevent loss of heat from those surfaces, thus helping to maintain the body temperature..
16. Oxygenated blood enters the left atrium through pulmonary vein. The oxygenated blood enters the left ventricle due to the opening of bicuspid valve or mitral valve.
17. Match the following:

    Eosinophils have bi-lobed nucleus and both the lobes are connected with a thin strand.
    (i) (d)

    Basophils secrete chemicals such as histamine, heparin and serotonin. Histamine produces an allergic reaction when an unwanted substance tries to enter our body.
    (ii) (a)

    Neutrophils engulf the pathogens invaded in our body by the process of phagocytosis. They act as body's natural antibiotics.
    (iii) (b)

    The main function of lymphocytes is the production of antibodies and thus, they provide immunity to our body.
    (iv) (c)

    Monocytes ingest microorganisms that intrude our body and also act as scavengers by removing the dead cells.
    (v) (e)

CHAPTER

7

Reproduction in Human Beings

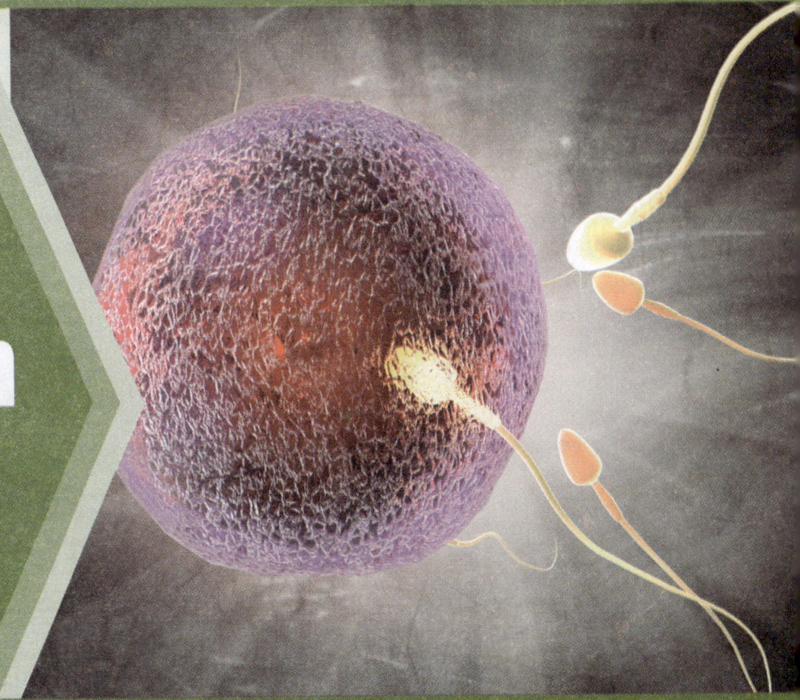

Remember

Before beginning this chapter, you should be able to:

- Recall basic modes of reproduction
- Remember the basic components of male and female reproductive systems

Key Ideas

After completing this chapter, you should be able to:

- Explain the male reproductive system
- Describe the female reproductive system
- Understand the phases in menstrual cycle
- Describe the events taking place during fertilization

A Tribute to Karl Ernst von Baer (1792–1876)

Karl Ernst von Baer (1792–1876) is regarded as a scientific titan for his ground-breaking contributions to embryology and human reproduction. Born in Estonian Province, this meticulous scientist discovered the mammalian egg cell, shedding light on the earliest stages of human life and paving the way for further research into reproductive biology. His seminal work, 'Developmental History of Animals,' encapsulated his profound insights into the developmental stages of animal embryos, laying the groundwork for modern embryology.

His exhaustive research not only unravelled the complexities of developmental biology but also advanced our understanding of human reproduction, in 1861, Von Baer was awarded the prestigious Copley Medal in recognition of his innovative scientific endeavours and unwavering pursuit of knowledge.

Von Baer's innovative spirit and lasting legacy continue to pervade the world of biology, providing critical perspectives and enriching the realms of developmental and reproductive sciences.

FUN TIME

CROSSWORD

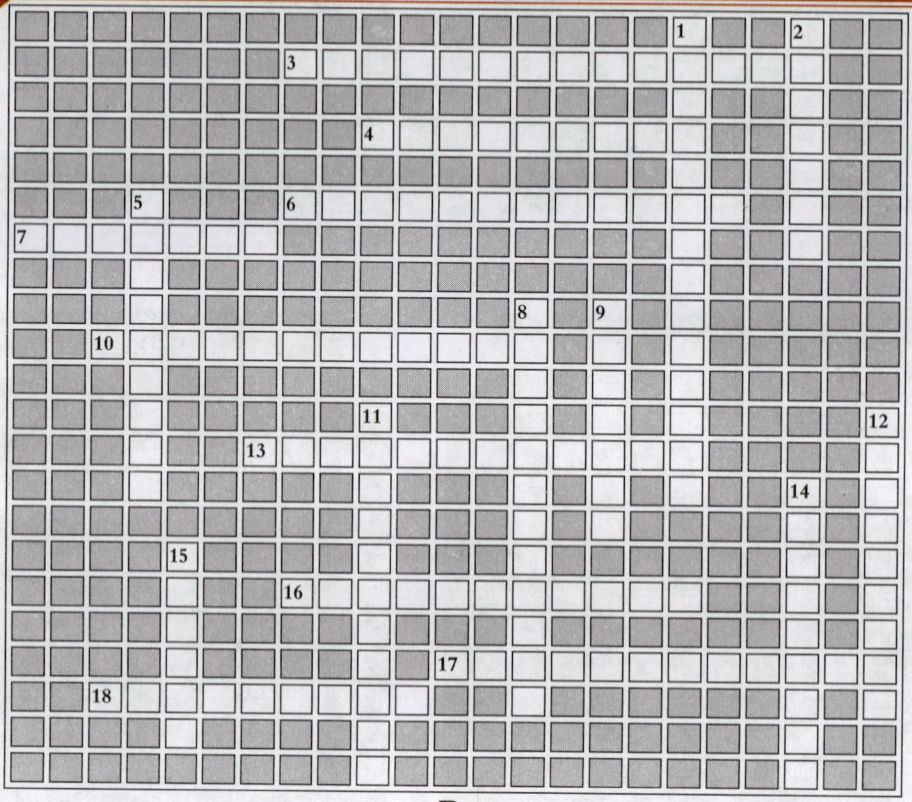

Across

3. The devices which are used to prevent pregnancy
4. The birth control operation performed in males
6. The phase of embryogenesis in which the formation of germ layers takes place
7. The pouch in which the testes are suspended in the abdominal cavity
10. Broad funnel-like structure that connects the ovary with the fallopian tube
13. The physiological changes which occur in sperm to make it ready for fertilisation
16. The thin outermost layer of the uterine wall composed of epithelial tissue
17. The hormone secreted by the corpus luteum
18. The embryonic membrane which forms the umbilical cord

Down

1. The extraembryonic membrane which is considered as vestigial organ in humans
2. The constricted part of the uterus lying between the fundus and the cervix
5. The process of formation of gametes in the female reproductive system
8. The fixation of the embryo to the endometrium of the uterus
9. Mode of asexual reproduction in hydra
11. The process of giving birth to the completely developed foetus by the mother
12. The hormone secreted by ovaries
14. Cell layer forms the outer layer of blastocyst
15. The mass of undifferentiated cells formed by the mitotic divisions of the zygote

INTRODUCTION

Reproduction is an inevitable process in the life of all living organisms for the perpetuation of the species. However, the modes of reproduction vary widely among the organisms. Asexual mode of reproduction is confined only to the lower organisms and plants. Sexual mode of reproduction is the only mode of reproduction in all higher animals. Sexual mode of reproduction as usual involves the process of fertilization to form zygote. This is followed by the process of development of zygote into a new individual. The various classes of animals differ widely with respect to the fertilization process and development. Human beings are at the pinnacle of evolutionary hierarchy, and hence show the highest level of complexity in the reproductive cycle. Humans show the distinct sexual dimorphism with striking secondary sexual characters in males and females. The human reproduction involves separate and complex male and female reproductive systems. The reproduction in humans involves internal fertilization followed by subsequent development of the baby inside the female reproductive system.

Modes of Reproduction in Animals

Depending upon the method followed for reproduction, it is classified into types:

- Asexual reproduction
- Sexual reproduction

Asexual Reproduction

This mode of reproduction involves only one parent. It does not involve formation of gametes, and hence, there is no blending of genetic material which gives rise to similar-looking offspring. The reproductive units may consist of either a portion of the parent body or the whole parent body. For example: many bacterial reproduce by the process of binary fission which involves splitting of the whole of the parent body into two daughter cells. These daughter cells then grow individually.

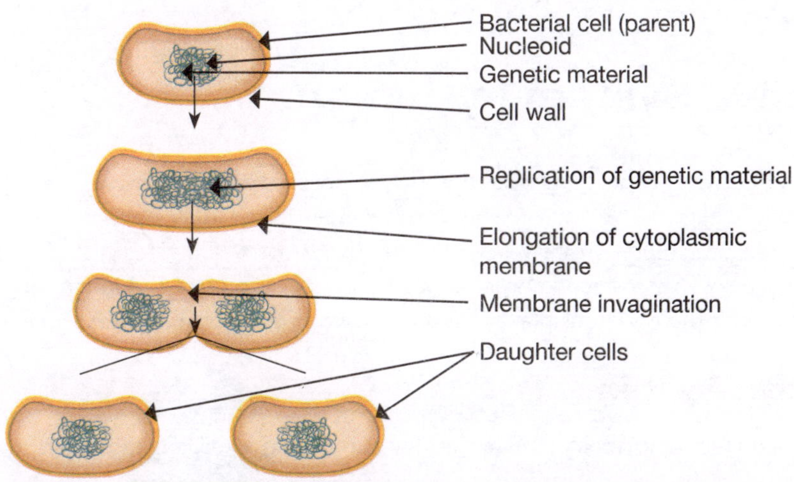

Figure 7.1 Illustration of binary fission in bacteria

Another example is of *Hydra* which reproduces by means of budding. In this mode, small buds grow out of the body of *Hydra*. These buds then get separated from the parent body and grow individually.

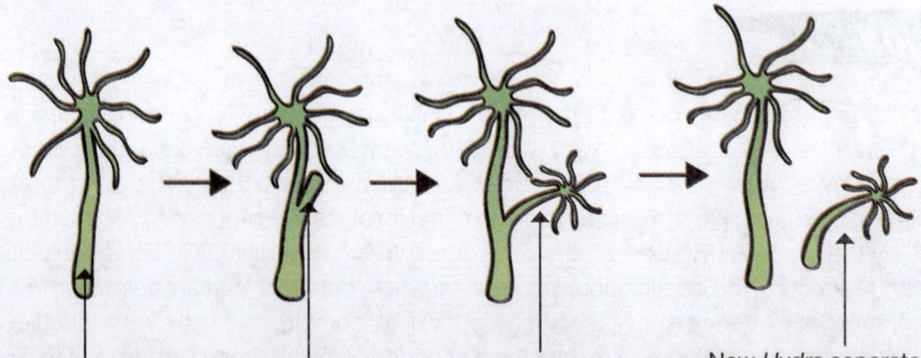

Figure 7.2 Illustration of budding in *Hydra*

Sexual Reproduction

This mode of reproduction involves two parents. It involves formation of gametes, and hence, there is blending of genetic material which gives rise to variation. The reproductive units may consist of either a portion of the parent body or the whole parent body. It involves participation of female and male reproductive structures which are discussed in detail in the successive section of this chapter.

Table 7.1 Differences between sexual and asexual modes of reproduction

Parameter	Asexual mode	Sexual mode
Gametes	Not involved	Involved
Parent	Uniparental	Biparental
Variation	Offspring genetically similar to parent	Offspring genetically different from parent
Number of offspring	Higher	Few
Meiosis	Not involved	Involved

Reproductive System In Humans

Both male and female reproductive systems comprise reproductive organs and accessory glands. Reproductive organs can be broadly classified into two categories: Primary reproductive organs; and Accessory reproductive organs. The organs concerned with the formation of gametes are primary reproductive organs. The organs that help in various processes of the reproductive cycle are accessory reproductive organs. Accessory glands secrete the hormones required throughout the reproductive cycle. Let us look at these various parts of reproductive system in males and females separately.

Male Reproductive System

Male reproductive system consists of primary and accessory reproductive organs along with accessory glands. These components are discussed below.

Primary Reproductive Organs

A pair of testes (singular: testis) is the primary reproductive organ in males.

Location of Testes

They are located outside the abdominal cavity and suspended in a pouch known as scrotal sacs or scrotum. The scrotal sacs or scrotum is present behind the penis.

Structure and Function of Testes

Chief morphological features of testis are given below:

- Oval in shape
- Pinkish in colour
- 4–5 cm long
- 2.5 cm wide
- 3 cm thick

Info Bytes!

An average human male produces about 1,500 sperm per second throughout his life.

Anatomy and Physiology

Testes are covered with a dense, fibrous tissue called tunica albuginea. There are ingrowths in tunica albuginea which are called septa. These septa divide each testis into 200–300 compartments called testicular lobules. Blood vessels and nerves are present in the testicular lobules. They are embedded in loose connective tissue. Each testicular lobule contains 1–4 highly coiled tube-like structures known as seminiferous tubules. Seminiferous tubules contain sertoli cells and germ cells. The diploid germ cells produce haploid male gametes, called sperms or spermatozoa by successive mitotic divisions, followed by meiotic division. At first, the immature non-motile sperms called spermatids are formed. On maturation, they become mature spermatozoa or sperms. This entire process of formation of sperms is called spermatogenesis. Sertoli cells provide nutrition to the germ cells. Leydig cells are interstitial cells that are present between the seminiferous tubules. Leydig cells secrete male sex hormone called testosterone. Testosterone hormone helps in the formation of sperms. The temperature maintained in testes is 2–3 degrees lower than the normal body temperature since they are present outside the abdomen. This temperature is conducive for the formation and maturation of sperms. The skin of the scrotum contracts or expands with the change in the temperature of the environment in different seasons so that the temperature in the testes is maintained.

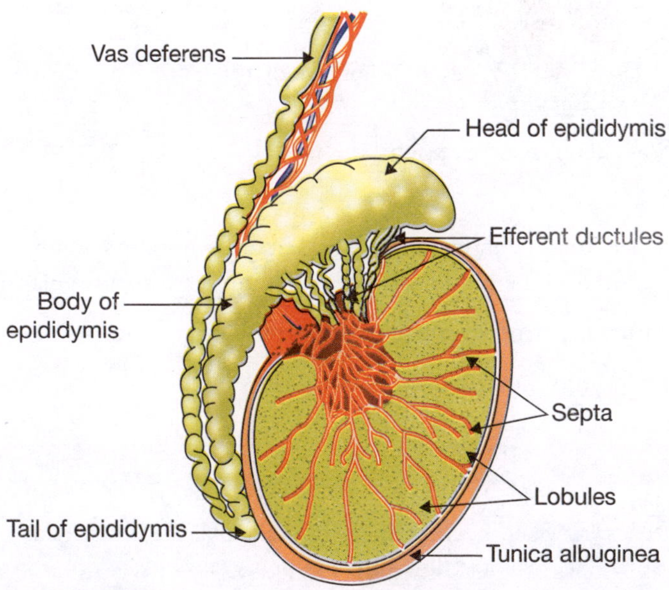

Figure 7.3 Illustration of longitudinal section of testis

Accessory Reproductive Organs in Male

The two accessory reproductive organs in male are: which are mentioned below.

1. Sperm ducts 2. Penis

Sperm Ducts

Sperm ducts are a series of different structures that originate from the seminiferous tubules in the testes and end at the ejaculatory organ that is penis. Sperm ducts transport the sperms from the testes to the penis. The different parts of the sperm ducts are:

- Rete testis
- Vasa efferentia
- Epididymis
- Vasa deferentia
- Ejaculatory duct

Rete testis: It is a network of tubules that transports sperms formed in testes to vasa efferentia.

Vasa efferentia: It is a convoluted tubular structure that leads to the epididymis. It carries sperms to the epididymis.

Epididymis: It is a long, coiled tube which is a temporary storage organ for spermatids. These undergo maturation and differentiation into mature sperms in the epididymis.

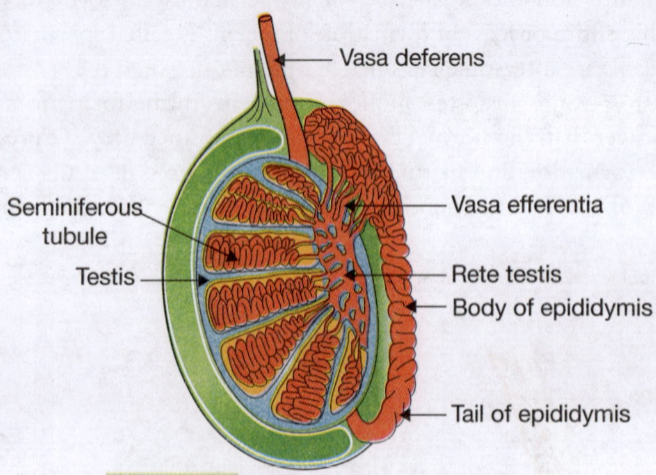

Figure 7.4 Illustration of sperm ducts

Info Bytes!

Vasectomy is a surgical procedure for male sterilization in which vas deferens are cut and tied.

Epididymis has three regions: upper, middle and hind regions. Sperms undergo maturation in the upper and middle regions of the epididymis and get stored in the hind region. Epididymis leads to a tubular part called vasa deferentia.

Vasa deferentia: It transports matured sperms from epididymis to the ejaculatory duct.

Ejaculatory duct: It delivers sperms into the urethra.

Penis

Penis is the muscular organ for ejaculation of sperms into the female sex organ. Hence, it is also called copulatory organ. Penis also helps in urination. But ejaculation and urination do not take place simultaneously. Sensory nerves are present in penis that help in sexual stimulation. Excess blood flow into the penis takes place due to sexual stimulation. Thus, penis becomes rigid and erected. This condition is called erection. During ejaculation, contraction of the sphincter muscles at the neck of the urinary bladder takes place. Thus, urine discharge does not take place during ejaculation.

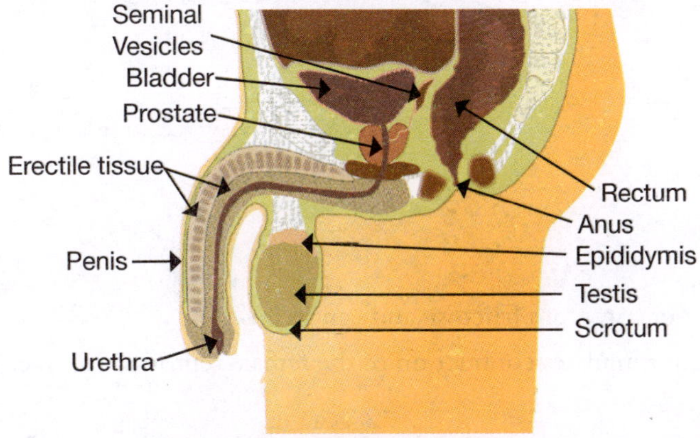

Figure 7.5 Male reproductive system

Accessory Glands of Male Reproductive System

There are three types of male accessory glands, which are:

1. A pair of seminal vesicles
2. A prostate gland
3. A pair of bulbourethral glands or Cowper's glands

Seminal Vesicles

The seminal vesicles are sac-like structure, they are located behind the urinary bladder, in front of the rectum and above the prostate gland. They secrete a fluid that has mild alkalinity (pH around 7.2) and acts as a medium for the transportation of sperms.

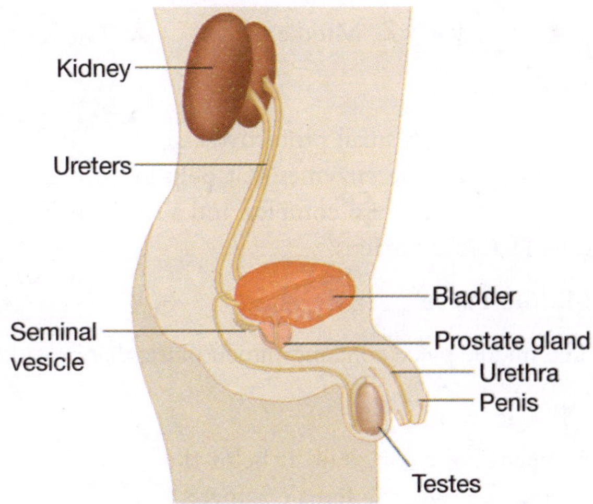

Figure 7.6 Illustration of prostate gland

Prostate Gland

All men have a prostate, an apricot-sized, muscular gland that produces prostate fluid. It sits just in front of the rectum and below the bladder. The prostate surrounds the urethra, the tube that carries urine from the bladder to the penis. It is vital for the proper functioning of the male reproductive system. The muscles of the prostate gland also help propel this seminal fluid into the urethra during ejaculation.

During ejaculation, millions of sperm move from the testes through tubes called the vas deferens into the area of the prostate. At this point, the prostate contracts, closing off the opening between the bladder and the urethra, releasing fluid into the urethra and pushing semen in through.

In most men, the prostate gland normally enlarges with age. This may be due to changes in sex hormone levels that occur with normal aging. In some men, the enlarged prostate causes few or no symptoms, while in others the symptoms can be very bothersome.

Bulbourethral or Cowper's Glands

A pair of bulbourethral or Cowper's glands is located below the prostate gland at the beginning of the penis. They are seen on either side of the urethra. They provide lubricating medium for urethra and the tip of the penis. They secrete an alkaline fluid containing mucus that neutralizes the fluid in the urethral region and thus, provides a clean pathway for ejaculation and transport of the sperms by expelling residue of urine and dead cells.

> **Info Bytes!**
>
> A total of 2.5–5 mL of semen is secreted during one ejaculation and 1 mL of semen contains 50–150 million sperms.

Semen

The fluids secreted by the seminal vesicles, prostate gland and Cowper's glands act as a medium for the transportation of sperms. This fluid mixture is called semen. The fluid from seminal vesicles constitutes 70 per cent of the semen. Semen contains the following substances as major constituents:

- Citrate
- Ascorbic acid
- Acid phosphatase
- Fructose
- Prostaglandin hormone

Function of Semen

- Spermatozoa or sperms get energy from fructose and can swim.
- The hormone, prostaglandin stimulates contraction of the female reproductive tract and helps in the fusion of male and female gametes.

Structure of Sperm

A sperm is a male reproductive cell that consists of following three parts:

1. Head **2.** Middle piece **3.** Tail

Head

Head contains a small protective cap-like structure, called acrosome. Acrosome covers the head of the sperm. Acrosome contains digestive enzymes that help in dissolving the outer coating of the female gamete (reproductive cell). Head also has a modified Golgi complex and a large nucleus. A single set of chromosomes is present in the nucleus, and hence, it is called haploid nucleus.

Middle Piece

The middle piece contains mitochondria that provide energy for the movement of the sperm.

Tail

A sperm has a long tail. It helps the sperm in swimming inside the female reproductive tract. This facilitates the male gamete to reach the female gamete.

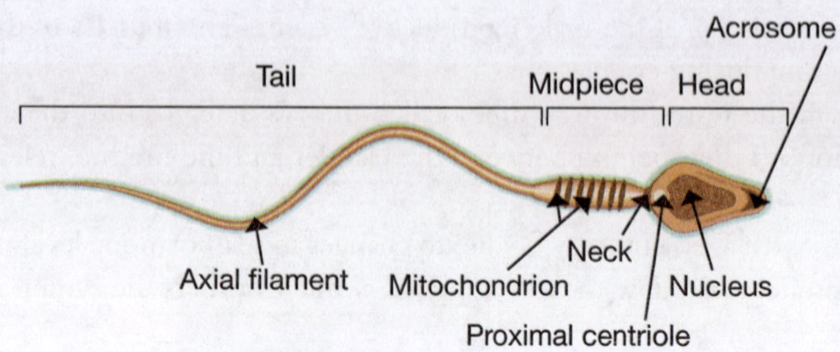

Figure 7.7 Illustration of a spermatozoon

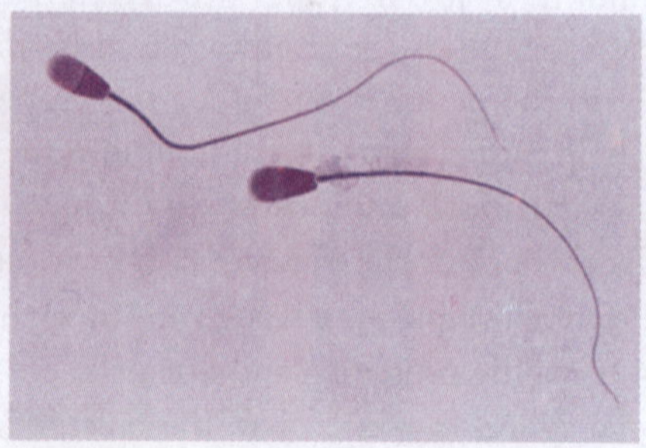

Figure 7.8 Microscopic view of sperm cells

Seminiferous tubules *(Produce sperms)* → Network of tubules → Efferent ducts → Upper part (head) of epididymis
↓
Middle part (body) of epididymis → Hind part (tail) of epididymis → Sperm duct (vas deferens) → Urethra (in penis)

Figure 7.9 Course of sperms in male reproductive system

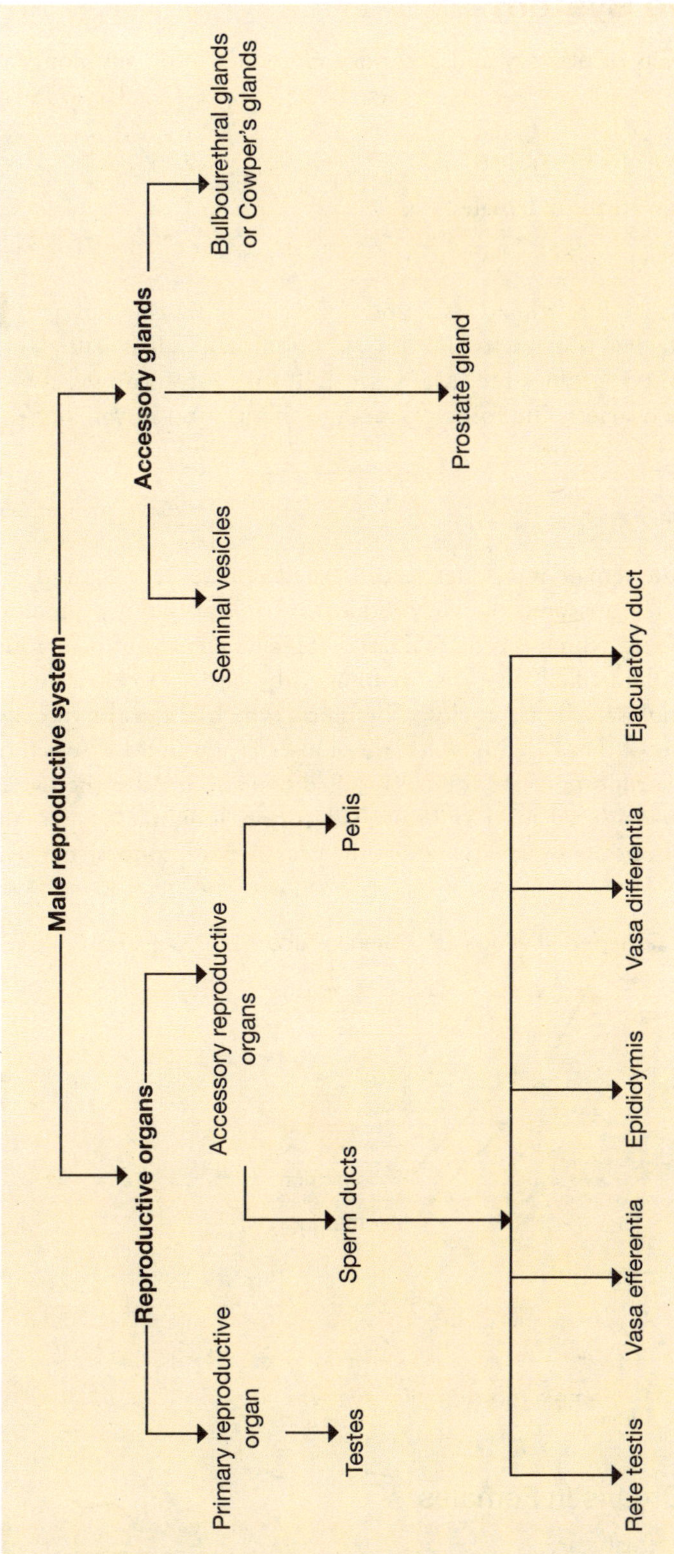

Figure 7.10 Schematic representation of male reproductive organs and glands

Female Reproductive System

Female reproductive system consists of primary and accessory reproductive organs along with accessory glands. These components are discussed below.

Primary Reproductive Organ in Females

A pair of ovaries is the primary sex organs in females.

Location and Structure of Ovaries

There is a pair of ovaries attached to the dorsal abdominal wall in the pelvic region. The mesentery that attaches ovaries to the dorsal abdominal wall is called mesovarium. Each ovary is about 3–4 cm wide. Many sac-like structures known as follicles are found in each of the ovaries. The follicles undergo maturation in various stages.

Info Bytes!

Mesentery is a set of tissues with the help of which an organ remains attached with the abdominal wall.

Function of Ovaries

Each follicle contains an immature female reproductive cell called oocyte. It is diploid. One oocyte gets matured in each ovary in alternate month. The matured oocyte produces a haploid ovum by meiotic division and the mature follicle in which the ovum is present, which is called Graafian follicle. The ovum is surrounded by a fluid-filled cavity inside the Graafian follicle. The fluid-filled cavity is surrounded by layers of cells called granulosa cells. These cells secrete oestrogen hormone. Granulosa cells are enclosed by theca, which is a group of cells that act as the coating of a follicle. The inner and outer layers of theca are known as theca interna and theca externa, respectively. Graafian follicle ruptures to release the ovum. The rupture of the follicle is called ovulation. After the ovulation, the remaining part of the follicle appears like a yellow-coloured mass and is called corpus luteum. Corpus luteum secretes progesterone hormone. The ovum is released from the ovary and enters the accessory reproductive organ called oviduct.

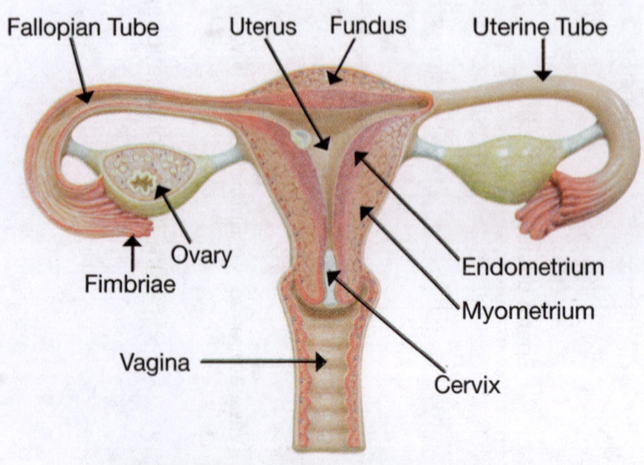

Figure 7.11 Female reproductive system

Info Bytes!

A female baby is born with all the eggs she will ever have in her life-time—around 1 to 2 million.

Accessory Reproductive Organs in Females

Accessory reproductive organs in females are:

- Oviduct or fallopian tube
- Uterus
- Vagina
- Vulva

Info Bytes!

An ovum is the largest human cell. Its diameter is about 120 micrometres.

Info Bytes!

Vagina is home to numerous microorganisms which thrive only in an acidic environment.

Oviduct

An oviduct is a muscular tube that transports ovum from the ovary to the uterus. The oviduct is also known as fallopian tube. The length of the oviduct is about 10–12 cm. The contraction and relaxation of the unstriped muscle fibres of the oviduct help in the propagation of the ovum. The inner wall of the oviduct is lined with granular ciliated epithelial cells. These ciliated cells help in the movement of ovum in a direction that is from the ovary to the uterus. Other than the transport of the ovum, the oviduct also provides a conductive environment for the

- Nourishment of the ovum
- Movement of the spermatozoa
- Fertilization

> **Info Bytes!**
> Tubectomy is a permanent method of contraception in women in which a portion of the fallopian tube is blocked.

The oviduct (fallopian tube) can be divided into three parts listed as follows:

1. Infundibulum
2. Ampulla
3. Isthmus

Infundibulum

- It is a broad funnel-like structure that connects the ovary with the fallopian tube.
- The aperture of infundibulum is called ostium and it collects ovum from the ovary.

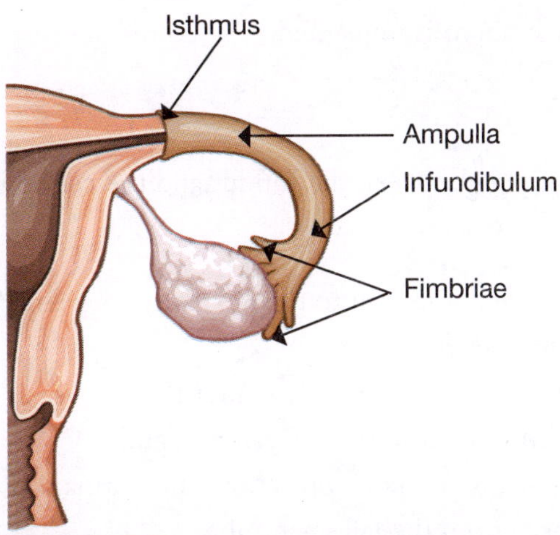

Figure 7.12 Parts of oviduct (fallopian tube)

- Ostium is surrounded by finger-like projections called fimbriae.
- Fimbriae help the ovum to enter the infundibulum from ovary.

Ampulla

- The part of the fallopian tube next to the infundibulum is ampulla.
- It is long, wide and convoluted.
- It is the site of fertilization.

Isthmus

- It is a small, narrow, thick-walled, tube-like structure.
- It is straight and provides the connectivity between the uterus and ampulla.
- It passes through the thick uterine wall and enters the uterine cavity.

Uterus

The fallopian tube leads into the next accessory reproductive organ which is called uterus.

The uterus, commonly called the womb, is a hollow pear-shaped cavity. It is present in the pelvic region behind the urinary bladder and in front of the rectum. It is the part of the female reproductive system where the fertilized ovum called embryo develops. The wall of the uterus is thick and comprises three layers of tissues. These are:

1. **Innermost layer or endometrium:** This layer contains many tubular glands and undergoes morphological changes during the menstrual cycle and the development of embryo.
2. **Middle layer or myometrium:** This is a smooth muscular layer which is composed of the major volume of the wall of the uterus.
3. **Innermost layer or perimetrium:** This layer is composed of epithelial tissues and acts as an envelope of the uterus.

Uterus has following three parts:

1. Fundus 2. Body or isthmus 3. Cervix

Fundus

- It is the upper part of the uterus and is connected to the fallopian tube.
- It has a dome-like structure.
- It is the place in the uterus where embryo is implanted.

Body or Isthmus

- The constricted part of the uterus lying between the fundus and the cervix is called isthmus of the uterus.

Cervix

- It is the lowermost part of the uterus and it leads into the next accessory female reproductive organ, which is vagina.
- It is the passage between the vagina and the uterus.
- It facilitates fertilization by allowing the spermatozoa to enter the uterus.
- After uterus, the next accessory female reproductive organ is vagina.
- The lowermost part of the uterus that is cervix extends upto the vagina.
- Uterus receives the ovum or embryo from the fallopian tube.
- It also provides shelter and nourishment to the fertilized ovum that is the embryo.

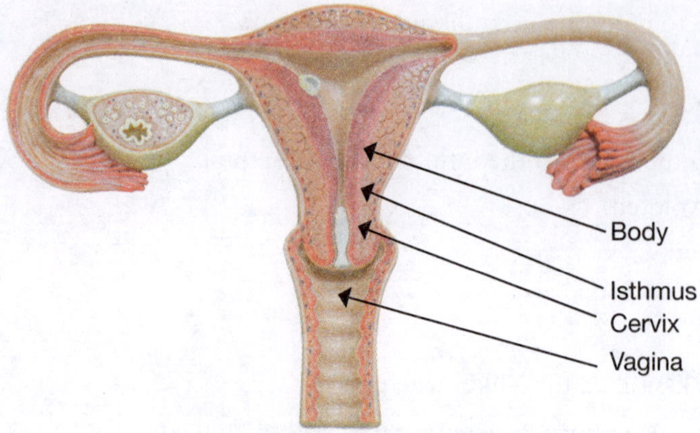

Figure 7.13 Parts of uterus

Vagina

The vagina has a muscular tube-like structure. It originates from the cervix and extends up to the external female genitalia named vulva. It is about 7.5-cm long and its inner wall is folded (bumps and ridges). This is called vaginal rugae. The inner wall of the vagina secretes mucus. Hymen is a thin membrane that partially closes the opening of the vagina. It is made up of highly delicate tissues, and hence usually gets ruptured during different rigorous activities such as exercise, cycling, horse riding, etc. If not, it gets ruptured during the first copulation of the female.

Functions of Vagina

Major functions of vagina are as listed below:

- Provides the passage for the sperms to reach the uterus.
- Allows the passage of menstrual flow.
- Undergoes stretching to facilitate the delivery of the newborn.

Vulva

The next and the external part of the female reproductive system is vulva. Vulva surrounds the vaginal opening. It comprises the following three parts.

- **Labia majora:** It is a pair of thick-folded skin constituted of adipose tissue. It protects the inner, delicate part of vulva.
- **Labia minora:** It is a pair of thin-folded skin covered by labia majora. It protects the clitoris, and vaginal and urethral openings.
- **Clitoris:** It is a small projected part of the vulva present above the urethral opening. It is an erectile tissue and contains sensory nerve endings. It is highly sensitive.

Accessory Female Reproductive Glands

There are two types of female reproductive glands, namely.

1. Bartholin's or large vestibular glands.
2. Mammary glands.

Bartholin's Glands

Bartholin's glands are small, round structures, located at either side of the vaginal opening. They secrete a fluid for the lubrication of the vagina and the vulva and help in copulation.

Mammary Glands

They are present in the breasts of the females. They help in lactation, that is, the production of milk when the new-born is delivered. Each breast has a circular pigmented area around the nipple. This is called areola. It only secretes a liquid that lubricates the nipple.

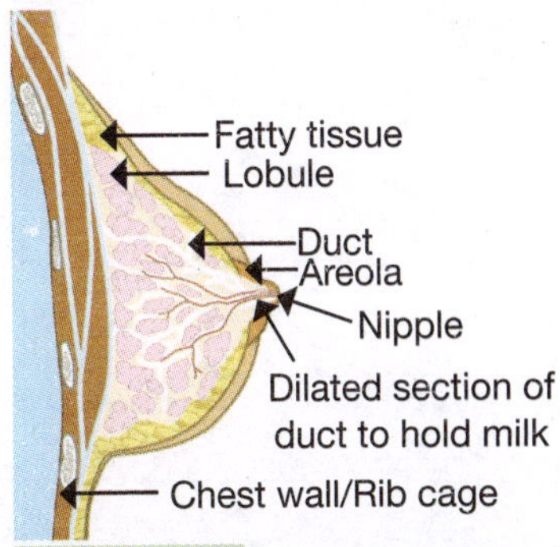

Figure 7.14 Mammary gland

Table 7.2 Comparative study of male and female reproductive systems

Reproductive organs/glands	Males	Females
Primary reproductive organ	A pair of testes	A pair of ovaries
Accessory reproductive organs	Sperm ducts Penis	Oviduct or fallopian tube Uterus Vagina Vulva
Accessory glands	A pair of seminal vesicles A prostate gland A pair of bulbourethral glands or Cowper's glands	Bartholin's or large vestibular glands Mammary glands

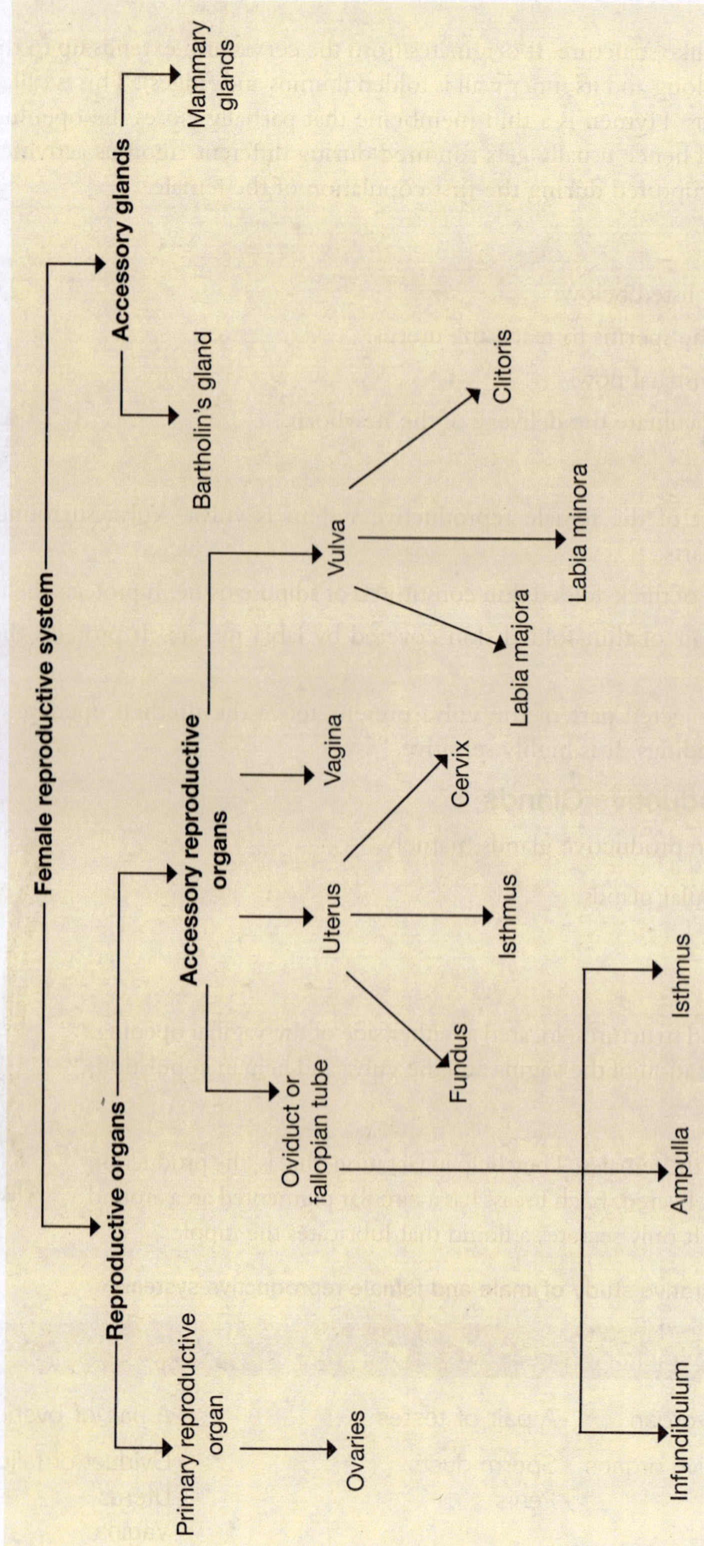

Figure 7.15 Schematic representation of female reproductive system

Quick Recap

✔ **What is the role of a Graafian follicle?**

A Graafian follicle is a small sac present in the ovary. At puberty, each ovary has a large number of immature follicles, each of which contains an immature oocyte. Between puberty and the onset of menopause, one of the follicles develops to maturity into a follicle, called Graafian follicle at every 28 days. The ovum within it becomes larger, the wall of the follicle becomes thicker and fluid gets accumulated in the follicle surrounding the ovum. The granulose cells surrounding the fluid-filled cavity in the Graafian follicle secrete oestrogen hormone that stimulates the uterus for endometrial thickening. As the follicle matures, it moves to the surface of the ovary. After maturation, the Graafian follicle ruptures and releases the ovum. This process is called ovulation. It occurs at around the 14th day of the menstrual cycle. The released ovum travels through the fallopian tube and reaches the uterus. During this period, empty Graafian follicle changes to a yellow mass, called corpus luteum. The corpus luteum secretes progesterone hormone that causes further changes in the endometrium of the uterus and nourishes the fertilized ovum and leads to the formation of the foetus.

✔ **What is the significance of huge length of seminiferous tubules?**

Seminiferous tubules are the site of three different functions—production of germ cells (sperm), maturation of sperms and their transportation. Sperm cells slowly flow through the seminiferous tubules for up to 60 days or more and finally reach sperm ducts. All the nutrients required for maturation of sperms are supplied by sertoli cells located at the wall of seminiferous tubules.

✔ **Explain the significance of sexual dimorphism in reproductive strategies and its implications for species survival.**

Sexual dimorphism, which is characterised by prominent secondary sexual characteristics, can influence a species' reproductive roles and strategies. This differentiation ensures diversification, which increases the chances of the species' survival and adaptation to different environments.

✔ **Investigate the significance of haploid gamete fusion in the formation of a diploid zygote. What is the significance of this transition for sexual reproduction?**

A diploid zygote is formed when haploid male (sperm) and female (ovum) gametes fuse. This restores the species' chromosome number, ensuring genetic diversity and continuity. It combines genetic material from both parents, resulting in beneficial variations for evolution.

✔ **Discuss the primary stages that guide the transformation of a single-celled zygote into a fully developed foetus.**

Embryogenesis is the process by which a zygote develops into a newborn. The zygote goes through several stages of cell division, differentiation, and organ formation during this process, ensuring the fetus's proper development and survival inside the womb.

✔ **Why is reproduction regarded as a necessary process in the lives of living organisms? How does it ensure the survival of species?**

Reproduction is essential for life to continue. It not only replaces old or deceased members, but it also introduces genetic variations that can be beneficial to a species' survival, ensuring the species' survival across generations.

✔ **Male and female reproductive systems are both complex. How do primary and secondary reproductive organs work together to facilitate reproduction?**

The primary reproductive organs (testes in males and ovaries in females) are in charge of gamete production. These gametes are transported, fed, and protected by accessory organs and glands. They work together to ensure successful fertilization and the survival of the species.

Biological Processes Involved in Reproductive Cycle

The entire process related to the reproductive cycle takes place in the reproductive system of females. The primary oocytes (immature) that are formed at birth enter into the maturation phase at the time of puberty. It is considered as the onset of reproductive age for the female. This onset of menstrual cycle at the time of puberty is called menarche. The maturation of the immature oocytes into mature ova and the subsequent events taking place in female reproductive system from the reproductive cycle is called menstrual cycle.

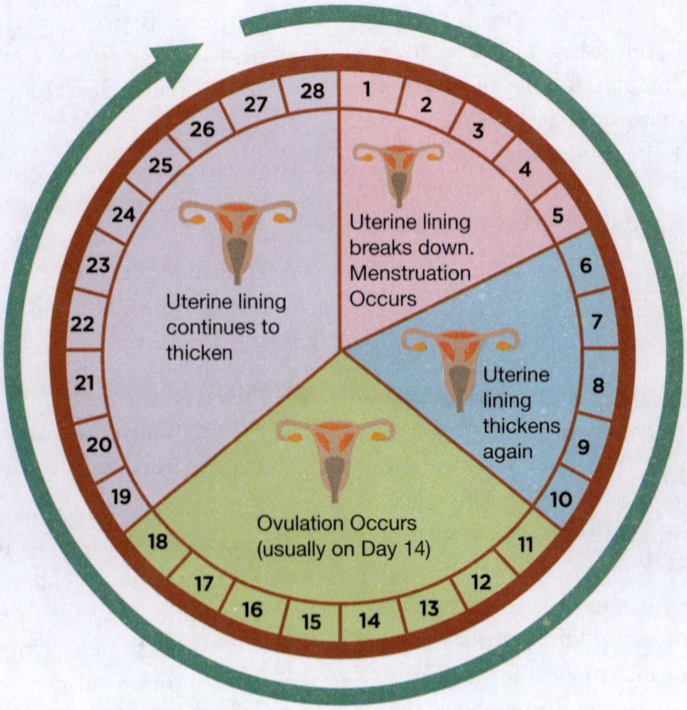

Figure 7.16 Phases of a menstrual cycle

Menstrual Cycle

It is a series of changes that the female reproductive organs undergo every month periodically, during the reproductive age. The average duration of a menstrual cycle is 28–30 days. There can be a minor variation in this duration. The menstrual cycle starts at an early teen age and ends at the age of around 50. Every month, the ovary generates a matured ovum that can undergo fertilization. During this period, the uterus undergoes certain changes so that it can provide shelter and nourishment to the fertilized egg. If the ovum does not get fertilized, the uterus sheds its lining and thus, the menstrual bleeding starts. A menstrual cycle can be divided into following four phases:

1. Menstrual phase
2. Proliferative phase or follicular phase
3. Ovulatory phase
4. Secretory phase or luteal phase

> **Info Bytes!**
> Menstrual cycle of orangutans is around every 23 days, and chimpanzees every 36 days.

Menstrual Phase

This phase is characterized by following events.

Changes in the ovary: It includes the modifications listed below.

- Degeneration of the unfertilized ovum takes place.
- Degeneration of corpus luteum takes place.
- Maturation of the oocyte in the follicle starts.

Changes in the uterus: It includes the modifications listed below.

- The endometrium lining of the uterus gets thickened for the implantation of the embryo prior to menstrual phase.
- Endometrium lining, blood vessels and degenerated ovum shed off and get discharged through the vagina. This is called menstrual bleeding.

Proliferative or Follicular Phase

This phase is characterized by following events.

Changes in the ovary: It includes the modifications listed below.

- Development of Graafian follicle takes place.
- Matured ovum is formed in the Graafian follicle.
- During the maturation of the ovum, Graafian follicle secrets oestrogen hormone.

Changes in the uterus: It includes the modifications listed below.

- The secretion of oestrogen stimulates the uterus for endometrial thickening.
- Oestrogen also helps in the development of the lining of blood vessels in the uterus.

Ovulatory Phase

This phase is characterized by following events.

Changes in the ovary: It includes the modifications listed below.

- The rupture of Graafian follicle takes place.
- The matured ovum is released from the ovary and enters the fallopian tube.
- Ovulation takes place in this phase.
- The ovum remains in the fallopian tube for 24 h.

Secretary Phase or Luteal Phase

This phase is characterized by following events.

Changes in the ovary: It includes the modifications listed below.

- Graafian follicle is converted to corpus luteum.
- Corpus luteum releases progesterone.

Changes in the uterus: It includes the modifications listed below.

- Progesterone helps in further thickening of the uterus.
- Uterus can provide conducive environment for the development of the embryo.
- If the ovum undergoes fertilization, it gets implanted in the uterus for its nourishment. Under these circumstances, menstrual cycle stops until the delivery of the newborn.
- If the ovum remains unfertilized, degeneration of the ovum takes place which results in menstrual bleeding.

> **Info Bytes!**
>
> During menstrual cycle, body temperature rises and falls slightly due to change in the levels of progesterone hormone.

Role of Hormones of Pituitary Gland in Reproduction

Two hormones released from the anterior lobe of pituitary gland play their role in reproduction in human beings. They are:

1. Follicle stimulating hormone (FSH)
2. Luteinizing hormone (LH)

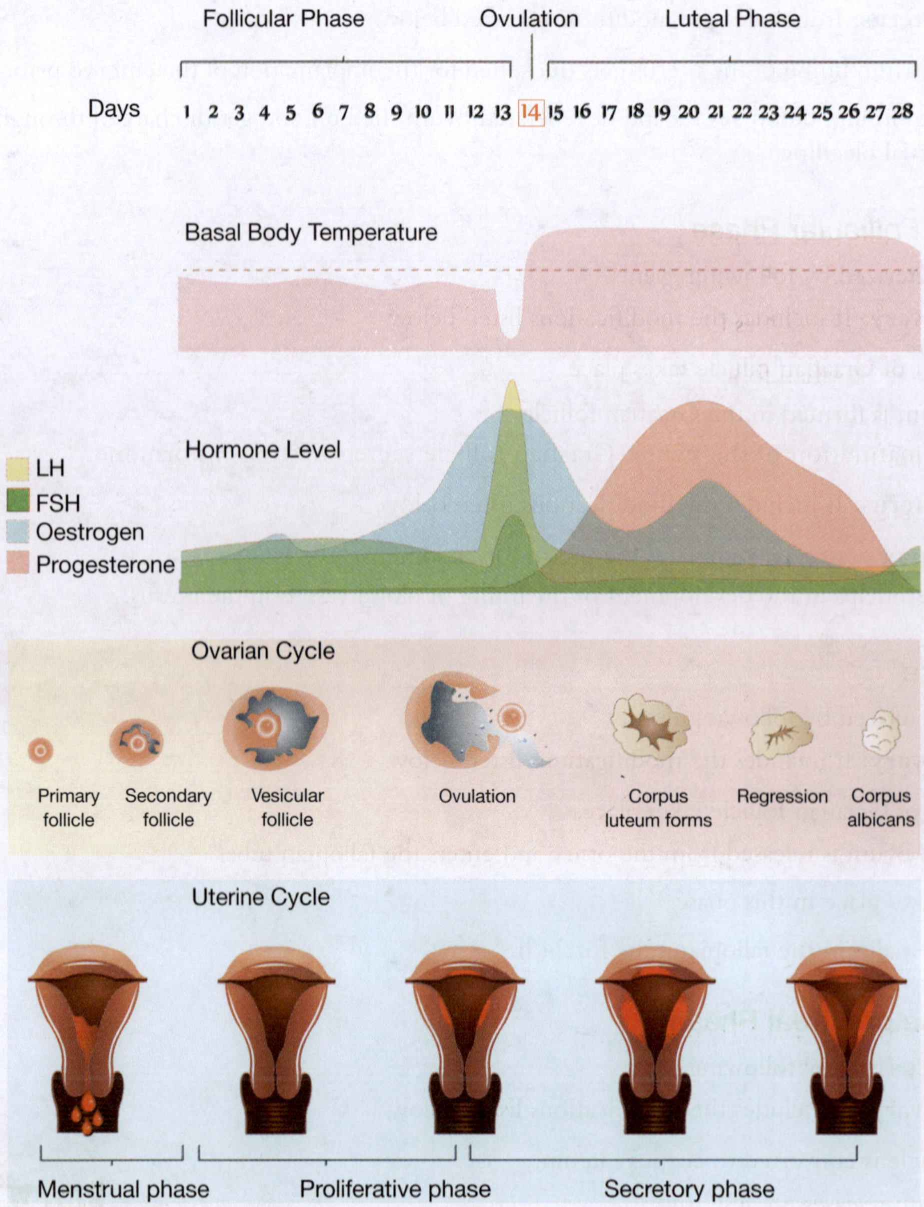

Figure 7.17 Illustration of detailed events of a menstrual cycle

Table 7.3 Role of pituitary hormones in reproduction

Hormones secreted from the anterior lobe of pituitary gland	Role in male reproductive system	Role in female reproductive system
Follicle stimulating hormone	Formation of spermatozoa	• Growth of Graafian follicle • Oestrogen secretion
Luteinizing hormone	Secretion of testosterone	• Ovulation • Development of corpus luteum • Secretion of progesterone

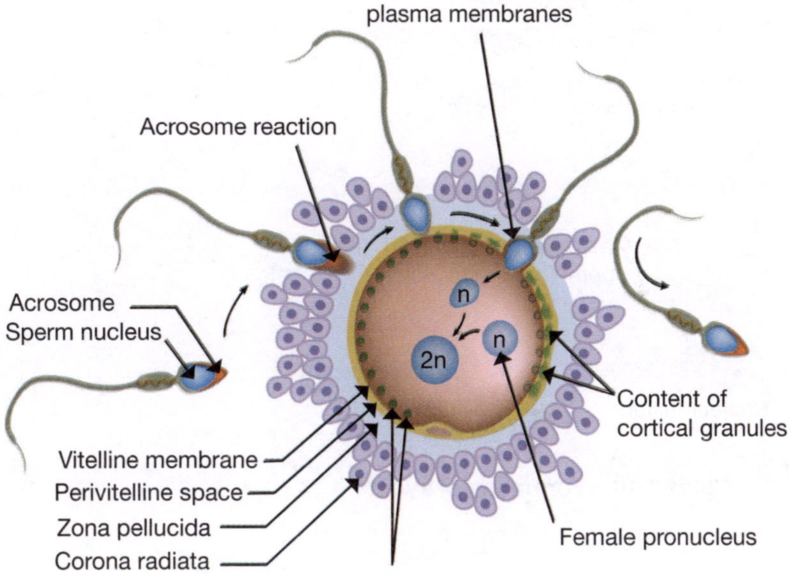

Figure 7.18 Fertilization of sperm with ovum

> **Info Bytes!**
>
> While millions of sperm are released during ejaculation, only about 200 or so sperm are serious contenders for reaching the awaiting egg, and only one gets to fertilize it.

Fertilization

Ovulation takes place by the rupture of Graafian follicle and the matured ovum enters the fallopian tube. After copulation, sperms travel from the vagina to the uterus and then enter the fallopian tube of the female reproductive system. Initially, the transportation of the sperms takes place by the contractions of uterus and fallopian tube. Later, they swim using their flagella to reach the ovum. The ovum gets surrounded by numerous sperms, but only one sperm enters it. As soon as one sperm enters the ovum, there is a series of chemical reactions that obstruct further entry of other sperms. The fusion of a haploid male gamete (sperm) and a haploid female gamete (ovum) to form a diploid zygote is called fertilization. It takes place in the ampulla of the fallopian tube of female reproductive system. Before fertilization, the sperm has to undergo capacitation.

Capacitation

The physiological changes that occur in the sperm to enable it to fertilize the ovum. These changes in the sperm are known as capacitation. The acrosome of the sperm secretes lytic enzymes. These enzymes help the sperm to penetrate the layers of cells clustered around the ovum. Then the sperm comes in contact with the ovum. The surface of the ovum secretes some chemicals that prevent the entry of the other sperms. This process ensures fertilization of ovum with only one sperm.

Formation of Zygote

The sperms actively swim with the help of the tails and pass through the cervix and reach uterus with a rate of about 1.5 mm per min. From uterus, they reach oviducts. If it happens that there is an ovum in the oviduct, the sperm fuses with the ovum.

The ovum and the sperm fuse to form zygote. After this process, corpus luteum formed from Graafian follicles secretes progesterone which helps in the development of the zygote.

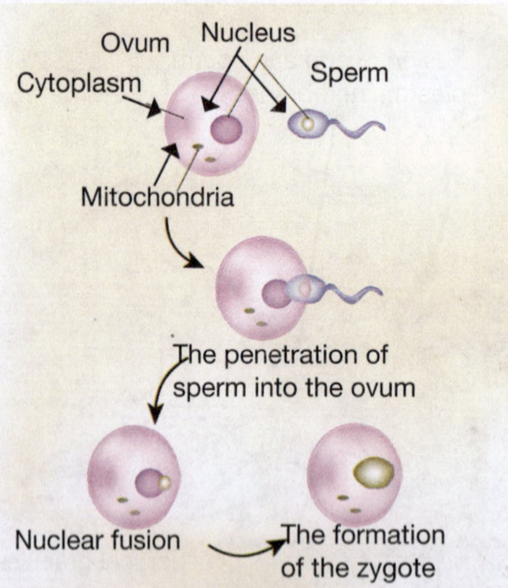

Figure 7.19 Formation of zygote

Embryogenesis

The entire process of development of a single-celled diploid zygote into a newborn child until its birth is called embryogenesis. The total time required for the development of the newborn until its delivery from a fertilized ovum (zygote) is 280 days. This period is called gestation period or pregnancy. The embryogenesis takes place in four stages, which are:

1. Cleavage
2. Blastulation
3. Gastrulation
4. Organogenesis

Cleavage

The zygote formed undergoes mitotic division and the number of cells increases in the zygote in geometric progression. This stage of the gestation is called cleavage and results in the formation of multicellular embryo from the single-celled zygote. This mass of undifferentiated cell is called morula.

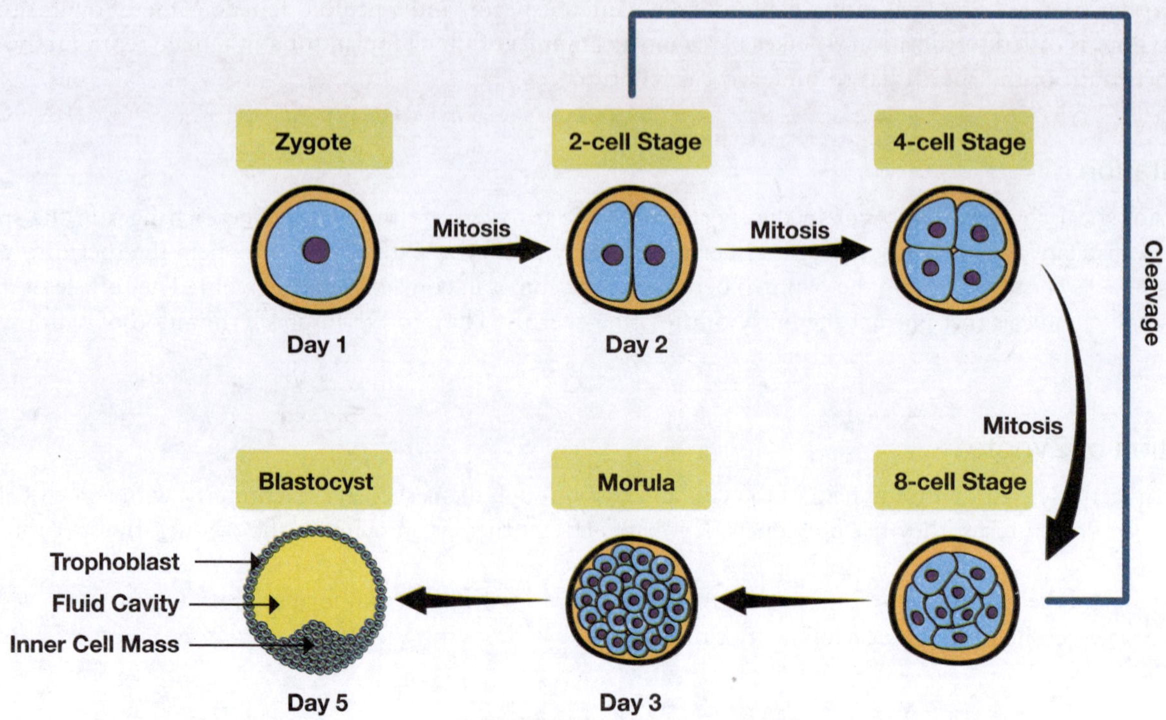

Figure 7.20 Steps of cleavage

Blastulation

Due to the rapid mitotic division of the morula, a multicellular mass comprising numerous cells is formed. These cells in the multicellular mass are called blastomeres. The blastomeres rearrange themselves into an outer layer called trophoblast and an inner group of cells called inner cell mass. The inner cell mass along with trophoblast is called blastocyst. The stage of gestation when the morula develops into a blastocyst is called blastulation. The blastocyst then travels towards the uterus from the fallopian tube. In the uterus, the blastocyst undergoes the next stage of gestation that is gastrulation. Further development of embryo takes place inside the uterus.

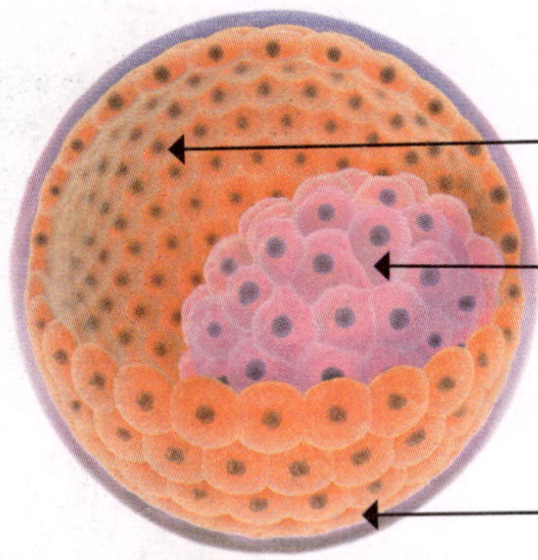

Figure 7.21 Illustration of blastocyst

Implantation

After reaching the uterus, the blastocyst gets embedded fixed to the endometrium of the uterus. This is called implantation. The layer of cells that forms the outer layer of the blastocyst is called trophoblast. The inner cellular mass is the actual embryo. The trophoblast leads to the formation of four extra embryonic membranes in the later period.

Gastrulation

The single-layered blastula gets converted to multi-layered gastrula. During gastrulation, the formation of the germ layers takes place in the embryo. The three germ layers are ectoderm, mesoderm and endoderm. The germ layers are the layers of partially differentiated cells.They undergo further cell division and cell differentiation that leads to the development of different organs in the embryo.

Organogenesis

The stage of gestation when the formation of different organs takes place in the embryo is called organogenesis. During organogenesis, the embryo also gets attached to the uterine wall. This process is called implantation. At this stage, the embryo is called foetus.

Embryonic Membranes

The extra embryonic membranes play the most significant role in the development process. They provide protection to the growing embryo and help the embryo to derive nutrition, and perform the vital functions of respiration, excretion, etc. The four membranes are:

1. Chorion
2. Amnion
3. Allantois
4. Yolk sac (vestigial organ)

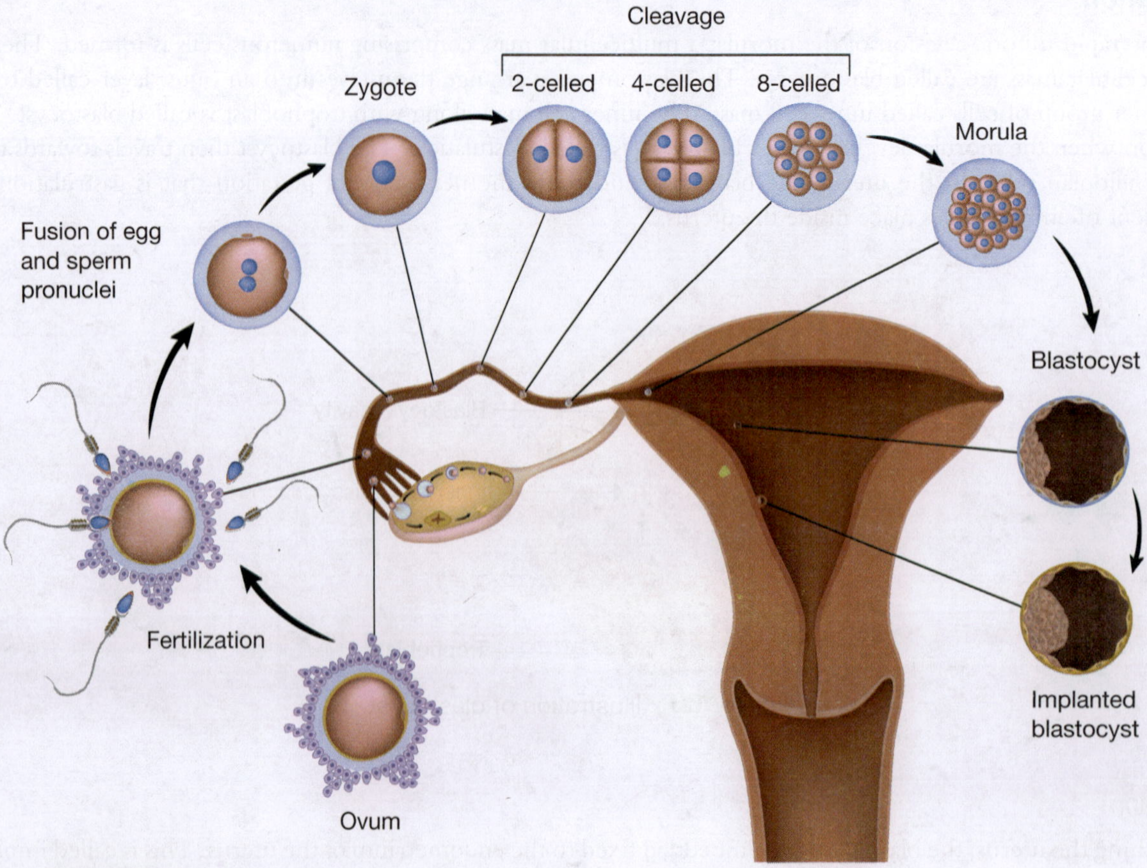

Figure 7.22 Human development from ovulation to implantation of blastocyst in the uterine wall

Chorion

The embryonic membrane, chorion develops finger-like projections called villi containing blood vessels. These villi lead to the development of an organ that connects the embryo to the uterine wall. This is called placenta. Another set of villi is developed from the uterine wall. The two sets of villi get interlocked, but the blood vessels inside them never open into each other. Thus, the blood of the embryo never mixes with the blood of the mother although the blood vessels come in close contact. The close contact of the blood vessels of the embryo and the mother ensures the diffusion of the following substances:

- The diffusion of oxygen and nutrients from the mother's blood to the embryo.
- The diffusion of carbon dioxide and other nitrogenous wastes from the blood of the embryo to the mother.

> **Info Bytes!**
>
> The placenta secretes hormones such as oestrogen, progesterone and human chorionic gonadotropin hormone required during embryogenesis.

Amnion

Amnion is a sac-like structure filled with amniotic fluid that surrounds the embryo. It is the inner most membrane. This amniotic fluid protects the embryo from any mechanical impact. Moreover, it prevents the adherence between the embryo and the amnion. This amniotic sac grows in size during the course of pregnancy to provide space for the growing foetus.

Allantois

Allantois is a sac-like structure that is developed from the gut of the embryo. It forms the umbilical cord that provides nutrition to the developing embryo and removes the waste material from the embryo. The umbilical cord establishes the connectivity between the foetus and the mother through the placenta for different biological processes. The umbilical cord attaches the placenta to the foetus. It carries foetal blood to placenta.

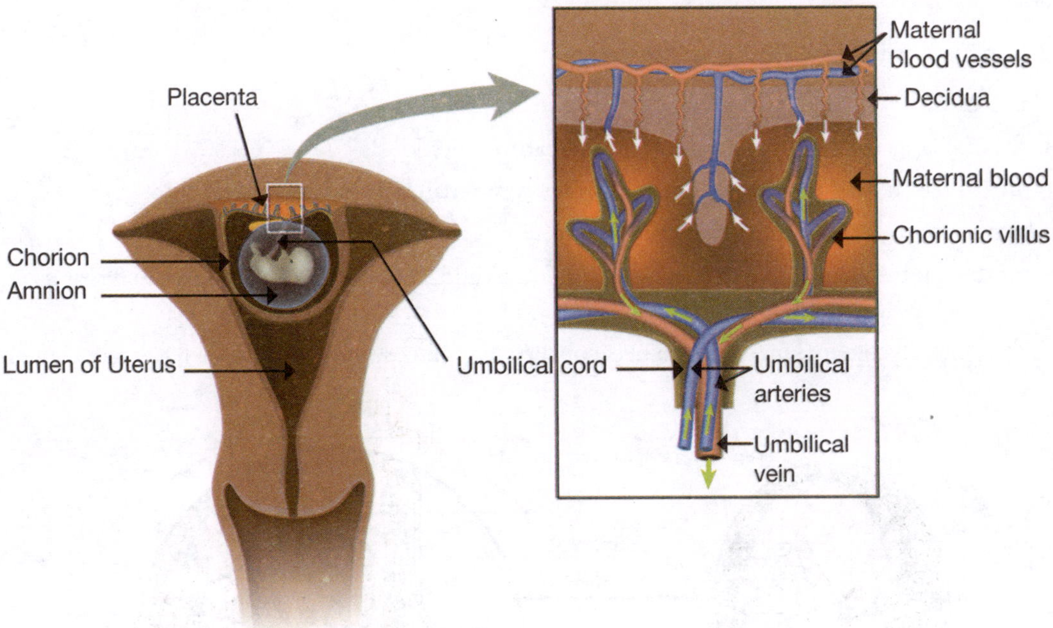

Figure 7.23 Illustration of umbilical cord

Yolk sac

Yolk sac serves to provide nourishment for the growing embryo in the earliest stages of development soon after implantation. It is the first extra embryonic membrane formed. It acts as the site of the formation of blood cells in the developing embryo up to 6 weeks. After 6 weeks, liver forms the blood cells and yolk sac starts shrinking. The process of implantation that started in the blastocyst stage continues until the foetus gets connected to the uterus by means of placenta. This means, implantation, formation of extra embryonic membranes and organogenesis take place rather simultaneously.

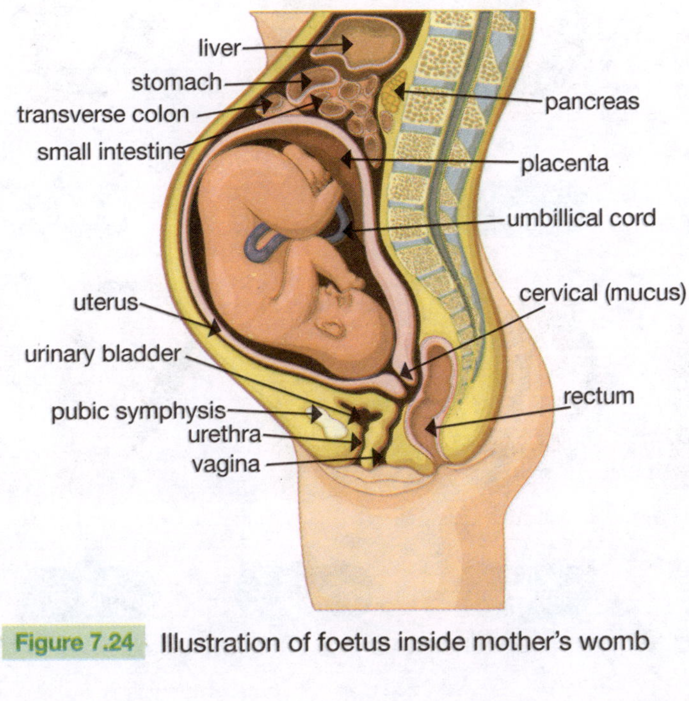

Figure 7.24 Illustration of foetus inside mother's womb

Role of Placenta

Functions of placenta are as follows:

- Provides nutrition
- Helps in the exchange of gases such as oxygen and carbon dioxide
- Helps in the excretion, that is, removal of nitrogenous waste material from the foetal blood to that of the mother
- Secretes hormones such as oestrogen and progesterone
- Provides protection by partitioning the blood of the foetus and the mother. Thus, unwanted materials such as germs cannot contaminate the blood of the foetus
- Acts as a storage of glycogen. This glycogen gets converted to glucose and fulfils the energy requirement of the foetus

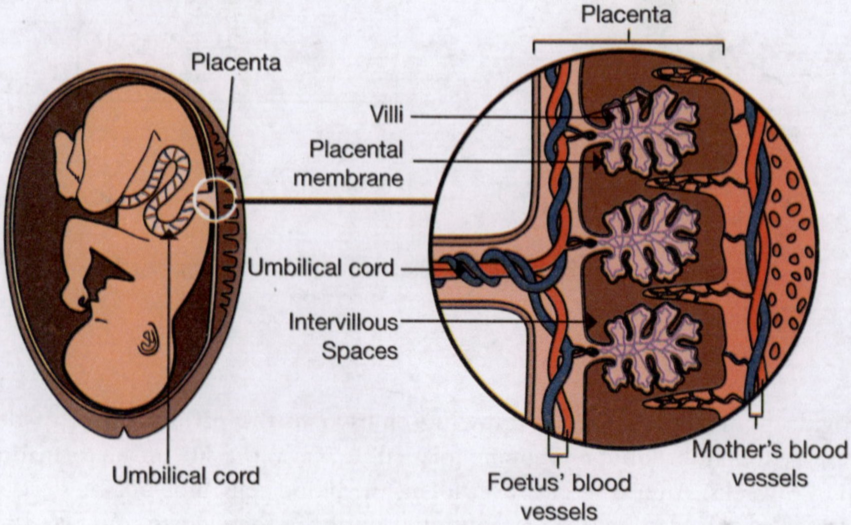

Figure 7.25 Illustration of placenta

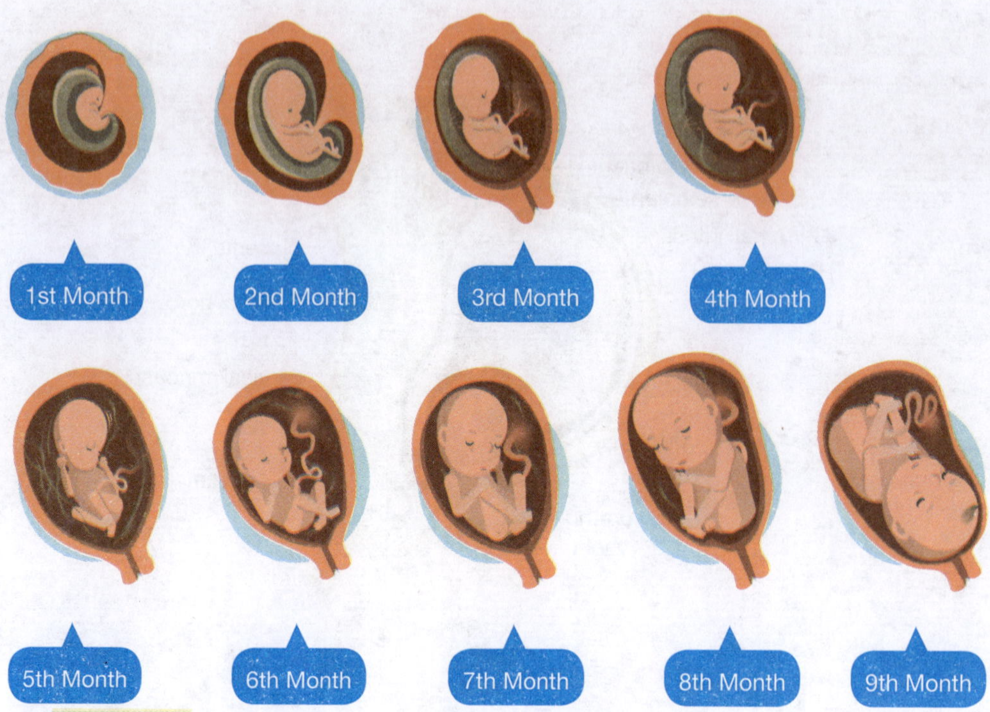

Figure 7.26 Illustration of human foetus inside the womb from 1st to 9th months

Parturition and Childbirth

The process of giving birth to the completely developed foetus is known as parturition. During parturition, the completely developed foetus is expelled from the uterus of the mother. This phenomenon of parturition involves various processes which provide driving force for the baby to come out. At first, strong contractions take place in the uterine wall. The head of the developed foetus gets pushed along the uterus due to the contraction of the uterine wall. The cervix gets widened to facilitate the expulsion of the child. The amniotic fluid is also expelled at this stage due to the rupture of the amniotic sac. Thus, the baby is delivered from the mother's womb along with umbilical cord. At this stage, shrinkage in the blood vessels of the umbilical cord takes place. The cord is cut after the delivery and clamped. The placenta gets detached from the uterine wall and expelled out of the uterus through the vagina. This is called after birth. The uterus of the mother shrinks back to the normal size after the delivery.

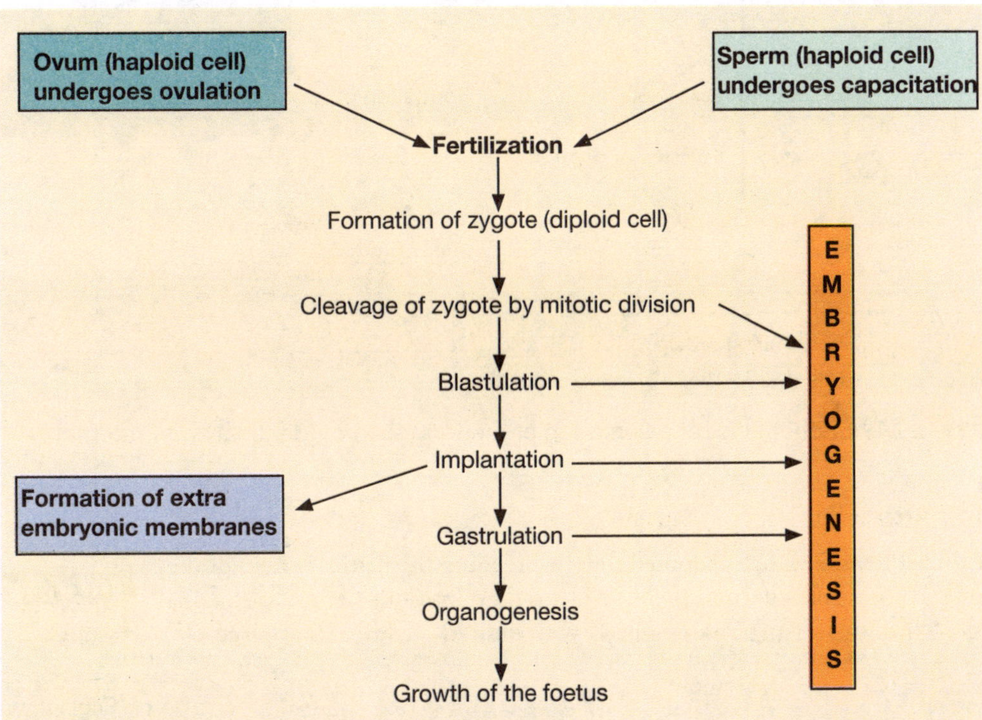

Figure 7.27 Different phenomena involved in the formation of an embryo and its development

Formation of Twins

Generally human beings produce single offspring. But occasionally, the development of two embryos together also takes place. Under this situation, twins are born. The formation of twins can happen in two following different ways:

1. Formation of identical twins
2. Formation of fraternal twins

Info Bytes!

Triplets are produced either by one single zygote or by splitting into two,and one of the split parts again splitting into two.

Identical Twins

Identical twins are also called monozygotic twins since they develop from a single zygote. Two separate embryos are formed due to the splitting of a single zygote. Since they originate from the same sperm and the same ovum, they are of same sex and have identical characteristics.

Fraternal Twins

Fraternal twins are also called dizygotic twins since they are formed due to the fertilization of two different ova by two different sperms. Usually only one ovum gets matured in 1 month. But sometimes the maturation of two ova simultaneously may happen. Fraternal twins may be of same or different sex and have different characteristics.

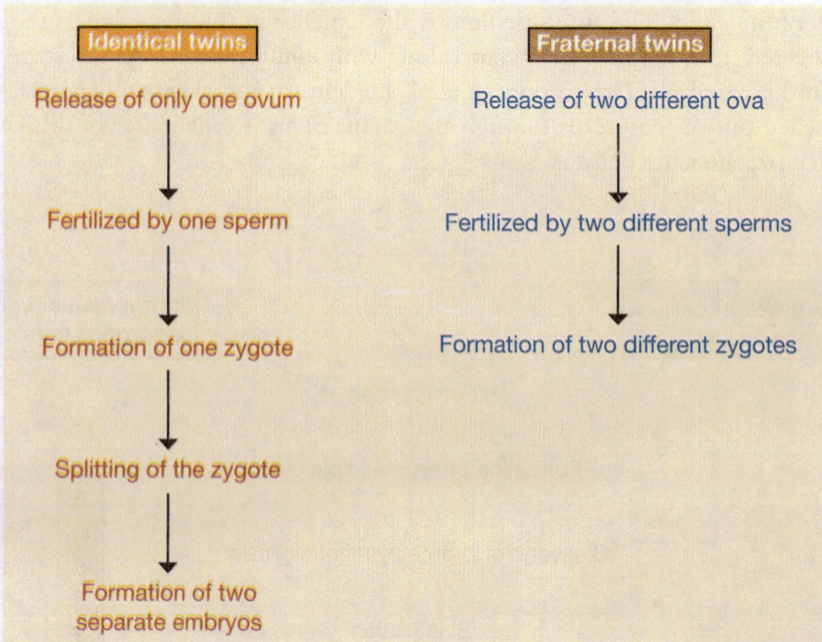

Figure 7.28 Schematic representation of the formation of Identical and Fraternal twins

Artificial Insemination

The method of artificial insemination is adopted for the breeding the cattle. Semen of the male cattle of good quality is collected and preserved. It is then introduced into the vagina of the female cattle. Thus, the formation of embryo with desired qualities takes place.

Info Bytes!

The first test tube baby was born in Lancashire, England on July 25, 1978. Her name is Louise Brown.

Test Tube Baby

Sometimes a woman cannot conceive in normal course. In such cases, the ovum is collected from the mother and the sperm is collected from the father. The sperm and the ovum are fertilized in a test tube in the laboratory. The zygote formed undergoes mitotic division in the test tube. When it attains a 32-cell stage, it is implanted in the uterus of the mother.

Info Bytes!

Condoms have been used for at least 400 years, with the earliest known versions being made from linen and animal intestines.

Reproductive Health

Population explosion is a major socio-economic issue in our country. Sustainable development is difficult in our country due to overpopulation. Sexually transmitted diseases are also increasing in our society due to various reasons. The most important measure to address the issues mentioned above is through public awareness regarding reproductive health. Reproductive health implies a responsible, safe and satisfying reproductive life. It is closely related to the physical, social and mental well-being. Healthy life also includes sound and safe reproductive health. Every individual must be aware of the consequences of the unsafe sexual life. Unsafe sexual life can give rise to the sexually transmitted diseases (STDs) such as gonorrhoea, syphilis, trichomoniasis, genital warts, etc. These diseases can be cured, but the most dreaded and incurable sexually transmitted disease is acquired immunodeficiency syndrome (AIDS). Apart from the vulnerability to sexually transmitted diseases, frequent pregnancies and pregnancy at a tender age also have adverse effects on the health of a woman. World Health Organization(WHO) laid down clear guidelines to enforce the public awareness regarding reproductive health. Government of India has established National Population Policy (NPP) and National Health Policy (NHP) to substantiate this awareness program. There are Non-Governmental Organizations (NGOs) that promote the awareness campaigns. Some devices and drugs have been developed to prevent pregnancy and to have a safe sexual life. They are called contraceptives. There are some surgical processes also to prevent pregnancy.

Table 7.4 Some contraceptives to prevent pregnancy

Contraceptives/surgical procedure	Adopted by males	Adopted by females
Physical Devices Prevents the entry of sperms into the female genital tract during copulation	Male condom	Female condom Diaphragm Cervical cap
Prevents the fertilized egg to be implanted in the uterus		Intrauterine devices (IUDs) such as Copper-T
Drugs Prevents ovulation		Oral pills
Act as spermicides		Vaginal pills
Surgical procedures **Vasectomy**: Prevents the entry of sperm into the uterus **Tubectomy**: Prevents the entry of the egg into the uterus	**Vasectomy** A small portion of vas deferens is removed or tied	**Tubectomy** A small portion of the fallopian tube is removed or tied.

Quick Recap

✔ **Why is the onset of menarche regarded as a significant event in the life of a female? What is the relationship between it and her reproductive potential?**

Menarche, or the start of the menstrual cycle, marks the beginning of puberty and reproductive maturity in females. It denotes the body's readiness for possible pregnancy and childbirth, signalling a significant transition in a female's reproductive capabilities.

✔ **Discuss the complexities of fertilization. Why is haploid gamete fusion required for the formation of a genetically unique individual?**

Fertilization is the joining of two haploid gametes to create a diploid zygote. This fusion ensures chromosome number restoration and the combination of genetic material from both parents, resulting in a genetically unique offspring, which is critical for biodiversity and evolution.

✔ **Describe the embryogenesis process. How does it ensure that a multicellular organism systematically grows from a single-celled zygote?**

Embryogenesis is a meticulously orchestrated process during which the zygote goes through cell division, differentiation, and morphogenesis. Each stage ensures the formation of tissues, organs, and systems, culminating in a complex, multicellular organism ready for birth.

POINTS TO REMEMBER

- ✔ Reproduction is an inevitable process in the life of all living organisms for the perpetuation of the species.
- ✔ The distinct sexual dimorphism with striking secondary sexual characters along with the complex male and female reproductive systems makes the process of reproduction complex.
- ✔ The male and female reproductive systems are constituted of primary and accessory reproductive organs and also accessory glands.
- ✔ A pair of testes is the primary reproductive organ in male. The testes are concerned with the production and maturation of sperms from the germ cells.
- ✔ The accessory glands in male are a pair of seminal vesicles, a prostate gland and a pair of bulbourethral glands.
- ✔ A pair of ovaries act as primary reproductive organs in females. These are concerned with the production of ova from the germ cells and their subsequent maturation.
- ✔ The reproductive cycle in females starts with menarche at the time of puberty. It is the onset of menstrual cycle.
- ✔ Menstrual cycle can be broadly divided into 4 phases. They are menstrual phase, follicular phase, ovulatory phase and secretary phase or luteal phase.
- ✔ The fusion of a haploid male gamete (sperm) and a haploid female gamete (ovum) to form a diploid zygote is called fertilization.
- ✔ The entire process of development of a single-celled diploid zygote into a newborn child until its birth is called embryogenesis.

DW

PRACTICE QUESTIONS CLASSROOM WING

Very Short Answer Type Questions

Directions for questions from 1 to 5.
Fill in the blanks.

1. Reproduction is essential for the _________ of the species.
2. The _________ phase marks the onset of the menstrual cycle.
3. The fusion of a male gamete and a female gamete result in a _________ zygote.
4. The testes in males are responsible for the production and maturation of _________.
5. The entire process from the formation of a diploid zygote to the birth of a child is called _________.

Directions for questions from 6 to 22.
For each of the following questions, four choices have been provided. Select the correct alternatives.

6. Which phase of the menstrual cycle involves the release of an egg from the ovary?
   (a) Ovulatory phase (b) Menstrual phase
   (c) Follicular phase (d) Luteal phase
7. Which of the following glands is NOT an accessory gland in males?
   (a) Ovaries (b) Seminal vesicles
   (c) Prostate gland (d) Bulbourethral glands
8. What defines the complex nature of the reproductive process in many organisms?
   (a) Presence of primary organs only
   (b) Absence of sexual dimorphism
   (c) Uniform secondary sexual characters
   (d) Presence of both male and female reproductive systems
9. The primary reproductive organ in females responsible for the production of ova is:
   (a) Uterus (b) Fallopian tubes
   (c) Vagina (d) Ovaries
10. Which process results in the formation of a diploid zygote?
    (a) Mitosis (b) Meiosis
    (c) Fertilization (d) Menstruation
11. What is a unique feature of gametes compared to other cells in the body?
    (a) They are diploid.
    (b) They are larger in size.
    (c) They can undergo mitosis.
    (d) They are haploid.
12. Which is not the accessory reproductive organ in the females?
    (a) Oviduct (b) Uterus
    (c) Vagina (d) Penis
13. The rupture of follicle is called _________.
    (a) Reproduction (b) Ovulation
    (c) Menstruation (d) Fertilization
14. _________ gland helps in copulation by lubricating vagina and vulva.
    (a) Bartholins (b) Mammary gland
    (c) Prostate gland (d) Bulboutheral gland
15. Identify the gland that helps in lactation.
    (a) Bartholins
    (b) Mammary gland
    (c) Prostate gland
    (d) Bulboutheral gland
16. Match the entries of Column 1 with those of Column 2.

Column 1	Column 2
A. Primary reproductive organ in females	(i) Sperm ducts
B. Accessory reproductive organ in females	(ii) Seminal vesicles
C. Male accessory gland	(iii) Vulva
D. Accessory reproductive organ of males	(iv) Ovaries

    (a) A→(iv), B→(iii), C→(ii), D→(i)
    (b) A→(iv), B→(iii), C→(i), D→(ii)
    (c) A→(iii), B→(iv), C→(ii), D→(i)
    (d) A→(i), B→(ii), C→(iii), D→(iv)

17. Which among the following is not a phase in menstrual cycle?
(a) Menstrual phase
(b) Secretory phase
(c) Ovulatory phase
(d) Copulation phase

18. During ________ the secretion of oestrogen stimulates the uterus for the thickening of the endometrium.
(a) Proliferative phase
(b) Luteal phase
(c) Menstrual phase
(d) Ovulatory phase

19. The release of progesterone by corpus luteum is during ________ in the menstrual cycle.
(a) Proliferative phase
(b) Luteal phase
(c) Menstrual phase
(d) Ovulatory phase

20. ________ is responsible for the growth of Graafian follicle in the female reproductive system.
(a) Lytic enzymes
(b) Germ layers
(c) Follicle stimulating hormone
(d) Lutenizing hormone

21. The physiological changes that occur in the sperm, enable it to fertilize the ovum. These changes in the sperm are known as ________.
(a) Ovulation
(b) Copulation
(c) Capacitation
(d) Fertilization

22. Match the entries of Column 1 with those of Column 2.

Column 1	Column 2
A. Diaphragm	(i) A small portion of vas deferens is removed
B. Copper-T	(ii) Acts as spermicides
C. Vaginal pills	(iii) Prevents the fertilized egg to be implanted in the uterus
D. Vasectomy	(iv) Prevents entry of sperms into female genital tract.

(a) A→(iv), B→(iii), C→(ii), D→(i)
(b) A→(iv), B→(iii), C→(i), D→(ii)
(c) A→(iii), B→(iv), C→(ii), D→(i)
(d) A→(i), B→(ii), C→(iii), D→(iv)

Short Answer Type Questions

23. Describe the significance of the menstrual cycle in females.

24. Explain the primary function of the testes and ovaries in reproduction.

25. How does the menstrual cycle prepare the female body for potential pregnancy?

26. Name the different parts of oviduct.

27. Mention the role of the following organs:
(a) Seminal vesicles
(b) Cowper's gland
(c) Rete testis

28. What is mesovarium?

29. Write a short note on the following
(a) Infundibulum
(b) Ampulla
(c) Isthmus

30. Name the different layers that make uterus thick and strong.

31. Which membrane closes the opening of vagina?

32. What are the different parts of uterus?

33. Explain the structure of the organ responsible for sperm formation.

34. Write about the journey of sperms from origin to ejaculatory organ.

35. Does the temperature of the testes remain same as that of the body temperature? Explain.

36. The male organ that is responsible for ejaculation also helps in discharge of urination. Explain the reason why discharge of urine does not take place during ejaculation.

37. Draw the structure of the male gamete.

38. Explain head part of the male gamete.

39. Where is the largest cell formed in the human female?

40. What are the different stages of the gestation period?

41. What is the main function of the accessory female reproductive organ where development of fertilized egg takes place?

42. Explain about the structure and function of the accessory female organ to which the lower most part of uterus is connected.

43. Define menstrual cycle.

44. What are the changes that take place in the uterus during the menstrual phase?

45. Name the hormones that are released by the anterior lobe of the pituitary gland.

46. What are the changes that take place in embryo during gestation period?

47. What happens during gastrulation?

48. What is the function of amnion?

49. What do you mean by implantation?

50. Name the phase of the menstrual cycle where oestrogen hormone is secreted.

51. Identify the phase and mention the changes that take place when Graafian follicle gets ruptured during the menstrual cycle.

52. Name the stage in which Graafian follicle gets converted to corpus luteum in the menstrual cycle.

Essay Type Questions

53. Mention the changes that take place in the uterus in the luteal or secretory phase.

54. The hormone that is responsible for secretion of testosterone in males also plays a significant role in females. Identify the hormone and mention its role in females.

55. How does the menstrual cycle ensure the regular possibility of fertilization in females?

56. What is the significance of the menstrual cycle in the female reproductive system, and how is it broadly divided?

57. What is the main role of the organ during development of foetus, which is formed by villi present in one of the membrane of trophoblast?

PRACTICE QUESTIONS COMPETITION WING

Level 1: Apply your Concepts

Directions for questions from 1 to 15.
Fill in the blanks.

1. While all organisms participate in reproduction, the ________ characteristics in some species add layers of complexity to the process.
2. The maturation of gametes in males and females, respectively, occurs in ________ and ________.
3. The ________ phase of the menstrual cycle is responsible for the release of the mature ovum.
4. Organs like seminal vesicles and prostate gland play a supporting role and are categorized as ________ in the male reproductive system.
5. Embryogenesis is a progression from a ________ entity to a multi-cellular organism.
6. ________ and ________ cells are present in seminiferous tubules.
7. ________ are interstitial cells that are present between seminiferous tubules.
8. ________ stimulates contraction of the female reproductive tract and helps in the fusion of male and female gametes.
9. ________ transports matured sperm from epididymis to the ejaculatory duct.
10. ________ part of the male gamete helps in swimming inside the uterus.
11. ________ is the period during which an embryo develops into a newborn until its birth.
12. The layers that contribute to the development of different organs in the embryo are known as ________.
13. The villi develops an organ that connects the embryo to the uterine wall which is known as ________.
14. An ________ is the sac-like structure with the fluid that surrounds the embryo.
15. The total period for the development of newborn baby until its delivery is called ________ or ________.

Directions for questions from 16 to 20.
For each of the following questions, four choices have been provided. Select the correct alternatives.

16. Which event signifies the transition from haploid cells to a diploid entity?
(a) Menstruation (b) Fertilization
(c) Menarche (d) Ovulation
17. Why are accessory glands important in the male reproductive system?
(a) Production of sperms
(b) Production of ova
(c) Providing nourishment and facilitating the movement of sperm
(d) Regulation of the menstrual cycle
18. Which phase of the menstrual cycle prepares the endometrium for possible implantation?
(a) Menstrual phase
(b) Follicular phase
(c) Ovulatory phase
(d) Luteal phase
19. The secondary sexual characters are most prominently observed during:
(a) Childhood (b) Puberty
(c) Menopause (d) Prenatal stage
20. Given the evolutionary importance of reproduction, why might the development of complex reproductive systems be beneficial?
(a) They increase the chances of mating.
(b) They ensure only the strongest organisms reproduce.
(c) They maximize the chances of successful fertilization and survival of offspring.
(d) They reduce the lifespan of organisms to ensure faster evolution.

Directions for questions from 21 to 25.
Correct the following statements.

21. If the sperm and ovum are fertilized in the uterus, then the baby born as a result is known as test tube baby.
22. The involvement of two organisms of same species to produce a new offspring is known as asexual reproduction.
23. The rupture of Graafian follicles to produce ovum is called capacitation.
24. Luteinizing hormone is responsible for the growth of Graafian follicle in the female reproductive system.
25. Tubectomy is a surgical procedure that prevents the entry of sperms into the uterus.

Directions for questions from 26 to 29:
Write the missing correlated terms.

26. Testes : Male : : ________ : Female.
27. ________ : Prostate gland : : Accessory reproductive organ : Penis.
28. Primary reproductive organ : ovaries : : ________ : Mammary gland.
29. Ampulla : ________ : : Uterus : Cervix .

Direction for Questions from 30 to 40.
Choose the correct option.

(a) Both A and R are true and R is the correct explanation for A.
(b) Both A and R are true, but R is not the correct explanation for A.
(c) A is true and R is false.
(d) A is false and R is true.

30. **Assertion (A)**: The skin of the scrotum contract or expand with the change in the ambient temperature.
Reason (R): Maturation of sperms requires a specific temperature.

31. **Assertion (A)**: During ejaculation, contraction of the sphincter muscles at the neck of the urinary bladder takes place.
Reason (R): Excess flow of blood into the penis takes place due to sexual stimulation.

32. **Assertion (A)**: Semen is alkaline in nature.
Reason (R): Semen contains fructose and prostaglandin hormone.

33. **Assertion (A)**: Fimbriae help the ovum to enter the infundibulum from ovary.
Reason (R): Fimbriae secrete some fluids that control the movement of ovum.

34. **Assertion (A)**: The secretion from Bartholin's gland helps in copulation.
Reason (R): Copulation ensures fertilization of the ovum.

35. **Assertion (A)**: Lactation happens at the adolescent stage of a female.
Reason (R): The secretion of different hormones during the later stage of pregnancy helps in milk production.

36. **Assertion (A)**: Artificial insemination is generally carried out in cattle.
Reason (R): Genetic selection can be done through artificial insemination.

37. **Assertion (A)**: During parturition, the head of the developed foetus gets pushed along the uterus due to the contraction of the uterine wall.
Reason (R): During parturition, cervical expansion takes place.

38. **Assertion (A)**: The placental barrier prevents the mixing of mother's blood with the fetal blood.
Reason (R): During implantation, placenta develops from the embryonic membrane called chorion.

39. **Assertion (A)**: Allantois finally converts to the umbilical cord.
Reason (R): Umbilical cord helps in mixing of body fluids of the mother and the foetus.

40. **Assertion (A)**: The presence of fructose in female genital tract indicates pregnancy.
Reason (R): Fructose is the major constituent of semen.

Level 2: Review your Concepts

Directions for questions from 41 to 52:

Answer the following questions.

41. The secretion of testosterone is maximum at adolescence and early adulthood in a male human being. Give reason.

42. Vasa efferentia contain ciliated cells. What purpose do they serve?

43. Sperms undergo maturation in the upper and middle regions of epididymis and get stored in the hind region. What kind of changes of sperms occurs in different regions of epididymis?

44. The secretion of male accessory glands makes the semen alkaline. What is the significance of alkaline nature of semen?

45. What is an ectopy or tubal pregnancy?

46. How are the diseases, salpingitis and infertility related?

47. Excess secretion of oestrogen leads to different problems in the pelvic region. Explain.

48. What are uterine fibroids? Why do they cause excess and continuous menstrual bleeding?

49. What is menorrhagia and what causes it?

50. What is the function of the accessory female reproductive glands?

51. Write about the function of vulva and identify its different parts.

52. Explain the method that is adopted by a woman to give birth to a child when she cannot conceive in a normal course.

Level 3: Assess Your Concepts

53. Menstrual cramp is a common problem that occurs during the beginning of menstrual period. What could be the reason for this?

54. What is fertilization and how does it relate to the terms 'haploid' and 'diploid'?

55. How does HIV get transmitted from the mother to the child? Does placenta play any role in the transmission of HIV? Explain.

56. What is chorioamnionitis? How does it occur?

57. How does vasectomy and tubectomy prevent fertilization?

58. In human females, yolk sac which is the embryonic layer becomes non-functional in the later part of the gestation period. Give reason.

AT

PRACTICE QUESTIONS NEET SPECIAL WING

Multiple-Answer Type Questions

Questions number 1 to 5 are multiple-choice questions. Each question has FOUR options (a), (b), (c), and (d). ONE OR MORE THAN ONE of these four option(s) is/are the correct answer(s).

1. The normal constituents of semen include:
   (a) Acid lipase (b) Fructose
   (c) Citrate (d) Ascorbic acid
2. Which pituitary hormones are secreted during ovulatory phase of the menstrual cycle?
   (a) FSH (b) LH
   (c) ADH (d) Progesterone
3. Which among the following are not roles of FSH?
   (a) Ovulation
   (b) Development of corpus luteum
   (c) Oestrogen secretion
   (d) Secretion of progesterone
4. Which of the following is true about Chorion?
   (a) It is developed from gut of the embryo
   (b) It has villi containing blood vessels
   (c) Helps in the development of placenta
   (d) It is filled with amniotic fluid that surrounds the embryo
5. Which of the following is true regarding identical twins?
   (a) Two different ova are released
   (b) Only one ovum is released which is fertilised by one sperm
   (c) One zygote splits into two
   (d) Two separate embryos are formed

Comprehension-Based Questions

A. Read the paragraph given below and answer the questions number 6 to 11:

The male reproductive system in humans consists of a pair of testes, sperm ducts and penis. The testes is required for production of male gametes that is sperms and the male sex hormone testosterone. Sperm ducts which consists of Rete testis, Vasa efferentia, Epididymis, Vasa differentia and ejaculatory duct helps with capacitation as well as transportation of sperms. Besides this there are accessory glands which nourish and produce transportation fluid for sperms which is semen. The sperm is the male gamete, consists of three parts that is head, tail and middle piece and shows motility.

6. Testes are present in the scrotal cavity because:
   (a) They give protection to testes
   (b) They provide alkaline medium for sperm production
   (c) They provide lower temperature for sperm production
   (d) They provide higher temperature for sperm production
7. The substance which is broken down to obtain energy for sperm motility is derived from:
   (a) Cowper's gland
   (b) Seminal vesicle
   (c) Prostate gland
   (d) Vas deferens
8. The cells that secrete testosterone are:
   (a) Primordial cells
   (b) Spermatogonia
   (c) Sertoli cells
   (d) Leydig cells
9. The part that carries sperms from rete testis is:
   (a) Vasa efferentia
   (b) Epididymis
   (c) Vasa differentia
   (d) Ejaculatory ducts
10. The part that helps the sperm to fuse with the egg is:
   (a) Middle piece
   (b) Centriole
   (c) Acrosome
   (d) Tail

11. Match the column:

Column – A	Column – B
(i) Epididymis	(a) Spermatid storage
(ii) Seminal vesicle	(b) Production of sperms
(iii) Cowper's glands	(c) Copulatory organ
(iv) Testes	(d) Alkaline fluid for transportation
(v) Penis	(e) Clean pathway for ejaculation

B. Read the paragraph given below and answer the questions number 12 to 17:

The female reproductive system consists of fallopian tubes, Uterus, vagina and vulva region. Every month alternate ovary produces the female gamete that is ovum. In case there is no fertilization, the egg along with the innermost uterine lining is shed causing menstruation. In the next few days new ovum is produced going through follicular stages and graafian follicle stage. In case of fertilization, the inner lining of the uterus is kept intact so the embryo can implant itself. This results in zygote formation and embryogenesis. All these processes take place under the influence of FSH, LH, oestrogen and progesterone. The embryo goes through cleavage, Blastulation, implantation, gastrulation and organogenesis for further development. The embryo consists of four main membranes which perform various functions for development, growth and upkeep of pregnancy.

12. Progesterone is secreted by:
   (a) Primary follicle
   (b) Graafian follicle
   (c) Corpus luteum
   (d) Secondary follicle

13. Which part is the highly sensitive erectile tissue in females?
   (a) Clitoris
   (b) Bartholin's glands
   (c) Vulva
   (d) Vestibular glands

14. Capacitation is:
   (a) the maximum capacity to store sperms
   (b) maturation of female gamete
   (c) progress of meiosis for female gamete formation
   (d) changes in sperms that allow them to fertilize the ovum

15. Which among the following is the stage for formation of morula?
   (a) 1 celled stage
   (b) 2 celled stage
   (c) 8 celled stage
   (d) 16 celled stage

16. The layer which is shed during menstruation:
   (a) endometrium
   (b) myometrium
   (c) perimetrium
   (d) ectometrium

17. Match the column:

Column – A	Column – B
(i) Fundus	(a) Lubricating fluid
(ii) Isthmus	(b) Connects uterus and ampulla
(iii) Cervix	(c) Protects orifices of vulva
(iv) Labia minora	(d) Dome like structure
(v) Bartholin's glands	(e) Lowermost part of uterus

ANSWER KEYS

Crossword

Across

3. Contraceptives
4. Vasectomy
6. Gastrulation
7. Scrotum
10. Infundibulum
13. Capacitation
16. Perimetrium
17. Progesterone
18. Allantois

Down

1. Dizygotic twins
2. Isthmus
5. Oogenesis
8. Implantation
9. Budding
11. Parturition
12. Oestrogen
14. Trophoblast
15. Morula

Classroom Wing

Very Short Answer Type Questions

1. Perpetuation
2. Menarche
3. Diploid
4. Sperms
5. Embryogenesis
6. (a)
7. (a)
8. (c)
9. (d)
10. (d)
11. (d)
12. (d)
13. (b)
14. (a)
15. (b)
16. (a)
17. (d)
18. (a)
19. (b)
20. (c)
21. (c)
22. (a)

Competition Wing

Level 1: Apply Your Concepts

1. Secondary sexual
2. Testes, ovaries
3. Ovulatory
4. Accessory glands
5. Single-celled
6. Sertoli cells, Germ cells
7. Leydig cells
8. Prostaglandin
9. Vasa deferentia
10. Tail
11. Gestation
12. Germ layers
13. Placenta
14. Amnion
15. Gestational period, Pregnancy
16. (b)
17. (c)
18. (d)
19. (b)
20. (c)
26. Ovaries
27. Accessory gland
28. Accessory gland
29. Oviduct
30. (a)
31. (b)
32. (b)
33. (c)
34. (c)
35. (d)
36. (a)
37. (b)
38. (b)
39. (c)
40. (d)

NEET Special Wing

Multiple-Answer Type Questions

1. (b, c, d) **2.** (a, b) **3.** (a, b, d) **4.** (b, c) **5.** (b, c, d)

Comprehension-Based Questions

6. (c) **7.** (c) **8.** (d) **9.** (a) **10.** (c)

11. (i) → (a); (ii) → (d); (iii) → (e); (iv) → (b); (v) → (c)

12. (c) **13.** (a) **14.** (d) **15.** (d) **16.** (a)

17. (i) → (d); (ii) → (b); (iii) → (e); (iv) → (c); (v) → (a)

Hints and Explanations

CLASSROOM WING

Short Answer Type Questions

23. The menstrual cycle in females is crucial as it prepares the body for potential pregnancy. It involves various phases like menstrual, follicular, ovulatory, and luteal, which regulate the release of eggs and maintain the uterine lining for embryo implantation.

24. The testes in males produce mature sperm, essential for fertilization. In females, the ovaries are responsible for producing and maturing ova (egg cells), which when fertilized, can develop into an embryo.

25. The menstrual cycle prepares the female body for a potential pregnancy through a series of cyclical changes. These include the maturation and release of an ovum, and the thickening of the uterus lining to support a potential embryo.

26. Oviduct is divided into three parts:
    (a) Infundibulum
    (b) Ampulla
    (c) Isthmus

27. (a) **Seminal vesicles:** Produces semen
    (b) **Cowper's gland:** Its secretion neutralizes the urethral region and provides a conducive environment.
    (c) **Rete testis:** Helps in the transportation of sperms from testis to vasa efferentia.

28. The mesentery that attaches the ovaries to the dorsal abdominal wall is called mesovarium.

29. (a) **Infundibulum:** It is the broad funnel-like structure that connects to the ovary with the fallopian tube. The aperture of this infundibulum is called ostium that collects ovum from the ovary. It is surrounded by finger-like projections called fimbriae. Fimbriae helps the ovum to enter the infundibulum from ovary.
    (b) **Ampulla:** The part of the fallopian tube next to the infundibulum is ampulla. It is long wide and convoluted and is the place for fertilization.
    (c) **Isthmus:** It is small narrow and thick-walled tubular structure. It is straight and provides the connectivity between the uterus and ampulla. It passes through the thick uterine wall and enters the uterine cavity.

30. The wall of uterus is thick and comprises three layers of tissues.
    (a) Endometrium: This layer comprises many tubular glands and undergoes morphological changes during the menstrual cycle.
    (b) Myometrium: It is the smooth muscular layer and composes the major volume of the wall of uterus.
    (c) Perimetrium: It is composed of epithelial cells and acts as an envelope of the uterus.

31. Hymen is the thin membrane that partially closes the opening of the vagina.

32. Uterus has three parts, namely:
    (a) Fundus
    (b) Body or isthmus
    (c) Cervix

33. Testes are responsible for the formation of sperms.
    - Testis is covered with a dense fibrous tissue called tunica albuginea.
    - The ingrowths present in tunica albuginea are called septa.
    - These septa are divided into 200–300 compartments called testicular lobules.
    - Each testicular lobule contains 1–4 highly coiled tube-like structures known as seminiferous tubules.
    - These tubules contain Sertoli cells and germ cells.
    - Germ cells produce male gametes and sertoli cells provide nutrition to them.
    - Leydig cells are interstitial cells that are present between the seminiferous tubules and they secrete male sex hormones called testosterone.
    - The testosterone helps in the formation of sperms.

34. Sperm duct is a series of different structures that starts from the seminiferous tubules in the testes and ends at the ejaculatory organ that is penis. The journey of sperms starts from the sperm duct and ends at the penis.

35. The temperature in testes is 2–3 degrees lower than the normal body temperature since they are present outside the abdomen. This temperature is conductive for the formation and maturation of sperms.

36. Penis is the muscular organ for ejaculation of sperms into the female sex organ. Hence, it is called copulatory organ. It also helps in urination.

The ejaculation and urination do not take place simultaneously. Because the sensory nerves that are present in the penis help in ejaculation and excess flow of blood takes place into the penis due to sexual stimulation. Hence, it becomes rigid and erect, this condition is called erection. Due to this, the urine does not ooze out during ejaculation.

37.

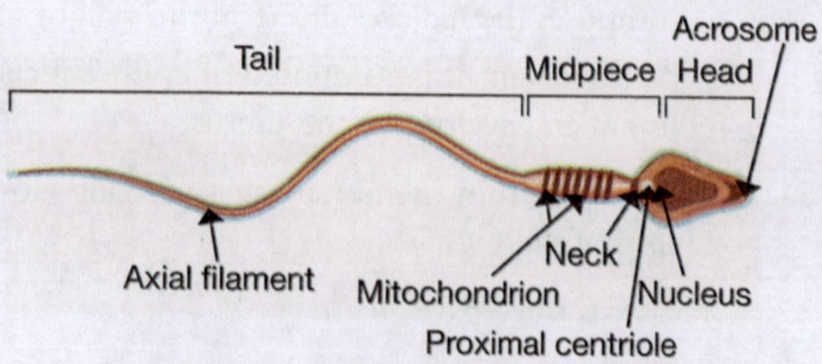

38. Head contains a small protective cap-like structure called acrosome, which covers the head of the sperm. It has a modified Golgi complex and a large nucleus. Acrosome contains digestive enzymes that help in dissolving the outer coating of the female gamete. A single set of chromosomes is present in the nucleus, and hence, it is called haploid nucleus.

39. An ovum is the largest human cell that is formed in the ovaries. Each follicle contains an immature reproductive cell called oocyte. One oocyte gets matured in each ovary in the alternative month. The matured oocyte is called an ovum and the follicle in which the ovum is present is called Graafian follicle.

40. Different stages of gestation are:
(a) Cleavage
(b) Blastulation
(c) Gastrulation
(d) Organogenesis

41. Womb is the place where development of fertilized egg takes place.
- It is a hollow pear-shaped cavity.
- It is present in the pelvic region behind the urinary bladder and in front of the rectum.
- It is a part of the female repr uctive system where the fertilized ovum called em yo develops.

The main functions of the uterus e as follows:
- Receving the ovum from the f. opian tube
- Providing shelter and nourishment to the fertilized ovum called embryo
- Delivering the newborn baby

42. Cervix is the lowermost part of the uterus which is connected to vagina, which is the next accessory female reproductive organ.
- It has a muscular tube-like structure.
- It originates from the cervix and extends up to the external female genitalia named vulva.
- It is 7.5 cm long and its inner wall is folded. This is called vaginal rugae which secrets mucus.
- Hymen is the membrane that partially closes the vagina and is made up of highly delicate tissues.

43. Menstrual cycle is a series of changes that the female reproductive organs undergo every month periodically.

44. During menstrual phase in the uterus, the endometrium lining of the uterus gets thickened for the implantation of the embryo prior to menstrual phase.

45. Two hormones are released by the anterior lobe of the pituitary gland. They are:
(a) Follicle stimulating hormone
(b) Luteinizing hormone

46. During gestation, following changes occur in the embryo:
(a) Cleavage
(b) Blastulation
(c) Gastrulation
(d) Organogenesis

47. During gastrulation, formation of germ layers takes place in the embryo, which contribute to the development of different organs in the embryo.

48. Amnion is a sac-like structure filled with amniotic fliud that surrounds the embryo.
- This fluid protects the embryo from any mechanical impact.
- It prevents the adherence between the embryo and amnion.

49. When the blastocyst gets embedded and fixed in the endometrium, this process is known as implantation.

50. Oestrogen hormone is secreted during the proliferative or follicular phase of the menstrual cycle.

51. The rupture c Graafian follicle takes place during the ovulatory ph of the menstrual cycle.

52. The convers 1 of Graafian follicle to corpus luteum takes place ing the secretary or luteal phase of the menstrual cycle.

Essay Type Questions

53. Following are the changes that take place in the uterus during the luteal or secretary phase:
    - Progesterone released by corpus helps in thickening of the uterus and also provides a conducive environment for the development of the embryo.
    - If the ovum gets fertilized, it gets implanted in the uterus for its nourishment and under these circumstances, menstrual cycle stops until the delivery of the newborn.

54. Luteinizing hormone is responsible for the secretion of testosterone in males. Following are the roles that are played by the female reproductive system:
    - Helps in ovulation
    - Development of corpus luteum
    - Secretion of progesterone

55. The menstrual cycle, comprising phases like menstrual, follicular, ovulatory, and luteal, coordinates the preparation, release, and possible fertilization of the ovum. The ovulatory phase releases a mature ovum, while the luteal phase prepares the endometrium for implantation. This cyclic process ensures that the female reproductive system is regularly primed for potential fertilization.

56. The menstrual cycle prepares the female body for a potential pregnancy on a cyclical basis. It starts with menarche at the time of puberty, marking the onset of the menstrual cycle. The menstrual cycle can be broadly divided into four phases: the menstrual phase, the follicular phase, the ovulatory phase, and the secretory or luteal phase. Each phase plays a specific role in the reproductive process, from shedding the uterine lining to the release of the mature ovum and preparation for potential implantation.

57. Placenta is the organ formed by villi, which is present in chorion membrane of trophoblast. Following are the main functions of placenta:
    - It provides nutrition.
    - It helps in exchange of gases such as oxygen and carbon dioxide.
    - Helps in the excretion of waste material from fetal blood to that of the mother.
    - Secretes hormones such as oestrogen and progesterone.
    - Provides protection from the germs to the foetus by partitioning the blood of the foetus and the mother.
    - Fulfils the requirements of foetus by storing glycogen

COMPETITION WING

Level 1: Apply your Concepts

21. If the sperm and the ovum are fertilized outside in a test tube and implanted back in the mother's womb, then the born baby is known as a test tube baby.

22. The involvement of two organisms of same species to produce a new offspring is known as sexual reproduction.

23. The rupture of Graafian follicles to produce ovum is known as ovulation.

24. Follicle stimulating hormone is responsible for the growth of Graafian follicles in female reproductive system.

25. Tubectomy is a surgical procedure that prevents the entry of egg to the uterus.

26. Testes : Male : : Ovaries : Female.

27. Accessory gland : Prostate gland : : Accessory reproductive organ : Penis.

28. Primary reproductive organ : ovaries : : Accessory gland : Mammary gland.

29. Ampulla : Oviduct : : Uterus : Cervix

30. The temperature maintained in testes is 2-3 degrees lower than the normal body temperature since they are present outside the abdomen. This temperature is conducive for the formation and maturation of sperms. The skin of the scrotum contracts or expands with the change in the temperature of the environment in different seasons so that the temperature in the testes is maintained.

Hence, the correct option is (a)

31. During ejaculation, contraction of sphincter muscles at the neck of the urinary bladder takes place so that urine does not come out of the bladder during ejaculation. Both ejaculation and urination take place through the urethra. Excess flow of blood in penis helps in erection of penis.

Hence, the correct option is (b)

32. Semen contains fructose which provides energy to sperm to swim and prostaglandin hormone stimulates the contraction of female reproductive tract. Semen is alkaline in nature because of secretion of alkaline substances by the accessory glands.

Hence, the correct option is (b)

33. Fimbriae are finger-like projections that mechanically support the movement of ovum from the ovary to the infundibulum.

Hence, the correct option is (c)

34. The secretion of Bartholin's glands helps in copulation. Copulation helps the sperm to enter the female reproductive tract, but it does not ensure fertilization.

Hence, the correct option is (c)

35. Milk ducts and glandular buds are developed at the adolescent stage, but lactation does not take place at this stage. Lactation takes place at the later stage of pregnancy due to the secretion of some hormones.

Hence, the correct option is (d)

36. In artificial insemination, the semen of good quality from potential male cattle is collected and stored. It is then deposited in the uterine tract of more than one female. Thus, an offspring having desirable genes can be produced.

Hence, the correct option is (a)

37. The head of the foetus comes out first during parturition since it is the best position for the baby to slide smoothly and effortlessly through the birth canal.

Cervix becomes naturally dilated during parturition for the expulsion of the baby.

Hence, the correct option is (b)

38. Placental barrier prevents the mixing of mother's blood with fetal blood to prevent the entry of harmful substances and maintains the blood pressure of the mother and the foetus. The placenta develops from the embryonic membrane, called chorion.

Hence, the correct option is (b)

39. Allantois is developed from the gut of the embryo and finally forms the umbilical cord that provides nutrition to the developing embryo and removes the waste material from the embryo. The umbilical cord establishes the connectivity between the foetus and the mother for different biological processes.

Hence, the correct option is (c)

40. The presence of fructose in female genital tract indicates that the girl had sexual intercourse. This is because fructose is the major constituent of semen and it is not present anywhere else in the body.

Hence, the correct option is (c)

Level 2: Review your Concepts

41. At the teenage stage, testosterone contributes to behavioral, structural and physiological development that transforms children into sexually reproductive adults.

    Testosterone plays a key role in the development of male reproductive tissues in testes and prostate, as well as promoting secondary sexual characteristics such as increased muscle and bone mass, and the growth of body hair. Since these changes occur at adolescent period and in early adulthood, maximum testosterone is secreted at this age.

42. Vasa efferentia transports sperms from the testes to epididymis. The ciliated cells in vasa efferentia serve to stir the fluid produced by testis. Stirring ensures homogeneous absorption of water from the fluid containing sperm. Absorption of water results in an increase in the concentration of luminal sperm.

43. Sperms remain immotile before entering epididymis. During their transit through epididymis, they become motile. Absorption of fluid also takes place in this region to increase the concentration of sperms. Since the sperms become motile in this region, large quantity of fluid is not required for their transportation.

    Decapacitation is a phenomenon that takes place in the hind region where sperms are stored. The epididymis secretes some proteins that block the receptors on the plasma membrane of sperm head which renders sperm infertile inside the male tract. This is called decapacitation. Capacitation of sperms takes place when they enter the female reproductive tract.

44. The normal environment of the vagina is acidic which is not conducive for sperms. The alkaline substances present in semen neutralize the acidic environment in the vagina. Thus, the DNA inside the sperms is protected from acidic denaturation.

45. The fertilization of ovum takes place in the fallopian tube and fertilized ovum stays there for 3–4 days before it proceeds towards the uterus. In uterus, the nourishment of the egg takes place. If the fertilized egg starts growing in the fallopian tube instead of proceeding towards the uterus, it is called ectopic pregnancy or tubal pregnancy. The fallopian tube is not a suitable place for the embryo to grow. Hence, the embryo cannot develop and it must be terminated.

46. Salpingitis is an inflammation of the fallopian tubes. This disease is caused by bacteria. The inflammation involves the secretion of extra fluid that gets accumulated in the fallopian tube. Without prompt treatment, the infection may permanently damage the fallopian tube and the ovum matured in each menstrual cycle can never be fertilized.

47. Oestrogen hormone causes thickening of the uterine wall. Excess secretion of oestrogen leads to abnormal enlargement of uterus that presses other organs such as urinary bladder, digestive tract, etc. This condition of uterus causes discomfort such as heaviness, pain in the pelvic region and frequent urination.

48. Uterine fibroids are benign tumors or non-cancerous abnormal growth in the uterus.

    Development of fibroids causes excess and continuous menstrual bleeding.

    At the end of the menstrual phase, uterine muscle contracts which causes enough clotting of blood and thus, the menstrual bleeding stops. But the fibroids developed in the uterus prevent the contraction of uterus and thus, the bleeding continues. Moreover, the fibroids stimulate the blood vessels of the uterus which results in excess blood flow.

49. Menorrhagia is the medical term for menstrual periods with abnormally heavy or prolonged bleeding.

    In a normal menstrual cycle, balance between the hormones, oestrogen and progesterone regulates the rebuilding of the lining of the uterus that is endometrium which is shed during menstruation. If there is an imbalance in the secretion of hormones, endometrium develops in excess and eventually sheds away resulting in heavy and continuous bleeding.

50. There are two accessory female reproductive glands.
    (a) Bartholin or vestibular gland: It helps in copulation by lubricating the vagina and vulva.
    (b) Mammary glands: It helps in lactation.

51. The main function of vulva is to protect vaginal and urethral openings. It constitutes of the following:
    (a) Labia majora
    (b) Labia minora
    (c) Clitoris

52. When a woman is unable to conceive in a normal course, in such cases, the ovum is collected from the mother and the sperm from the father. They are made to fertilize in the test tube in a laboratory. The zygote formed undergoes mitotic division in the test tube. When it attains a 32-cell stage it is then implanted in the uterus of the mother. The baby so born is known as a test tube baby.

Level 3: Assess Your Concepts

53. Shortly before a menstrual period begins, the endometrial cells that form the lining of the uterus produce large amounts of a hormone-like substance called prostaglandin. The functions of prostaglandin are the contraction and relaxation of smooth muscle, the dilation and constriction of blood vessels, control of blood pressure and modulation of inflammation. During the menstrual cycle, prostaglandin constricts the blood vessels in the uterus and makes its muscle layer contract causing painful cramps. If the uterus contracts too strongly, it can press against nearby blood vessels, cutting off the supply of oxygen to the muscle tissue of the uterus. Severe pain results when part of the muscle briefly loses its supply of oxygen.

54. Fertilization is the fusion of a haploid male gamete (sperm) and a haploid female gamete (ovum) to form a diploid zygote. The term 'haploid' refers to cells with a single set of chromosomes, like sperm and ovum. When these haploid cells merge during fertilization, they form a 'diploid' cell, the zygote, which contains two sets of chromosomes – one from each parent. This diploid zygote then undergoes numerous divisions and differentiations to develop into a multicellular organism.

55. No, HIV does not generally get transmitted from the mother to the foetus through placenta provided the disease is not at an acute stage. If the placenta is damaged and blood from the mother gets transferred into the blood of the foetus, the transmission of this disease is possible. Transmission of HIV can take place during delivery from the infected mother. When a baby passes through the birth canal, the baby gets exposed to HIV in the mother's blood and other fluids. Since HIV is transmitted through body fluid, breast feeding also transmits the disease.

56. Chorioamnionitis is a bacterial infection in amnion and chorion (foetal membranes).

The infection can occur when bacteria that are normally present in the vagina of the mother ascend into the uterus, where the foetus is located. The amniotic fluid and placenta as well as the baby can be infected by these bacteria. Examples of such bacteria are *E. coli,* group B *Streptococcus* and anaerobic bacteria.

57. Sperms leave the testes through a pair of tubes, called vas deferens and mix with other fluid, forming semen. The sperm in the semen can cause pregnancy if it gets into the vagina.

Vasectomy blocks or cuts each vas deferens so that the sperms cannot enter the urethra of the male. Hence, semen of the male will not contain any sperm. Sperm cells stay in male testes and are absorbed by the body.

Tubectomy is a surgical procedure done on women as a permanent method of contraception. The ovum released from the ovary enters the fallopian tube. If sperm is present in the fallopian tube, the ovum gets fertilized and the resulting embryo moves into the uterus. In tubectomy, the fallopian tubes are blocked and thus the entry of embryo to uterus is prevented.

58. Yolk sac is the first layer of embryo that is developed in the initial phase of gestation period. The yolk sac provides nourishment to the growing embryo. Once the placenta is fully formed, the function of transfer of nutrients to eth mother is carried out by the placenta. Hence, yolk sac becomes non-functional.

NEET SPECIAL WING

Multiple-Answer Type Questions

1. The normal constituents of semen include- Citrate, ascorbic acid, acid phosphatase, fructose prostaglandin hormone.

2. During ovulatory phase of the menstrual cycle there is a surge of both FSH and LH. These hormones cause the ovary to produce more oestrogen and the LH surge ultimately helps the ovary to release the ovum.

3. FSH has two main functions that is growth of graafian follicle and oestrogen secretion. Rest of the functions are that of LH.

4. The embryonic membrane, chorion develops finger-like projections called villi containing blood vessels. These villi lead to the development of an organ that connects the embryo to the uterine wall. This is called placenta. The close contact of the blood vessels of the embryo and the mother ensures the diffusion of oxygen and nutrients from the mother's blood to the embryo. The diffusion of carbon dioxide and other nitrogenous wastes from the blood of the embryo to the mother

5. Identical twins are also called monozygotic twins since they develop from a single zygote. Two separate embryos are formed due to the splitting of a single zygote. Since they originate from the same sperm and the same ovum, they are of same sex and have identical characteristics.

Comprehension-Based Questions

A.

6. The scrotal bag is present in the extra abdominal cavity and provides 2-3 degrees lower temperature than the body temperature thus favouring sperm production.

7. It is the prostate gland which produces fluid rich in substances that give energy for sperm motility.

8. Leydig cells are interstitial cells that are present between the seminiferous tubules. Leydig cells secrete male sex hormone called testosterone. Testosterone hormone helps in the formation of sperms.

9. Vasa efferentia is a convoluted tubular structure that leads to the epididymis. It carries sperms to the epididymis from the rete testis.

10. Head contains a small protective cap-like structure, called acrosome. Acrosome covers the head of the sperm. Acrosome contains digestive enzymes that help in dissolving the outer coating of the female gamete (reproductive cell).

11. Match the following:

    Epididymis is a long, coiled tube which is a temporary storage organ for spermatids.
    (i) (a)

    The seminal vesicles secrete a fluid that has mild alkalinity (pH around 7.2) and acts as a medium for the transportation of sperms.
    (ii) (d)

    Cowper's glands secrete an alkaline fluid containing mucus that neutralizes the fluid in the urethral region and thus, provides a clean pathway for ejaculation and transport of the sperms by expelling residue of urine and dead cells.
    (iii) (e)

    Production of sperms takes place in the testes.
    (iv) (b)

    Penis is the muscular organ for ejaculation of sperms into the female sex organ. Hence, it is also called copulatory organ.
    (v) (c)

B.

12. Graafian follicle is converted to corpus luteum. Corpus luteum releases progesterone.

13. Clitoris is a small projected part of the vulva present above the urethral opening. It is an erectile tissue and contains sensory nerve endings. It is highly sensitive.

14. The physiological changes that occur in the sperm to enable it to fertilize the ovum. These changes in the sperm are known as capacitation. The acrosome reaction can occur only following the completion of capacitation.

15. The zygote formed undergoes mitotic division and the number of cells increases in the zygote in geometric progression. This stage of the gestation is called cleavage and results in the formation of multicellular embryo from the single-celled zygote. This mass of

undifferentiated cell is called morula which is at the 16 celled stage.

16. Innermost layer or endometrium is the layer that contains many tubular glands and undergoes morphological changes during the menstrual cycle and the development of embryo. It is the layer which is shed during menstruation and during pregnancy is kept for implantation of the embryo.

17. Match the following:

Fundus is the upper part of the uterus and is connected to the fallopian tube. It has a dome-like structure. It is the place in the uterus where embryo is implanted.
(i) (d)

Isthmus is a small, narrow, thick-walled, tube-like structure. It is straight and provides the connectivity between the uterus and ampulla.
(ii) (b)

Cervix is the lowermost part of the uterus and it leads into the next accessory female reproductive organ, which is vagina. It is the passage between the vagina and the uterus.
(iii) (e)

Labia majora is a pair of thick-folded skin constituted of adipose tissue. It protects the inner, delicate part of vulva.
(iv) (c)

Bartholin's glands are small, round structures, located at either side of the vaginal opening.
They secrete a fluid for the lubrication of the vagina and the vulva and help in copulation.
(v) (a)

CHAPTER

8

Control and Coordination

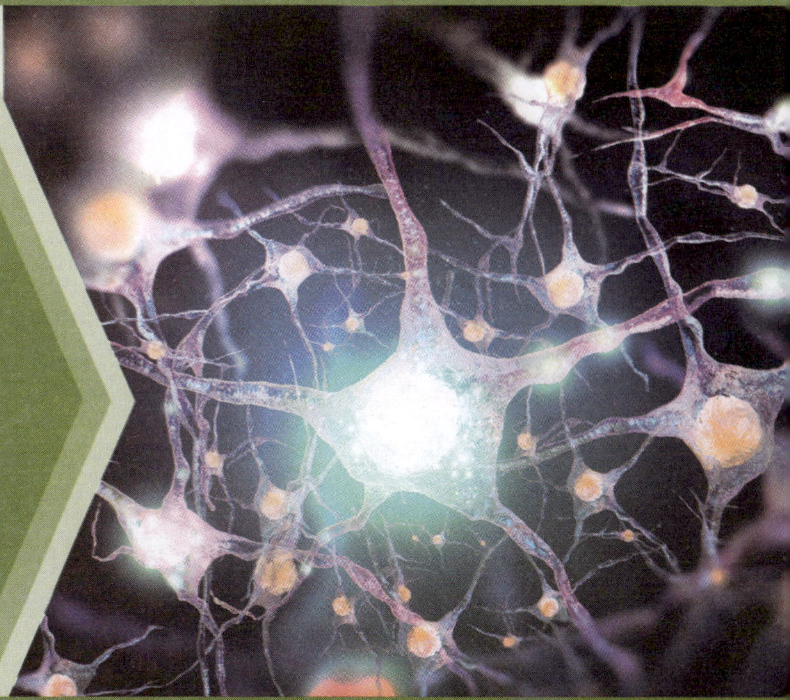

Remember

Before beginning this chapter, you should be able to:

- Remember the basic structure and function of neuron
- Recall basic life processes associated with human life
- Recall chemical nature of basic biomolecules

Key Ideas

After completing this chapter, you should be able to:

- Understand the components and functions of nervous system
- Explain the components and functions of endocrine system
- Relate the regulatory mechanism of hormones in human beings
- Understand the role of phytohormones

A Tribute to Ivan Petrovich Pavlov (1849–1936)

Ivan Petrovich Pavlov (1849–1936) was a seminal figure in physiology, making invaluable contributions to our understanding of control and coordination within living organisms. Pavlov, who was born in Ryazan, Russia, pioneered digestive physiology research that led to the discovery of the conditioned reflex, a concept that revolutionised our understanding of learning, memory, and behavioural conditioning.

He brilliantly demonstrated how external stimuli could elicit involuntary responses in dogs, resulting in the theory of classical conditioning. This was demonstrated when dogs, who had previously only salivated in response to food, began salivating in response to a ringing bell, which had previously been associated with the arrival of food.

His pioneering work was recognised with the Nobel Prize in Physiology or Medicine in 1904, demonstrating the significance and influence of his scientific investigations.

FUN TIME

CROSSWORD

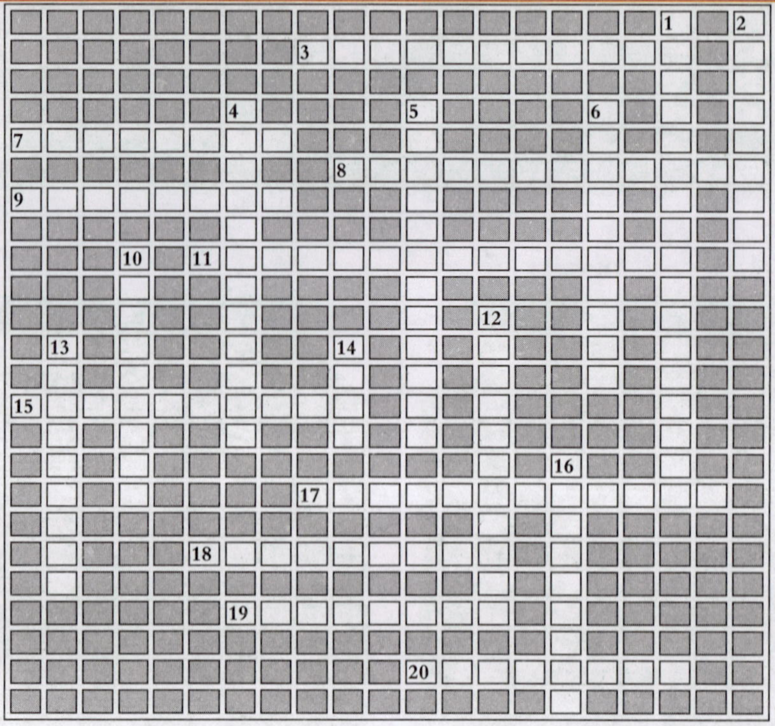

Across

3. Example of mineralocorticoid hormone
7. Hormones that induce labour pains
8. ____hormone Inhibits insulin and glucagon
9. Gaseous phytohormone
11. The state in which the depolarised state of the axon comes back to the state of resting potential
15. _____hormone regulates calcium level in blood
17. Male gamete to ovule follow___movement
18. Branched tree projections from the neurons
19. Protective membranes covering brain and spinal cord
20. Hormone that increases blood sugar level

Down

1. _____ facilitate transmission of nerveimpulse
2. Retarded physical and mental development in childhood caused due to hyposecretion of thyroxine
4. ____ part connects forebrain with the midbrain
5. ____Region of brain possesses speech and memory information
6. Plant hormones concerned within cell division
10. Hormone secreted by the anterior lobe of pituitary gland concerned with the secretion of milk
12. Term for maintenance of normal glucose conc. in blood
13. Meninges' middle layer covering the brain & spinal cord.
14. Round bulge between midbrain and medulla oblongata
16. Single pair of nerves at the spinal cord's end

INTRODUCTION

All living organisms have a common characteristic of responding to the changes in the surrounding environment. These changes in the surrounding environment are called stimuli (singular: stimulus). Examples of external stimuli are light, heat, cold, sound, smell, taste, touch, pressure, pain, water, gravity, etc. Living organisms respond to such stimuli by using certain parts of the body. Plants respond to the stimuli of light, water, gravity, etc. However, the response of the plants to the stimuli is not as conspicuous as it is observed in the animals. For example, sunflower always faces the sun and the leaves of the touch-me-not plant of *Mimosa* family droop down on touch. The responses to various stimuli in animals are very conspicuous. So, on quick removal of hands or suddenly touching a very hot / cold object or mouth becoming watery on the perception of the aroma of a delicious food, are responses to various stimuli. In case of animals, the response to a certain stimulus involves different organs. A proper communication among the organs involved can give rise to appropriate response.

The systematic involvement of different organs in order to respond to a stimulus to generate a proper response is called coordination. Coordination in animals involves nervous and endocrine systems. Nervous system coordinates through the electrical impulses whereas endocrine system coordinates by generating chemicals known as hormones.

Nervous System

Nervous system comprises the network of nerve cells and fibres which are involved in transmitting signals between different parts of the body.

Need for Nervous System

Nervous system plays a major role in sustenance of life because of the following functions that it performs.

- With the help of our sense organs, we are informed about the outside world.
- It controls and regulates vital activities of our body which are involuntary, for example, breathing.
- It enables us to remember information.
- All voluntary activities that we perform are controlled and coordinated by the nervous system.

Parts of Nervous System

In human beings, the nervous system can be broadly divided into two parts, namely:

1. Central nervous system
2. Peripheral nervous system

Central nervous system comprises the brain and spinal cord. The analysis of all sorts of information collected takes place in the central nervous system. Peripheral nervous system is a complex network of nerve cells or neurons responsible for the transmission of responses.

Neuron

The structural and functional unit of nervous system is a nerve cell or neuron. Structure wise, a neuron can be divided distinctly into following three regions:

1. Cell body or cyton
2. Dendrites
3. Axon

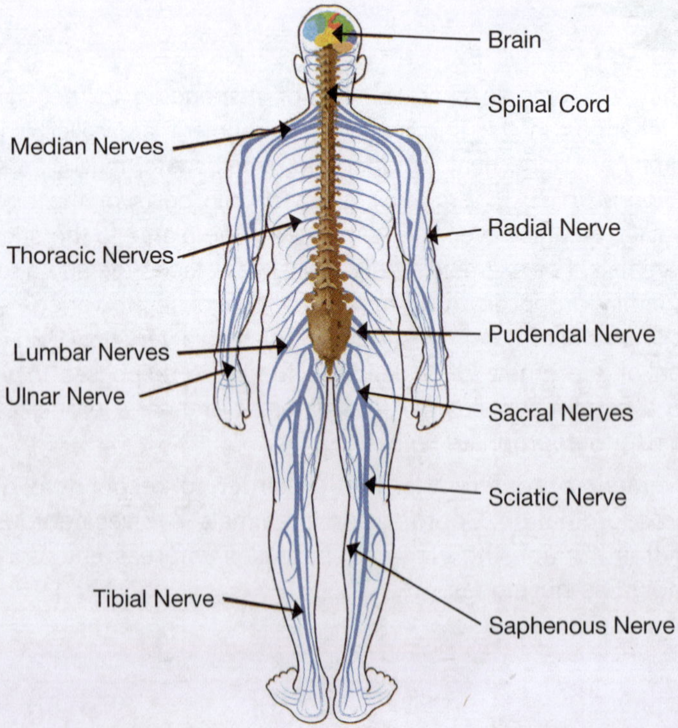

Figure 8.1 Illustration of nervous system

Cell Body or Cyton

Cell body comprises a centrally located nucleus that is surrounded by the granular cytoplasm. Different cell organelles such as lysosomes, mitochondria and Golgi complex are present in the cytoplasm to carry out specific metabolic activities. Centrosome is not found in the cell body since nerve cells do not undergo cell division. The cytoplasm in the cell body contains Nissl granules that are rich in RNA.

> **Info Bytes!**
> Nerve impulses are electrical signals travelling along a neuron.

Dendrites

The tree-like highly branched extensions of cytoplasm of the cell body are called dendrites. The fine branches of dendrites can conveniently reach the narrowest part of the body. Dendrites are the regions in the neuron that receive stimuli.

Axon

Axon is the long, slender projection of a neuron. The length of an axon varies from a few millimetres to more than a metre depending on its location. Axon conducts the electrical impulses away from the cell body of the neuron. Axons of many neurons are coated by a white, multi-layered fatty substance, called myelin sheath. Axons without the myelin sheath are called non-myelinated axons. The neurons with such axons are called non-myelinated neurons. Myelin sheath facilitates rapid conduction of electrical impulses and provides insulation for the axon. The periodic gaps in the myelin sheath over the axon in myelinated neurons are called nodes of Ranvier. Axon endings are placed near the dendrites of another neuron/s. There is a gap in between them which is called synaptic cleft.

> **Info Bytes!**
> The longest axon in a human body originates from the base of the spine and runs to the toes of each foot.

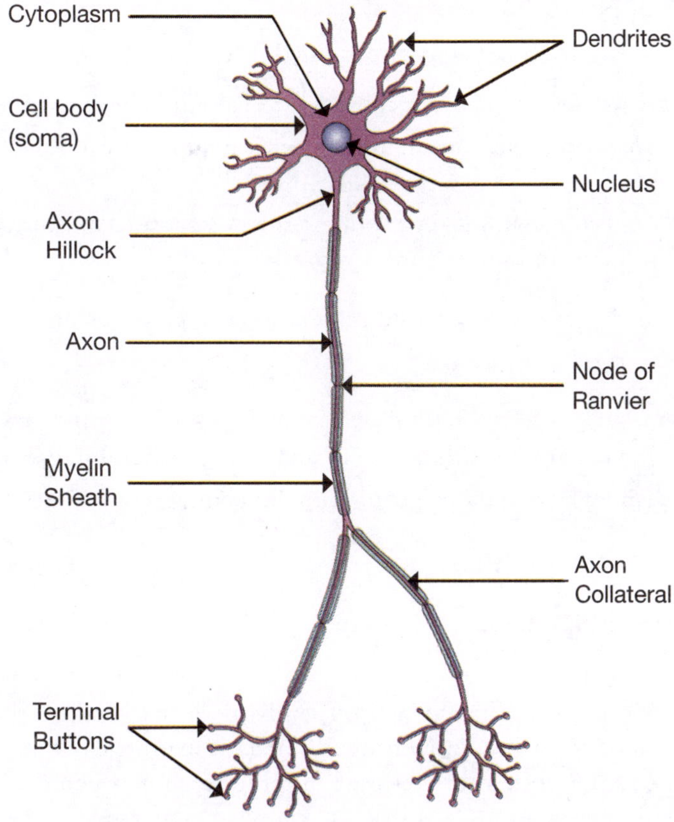

Figure 8.2 Generalized structure of a neuron

Structural Classification of Neurons

Neurons can be structurally divided into three categories on the basis of branching of cell body. These are:

1. **Unipolar neuron:** Unipolar neurons have only one cytoplasmic extension from the cell body. This means that they do not have dendrites and they possess a single axon.
2. **Bipolar neuron:** Bipolar neurons comprise a single dendrite and an axon.
3. **Multipolar neuron:** Multipolar neurons have several dendrites.

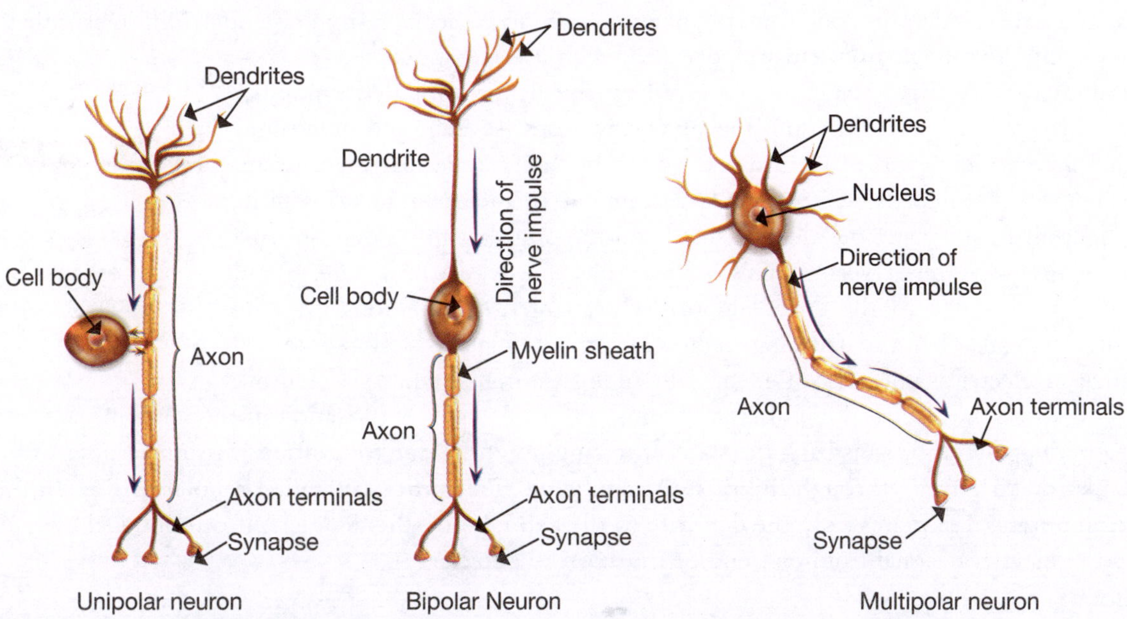

Figure 8.3 Illustration of unipolar, bipolar and multipolar neurons

Functional Classification of Neurons

Neurons can be functionally divided into three categories as listed below:

1. **Sensory or afferent neurons:** Sensory neurons convert external stimuli to internal electrical impulses.
2. **Motor or efferent neurons:** Motor neurons transmit electrical impulses from the brain and the spinal cord to the muscles of different organs.
3. **Connector neurons:** Connector neurons interconnect the sensory and motor neurons and they are located in the central nervous system (brain and spinal cord).

Before discussing further about the processes involved in nervous system, let us understand the meaning of few basic terms involved.

- **Response:** The reaction/change generated in our body due to a given stimulus is called response.
- **Receptor:** Specialized cell which receives the stimulus and sets up nerve impulses is called receptor.
- **Effector:** A muscle or a gland which upon receiving stimulus contracts or secretes substances, respectively, is called effector.

Conduction of Nerve Impulse

A nerve impulse is an electrical signal that gets transmitted from one neuron to another. Neurons communicate with each other with the help of axons and dendrites. A neuron sends an electrical signal through the axon. An electrical signal is converted into a chemical signal at the axon terminal. Then the axon releases molecules of chemical messengers called neurotransmitters. The neurotransmitters are released into the space between the end of an axon of one neuron and the tip of the dendrite of another neuron. This space is known as synapse. The neurotransmitters travel through the synapse and are finally received by the dendrite of another neuron. The dendrite then converts the chemical signal into electrical signal. Thus, the conduction of nerve impulses takes place.

Mechanism of Conduction of Nerve Impulses

The axons or nerve fibres are immersed in an extracellular fluid. This extracellular fluid and the cytoplasm in the axon contain various ions, which are sodium, potassium and calcium ions. In the absence of a stimulus, the extracellular fluid outside the neuron possesses larger concentration of Na^+ ions. Due to this, the electrical charge outside the plasma membrane is positive. The charge is negative inside the plasma membrane of the neuron. This condition is called polarized state. Under this condition, the neuron is said to be at the resting potential. This means that the plasma membrane surrounding the neuron remains polarized when it is not stimulated.

The stimulus for the nerve impulse is received by the dendrites and the impulse is transmitted to the axon. The transmission of positive ions (sodium and potassium) through the plasma membrane of neuron takes place by active transport mechanism. When the neuron is stimulated, entry of a large number of sodium ions takes place inside the neuron. At this state, the electric charge on the outside and inside of plasma membrane of the axon gets reversed. This is known as the depolarized state. Thus, depolarization occurs due to the entry of positively charged sodium ions into the cytoplasm of the axon. Then the neuron generates action potential. An action potential is the change in electrical potential of an impulse along the membrane of a neuron. Under this situation, the electrical impulses get transmitted to the adjacent location of the neuron.

> **Info Bytes!**
>
> Potassium and sodium ions are necessary and indispensable for the functioning of the nervous system.

The area of depolarization gets back the state of resting potential due to the transmission of potassium ions from inside the neuron to outside through the plasma membrane. This process is called repolarization. In this way, the area of action potential migrates from the dendrite to the axon. Thus, the depolarization followed by repolarization propagates the electrical signal from one end of the axon to another.

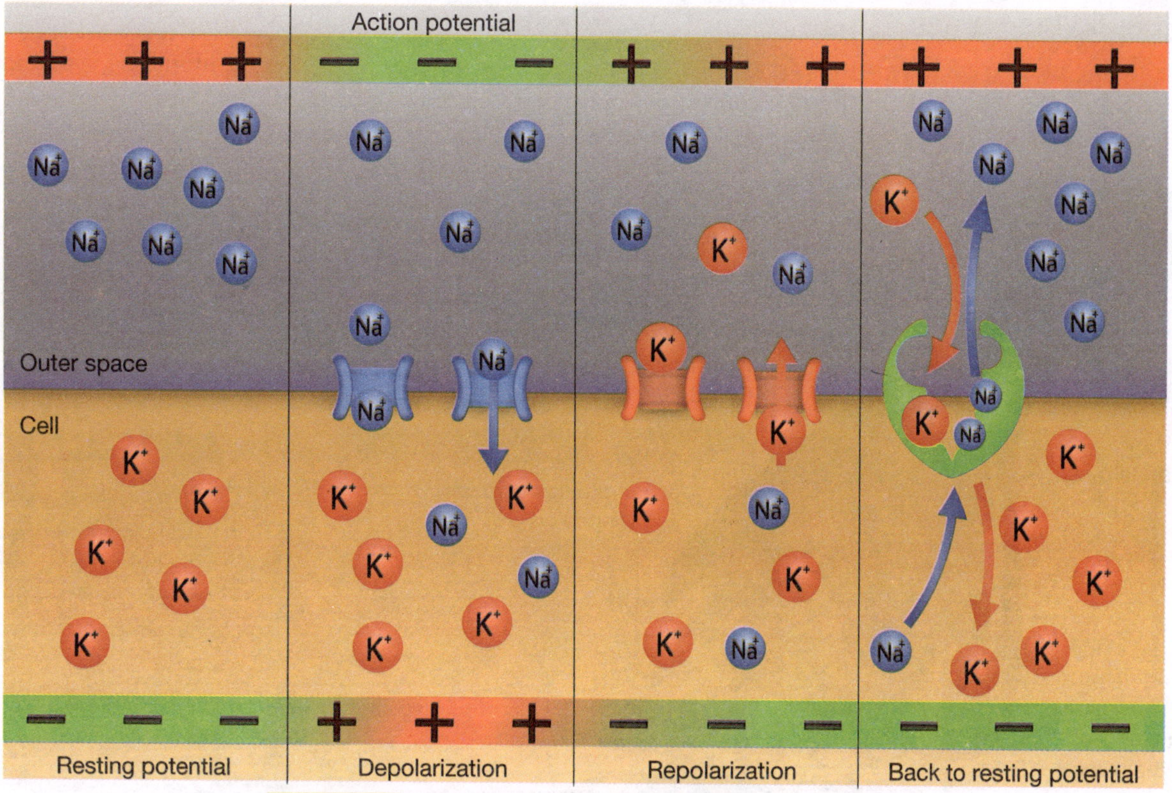

Figure 8.4 Illustration of conduction of nerve impulse

Synapse

The junction between the two nerve cells facilitates the transmission of impulses from one neuron to another and is known as synapse. Synapse is composed of three elements:

1. Presynaptic membrane
2. Synaptic cleft
3. Postsynaptic membrane

Presynaptic Membrane

The membrane at the axon terminal of a neuron is called presynaptic membrane. When the action potential reaches the terminal of the axon, the inflow of calcium ions takes place in this area. Small secretory vesicles are present inside the axon near the presynaptic membrane. These secretory vesicles are known as synaptic vesicles and they contain neurotransmitters. Neurotransmitters are the molecules of a chemical substance that transmit the impulse from one neuron to another through the synapse. Calcium ions help the synaptic vesicles move towards the presynaptic membrane. They finally fuse with the presynaptic membrane. Then neurotransmitters, the content of synaptic vesicles, are transported to the next element of the synapse, the synaptic cleft. Thus, the electrical impulses get converted to chemical impulses by the release of neurotransmitters.

Synaptic Cleft

The space between the two neurons across which a nerve impulse is transmitted by neurotransmitters is called synaptic cleft. Neurotransmitters move across the synaptic cleft and get adhered to the next element of the synapse, that is, postsynaptic membrane of another neuron.

Postsynaptic Membrane

Postsynaptic membrane encloses some part of the dendrite of a neuron. When the neurotransmitters get attached with the postsynaptic membrane of another neuron, active transport of sodium ions takes place in its dendrite. Thus, the next neuron attains the state of action potential and chemical impulses get converted to electrical impulses.

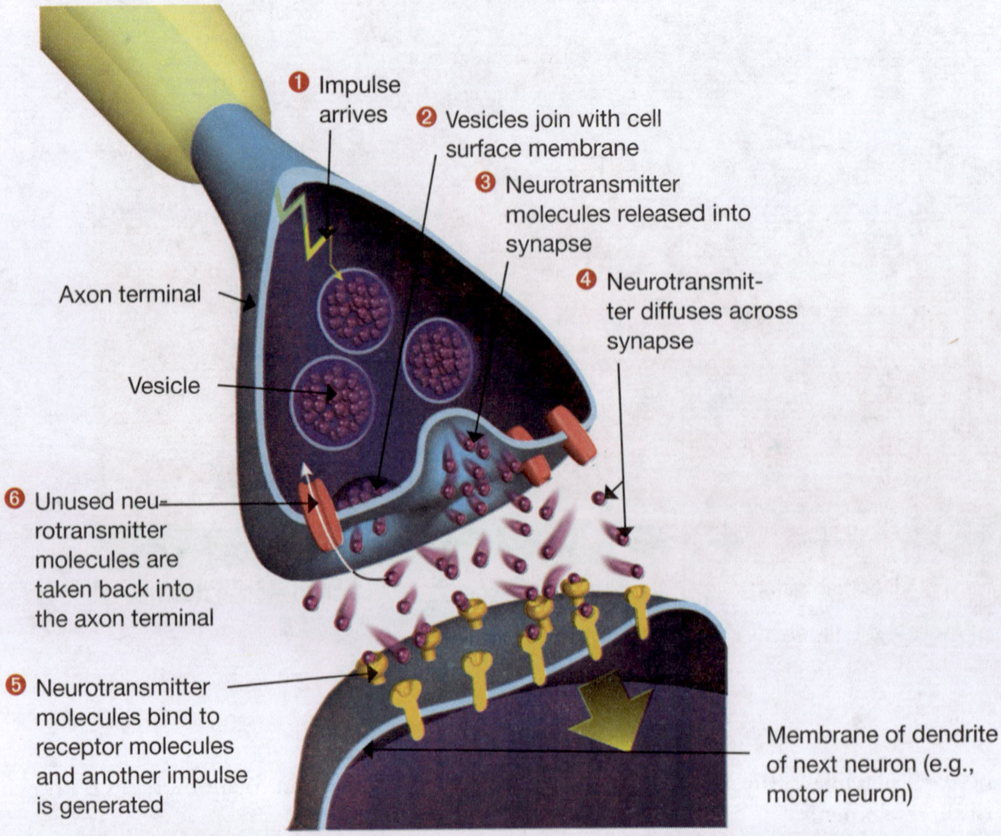

Figure 8.5 Illustration of neurotransmitter release mechanism

> **Info Bytes!**
> There are approximately 86 billion neurons in the human brain. That's nearly 14 times the human population on Earth.

Nerves

Nerves are cable-like glistening white structures containing a bundle of neurons. They emerge from the central nervous system (brain and spinal cord) and branch out to almost all parts of the body. Nerves present throughout the nervous system can be categorized into three types:

1. **Sensory nerves:** Sensory nerves receive the stimulus from the sense organs and transmit the impulse to the central nervous system. Sense organs are the organs of the body that respond to the external stimuli and convey the impulses to the sensory nerves. For example, optic nerve.
2. **Motor nerves:** Motor nerves transmit impulses from the central nervous system to muscles and glands, and thus, help them to take the appropriate action. For example, trochlear nerve.
3. **Mixed nerves:** Mixed nerves contain both sensory nerves and motor nerves, and thus, carry both incoming sensory information and outgoing muscle commands in the same bundle. For example, vagus nerve.

> **Info Bytes!**
> Ganglia (singular: ganglion) are the bundles of cell bodies, usually linked at synapses.

Central Nervous System

Central nervous system comprises the brain and spinal cord.

Brain

The brain in the human beings is the largest and the most developed among all the animals. It is protected by eight cranial bones that are the part of the skull. The three membranes that cover the brain and the spinal cord are together called meninges. The three layers are as follows:

1. Outermost dura mater
2. Middle arachnoid
3. Innermost pia mater

A clear, colourless fluid is present between the inner two layers and is known as cerebrospinal fluid. Cerebrospinal fluid has following three major functions:

- It protects the brain.
- It supplies nutrients to the nervous system.
- It removes waste products generated by the metabolism process in the brain.

A choroid plexus that secretes the cerebrospinal fluid is a network of capillaries present in the roof of the brain. The weight of an adult human brain is approximately 1400 g. The brain can be divided into three major regions:

Info Bytes!

12 pairs of nerves control the head and neck.

1. Forebrain which comprises cerebrum, diencephalon and olfactory lobes.
2. Mid brain which comprises optic lobes and cerebral peduncles.
3. Hindbrain which comprises cerebellum, pons and medulla oblongata.

Forebrain

The forebrain is the most important part of the brain in terms of functioning and a well-developed forebrain distinguishes the nervous system of human beings from that of other animals. It comprises the cerebrum, diencephalon and olfactory lobes.

Cerebrum

It is the largest part of the brain and comprises a folded mass of the nervous tissue. It makes up the major part of the brain. It is divided into the right and left halves called cerebral hemispheres that are connected together by a sheet of nerve fibres called corpus callosum. Corpus callosum helps in communication between the two hemispheres. The outer layer of the cerebrum is called cerebral cortex. The outer region of the cerebral cortex contains cell bodies of the neurons and appears greyish in colour. Hence, it is called grey matter. The grey matter is highly convoluted with ridges and grooves. These convolutions in the grey matter increase its surface area. The grey matter comprises cell bodies of neurons. Inner region of the cerebrum comprises axons of the neurons and is known as white matter.

Info Bytes!

Neurons change their shape many times throughout their life.

Functionally, cerebrum can be divided into four lobes.

1. **Frontal lobe:** The function of this lobe is planning and reasoning. It is also involved in the expression of emotions and problem-solving. The motor nerves are present at the rear part of the frontal lobe. They receive information from other parts of the brain and ensure that the action is carried out by the body.
2. **Occipital lobe:** It is mainly responsible for receiving the information from the retina in the eyes and processing visual information.
3. **Parietal lobe:** It perceives various stimuli, helps in recognition, processes the senses received by the body.
4. **Temporal lobe:** It processes auditory information and is associated with speech and memory. Hence, any damage to this area can lead to memory problems and language deficiency.

Info Bytes!

Brain uses more than 20% of the body's total energy generation.

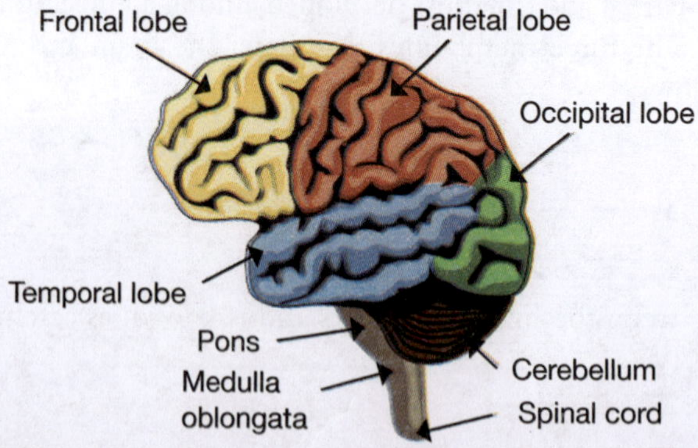

Figure 8.6 Location of lobes in the cerebrum of human brain

On the whole, the left hemisphere of the cerebrum controls right-handedness and is mainly concerned with logical and analytical thinking. The right hemisphere of the cerebrum altogether controls left-handedness and is associated with creative skills.

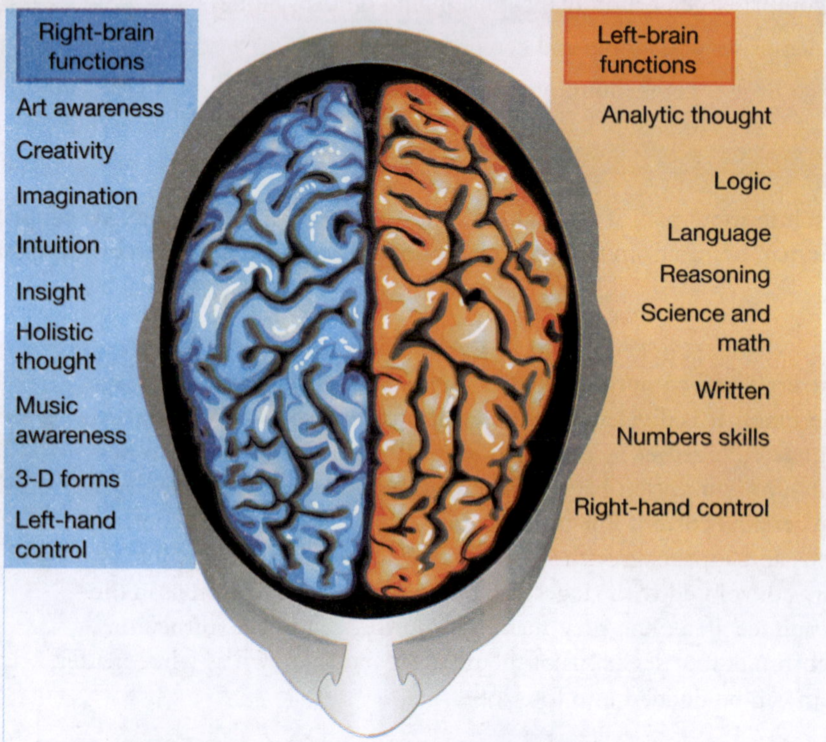

Figure 8.7 Human brain—left and right functions

Diencephalon

Diencephalon is a part of the forebrain which connects the forebrain to the mid brain. It is divided into two parts, namely thalamus and hypothalamus. The main function of thalamus is relaying motor and sensory signals to the cerebrum. Hypothalamus links nervous system to the endocrine system and controls pituitary gland, a part of endocrine system. It also plays role in maintaining body temperature, blood pressure, thirst, etc.

Olfactory Lobes

A pair of olfactory lobes is located in the forebrain. They are club-shaped solid structures and are involved in the relay of sense of smell.

Mid Brain

Mid brain connects the forebrain to the hindbrain. This part of the brain is mainly involved in auditory and visual processing. It comprises optic lobes and cerebral peduncles.

Optic Lobes

A pair of optic lobes is located at the dorsal side of the midbrain and controls vision.

Cerebral Peduncles

Cerebral peduncles are the paired structures located at the ventral side of the midbrain. They connect cerebellum, a part of hindbrain to the midbrain. They relay motor impulses from the cerebral cortex to the pons, a part of the hindbrain and spinal cord. They also relay sensory impulses from the spinal cord to the thalamus.

Hindbrain

It comprises the cerebellum, pons and medulla.

Cerebellum

The cerebellum is located below the cerebrum and above the medulla. It can be divided into two lateral hemispheres and a narrow middle zone, called vermis. Two hemispheres contain numerous furrows, but they are not convoluted. A bridge of nervous fibre, called pons Varolii connects the two hemispheres of the cerebellum. Muscular movements of both sides of the body are coordinated by the transmission of impulses between the two hemispheres of the cerebellum across the bridge. Cerebellum comprises the grey and white matter. Grey matter is located at the surface of the cerebellum and is folded in appearance. It is called cerebellar cortex. White matter is located below the cerebellar cortex and a tree-like appearance. A bundle of nerve fibres or axons present in the white matter are connected to the cerebrum and medulla oblongata, another part of the hindbrain. The function of cerebellum is receiving information from the sensory systems, the spinal cord and other parts of the brain. It also regulates the voluntary movements such as posture, balance, coordination, etc., and thus, balances the activities of the muscles.

Pons

Pons appears like a round bulge located between the midbrain and medulla oblongata, another part of the hindbrain. It controls the respiratory functions.

Medulla Oblongata

Medulla oblongata is the lowermost part of the brain. It has a cone-shaped structure and it forms the connection between the spinal cord and the brain. It is connected to the midbrain by the pons. It has both grey matter and white matter. Grey matter comprises the myelinated nerve fibres, while white matter is composed of non-myelinated nerve fibres. White matter is in the outer side and grey matter lies in the inner side. A choroid plexus that secretes the cerebrospinal fluid is present at the roof of medulla oblongata. It is the centre for controlling respiratory and circulatory systems. It controls all autonomic functions such as regulating the contractions of heart and blood vessels, digestion, sneezing, coughing, swallowing, vomiting, etc. Another part of the central nervous system is spinal cord.

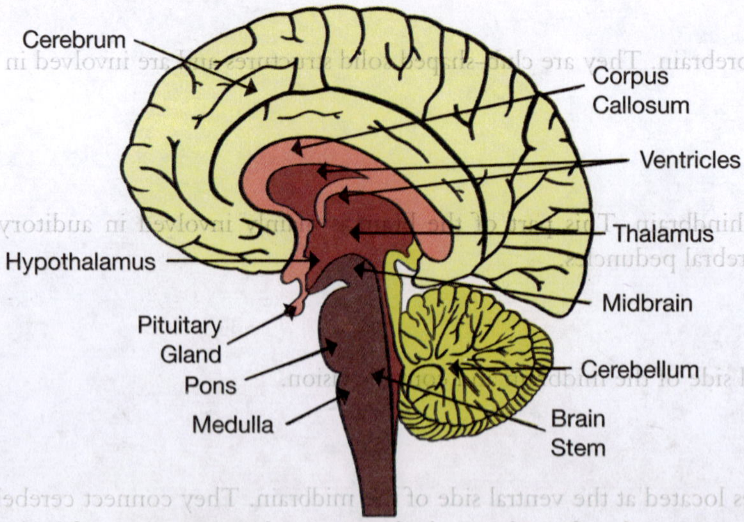

Figure 8.8 Major portions of human brain

> **Info Bytes!**
> Jellyfish and starfish don't have brains. Instead, they have a simple network of nerves.

Spinal Cord

Spinal cord is a long and thin tube-like bunch of nervous tissue and cells that from the medulla oblongata to the vertebral column.

Structure

Spinal cord has a long, cylindrical structure and it is composed of nerves. It is originated from the brain and runs through the vertebral canal. The core of the spinal cord contains grey matter and the contents of grey matter are cell bodies, dendrites, supporting cells. White matter contains axons and surrounds the grey matter. Cross section of grey matter shows H-shaped or butterfly-shaped grey matter surrounded by white matter. Each side of the butterfly-shaped grey matter has a posterior horn called dorsal horn and an anterior horn called ventral horn. The central canal of the grey matter contains cerebrospinal fluid which acts as a cushion to protect the nerves. Cerebrospinal fluid also supplies nutrients to nerves and removes wastes generated due to cerebral metabolism.

Three layers of membranes, called meninges which protect the spinal cord are:

1. **Dura mater:** It is the outermost layer which connects the meninges to the skull and vertebral column. It contains tough and fibrous connective tissue.
2. **Arachnoid mater:** It is the middle layer of the meninges which connects the dura mater and pia mater.
3. **Pia mater:** It is the innermost layer of the meninges which is in direct contact with the cerebral cortex and spinal cord. This layer has a rich supply of blood vessels.

Functions

The functions of spinal cord are as follows:

- It controls the reflexes taking place in the body parts located below the neck region.
- Sensory impulses from the skin and muscles are transmitted to the brain through the spinal cord.
- It also transmits motor responses from the brain to the muscles of trunk and limbs.

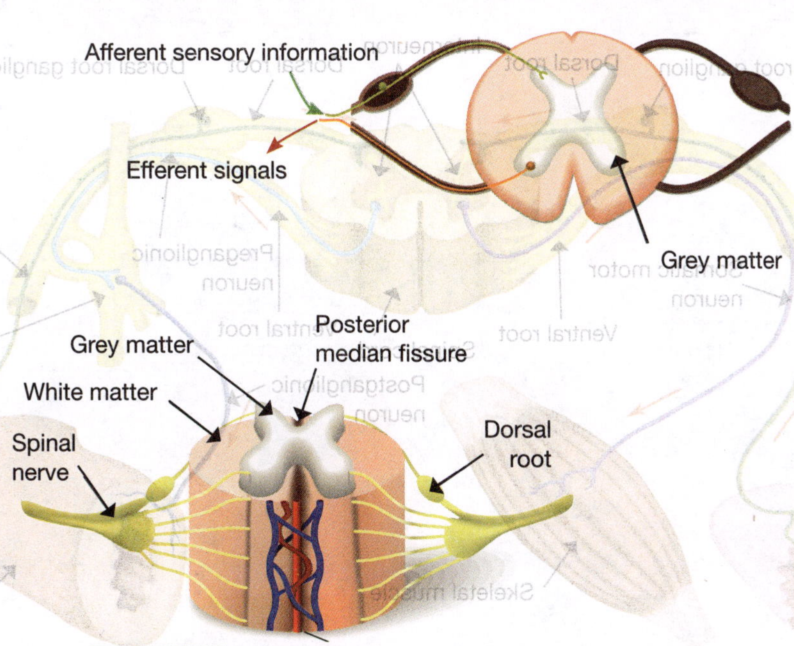

Figure 8.9 Illustration of cross-section of spinal cord

Peripheral Nervous System

Peripheral nervous system comprises nerves that connect the different organs, limbs and skin to the central nervous system. Peripheral nervous system can be divided into two categories based on their functions. They are as follows:

1. Somatic nervous system
2. Autonomic nervous system

Somatic Nervous System

Somatic nervous system regulates the voluntary movements of the body. The nerves associated with the somatic nervous system can be classified into following two categories.

1. Cranial nerves
2. Spinal nerves

Cranial Nerves

Cranial nerves originate directly from the brain. There is a set of 12 pairs of cranial nerves. They are of following three categories:

1. **Sensory nerves:** They carry signals towards the brain and spinal cord. For example, olfactory, optic and auditory nerves
2. **Motor nerves:** They carry signals from central nervous system to the muscles. For example, oculomotor and trochlear nerves
3. **Mixed nerves:** They are composed of both sensory and motor nerve fibres and carry signals in both directions. For example, trigeminal and facial nerves

Spinal Nerves

Spinal nerves originate from the spinal cord and they transmit signals between the spinal cord and the body. Spinal nerves are mixed nerves since they contain both sensory and motor fibres. The two types of nerves are separated inside the grey matter of the spinal cord. Sensory fibres are connected to dorsal horn and motor fibres are connected to ventral horn of the grey matter through dorsal and ventral roots, respectively. There are 31 pairs of spinal nerves.

- 8 pairs of cervical nerves
- 12 pairs of thoracic nerves
- 5 pairs of lumbar nerves
- 5 pairs of sacral nerves
- 1 pair of coccygeal nerves

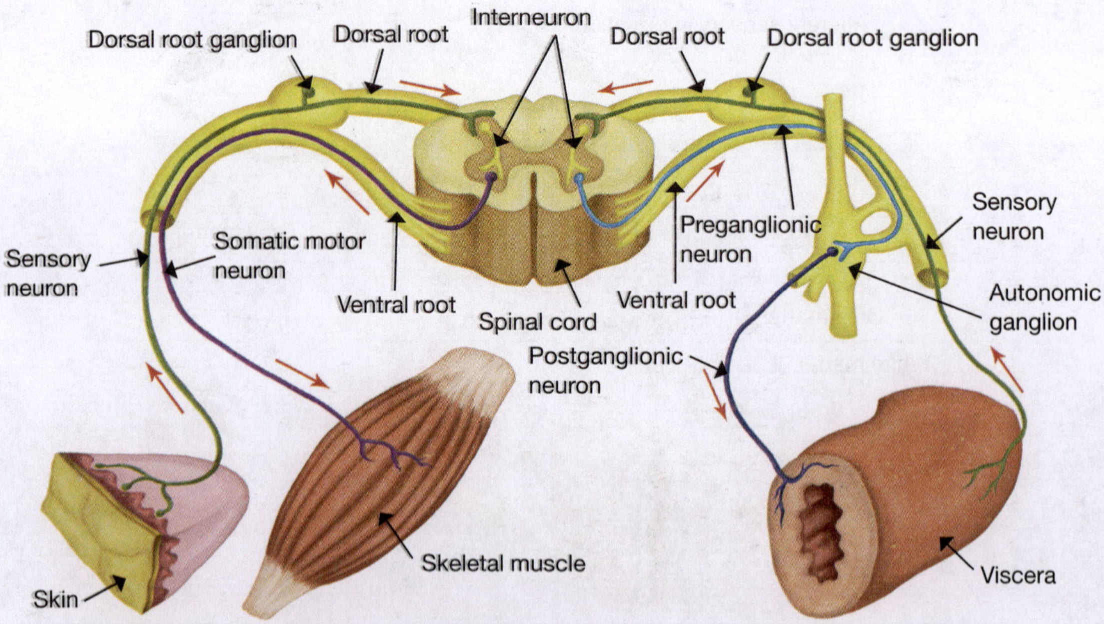

Figure 8.10 Illustration of somatic (left) and autonomic (right) nervous systems

Autonomic Nervous System

Autonomic nervous system controls and regulates the internal organs without any conscious effort by the human body. Two antagonistic (opposing each other) sets of nerves constitute autonomic nervous system. Hence, autonomic nervous system is divided into sympathetic and parasympathetic nervous systems. If one nervous system contracts a muscle, the other one relaxes it. Proper balancing between the two nervous systems accurately regulates the involuntary movements in the human body. They are present on either sides of the spinal cord.

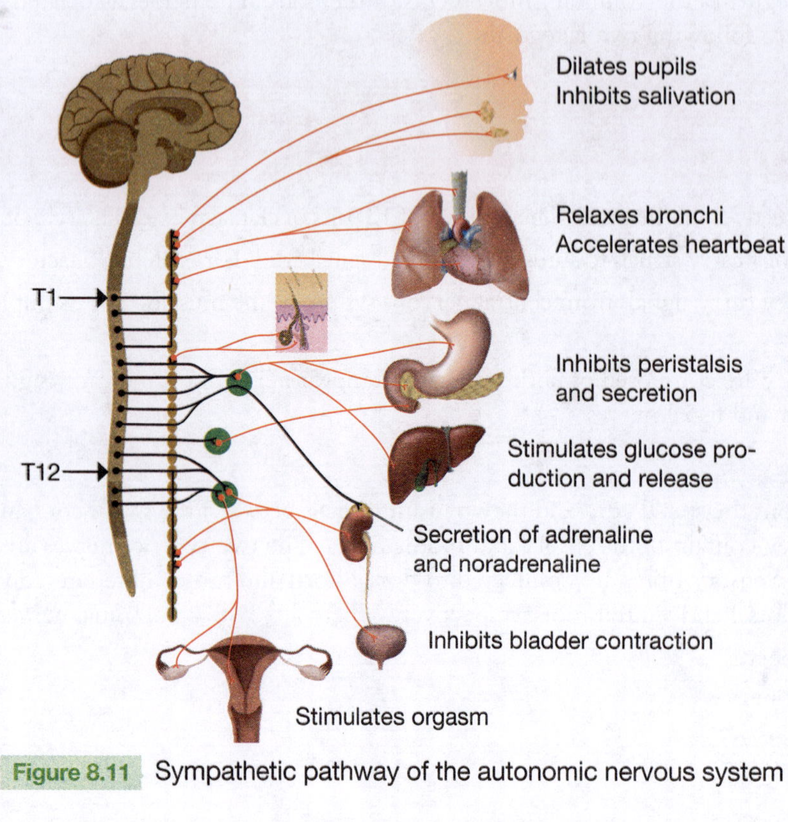

Figure 8.11 Sympathetic pathway of the autonomic nervous system

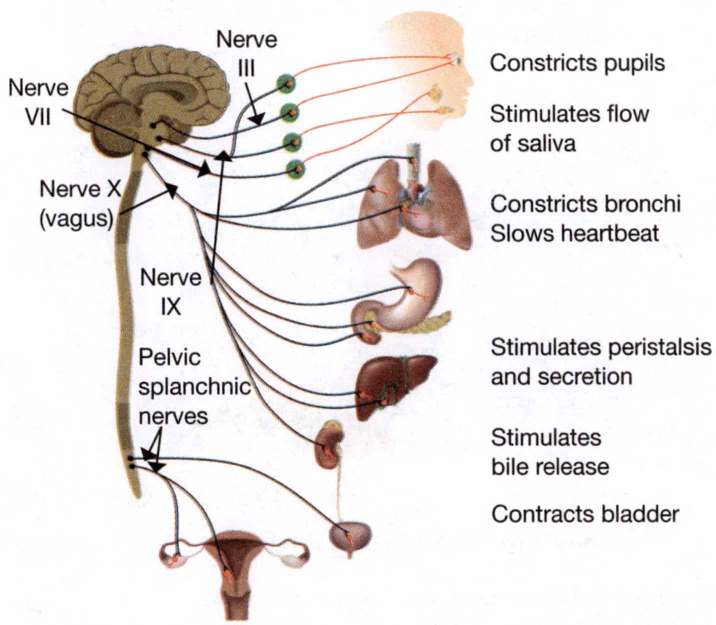

Figure 8.12 Parasympathetic pathway of the autonomic nervous system

Table 8.1 Difference between sympathetic and parasympathetic nervous systems

Organ	Sympathetic nervous system	Parasympathetic nervous system
Body	Prepares for an action	Prepares for relaxation
Pupil	Dilation	Constriction
Urinary bladder	Contraction of sphincter	Relaxation of sphincter
Lungs	Dilates bronchi	Constricts bronchi
Heart	Acceleration of heart beat	Retardation of heart beat
Blood vessel	Constriction (except coronary vessels)	Dilation (except coronary vessels)
Salivary glands	Inhibition of saliva secretion	Stimulation of saliva secretion

Reflex Action

A reflex action is an involuntary and almost instantaneous response to a stimulus. An example of reflex action is contraction of pupils of the eyes when they are exposed to bright light. Other examples are removing the hands from the hot object after touching them and watering of mouth on inhaling the aroma of food. The nerve pathway along which the impulses transmit to generate a reflex action is called reflex arc.

Table 8.2 Components of a reflex arc

Component	Description
The stimulus	Receptors perceive the stimulus
Sensory neurons	These neurons transmit the impulse to the spinal cord.
The spinal cord	Relay neurons (present in the brain and the spinal cord) connect the sensory neurons and the motor neurons in the spinal cord.
Motor neurons	These neurons send nerve impulses away from the central nervous system to the effector (glands or organs).

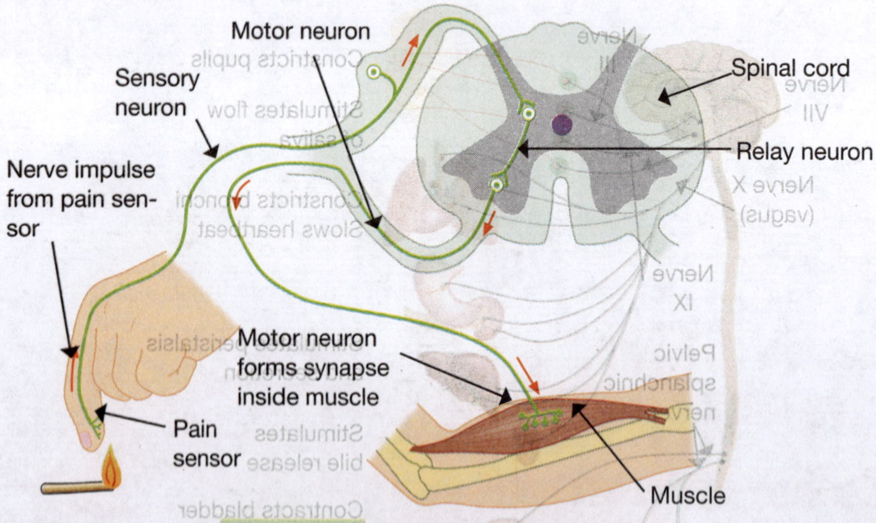

Figure 8.13 Illustration of a reflex arc

Table 8.3 Differences between reflex and voluntary actions

Parameter	Reflex action	Voluntary action
Initiation	By a stimulus	By a voluntary thought
Reason	Mainly self-defence	Fulfilment of a goal
Organs involved	Muscles and glands	Muscles
Command	Originates mainly in the spinal cord and autonomic nervous system	Originates in brain

The reflexes are of two types—conditioned (conditional) and unconditioned (unconditional) reflexes.

1. **Conditioned reflexes**—These are learned by individuals through the interaction with the stimuli during their lifetime. This reflex is not shown when the stimulus is not experienced previously by the person. These reflexes are controlled by the cerebral cortex. For example, watering of the mouth at the sight or smell of food.
2. **Unconditioned reflexes**—These are unconscious responses to a given stimuli and they are inborn reflexes. For example, suckling of mother's breast by a new born baby, and yelping of a person in response to the bite of an insect, etc.

Nervous system works in coordination with the endocrine system for the most effective and efficient communication system in the body. These two systems are together involved in control and coordination of the functions of different parts of the body.

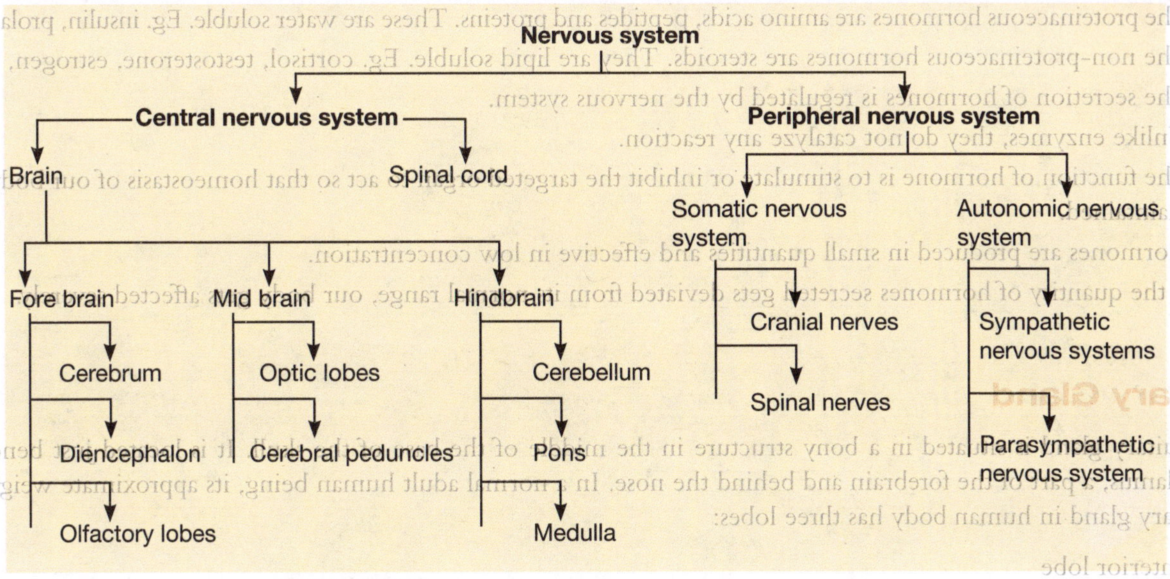

Figure 8.14 Classification of human nervous system

Endocrine System

Endocrine system is the collection of ductless glands that secrete certain chemical substances directly into the blood. These chemical substances are called hormones. Hormones are chemical substances secreted by stimulated cells. These hormones regulate different life processes. Main endocrine glands in our body are:

- Adrenal
- Pituitary
- Thyroid
- Thymus
- Parathyroid
- Testes (in men)
- Ovaries (in women)

Need for Endocrine System

At any given time, there are various complex activities happening inside our cells that are essential for proper metabolic functioning of our body. For such various activities, there are various systems involved. These activities need to be tightly regulated. Hence, there is an endocrine system in place that takes care of regulating and coordinating all functions in our body.

Hormones are chemical messengers secreted directly into the blood in response to the changes inside or outside the body and transported to organs and tissues of the body to exert their functions.

Characteristics of Hormones

Following are the main characteristic features of hormones:

- Hormones are circulated through the bloodstream.
- The site of secretion of hormone and the site of action are different.
- They could be proteinaceous or non-proteinaceous (steroid).

Info Bytes!

The word 'hormone' is originated from a Greek term, the meaning of which is 'to excite'.

- The proteinaceous hormones are amino acids, peptides and proteins. These are water soluble. Eg. insulin, prolactin, etc.
- The non-proteinaceous hormones are steroids. They are lipid soluble. Eg. cortisol, testosterone, estrogen, etc.
- The secretion of hormones is regulated by the nervous system.
- Unlike enzymes, they do not catalyze any reaction.
- The function of hormone is to stimulate or inhibit the targeted organ to act so that homeostasis of our body can be maintained.
- Hormones are produced in small quantities and effective in low concentration.
- If the quantity of hormones secreted gets deviated from its normal range, our body gets affected severely.

Pituitary Gland

The pituitary gland is situated in a bony structure in the middle of the base of the skull. It is located just beneath the hypothalamus, a part of the forebrain and behind the nose. In a normal adult human being, its approximate weight is 1.5 g. Pituitary gland in human body has three lobes:

1. Anterior lobe
2. Intermediate lobe
3. Posterior lobe

Function of Pituitary Gland

The pituitary gland is often called 'master gland' since it controls the activity of other endocrine glands such as thyroid, adrenal, ovaries and testes.

Info Bytes!

The term 'tropic' refers to hormones that stimulate other endocrine glands.

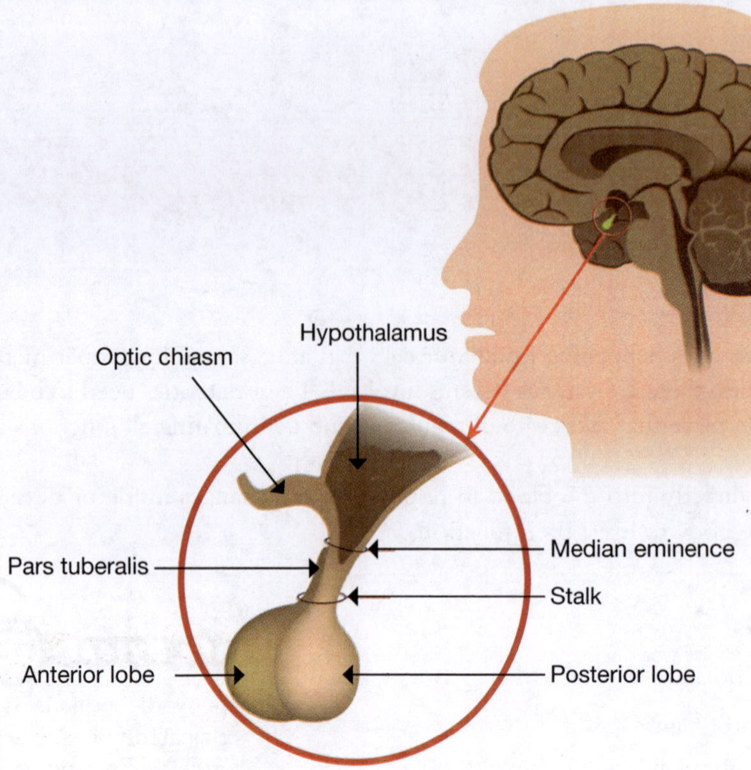

Figure 8.15 Location and structure of pituitary gland

Table 8.4 Hormones secreted by three lobes of the pituitary gland

Hormones secreted	Function of the hormones
Anterior lobe of the pituitary gland	
Somatotropic or growth hormone (STH or GH)	• Stimulates the growth of all tissues of the body including bones • Controls cell metabolism
Thyroid stimulating hormone (TSH)	• Secretion is controlled by thyrotropin-releasing factor produced by the hypothalamus • Stimulates thyroid to produce thyroxine hormone • Hyposecretion develops thyroid atrophy which leads to progressive destruction of the thyroid glands
Adrenocorticotropic hormone (ACTH)	• Stimulates the adrenal cortex to secrete glucocorticoid and minerelocorticoid hormones
Follicle stimulating hormone (FSH)	**In females** • Stimulates the growth of Graafian follicle and secretion of oestrogen hormone **In males** • Controls the production of sperms
Luteinizing hormone (LH)	**In females** • Stimulates ovulation • Stimulates formation of corpus luteum and secretion of progesterone hormone **In males** • It is called Interstitial Cell Stimulating Hormone (ICSH) • Stimulates secretion of testosterone hormone.
Prolactin	• Controls enlargement of breasts during pregnancy • Controls secretion of milk after delivery
Intermediate lobe of the pituitary gland	
Melanocyte stimulating hormone (MSH)	• Stimulates the formation of the black pigment (melanin) in the skin
Posterior lobe of the pituitary gland	
Vasopressin or antidiuretic hormone (ADH)	• Maintains the water content in the blood, and thus, concentration of electrolyte is balanced • Increases blood pressure by contracting blood vessels
Oxytocin	• Causes contraction of the uterine muscles during parturition • Helps in the secretion of milk in female breasts during lactation

Disorders Related to The Activity of Pituitary Gland

Dwarfism: The deficiency of growth hormone in childhood results in dwarfism which is characterized by short stature, slower growth of bones and other body organs.

Gigantism: It results from over-secretion of growth hormone in childhood. Bones lengthen beyond normal limit and results in very tall heights.

> **Info Bytes!**
> FSH and LH are called gonadotropins.

Acromegaly: It results from over-secretion of growth hormone in an adult. It is characterized by abnormal increase in facial and limb bones.

Thyroid Glands

There are two lobes in the thyroid gland that lie on either side of the trachea. Two lobes are connected by the isthmus. It appears like a butterfly and is located at the base of the neck, below the larynx.

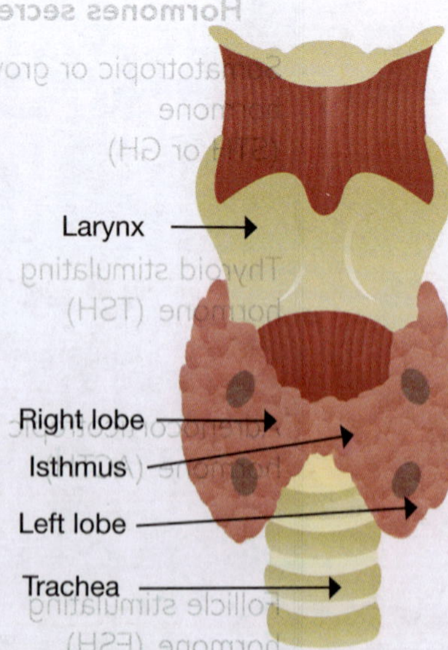

Figure 8.16 Location and structure of thyroid gland

Functions of Thyroid Gland

Two hormones are secreted by the thyroid gland. These are:

1. **Thyroxine**
   - Controls metabolism in tissues, and thus, controls growth
   - Influences bone ossification, that is, formation of bone
   - Maintains body temperature
   - Maturation of brain
2. **Calcitonin**
   - Regulates concentration of calcium in blood
   - Participates in phosphorous metabolism

Disorders Related to the Activity of the Thyroid Gland

Hyposecretion of Thyroxine

It leads to the following diseases.

- **Cretinism in children:** Retarded physical and mental development in childhood.
- **Myxoedema in adults:** Decrease in basal metabolism which leads to physical and mental dullness.
- **Goitre:** Swelling in the neck.

Hypersecretion of Thyroxine

This condition causes the following diseases.

- **Hyperthyroidism:** Accelerates metabolism in the body, increases heart and ventilation rate
- **Exopthalmic goitre:** A form of hyperthyroidism which causes protrusion of eyeballs.

Adrenal Glands

Adrenal gland is a paired structure and is located on the top of the kidneys. Hence, it is called supra-renal gland. Adrenal gland can be divided into two parts.

1. Adrenal medulla
2. Adrenal cortex

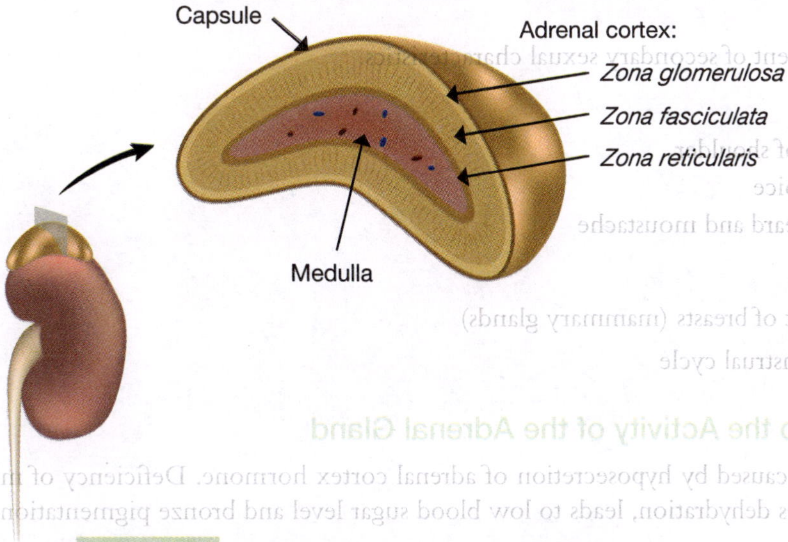

Figure 8.17 Location and structure of adrenal gland

Adrenal Medulla

This part of adrenal gland secretes adrenaline (epinephrine and norepinephrine) hormones. Adrenaline hormones have following functions:

- They are released to cope with the stress.
- They increase heartbeat, blood pressure, supply of blood to the muscle.
- They trigger the release of glucose.

Adrenal Cortex

This part of the adrenal gland secretes cortical hormones. Some of the cortical hormones are:

Mineralocorticoids

- They regulate electrolytic and fluid balance by maintaining the ratio of sodium and potassium ion.
- Aldosterone facilitates active reabsorption of sodium, passive reabsorption of water and excretion of potassium from the kidneys. For example, aldostrerone.

Glucocorticoids

- These hormones are released at the time of stress and if any disturbance of homeostasis of any nutrients occurs in our body.
- They regulate metabolism of all sorts of nutrients.
- Glucocortcoids promote gluconeogenesis. Gluconeogensis is the process of synthesis of glucose from non-carbohydrate source. Thus, they maintain homeostasis of glucose.
- They also decrease the rate of protein synthesis and stimulate the formation of fat droplets from fats.
- Glucocorticoids suppress immunity by reducing the number of eosinophils and lymphocytes which form antibodies. For example, cortisol and cortisone.

Corticosteroids

They stimulate development of secondary sexual characteristics.

In males

- Broadening of shoulder
- Change in voice
- Growth of beard and moustache

In females

- Development of breasts (mammary glands)
- Onset of menstrual cycle

Disorders Related to the Activity of the Adrenal Gland

Addison's disease: It is caused by hyposecretion of adrenal cortex hormone. Deficiency of minerelocorticoids disturbs electrolytic balance, causes dehydration, leads to low blood sugar level and bronze pigmentation of skin.

Cushing's syndrome: It is caused due to excess secretion of glucocortcoids which increases blood sugar and blood pressure. Excretion of sugar takes place with urine in such condition.

Conn's Syndrome (Aldosteronism): It is caused by excess of aldosterone which increases the sodium–potassium ratio, with increase in blood pressure due to excess retention of water. Symptoms are weakness and cramps in muscles and even paralysis.

Adrenal Virilism: Excess secretion of sex corticoids in females leads to the development of male characteristics such as beard, moustache and change in voice in the females. This condition is called adrenal virilism. Excess secretion of these hormones in early age leads to sexual maturity.

Pancreas

Pancreas is a soft and elongated organ. It is located behind the stomach and surrounded by spleen, liver and small intestine. It has both exocrine (with duct) and endocrine (ductless) parts, and hence, it is called heterocrine gland.

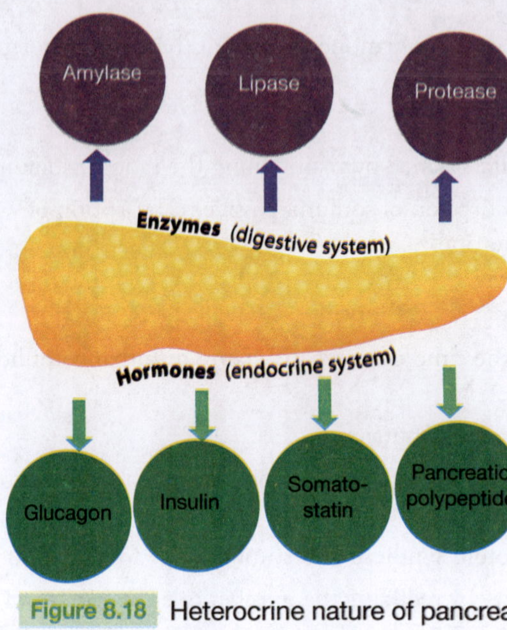

Figure 8.18 Heterocrine nature of pancreas

As an endocrine gland, it has specific groups of cells, called Islets of Langerhans which secrete different hormones. Islets of Langerhans contain three types of cells, called alpha, beta and delta cells.

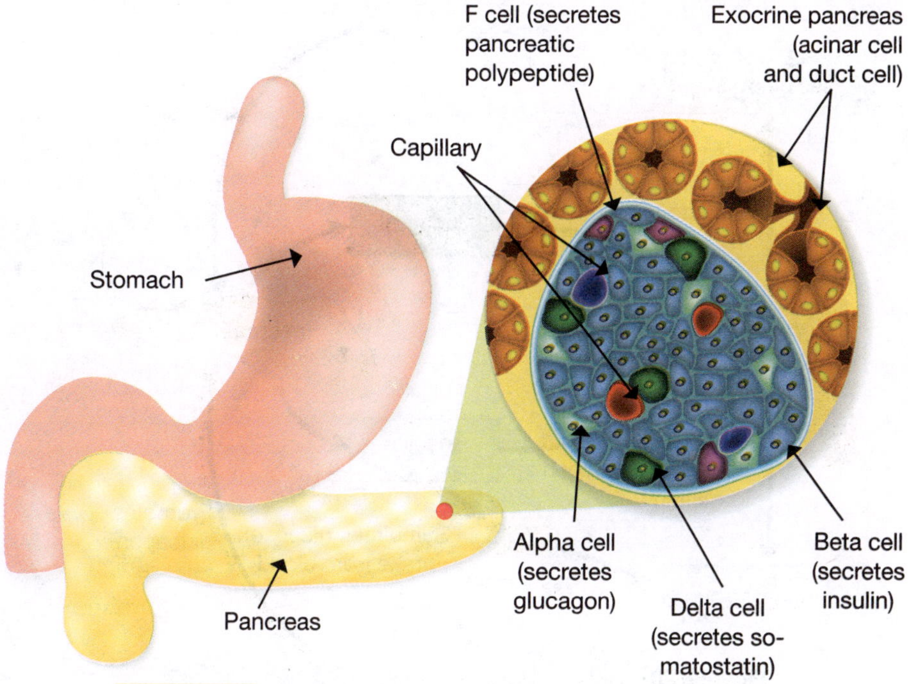

Figure 8.19 Location and structure of islets of Langerhans

Functions of Pancreas

Table 8.5 Different hormones released by Islets of Langerhans and their functions

Type of cells	Hormone released	Functions
Alpha cells	Glucagon	• Converts glycogen to glucose • Thus, raises blood sugar
Beta cells	Insulin	• Initiates deposition of extra glucose in the form of glycogen in liver and muscles • Thus, lowers blood sugar level • Increases oxidation of glucose to release energy
Delta cells	Somatostatin	• It is also called growth hormone inhibiting hormone (GHIH) • Inhibits secretion of insulin and glucagon

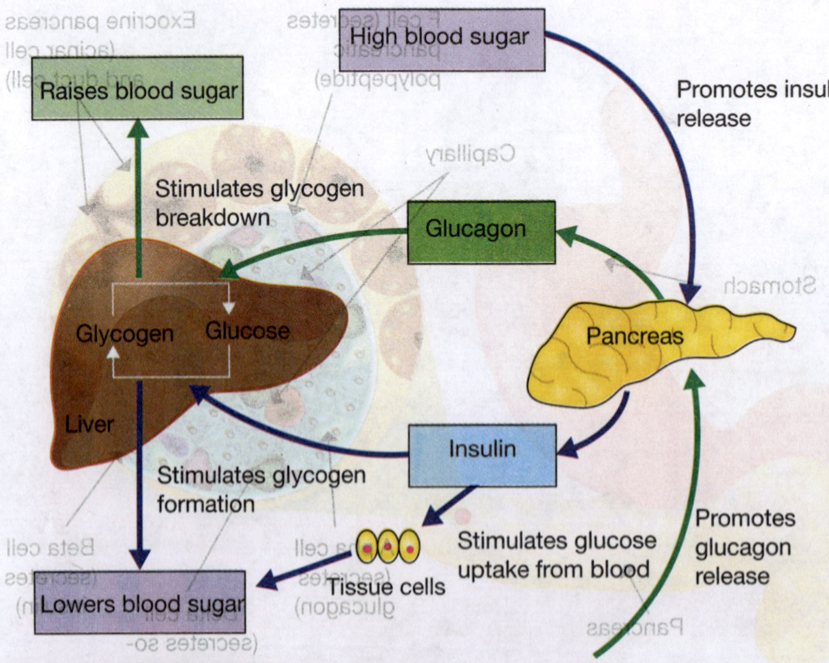

Figure 8.20 Role of hormones secreted by pancreas

Disorders Related to the Activity of the Pancreas

Hyperglycemia: Due to deficiency in secretion of insulin, conversion of glucose to glycogen does not take place properly, and thus, sugar level in blood increases. Sometimes, sugar is found in urine sample also.

Hypoglycemia: Excess secretion of insulin decreases sugar level in blood.

Feedback Control of Hormone Secretion

A hormone can act effectively if its concentration in the circulatory system is maintained in the normal range. Deviation from the normal range affects the body severely. The secretion of a hormone takes place in response to chemical stimuli and its secretion can be inhibited by the hormone itself.

Example 1

Let us take a look at the following points to understand this example.

- An increase in the concentration of glucose in plasma stimulates the secretion of insulin from pancreas.
- Release of insulin decreases the concentration of glucose in the blood.
- This condition leads to the inhibition of secretion of insulin from pancreas.
- This closed-loop system for the inhibition of secretion of a hormone is known as negative feedback control.
- Most of the endocrine glands are under negative feedback control for maintaining their concentration in a normal range.

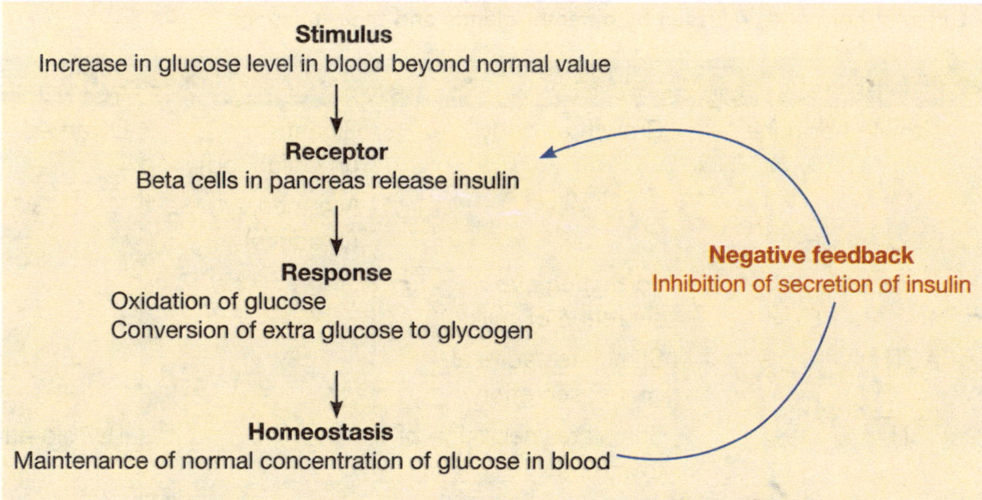

Figure 8.21 Negative feedback control of blood glucose level

Example 2

Let us take a look at the following points to understand this example.

- Metabolic need induces the hypothalamus to secrete **thyrotropin releasing hormone (TRH)**.
- TRH stimulates pituitary gland to release thyroid stimulating hormone (TSH).
- TSH stimulates thyroid gland to produce thyroxine (T4) and triiodothyronine (T3) which regulate the metabolism.
- Increase in level of T3 and T4 inhibits the secretion of TSH which in turn inhibits the secretion of TRH. Thus, this is how negative feedback control of T3 and T4 works.

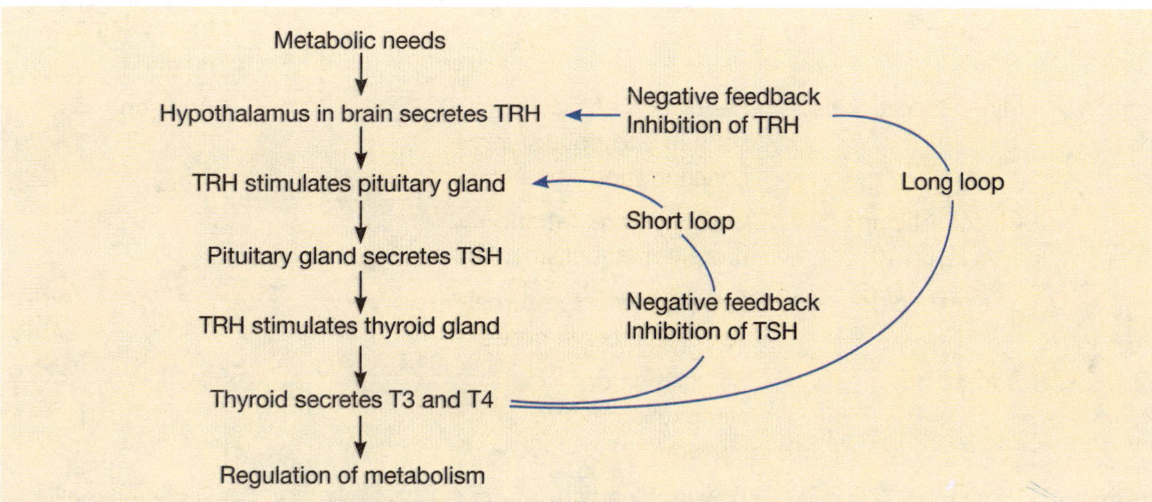

Figure 8.22 Negative feedback control of T3 and T4

Table 8.6 Different hormones released by different glands and their functions

Gland	Hormone	Function	Over-secretion	Under-secretion
Anterior pituitary	Growth hormone	Growth of body	Gigantism (in childhood) Acromegaly (in adults)	Dwarfism
	Prolactin	Formation and secretion of milk		
	ACTH	Stimulates adrenal cortex secretion		
	TSH	Stimulates secretion of thyroxine		Thyroid atrophy
	FSH	Growth of Graafian follicle in females; spermatogenesis in males		
	LH	Ovulation in females; testosterone secretion in males		
Posterior pituitary	Vasopressin	Reabsorption of water from kidneys	Increase in blood pressure	Diabetes insipidus
	Oxytocin	Contraction of uterine muscle during childbirth		
Thyroid	Thyroxine	Tissue metabolism	Exophthalmic goitre	Simple goitre, cretinism in children, myxoedema in adults
Adrenal glands	Mineralocorticoids	Regulation of plasma sodium and potassium concentration		Addison's disease
	Glucocorticoids	Carbohydrate, fat and protein metabolism		
	Sex corticoids	Development of external sex characters in males		
	Adrenaline	Stimulation of sympathetic nervous system		
Pancreas	Insulin	Lowers blood sugar level		Diabetes mellitus
	Glucagon	Increases blood sugar level		
	Somatostatin	Inhibits secretion of glucagon and insulin		

Control and Coordination in Plants

In plants, coordination takes place only with the help of hormones since they do not have a nervous system. Plants respond to the stimuli such as light, gravity, chemicals, water and touch by hormonal action. Plant hormones are called phytohormones as the word, phyto means plants. In plants, a hormone is generated in one part of the plant and diffuses away to the area of action. The major functions of phytohormones are controlling growth of the plant and responding to stimuli. Five major hormones secreted in plants are as follows:

1. Auxins
2. Gibberellins
3. Cytokinins
4. Abscisic acid
5. Ethylene

Auxins and gibberellins take part in the growth of the plants. Cytokinins help in cell division. Abscisic acid inhibits growth.

The direction of the growth of different parts of the plant is controlled by hormones in response to different environmental stimuli. The movement of plants due to the growth in a particular direction as a response to the external stimulus is called tropic movement. Tropic movements can be largely divided into four types:

1. Phototropism
2. Geotropism
3. Hydrotropism
4. Chemotropism

Phototropism

Phototropism is the process of growth of the plant in response to light. Auxins play a vital role in phototropism and they are synthesized at the tip of the shoot. Whenever plant cells are stimulated by light, auxin hormone moves to the side of the shoot which is away from the light. Since auxins are involved in growth, the shady part of the shoot grows longer. Thus, shoot of the plant bends towards the light.

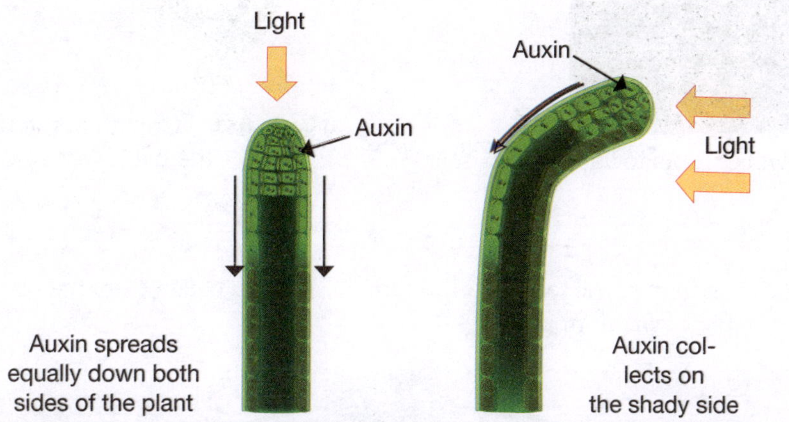

Figure 8.23 Illustration of auxins involved in plant body development

Geotropism

The movement of plant due to its growth under the influence of gravity is called geotropism. The growth of the roots takes place towards the gravity and this is an example of geotropism.

Figure 8.24 Sunflower seedling showing geotropic response a few days after being tipped over.

Info Bytes!

The growth of a pollen tube during fertilization in plants is due to chemotropism, directed by chemicals from the ovule.

Hydrotropism

The growth of the part of a plant towards water is called hydrotropism. The growth of the root towards the moist soil is an example of hydrotropism.

Figure 8.25 Growth of roots towards moist soil

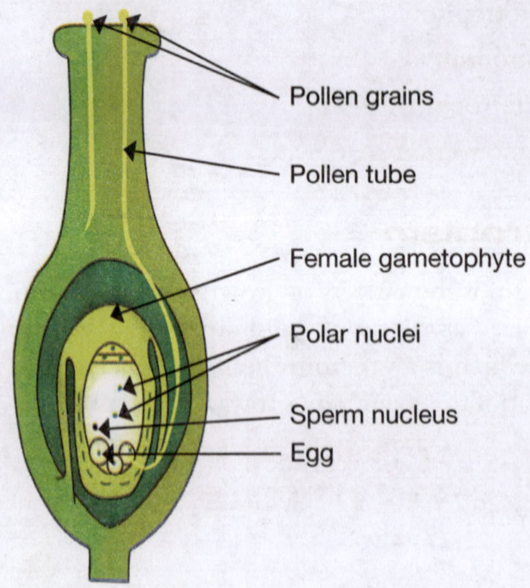

Figure 8.26 Growth of the pollen tube towards the ovule—chemotropism

Chemotropism

The movement of part of a plant in response to a chemical stimulus is called chemotropism. The growth of the pollen tube towards the ovules is an example of chemotropism.

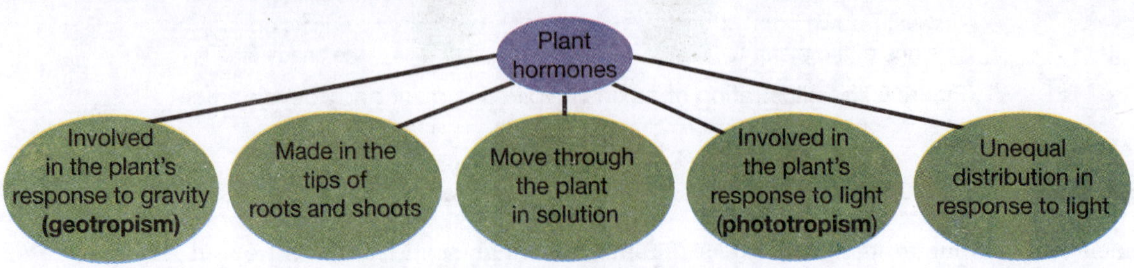

Figure 8.27 Role of plant hormones

Quick Recap

✔ **Given that all living organisms respond to stimuli, how do plant and animal responses differ fundamentally? Explain each with an example.**

Plants primarily respond to stimuli through growth movements, also known as tropisms. Phototropism, for example, is when a plant grows toward a light source. Animals, on the other hand, can respond with immediate movements, such as a cat jumping in response to a loud noise. Plants do not have muscles to move quickly, so they adapt by changing the direction of their growth. Animals, which have muscles and a more complex nervous system, can exhibit immediate and diverse responses.

✔ **What happens when the following parts of the brain are damaged due to injury?**

(a) Cerebrum

(b) Cerebellum

(c) Medulla oblongata

(a) When cerebrum is damaged, the person may lose the ability to think, analyse and make decisions. The long-term memory may also be affected in case of severe damage.

(b) When cerebellum is damaged, the motor functions may be affected because the cerebellum controls the voluntary muscle movements. The person may also find it difficult to maintain balance and posture as the main function of cerebellum is maintaining balance, equilibrium and posture.

(c) When medulla oblongata is damaged, it becomes fatal as it controls the involuntary and life supporting activities such as breathing, heartbeat, etc.

✔ **How do the nervous and endocrine systems collaborate in animals to regulate control and coordination?**

The nervous system uses electrical impulses to provide rapid, targeted responses, whereas the endocrine system uses hormones to provide slower, more widespread responses. Both systems work in tandem, with the nervous system frequently triggering endocrine responses. Animals require both the immediacy of the nervous system and the enduring effects of hormones for comprehensive coordination, ensuring a mix of quick and prolonged reactions.

✔ **Differentiate between the central and peripheral nervous systems. What role does each play in the overall functioning of the nervous system?**

The brain and spinal cord comprise the central nervous system (CNS), which is in charge of information processing and decision-making. The peripheral nervous system (PNS) connects the central nervous system (CNS) to the rest of the body, transmitting sensory and motor outputs. While the CNS serves as the primary command and control centre, the PNS serves as the communication network, ensuring that information flows smoothly throughout the body.

✔ **What distinguishes a reflex action from other types of voluntary actions? Please provide an example of a reflex action.**

A reflex action is an automatic response to a stimulus that is not prompted by conscious thought. The knee-jerk reflex, which occurs when the knee tendon is tapped, is one example. Reflex actions bypass the brain in order to provide rapid responses, instead relying on simpler neural pathways known as reflex arcs to ensure immediate responses to potential threats or specific stimuli.

✔ **Which hormone is in greater concentration in fruits and seeds? Why?**

Cytokinin is the plant hormone present in greater concentrations in the fruits and seeds. This is because of the fact that cytokinins induce cell division and are concentrated in the parts or regions where cell division takes place vigorously.

POINTS TO REMEMBER

- ✔ All living organisms have a common characteristic of responding to the changes in the surrounding environment which are called stimuli.
- ✔ The response of the plants to the stimuli is not as conspicuous as it is observed in the animals.
- ✔ The systematic involvement of different organs in order to respond to a stimulus to generate a proper response is called coordination.
- ✔ Coordination in animals involves nervous and endocrine systems.
- ✔ All voluntary activities that we perform are controlled and coordinated by the nervous system.
- ✔ Central nervous system comprises the brain and spinal cord.
- ✔ Peripheral nervous system is a complex network of nerve cells or neurons responsible for the transmission of responses.
- ✔ The structural and functional unit of nervous system is a nerve cell or neuron.
- ✔ A reflex action is an involuntary and almost instantaneous response to a stimulus.
- ✔ Endocrine system is the collection of ductless glands that secrete certain chemical substances directly into the blood.
- ✔ Hormones are chemical messengers secreted directly into the blood in response to the changes inside or outside the body and transported to organs and tissues of the body to exert their functions.

DW

PRACTICE QUESTIONS CLASSROOM WING

Very Short Answer Type Questions

Directions for questions from 1 to 14.
Fill in the blanks.

1. The responses of plants to external stimuli are not as ________ as observed in animals.
2. The periodic gaps in the myelin sheath over the axon in myelinated neurons are called ________.
3. In the absence of a stimulus, the extracellular fluid outside the neuron has a larger concentration of ________ ions.
4. Nerves that contain both sensory nerves and motor nerves are termed as ________.
5. The largest part of the brain that comprises a folded mass of the nervous tissue is called ________.
6. The ________ connects the forebrain to the midbrain.
7. Hormones are produced in ________ quantities and are effective in ________ concentration.
8. ______ and ______ are the hormones released at the time of stress by glucocorticoids.
9. Glucagon hormone is released by ______.
10. ______ and ______ hormones are secreted by thyroid gland.
11. Delta cells release ______.
12. Plant hormones are known as ______.
13. ______ is the hormone that helps in cell division in plants.
14. The process of growth of the plant in response to light is known as ______.

Directions for questions from 15 to 22.
For each of the following questions, four choices have been provided. Select the correct alternative.

15. Which of the following is NOT a function of the nervous system?
    (a) Regulation of involuntary activities like breathing
    (b) Helps us remember information
    (c) Facilitates digestion of food
    (d) Informs us about the outside world with the help of our sense organs
16. A neuron that has several dendrites is termed as:
    (a) Unipolar neuron (b) Bipolar neuron
    (c) Multipolar neuron (d) Sensory neuron
17. The change in electrical potential of an impulse along the membrane of a neuron is termed as:
    (a) Synapse (b) Dendrite impulse
    (c) Action potential (d) Stimulus response
18. What is the function of the cerebrospinal fluid?
    (a) Producing energy
    (b) Removal of waste products from the brain
    (c) Producing new nerve cells
    (d) Sending signals to the spinal cord
19. Which part of the brain regulates voluntary movements such as posture, balance, and coordination?
    (a) Cerebrum (b) Medulla oblongata
    (c) Cerebellum (d) Diencephalon
20. Which part of the brain controls autonomic functions such as regulating heart contractions and blood vessel movements?
    (a) Cerebellum (b) Medulla oblongata
    (c) Cerebrum (d) Diencephalon
21. Which of the following hormones is NOT proteinaceous?
    (a) Insulin (b) Glucagon
    (c) Aldosterone (d) Somatostatin
22. Which lobe of the pituitary gland secretes Vasopressin or antidiuretic hormone (ADH)?
    (a) Anterior lobe
    (b) Intermediate lobe
    (c) Posterior lobe
    (d) None of the above

Directions for questions 23 and 24.

Match the entries of Column 1 with those of Column 2.

23.

Column 1	Column 2
A. Synapse	(i) Cyton
B. Neuron	(ii) Cerebral peduncles
C. Hindbrain	(iii) Synaptic cleft
D. Mid brain	(iv) Pons

(a) A → (iii), B → (i), C → (iv), D → (ii)
(b) A → (ii), B → (i), C → (iv), D → (iii)
(c) A → (iii), B → (iv), C → (i), D → (ii)
(d) A → (iii), B → (i), C → (ii), D → (iv)

24.

Column 1	Column 2
A. Glucocorticoids	(i) Somatotropic hormone
B. Calcitonin	(ii) Adrenal medulla
C. Adrenaline	(iii) Thyroid gland
D. Dwarfism	(iv) Adrenal cortex

(a) A → (iv), B → (iii), C → (ii), D → (i)
(b) A → (iii), B → (i), C → (iv), D → (ii)
(c) A → (ii), B → (ii), C → (iv), D → (ii)
(d) A → (i), B → (ii), C → (iii), D → (iv)

Short Answer Type Questions

25. Describe the role of neurotransmitters in the conduction of nerve impulses.

26. What is the significance of the polarized state in a neuron?

27. What are the three layers that cover the brain and spinal cord?

28. Differentiate between grey matter and white matter in the context of the cerebrum.

29. Write in brief about olfactory lobes.

30. What are the different regions present in a neuron?

31. Explain about the transmission of electrical signals in our body.

32. Explain the type of action involved in the contraction of pupil when the eyes are exposed to the bright light.

33. What is meant by reflex action? Explain the formation of reflex arc by means of schematic diagram.

34. Differentiate among conditioned reflexes and unconditioned reflexes.

35. What kinds of movements does a germinating seed exhibit?

36. Identify the type of neurons associated with the following:

(a) Perception of fragrance of flowers
(b) Instruction to climb up a staircase
(c) Picking up a stone to throw away a dog

37. Which part of the brain keeps working even when we are sleeping? Explain.

38. Name the different endocrine glands in the human body.

39. Define hormones.

40. What do you mean by the endocrine system?

41. What is the main function of the pituitary gland?

42. Write about the structure and position of the thyroid gland.

43. Explain about the following diseases:

(a) Exophthalmic goitre
(b) Cretinism in children
(c) Goitre

44. What is the major function of phytohormones?

45. What is the position of the master gland in human body? Explain its structure.

46.

Function of the hormone	Hormone secreted
(a) Causes contraction of the uterine muscles during parturition.	
(b) Increases the blood pressure by contracting blood vessels	
(c) Stimulates the secretion of testosterone	
(d) Secretion of oestrogen	

Essay Type Questions

47. Explain the complex interplay between different types of neurons in receiving a stimulus and generating an appropriate response.

48. Discuss the importance of the cerebrospinal fluid in the central nervous system and how its imbalance can affect the functioning of the brain.

49. How does secretion of insulin vary according to the sugar level in blood?

50. Why are hormones referred to as chemical messengers?

PRACTICE QUESTIONS COMPETITION WING

Level 1: Apply your Concepts

Directions for questions from 1 to 5.
Fill in the blanks.

1. The pituitary gland controls the activity of other endocrine glands such as thyroid, adrenal, ________ and ________.
2. Pancreas is a ________ gland because it has both exocrine and endocrine parts.
3. Plants do not have a nervous system; hence they respond to stimuli such as ________ by hormonal action.
4. The movement of plants due to growth in a specific direction in response to external stimulus is called ________.
5. ________ is the process of the growth of the plant in response to light.

Direction for Questions from 6 to 15.
Choose the correct option.

(a) Both A and R are true and R is the correct explanation for A.
(b) Both A and R are true, but R is not the correct explanation for A.
(c) A is true and R is false.
(d) A is false and R is true.

6. **Assertion:** Hormones do not catalyse any reaction.
Reason: Hormones act as chemical messengers.
7. **Assertion (A):** Auxins are synthesized at the tip of the shoot.
Reason (R): The shady part of the shoot grows longer due to auxins.
8. **Assertion (A):** Action potential is generated due to the exit of sodium ions from the neuron through the plasma membrane.
Reason (R): Movement of sodium ions through the plasma membrane takes place under the influence of a stimulus.
9. **Assertion (A):** White matter of brain and spinal cord comprises axons.
Reason (R): Axon of a neuron is coated with myelin sheath.
10. **Assertion (A):** A person yelps in response to the bite of an insect.
Reason (R): Conditioned reflexes are learned by an individual through interaction with the stimuli during the lifetime.
11. **Assertion (A):** If the quantity of hormones secreted gets deviated from its normal range, our body gets affected severely.
Reason (R): The function of hormone is to stimulate or inhibit the targeted organ to act so that homeostasis of our body can be maintained.
12. **Assertion (A):** The pituitary gland is the master gland of our body.
Reason (R): The pituitary gland controls the activity of other endocrine glands such as thyroid, adrenal, ovaries and testes.
13. **Assertion (A):** Excessive thirst is a symptom of diabetes.
Reason (R): Insulin controls the water content of the body.
14. **Assertion (A):** Thyroid glands are called supra-renal gland.
Reason (R): T3 and T4 are secreted from thyroid that regulate metabolism in our body.
15. **Assertion (A):** Phototropism is the process of growth of the plant in response to light.
Reason (R): Auxins are involved in growth.

Directions for questions from 16 to 17.
For each of the following questions, four choices have been provided. Select the correct alternative.

16. Which hormone is responsible for the growth of the pollen tube towards the ovules?
(a) Auxins (b) Gibberellins
(c) Ethylene (d) None of the above
17. Which of the following tropic movements involves growth under the influence of gravity?
(a) Phototropism
(b) Geotropism
(c) Hydrotropism
(d) Chemotropism

Directions for questions from 18 to 21.

Write the missing correlated terms.

18. Dendrites: Receive Stimuli:: Axon: ________

19. Cerebrum: Cerebral cortex:: Cerebellum: ________.

20. Thyroid: Thyroxine:: Pancreas: ________.

21. Phototropism: Light:: ________: Chemicals

Level 2: Review your Concepts

22. Conduction of electrical impulse is faster in myelinated neuron than in non-myelinated neuron. Give reason.

23. Nerve impulses in axon are unidirectional. Give reason.

24. State the difference between action potential and resting potential.

25. Food tastes odd when we are suffering from cold. Give reason.

26. Head injury leading to vomiting and loss of consciousness is considered fatal. Give reason.

27. Damage on the right side of the brain leads to paralysis of the left part of the body. Give reason.

28. A drunken driver does not have complete control over the vehicle. Give reason.

29. Hypothalamus helps maintain body temperature. Give reason.

30. What is Parkinson's disease? How does it occur?

31. How does autonomic nervous system control blood pressure?

32. How does geotropism take place?

33. How does pollen tube grow towards the ovary of the flower?

34. What is the main function of thalamus and hypothalamus?

35. Identify and write the function of the different categories of the nervous system, in which the nerves connect the different organs, limbs and skin to the central nervous system.

36. What are the main functions of the long cylindrical structure that has originated from the brain and runs through the vertebral column?

37. Explain the process of gluconeogenesis.

38. What do you mean by sex corticoids?

39. Explain about the disease that is caused by the hyposecretion of the insulin hormone.

40. What role do auxins play in phototropism?

41. How does the growth of roots towards moist soil demonstrate a specific tropic movement?

42. Identify the type of neurons associated with the following:
    (a) Perception of fragrance of flowers
    (b) Instruction to climb up a staircase
    (c) Picking up a stone to throw away a dog

43. Identify the activities controlled by medulla oblongata.
    (a) Functioning of kidneys
    (b) Walking on a rope
    (c) Release of hormones into blood
    (d) Becoming alert on hearing a sudden and loud noise

44. A person who consumes more alcohol than a specified quantity cannot walk properly or cannot balance a bicycle. Give reason.

45. Running along a straight line is coordinated by cerebrum. Explain.

46. Reflex actions are controlled by brain. Explain.

47. The brain does not get easily damaged even when there is a minor mechanical injury to the head. Give reason.

48. Which part of the nervous system acts as a connecting link between the central nervous system and the various parts of the body?

Level 3: Assess Your Concepts

49. When we perceive the aroma of a delicious food, our mouth becomes watery. Explain.

50. Availability of iodized salt in the market virtually eliminated the disease, goitre. Give reason.

51. How does stress cause diabetes or hyperglycemia?

52. What is an autoimmune disease? Glucocorticoids are prescribed for treating autoimmune diseases. Give reason.

53. FSH and LH are called gonadotropins. Give reason.

54. Discuss the interrelationship between the nervous system and the endocrine system in maintaining body homeostasis.

55. How is sugar level in blood maintained by pancreas? Explain.

AT

PRACTICE QUESTIONS NEET SPECIAL WING

Multiple-Answer Type Questions

Questions number 1 to 5 are multiple-choice questions. Each question has FOUR options (a), (b), (c), and (d). ONE OR MORE THAN ONE of these four option(s) is/are the correct answer(s).

1. Which of the following statements are true regarding hormonal control of T_3 and T_4?
   (a) Hypothalamus gets stimulated to release TSH
   (b) TRH stimulates pituitary
   (c) TSH stimulates thyroid gland
   (d) Increase in the level of T_3 and T_4 inhibits secretion of TSH

2. Identify amongst the following the functions of glucocorticoids.
   (a) They are released at the time of stress
   (b) They regulate the balance of sodium and potassium ion
   (c) They decrease the rate of protein synthesis
   (d) They stimulate the formation of fat droplets from fats

3. Which of the following are unconditioned reflexes?
   (a) Yelping in response to insect bite
   (b) Feeling of hunger on smelling good food
   (c) Watering of mouth on sight of good food
   (d) Suckling of mother's breast by new born baby

4. Which of the following is true regarding conduction of nerve impulse?
   (a) Extra cellular fluid has higher concentration of sodium ions in absence of stimulus
   (b) Polarised state is when the inside of the plasma membrane of neuron is positive
   (c) Transmission of positive ion across plasma membrane of neuron takes place via active transport
   (d) Depolarization occurs due to the entry of positively charged sodium ions into the cytoplasm of the axon.

5. Which of the following are true regarding the different phytohormones?
   (a) Auxins help the shady part of the shoot to grow longer
   (b) Abscisic acid inhibits growth
   (c) Cytokinins help in cell division
   (d) Ethylene helps in fruit ripening

Comprehension-Based Questions

A. Read the paragraph given below and answer the questions number 6 to 11:

Endocrine system consists of ductless glands that secrete certain chemical substances directly into the blood. These chemical messengers are called hormones. Hormones are chemical substances secreted by stimulated cells. These hormones regulate different life processes. Main endocrine glands in our body are: Adrenal, pituitary, thyroid, thymus, parathyroid, testes (in men) and ovaries (in women). Excess or less secretions of the endocrine glands leads to various disorders in the body for example, hyposecretion of growth hormone leads to dwarfism wherein the person has short stature and slower growth of bones and other body organs.

6. Which is the hormone secreted in greatest amount by anterior pituitary?
   (a) ACTH (b) TSH
   (c) GH (d) LH

7. Which of the following hormone converts glycogen to glucose?
   (a) Glucagon (b) Insulin
   (c) Somatostatin (d) Thyroxine

8. Which of the following is not a function of thyroid hormone?
   (a) Maintenance of body temperature
   (b) Maturation of brain

(c) Controlling metabolism
(d) Increasing heart beat and blood pressure

9. The hormone which stimulates secretion of sex hormone testosterone is:
(a) FSH
(b) ICSH
(c) ACTH
(d) TSH

10. Which of the following endocrine glands is most active during emotional stimulation?
(a) Adrenal cortex
(b) Adrenal medulla
(c) Thyroid
(d) Pituitary

11. Match the column:

Column – A	Column – B
(i) Cretinism	(a) Hyposecretion of mineralocorticoids
(ii) Addison's disease	(b) Hypersecretion of Aldosterone
(iii) Acromegaly	(c) Hypersecretion of sex corticoids
(iv) Conn's Syndrome	(d) Hyposecretion of Thyroxine
(v) Adrenal Virilism	(e) Hypersecretion of growth hormone

B. Read the paragraph given below and answer the questions number 12 to 17:

The nervous system is divided into two main systems that is the central nervous system (CNS) and the peripheral nervous system (PNS). The CNS consists of the brain and spinal cord. The brain is divided into three main parts, i.e., fore brain, mid brain and hind brain. The fore brain consists of cerebrum, diencephalon and olfactory lobes. The mid brain consists of optic lobes and cerebral peduncles. The hind brain consists of cerebellum, pons and medulla oblongata. The peripheral nervous system (PNS) is further divided into the somatic nervous system and autonomic nervous system (ANS). The somatic nervous system consists of cranial nerves and spinal nerves. The ANS is further divided into sympathetic nervous system and parasympathetic nervous system.

12. The function of efferent neurons is to carry nerve impulses from:
(a) CNS to effector organs
(b) CNS to spinal cord
(c) effector organs to CNS
(d) Effector organs to spinal cord

13. Action potential is caused due to:
(a) Entry of sodium ions into the cytoplasm of axon
(b) Exit of sodium ions from the cytoplasm of axon
(c) Exit of potassium ions from the cytoplasm of axon
(d) Entry of potassium ions into the cytoplasm of axon

14. Which one of the following is the function of parasympathetic nervous system?
(a) Dilation of pupil
(b) Constriction of bronchi
(c) Inhibition of saliva secretion
(d) Contraction of sphincter of urinary bladder

15. Vomiting, coughing and sneezing are the reflexes which are controlled by:
(a) Mid brain
(b) Spinal cord
(c) Medulla oblongata
(d) Cerebellum

16. Which of the following is the function of cerebellum?
(a) controls posture and balance
(b) controls heart
(c) controls vision
(d) relays sense of smell

17. Match the column:

Column – A (Part of brain)	Column – B (Function)
(i) Frontal lobe	(a) Perceives stimuli
(ii) Occipital lobe	(b) Sense of smell
(iii) Parietal lobe	(c) Planning and reasoning
(iv) Temporal lobe	(d) Vision
(v) Olfactory lobe	(e) Speech and memory

ANSWER KEYS

Crossword

Across

3. Aldosterone 7. Oxytocin 8. Somatostatin 9. Ethylene 11. Repolarisation
15. Calcitonin 17. Chemotropism 18. Dendrites 19. Meninges 20. Glucagon

Down

1. Neurotransmitters 2. Cretinism 4. Diencephalon 5. Temporal lobe
6. Cytokinins 10. Prolactin 12. Homeostasis 13. Arachnoid 14. Pons
16. Coccygeal

Classroom Wing

Very Short Answer Type Questions

1. Conspicuous 2. Nodes of Ranvier 3. Na^+ (or sodium) 4. Mixed nerves 5. Cerebrum
6. Diencephalon 7. Small, low 8. Cortisol, Cortisone 9. Alpha cells
10. Thyroxine, Calcitonin 11. Somatostatin hormone
12. Phytohormones 13. Cytokinin 14. Phototropism 15. (c) 16. (c)
17. (c) 18. (b) 19. (c) 20. (b) 21. (c)
22. (c) 23. (a) 24. (a)

Competition Wing

Level 1: Apply Your Concepts

1. Ovaries, testes 2. Heterocrine 3. Light, gravity, chemicals, water and touch
4. Tropic movement 5. Phototropism 6. (b) 7. (a) 8. (d)
9. (b) 10. (b) 11. (b) 12. (a) 13. (c)
14. (d) 15. (b) 16. (d) 17. (b)
18. Conducts electrical impulses 19. Cerebellar cortex 20. Insulin 21. Chemotropism

NEET Special Wing

Multiple-Answer Type Questions

1. (b, c, d) 2. (c, d) 3. (a, d) 4. (a, c, d) 5. (a, b, c, d)

Comprehension-Based Questions

6. (c) 7. (a) 8. (d) 9. (b) 10. (b)
11. (i) → (d); (ii) → (a); (iii) → (e); (iv) → (b); (v) → (c)
12. (a) 13. (a) 14. (b) 15. (c) 16. (a)
17. (i) → (c); (ii) → (d); (iii) → (a); (iv) → (e); (v) → (b)

Hints and Explanations

CLASSROOM WING

Short Answer Type Questions

25. Neurotransmitters are chemical messengers that facilitate the transmission of nerve impulses. When an electrical signal reaches the axon terminal, it is converted into a chemical signal, leading to the release of neurotransmitters from synaptic vesicles. These neurotransmitters travel across the synaptic cleft and are received by the dendrite of the next neuron, where they are then converted back into an electrical signal.

26. The polarized state in a neuron refers to the condition where the electrical charge outside the plasma membrane is positive due to a higher concentration of $Na+$ ions, while the inside is negative. This resting potential indicates that the neuron is not stimulated. The polarized state is crucial for maintaining the neuron's readiness to transmit an impulse once stimulated.

27. The three layers that cover the brain and the spinal cord are the outermost dura mater, the middle arachnoid, and the innermost pia mater.

28. The grey matter in the cerebrum contains the cell bodies of neurons and appears greyish in colour, while the white matter comprises axons of the neurons.

29. A pair of olfactory lobes is located at the forebrain. They are club-shaped solid structures and are involved in the relay of sense of smell.

30. A neuron can be divided distinctly into three regions:

(a) Cell body or cyton

(b) Dendrites

(c) Axon

31. Nerve impulses are known as electrical impulses that get transmitted from one neuron to another.

(a) Neurons communicate with each other with the help of dendrites and axons.

(b) It sends the electrical impulse through axons.

(c) An electrical impulse is converted to chemical signal at the terminal of the axon. And then the chemical messengers known as neurotransmitters, are released by them.

(d) These are released into the space between the end of an axon of a neuron and the tip of the dendrite of another neuron. This space is known as synapse.

(e) The dendrite converts the chemical signals into the electrical signals. Thus, conduction of nerve impulses takes place.

32. Reflex action is contraction of pupil of the eyes when they are exposed to bright light.

(a) A reflex action is an involuntary and almost instantaneous response to a stimulus.

(b) The nerve pathway along which the impulses transmit to generate a reflex action is called reflex arc.

(c) The pathway has the following components:

(i) Stimulus—receptor perceives the stimulus

(ii) Sensory neurons—these neurons transmit the impulse to the spinal cord

(iii) Spinal cord—relay neurons connect the sensory neurons and the motor neurons in the spinal cord.

(iv) Motor neurons—these neurons send nerve impulses away from the central nervous system to the effector.

33. Reflex action can be defined as a quick and immediate response to sudden stimulus from the environment without the concern of brain. This is achieved by producing a reflex arc in the spinal cord much before the messages reach the brain.

34.

Conditioned reflexes	Unconditioned reflexes
These are the reflexes learned by an individual through interaction with the stimuli during the lifetime. These are controlled by the cerebral cortex.	These are unconscious responses to a given stimuli and they are in-born reflexes.

35. A germinating seed exhibits two kinds of movements. Lower radicle shows gravitropic and hydrotropic movements while the upper plumule shows phototropism.

36. (a) Perception of fragrance of flowers—Sensory neurons
(b) Instruction to climb up a staircase—Motor neurons
(c) Picking up a stone to throw away at a dog–Association neurons

37. Medulla oblongata keeps working continuously even when we are sleeping as it controls the involuntary activities such as digestion, blood circulation, respiration and so on.

38. The main endocrine glands in our body are as follows:
(a) Adrenal gland
(b) Pituitary gland
(c) Thyroid gland
(d) Thymus gland
(e) Parathyroid gland
(f) Testes
(g) Ovaries

39. Hormones are the chemical messengers secreted directly into the blood in response to the changes in or outside the body and transported to organs and tissues of the body to exert their function.

40. Endocrine system is the collection of ductless glands that secrete hormones directly into the blood.

41. Pituitary gland is known as the master gland. The main function of pituitary gland is to control the activities of the other endocrine glands such as thyroid, adrenal, ovaries and testes.

42. Thyroid gland appears like butterfly and is located at the base of the neck, below the larynx. There are two lobes that lie on the either side of the trachea and are connected by isthmus.

43. Diseases:
(a) **Exophthalmic goitre:** A form of hyperthyroidism that causes protrusion of eyeballs.
(b) **Cretinism in children:** Retarded physical and mental development in the childhood.
(c) **Goitre:** Swelling of the neck.

44. The major function of phytohormones are controlling the growth of the plant and responding to stimuli.

45. Pituitary gland is known as the master gland and it is situated in a bony structure in the middle of the base of the skull. Located beneath the hypothalamus, it has three lobes, namely:
(a) Anterior lobe
(b) Intermediate lobe
(c) Posterior lobe

46.

Function of the hormone	Hormone secreted
Causes contraction of the uterine muscles during parturition.	Oxytocin hormone
Increases the blood pressure by contracting blood vessels	Vasopressin or antidiuretic hormone
Stimulates the secretion of testosterone	Luteinizing hormone
Secretion of estrogen	Follicle-stimulating hormone

Essay Type Questions

47. The nervous system operates through a precise sequence of events involving various types of neurons. First, sensory or afferent neurons convert external stimuli into internal electrical impulses. These impulses are then transmitted to connector neurons located in the central nervous system. These connector neurons serve as intermediaries, processing the information and determining the appropriate response. Following this, the electrical impulses are conveyed to the motor or efferent neurons, which then transmit these impulses to muscles or organs to generate the required response. This intricate relay of information, from stimulus reception to response execution, ensures efficient and rapid coordination within the body.

48. Cerebrospinal fluid (CSF) plays a pivotal role in the central nervous system. Firstly, it acts as a cushion or buffer for the brain, providing basic mechanical and immunological protection to the brain inside the skull. Additionally, CSF serves a vital function in the cerebral autoregulation of cerebral blood flow. It provides nutrients to the nervous system and also removes waste products generated by the metabolism process in the brain. An imbalance or disruption in the production or drainage of this fluid can lead to conditions such as

hydrocephalus, where there is an excessive accumulation of CSF in the brain. This can increase intracranial pressure, leading to brain damage, and can manifest in symptoms ranging from headaches and dizziness to cognitive issues and loss of coordination. Proper maintenance and balance of CSF are crucial for the optimal functioning and health of the brain.

49. Hormones are generally secreted as per the requirement. The quantity and the time of release of a particular hormone are regulated by feedback mechanisms. When the sugar level in blood rises, it is detected by the cells of pancreas that respond to the situation by producing more amount of insulin. When the sugar level in blood falls, the secretion of insulin is reduced.

50. Hormones are the chemical substances released into blood and control the functioning of various systems of the body. These substances work in coordination with the nervous system and send instructions to the various organs to respond to the surroundings. Hence, they are called chemical messengers.

COMPETITION WING

Level 1: Apply your Concepts

6. While hormones indeed don't catalyze reactions like enzymes do, their primary role is as chemical messengers, but this doesn't explain why they don't catalyze reactions.
Hence, the correct option is (b)

7. Auxins play a vital role in phototropism and when stimulated by light, they move to the shady side of the shoot, promoting its growth.
Hence, the correct option is (a)

8. Action potential is generated due to the entry of sodium ions inside the neuron through the plasma membrane. Movement of sodium ions through the plasma membrane takes place under the influence of a stimulus.
Hence, the correct option is (d)

9. White matter of brain and spinal cord comprises axons and axons of neurons coated with myelin sheath which is white in colour.
Hence, the correct option is (b)

10. A person yelps in response to the bite of an insect and it is a reflex action controlled by the spinal cord.
Conditioned reflexes are the reflexes learned by an individual through interaction with the stimuli during the lifetime.
Hence, the correct option is (b)

11. If the quantity of hormones secreted gets deviated from its normal range, our body gets affected severely since a particular concentration of hormone in blood is required for maintaining homeostasis of our body.
The function of hormone is to stimulate or inhibit the targeted organ to act so that homeostasis of our body can be maintained.
Hence, the correct option is (b)

12. The pituitary gland is the master gland of our body since the pituitary gland controls the activity of other endocrine glands such as thyroid, adrenal, ovaries and testes.
Hence, the correct option is (a)

13. Excessive thirst is a symptom of diabetes since frequency of urination increases if a person has diabetes. Antidiuretic hormone controls the water content of the body.
Hence, the correct option is (c)

14. Adrenal gland is called suprarenal gland since this gland is located on the top of the kidneys. T3 and T4 are secreted from the thyroid which regulate metabolism in our body.
Hence, the correct option is (d)

15. Whenever plant cells are stimulated by light, auxin hormone moves to the side of the shoot which is away from the light.
Since auxins are involved in growth, the shady part of the shoot grows longer.
Thus, shoot of the plant bends towards the light.
Hence, the correct option is (b)

Level 2: Review your Concepts

22. In myelinated neurons, the exit and entry of potassium ions and sodium ions respectively take place through the nodes of Ranvier whereas it takes place throughout the axon in nonmyelinated neurons. So, action potentials are generated only at the nodes and they jump from one node to another. This phenomenon is known as saltatory conduction, and serves as a means of increasing the rate of propagation of an action potential.

23. The nerve impulses that are transmitted along the axon from one end to another end are unidirectional. When the electric signal corresponding to one impulse is passed onto the next region, the previous region which was in depolarized state gets polarized and comes back to the resting potential state. This is called repolarization. Until the completion of repolarization, the region of axon cannot receive the next impulse. This period between the depolarization and repolarization is called refractory period. Therefore, the impulse is transmitted in only one direction.

24.

Resting potential	Action potential
Resting potential is the voltage difference across the plasma membrane of the neuron when it is not transmitting the signals.	Action potential is the voltage difference across the neuron membrane when it is transmitting the signals along the axons in response to a stimulus.
More Na+ ions and less K+ ions outside the plasma membrane in the extracellular fluid when the resting potential sets in.	More Na+ and less K+ ions inside the axon when the action potential sets in.
The membrane of the neuron is said to be in the polarized state.	The membrane of the neuron is said to be in the depolarized state.

25. The olfactory receptors are present at the back of the nose, and hence, when we inhale, smell enters the back of the nose. They also rise up from the back of the mouth as we eat food. Therefore, smell is such an important part of tasting and enjoying food. When we have cold, the nasal organs become inflamed and the sense of smell is temporarily lost. As a result, food also does not taste good as we cannot relish the flavor.

26. Medulla oblongata in the brain is the main centre for cardiac, respiratory and vasomotor activities. This part of the brain coordinates reflexes such as swallowing, coughing, sneezing and vomiting. Any head injury causing damage to the medulla oblongata results in vomiting followed by the loss of consciousness. Since the life supporting activities are controlled by medulla oblongata, its damage may result in death.

27. Each side of the brain actually controls the opposite side of the body. Therefore, when right part of the brain is affected, left side of the body gets paralyzed and vice versa.

28. The cerebellum coordinates the movement of muscles. In addition of coordinating voluntary muscle movements, the cerebellum also coordinates the fine muscle movements involved in maintaining your balance. Since alcohol affects the cerebellum, a drunken driver does not have complete control over the vehicle.

29. When our hypothalamus senses that the body temperature is increasing, it sends signal to our sweat glands to generate sweat and our body temperature comes down. When hypothalamus senses that our body temperature is decreasing, it sends signals to our muscles to shiver and create warmth.

30. Parkinson's disease is a progressive degenerative disorder that affects nerve cells in deep parts of the brain. Nerve cells in a specific area in the deep part of the brain produce a type of neurotransmitter molecules called dopamine that are responsible for relaying messages that plan and control body movement. In some individuals, these dopamine-producing nerve cells get destroyed. When 80 per cent of dopamine is lost, symptoms of Parkinson's disease such as tremor, sluggish movement, stiffness and sense of imbalance take place.

31. The autonomic nervous system regulates the degree of constriction or dilation of the blood vessels in the body. Constriction of the blood vessels results in an increase in the blood pressure and dilation of the blood vessels results in a decrease in the blood pressure.

The autonomic nervous system also alters the cardiac output, which influences the blood pressure. Cardiac output is determined by multiplying the heart rate with the stroke volume. The stroke volume is the amount of blood ejected from the heart with each beat. The sympathetic nervous system increases the heart rate and the strength of heart contraction leading to a greater stroke volume.

This increased cardiac output results in an elevation in the blood pressure. The parasympathetic nervous system decreases heart rate and stroke volume. The two antagonistic actions maintain the blood pressure.

32. There is a root cap at the end of the root. Root cap contains specialized cells with sensors called statoliths. Statoliths allow the plants to sense gravity and expand faster in a downward direction.

33. Pollen tube grows towards the ovary since the ovary releases chemicals. In response to that chemical stimulus, growth of pollen tube takes place towards the ovary.

34. Thalamus: It relays motor and sensory signal to the cerebrum.

Hypothalamus: it actually links the nervous system to the endocrine system and controls pituitary gland. It helps in maintaining the body temperature, blood pressure, thirst, etc.

35. Peripheral nervous system comprises nerves that connect different organs, limbs and skin to the central nervous system.

It is divided into two categories based on their functions. They are as follows:

(a) Somatic nervous system: The nerves in this system are classified into two types:
   (i) Cranial nerves
   (ii) Spinal nerves

(b) Autonomic nervous system—It controls and regulates the internal organs without any conscious effort by the human body.

36. The long cylindrical structure that is originated from the brain and runs through the vertebral column is the spinal cord. The functions of spinal cord are:

(a) It controls reflexes below the neck.

(b) Sensory impulses from the skin and the muscles are transmitted to the brain through the spinal cord.

(c) It transmits motor responses from the brain to the muscles of the trunk and the limbs.

37. Gluconeogenesis is the process of synthesis of glucose from no carbohydrate source, and hence, they maintain glucose homeostasis.

38. Sex corticoids are the cortical hormones secreted by the adrenal cortex. They stimulate the development of the secondary sexual characteristics in males and females.
   (a) In males:
      - Broadening of shoulders
      - Change in voice
      - Growth of beard and moustache
   (b) In females:
      - Development of breasts
      - Starting of the menstrual cycle.

39. Hypersecretion of the insulin leads to hypoglycemia.
   (a) In this disease, excess secretion of the insulin decreases sugar level in the blood.
   (b) Drastic fall in the sugar level may lead to the condition of coma.

40. Auxins play a vital role in phototropism by getting synthesized at the tip of the shoot. When plant cells are stimulated by light, the auxin hormone moves to the side of the shoot that's away from the light, resulting in the shady part of the shoot growing longer and the shoot bending towards the light.

41. The growth of roots towards moist soil demonstrates hydrotropism. Hydrotropism refers to the growth of a part of the plant in the direction of water, and in this case, the moist soil provides the necessary water stimulus.

42. (a) Perception of fragrance of flowers—sensory neurons
   (b) Instruction to climb up a staircase—motor neurons
   (c) Picking up a stone to throw away at a dog –association neurons

43. Functioning of kidneys and release of hormones into the blood are the involuntary activities, and hence are controlled by the medulla oblongata.

44. Consumption of alcohol by a person affects the cerebellum of the brain. Since the cerebellum is responsible for carrying out the function of maintaining balance and body posture along with motor functions, the person loses balance and cannot walk steadily or balance a bicycle.

45. Running along a straight line is coordinated by cerebellum.

46. Reflex actions are controlled by the spinal cord.

47. Brain is composed of a soft and delicate tissue. However, it is enclosed in a hard bony structure called cranium. Protective membranes called meninges are also present in the space between the cranium and brain. Additionally, a fluid called cerebrospinal fluid fills the spaces between the meninges. This fluid provides protection for the brain by absorbing the mechanical shocks. Hence, the brain does not get damaged by minor mechanical injury to the head.

48. Peripheral nervous system forms a connecting link between the various organs of the body and the central nervous system.

Level 3: Assess Your Concepts

49. It is a reflex action.

    The stimulus: Aroma of the food is the stimuli.

    Recepor: Nose is the receptor.

    Sensory neurons: These neurons in the nose transmit the impulse to the spinal cord.

    The spinal cord: Relay neurons (present in the brain and the spinal cord) connect the sensory neurons and the motor neurons in the spinal cord.

    Motor neurons: These neurons send nerve impulses away from the central nervous system to the effector. Here the effectors are salivary glands. Salivary glands secrete saliva and our mouth becomes watery.

50. Our body does not generate iodine. Iodine intake must take place through our diet.

    Thyroid cells are the only cells in the body that can absorb iodine. These cells combine iodine and the amino acid, called tyrosine to make T3 and T4 hormones. Goitre is a disease that occurs due to the hyposecretion of thyroxine (T4). Hyposecretion of thyroxine takes place due to deficiency of iodine. Salt is used in our daily meal. Iodine is added to the salt in the form of iodized salt. Thus, deficiency of iodine in our body can be replenished.

51. Whenever we are under stress, our body prepares to release stress. The adrenal gland secretes adrenaline hormones to cope with the stress. Adrenaline hormones trigger the release of glucose in the blood. If somebody is under stress for a long period, the sugar level in the blood remains high which eventually results in diabetes.

52. An autoimmune disease is a condition in which our immune system mistakenly attacks your body. The immune system normally guards against pathogens like bacteria and viruses. When it senses these foreign invaders, it generates antibody to fight against the diseases. Normally, the immune system can understand the

difference between foreign cells and our own body cells. In an autoimmune disease, the immune system releases proteins called autoantibodies that attack healthy cells. Glucocorticoids suppress immunity by reducing the number of eosinophils and lymphocytes that form antibodies. Hence, it is used to treat autoimmune diseases.

53. Gonads are the organs that produce gametes like a testis or an ovary.

Gonadotropins are hormones that stimulate gonads to secrete hormones required for reproduction.

The following are the functions of FSH and LH:

Hormone	Functions
Follicle Stimulating Hormone (FSH)	**In females** • Stimulates the growth of Graafian follicle and secretion of estrogen hormone **In males** • Controls the production of sperms
Luteinizing Hormone (LH)	**In females** • Stimulates ovulation • Stimulates formation of corpus luteum and secretion of progesterone hormone **In males** • It is called interstitial cell stimulating hormone (ICSH) • Stimulates secretion of testosterone hormone

Hence, FSH and LH are called gonadotropins.

54. The nervous and endocrine systems are two primary systems that work in tandem to regulate and maintain body functions. The nervous system responds quickly to immediate changes by sending rapid electrical impulses. In contrast, the endocrine system acts by sending out chemical messengers called hormones, which may have prolonged effects. For instance, the secretion of many hormones is regulated by the nervous system. The hypothalamus, a part of the brain, directly links the two systems by sending signals to the pituitary gland to release specific hormones. These hormones can then stimulate other glands to produce their hormones. Additionally, feedback mechanisms exist, where the level of certain hormones in the blood can affect their further release. Through these intricate interactions, the body achieves a state of balance or homeostasis.

55. Glucagon secreted by pancreas converts glycogen to glucose, thus, raises blood sugar level. Beta cells in pancreas secrete insulin which initiates deposition of extra glucose in the form of glycogen in liver and muscles. Thus, it lowers blood sugar level and increases oxidation of glucose to release energy.

NEET SPECIAL WING

Multiple-Answer Type Questions

1. The various steps in secretion of T_3 and T_4 are as follows: Metabolic need induces the hypothalamus to secrete TRH.
   TRH stimulates pituitary gland to release thyroid stimulating hormone (TSH).
   TSH stimulates thyroid gland to produce thyroxine (T_4) and triiodothyronine (T_3) which regulate the metabolism.
   Increase in level of T_3 and T_4 inhibits the secretion of TSH which in turn inhibits the secretion of TRH. Thus, this is how negative feedback control of T_3 and T_4 works.
2. Regulation and maintenance of ratio of sodium and potassium ions is brought about by mineralocorticoids and not a function of glucocorticoids. Catecholamines are released at the time of stress.
3. Unconditional reflexes are unconscious responses to a given stimuli and they are inborn reflexes. For example, suckling of mother's breast by a new born baby, and yelping of a person in response to the bite of an insect, et
4. In the absence of a stimulus, the extracellular fluid outside the neuron possesses larger concentration of Na^+ ions. Due to this, the electrical charge outside the plasma membrane is positive. The charge is negative inside the plasma membrane of the neuron. This condition is called polarized state.
5. Whenever plant cells are stimulated by light, auxin hormone moves to the side of the shoot which is away from the light. Since auxins are involved in growth, the shady part of the shoot grows longer. Thus, shoot of the plant bends towards the light. Besides this auxin and gibberellin take part in the growth of the plants. Cytokinins help in cell division. Abscisic acid inhibits growth.

Comprehension-Based Questions

A.

6. Growth hormone is the most abundant hormone produced by anterior pituitary. It stimulates the growth of all tissues of the body including bones and controls cell metabolism.
7. Glucagon secreted by the alpha cells of pancreas converts glycogen to glucose and raises the blood sugar level.
8. The two hormones of thyroid gland are thyroxine and calcitonin. Thyroxine controls metabolism in tissues, and thus, controls growth, influences bone ossification, maintains body temperature and maturation of brain. Calcitonin regulates concentration of calcium in blood and participates in phosphorous metabolism.
9. In males Luteinizing hormone is called as Interstitial Cell Stimulating Hormone (ICSH). It stimulates secretion of testosterone hormone.
10. Adrenal medulla secretes adrenaline (epinephrine and norepinephrine) hormones.
    They are released to cope with the stress. They increase heartbeat, blood pressure, supply of blood to the muscle. They trigger the release of glucose
11. Match the following:
    Cretinism is caused due to the hyposecretion of thyroxine. It causes retardation of physical and mental development in childhood.
    (i) (d)

    Addison's disease: It is caused by hyposecretion of adrenal cortex hormone. Deficiency of mineralocorticoids disturbs electrolytic balance, causes dehydration, leads to low blood sugar level and bronze pigmentation of skin.
    (ii) (a)

    Acromegaly results from over-secretion of growth hormone in an adult. It is characterized by abnormal increase in facial and limb bones.
    (iii) (e)

    Conn's Syndrome (Aldosteronism) is caused by excess of aldosterone which increases the sodium–potassium ratio, with increase in blood pressure due to excess retention of water. Symptoms are weakness and cramps in muscles and even paralysis.
    (iv) (b)

    Excess secretion of sex corticoids in females leads to the development of male characteristics such as beard, moustache and change in voice in the females. This condition is called adrenal virilism. Excess secretion of these hormones in early age leads to sexual maturity.
    (v) (c)

B.

12. Efferent neurons also called as motor nerves transmit impulses from the central nervous system to muscles and glands, and thus, help them to take the appropriate action. For example, trochlear nerve.

13. When the neuron is stimulated, entry of a large number of sodium ions takes place inside the neuron. At this state, the electric charge on the outside and inside of plasma membrane of the axon gets reversed. This is known as the depolarized state. Thus, depolarization occurs due to the entry of positively charged sodium ions into the cytoplasm of the axon. Then the neuron generates action potential. An action potential is the change in electrical potential of an impulse along the membrane of a neuron. Under this situation, the electrical impulses get transmitted to the adjacent location of the neuron.

14. Constriction of bronchi of lungs is brought about by the parasympathetic nervous system.

15. Medulla oblongata is the centre for controlling respiratory and circulatory systems. It controls all autonomic functions such as regulating the contractions of heart and blood vessels, digestion, sneezing, coughing, swallowing, vomiting, etc.

16. The function of cerebellum is receiving information from the sensory systems, the spinal cord and other parts of the brain. It also regulates the voluntary movements such as posture, balance, coordination, etc., and thus, balances the activities of the muscles

17. Match the following:

The function of frontal lobe is planning and reasoning. It is also involved in the expression of emotions and problem-solving. The motor nerves are present at the rear part of the frontal lobe. They receive information from other parts of the brain and ensure that the action is carried out by the body.
(i) (c)

Occipital lobe is mainly responsible for receiving the information from the retina in the eyes and processing visual information.
(ii) (d)

Parietal lobe perceives various stimuli, helps in recognition, processes the senses received by the body.
(iii) (a)

Temporal lobe processes auditory information and is associated with speech and memory.
Hence, any damage to this area can lead to memory problems and language deficiency.
(iv) (e)

A pair of olfactory lobes is located in the forebrain. They are club-shaped solid structures and are involved in the relay of sense of smell.
(v) (b)

CHAPTER

9

Genetics

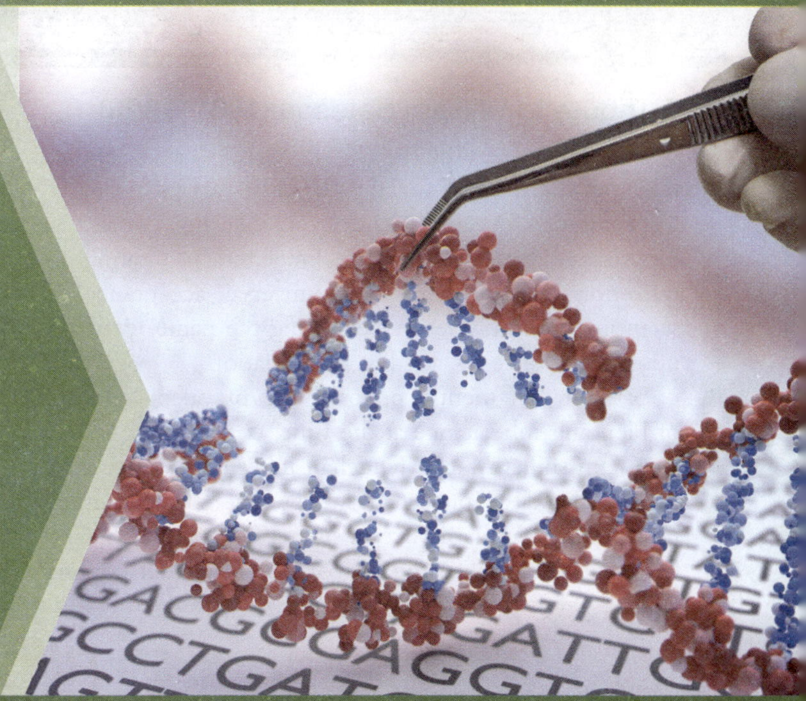

Remember

Before beginning this chapter, you should be able to:

- Differentiate asexual mode from sexual mode of reproduction
- Remember structure and function of nucleus
- Recall the DNA structure and chromosome numbers

Key Ideas

After completing this chapter, you should be able to:

- Understand the concepts of heredity and variation
- Explain Mendel's monohybrid and dihybrid crosses
- Understand the concept of sex determination
- Discuss different types of genetic disorders

A Tribute to William Bateson (1861–1926)

William Bateson (1861–1926) is regarded as a seminal figure in the field of genetics. Bateson was instrumental in bringing Gregor Mendel's pioneering work on inheritance patterns into the limelight, facilitating its transition from obscurity to universal acceptance in scientific communities by bestowing the name 'genetics' upon the science of heredity and variation.

Bateson vehemently opposed the prevalent concept of blending inheritance at the time, contributing to the paradigm shift toward Mendelian inheritance principles. He elucidated the intricate networks of hereditary units by introducing seminal concepts such as homozygosity and heterozygosity, paving the way for a deeper understanding of genetic science. His meticulous investigation into the dynamics of heredity laid the groundwork for subsequent advances in genetics and evolutionary biology.

Even in the face of widespread scepticism and opposition, his commitment to Mendelian principles was unwavering. He worked tirelessly to reconcile Mendelism with contemporary evolutionary theories, culminating in the development of a more comprehensive and cohesive framework of evolutionary genetics.

Though he did not receive a Nobel Prize, Bateson's revolutionary contributions earned him eternal respect and a place in the annals of biological sciences.

FUN TIME

CROSSWORD

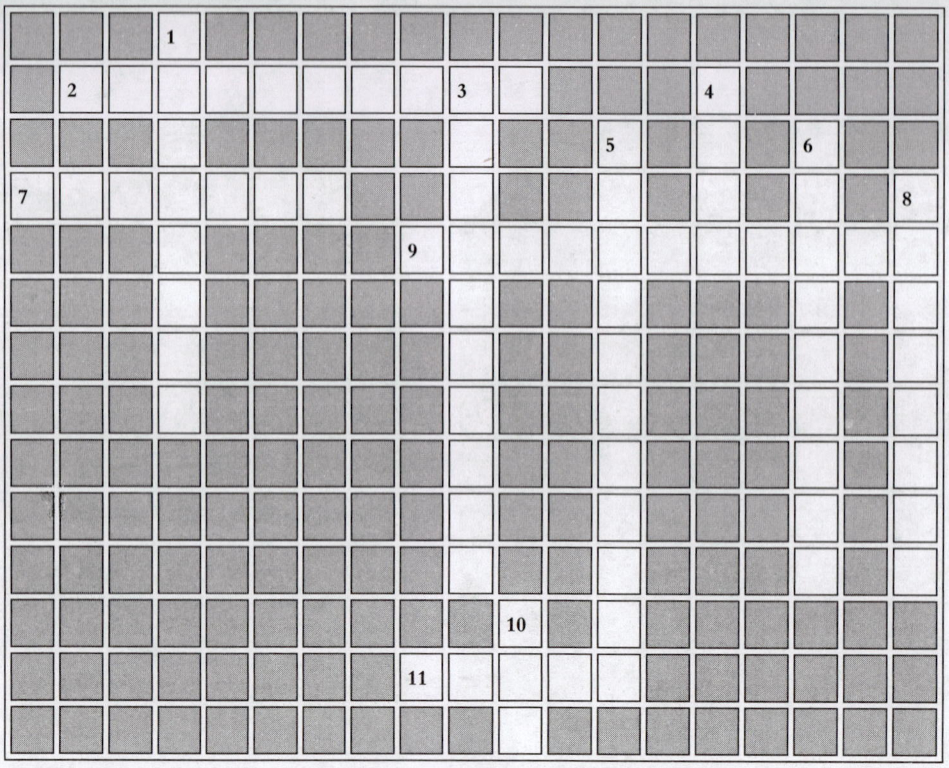

Across

2. Phenomenon where one allelic gene pair may influence more than one character
7. The contrasting forms of genes (factors) representing a particular character
9. The transmission of characters and variations along the forthcoming generations
11. The physical units of heredity

Down

1. Study of heredity and variation is called____
3. The ratio of visible features
4. The cross between the individual of the F1 generation with the recessive parent
5. Present in the nucleus of living cells, they serve as the vehicles of transmission of characters
6. The ratio of genetic features
8. Inheritance of characters from parents to the offspring
10. The molecular or chemical unit of heredity

INTRODUCTION

The branch of biology that deals with the study of heredity and variations is called genetics. The study of genetics enables us to understand how the characters of parents are transmitted to the children and then to the subsequent generations. Genetics also helps us to understand how and why individuals of the same species show variations in their characters. The progress of genetics have resulted in major advancements in various fields such as agriculture, medicine, forensic science, and so on. Though genetics is relatively a new branch of science, yet it is considered as the most important area of science that leads to dramatic breakthrough in the modern world as it contributed to the transformation of society in a big way.

Heredity and Variation

Table 9.1 Contributors in the field of genetics

Scientist	Year	Contribution
Gregor Johann Mendel	1865	Breeding experiments on garden pea; laws of heredity; Father of genetics
Hugo de Vries	1886	Mutations
J. Kolreuter and F. Galton	1883	Quantitative inheritance
Sutton and Boveri	1902–1903	Chromosome theory of inheritance
Thomas Hunt Morgan	1908	Genetic experiments on fruit fly (*Drosophila melanogaster*); Father of experimental genetics
H.G. Khorana	1960s	Synthesis of artificial gene
W. Bateson	1905	Coined the term 'genetics'

Reproduction is the process by which all the living organisms produce their offspring. The characters are passed on from one generation to the next by this process. Asexual mode of reproduction produces offspring that are almost exactly similar to the parents. They show very little differences from their parents. As only one parent is involved in asexual mode of reproduction, their offspring are called clones. The clones produced inherit all the characters of the parent, and hence closely resemble the parent organism. However, in the higher organisms, sexual reproduction is the principal mode of reproduction. It results in offspring that show some differences from their parents. This degree of differences between offspring and the parents is called variation. That means, some variations are produced during the process and these variations may be transmitted from one generation to the next. This transmission of characters and variations along the forthcoming generations is known as inheritance. This phenomenon of exhibiting inheritance is called heredity.

Info Bytes!

The word 'genetics' originated from the Greek word 'genesis' that means to grow into or to become.

Heredity results in some resemblances and differences between the parents and their offspring. The characters that are transmitted to the succeeding generations are called inherited traits. Some commonly observed inherited characters in human beings include skin colour, eye colour, hair colour, height, shape of the ear lobes, eye brows, etc. Apart from these observable features, there are certain anatomical features such as blood group that offspring inherit from their parents. Some behavioural patterns such as use of hand, pattern of walk and intelligence also seem to be inherited across the generations.

Info Bytes!

The inheritance of characters from the parents to the offspring is known as heredity.

Units of Heredity

The chromosomes present in the nucleus of living cells serve as the vehicles of transmission of characters. The chromosomes possess DNA that is the genetic material and is passed on from one generation to the next. The segment of DNA with a specific sequence of nucleotides is called gene. Hence, genes are the physical units of heredity and DNA is the molecular or chemical basis of heredity. Nucleus in the mature cells of all higher organisms contains chromatin material in the form of inter-woven network of fibres. The chromatin material consists of DNA as the genetic material. The chromatin material gets organized into chromosomes at the time of cell division. A particular species of organisms is characterized by a certain number of chromosomes as counted at the time of cell division.

Table 9.2 Number of chromosomes in selected organisms

Organism	Number of Chromosomes
Garden pea (*Pisum sativum*)	14
Fruit fly (*Drosophila melanogaster*)	6
Female Honey bee	32
Tobacco plant	48
Human beings	46

Info Bytes!

The word 'chromosome' comes from the Greek word, chrome meaning colour. Chromosomes got their name owing to being stained by dyes.

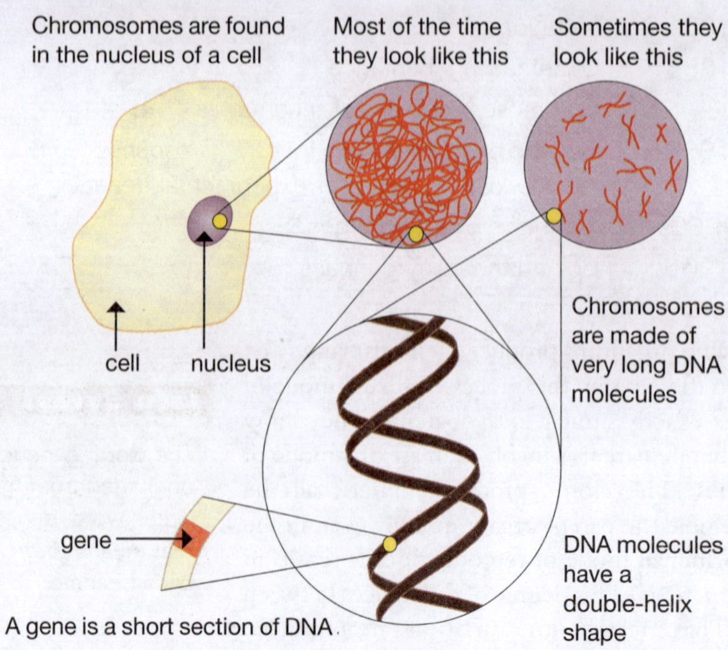

Figure 9.1 Diagram showing magnification of chromosomes and DNA in cell nucleus

Info Bytes!

The term "genetics" was coined by William Bateson in 1905.

During the interphase, the chromosomes organize themselves as pairs in each cell and are called homologous chromosomes. One from each homologous pair is derived from each parent. The chromosomes which determine the sex of an individual are termed as sex chromosomes or allosomes. The chromosomes other than sex chromosomes are called autosomes.

For example, human cell consists of 23 pairs of homologous chromosomes, that is, 22 pairs of autosomes and one pair of allosomes or sex chromosomes (XY in males and XX in females).

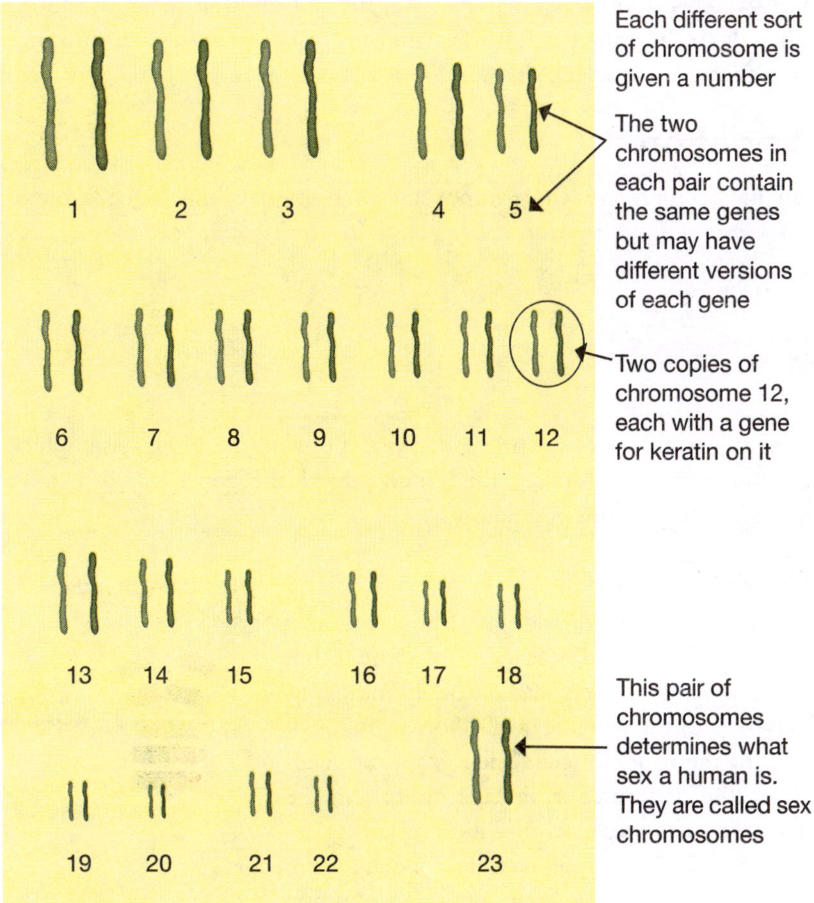

Figure 9.2 Illustration of homologous chromosome in humans

Allele

The two chromosomes in a homologous pair possess genes representing the same characters. Each character is present as a pair of contrasting traits called alleles.

For example, a particular gene represents height of the organism. There are three possible combinations of the pair of genes representing the height. These are:

1. The genes on both the chromosomes may correspond to tallness.
2. The gene on one chromosome may correspond to tallness and that on other chromosome may correspond to dwarfness.
3. The genes on both the chromosomes may correspond to dwarfness.

In this case, height of the organism is the character under consideration. The tallness and dwarfness are the contrasting traits. The genes that represent the two contrasting traits are called alleles. The distribution of chromosomes containing genes during cell division is the basis of the phenomenon of heredity.

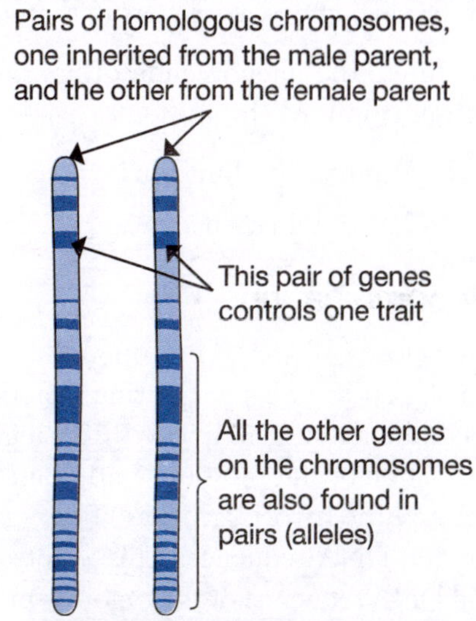

Figure 9.3 Illustration of a pair of homologous chromosome

Cell Division and Heredity

During the process of cell division, the homologous chromosomes get separated and are distributed into the daughter cells. Somatic cells in the body of an organism undergo mitotic cell divisions in order to produce daughter cells with exactly same DNA sequence. This results in the growth and development of the organism. Germ cells in the body of an organism undergo meiotic cell divisions to produce male or female gametes as the case may be. Meiosis cell division involves the distribution of homologous chromosomes of the germ cells to the gametes. This distribution of homologous chromosomes in meiotic cell division takes a different course from that in mitotic cell division. This is the basis of mechanism of heredity.

Mechanism of Variation

The mechanism of heredity basically involves three important phenomena taking place in meiotic cell division. They are:

1. DNA replication
2. Linkage and crossing over
3. Genetic recombination

DNA Replication

This takes place in the same way as in case of mitotic cell division during the interphase, which is the preparatory phase. The homologous chromosomes paired up during this phase possess the genes of both the parents. This leads to the transmission of characteristics of the previous generations.

Linkage and Crossing Over

These processes are exclusive to meiotic cell division and are responsible for inheritance of some characteristics and variation in some other characteristics. In meiotic cell division, all the genes on the homologous chromosomes are not transmitted to the daughter cells. Some groups of genes are together passed on to the daughter cell. Such group of genes that is normally inherited together is termed as linkage group and the genes are called linked genes. The phenomenon in which certain genes present on a chromosome are together carried on to daughter cell during meiotic cell division is called linkage. If all the genes on a chromosome are transferred, it is called complete linkage. If some of the genes are transferred, it is called incomplete linkage. Linkage is responsible for the inheritance of characters to the successive generations. Crossing over is a somewhat opposite phenomenon of linkage. The phenomenon of the exchange of segments of non-sister chromatids (genes) of homologous chromosomes is known as crossing over. Although linkage serves to preserve the characters of parental generation, crossing over gives scope for producing new characters in the successive generations.

Due to the phenomenon of linkage and crossing over, two probable combinations of chromosomes can be visualized, namely:

1. Parental combination
2. Recombination

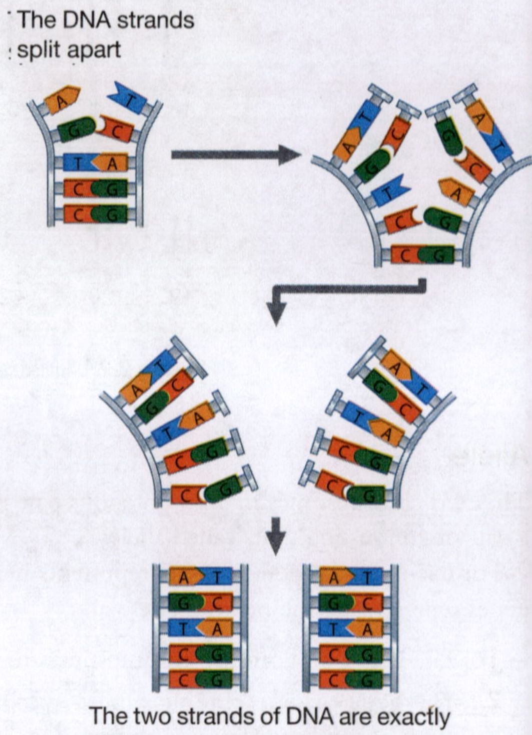

Figure 9.4 Illustration of DNA cell replication

Recombination

Linkage of all the genes on the chromosomes results in parental combination, which usually does not happen during meiotic cell division. Crossing over is generally followed by recombination. This involves exchange of genetic material between the chromosomes and formation of chromosomes with some new sets of genes in the daughter cells. The daughter cells are the haploid gametes. These gametes undergo gametic fusion to form zygote with unique DNA sequence. This zygote undergoes repeated mitotic cell divisions in which the DNA sequence of the zygote is preserved. Consequently, the new organism (offspring) formed has a DNA sequence unique to itself and is considerably different from the parents. The new characters that are acquired by the offspring due to the new genetic combination are called variations. Therefore, linkage is responsible for parental combination.

Info Bytes!

Independent assortment during meiosis and the fusion of gametes at fertilization also contribute to genetic recombination and the generation of genetic diversity in offspring.

For example,

Father with dark complexion and long stature.
Mother with fair complexion and short stature.
Offspring with dark complexion and short stature is one recombination.
Offspring with fair complexion and long stature is another recombination.
Offspring with medium complexion and medium stature shows variations.

The differences existing among the individuals of a species from one generation to the next and also among the offspring of the same parents are called variations.

Mendelian Inheritance

Gregor Johann Mendel, an Augustinian priest and scientist, made a lot of progress in the study of the inheritance of various traits from one generation to the next. For this reason, he is regarded as the 'father of genetics.' Mendel conducted various experiments to study the mechanism of inheritance from parents to offspring by choosing pea plant (*Pisum sativum*) as the experimental material.

Figure 9.5 Gregor—Johann Mendel 'Father of Genetics'

Reasons for Choosing Pea Plants for Mendel's Experiments

Mendel had selected pea plant for various reasons listed below.

- Easy cultivation of pea plants
- Pea is an annual plant that gives results within a year
- Pea plant is normally self-pollinated, however, it could be cross-pollinated by removing male and female reproductive parts.
- Large number of varieties with observable alternative forms for a trait in pea plants are available with a number of contrasting traits. This makes it convenient for taking plants with various contrasting features and studying the transmission of those traits to the next generations.

Mendel's Experiments

Mendel selected pea plants having one or two of the contrasting traits and conducted the experiments. According to Mendel, one of the contrasting traits was considered to be dominant and the other one to be recessive. According to

Mendel, the contrasting traits are carried by factors that are now called genes. The dominant trait of each character is represented by the first letter of that trait with capital letter. Recessive traits of each character are represented by indicating them with small letters of the corresponding letter for the dominant trait.

Table 9.3 Seven pairs of contrasting features of garden pea

	Dominant factor		Recessive factor	
Character	**Trait**	**Representation**	**Trait**	**Representation**
Stem height	Tall	T	Dwarf	t
Flower colour	Purple	P	White	p
Flower position	Axial	A	Terminal	a
Pod colour	Green	G	Yellow	g
Pod shape	Full	F	Constricted	f
Seed colour	Yellow	Y	Green	y
Seed shape	Round	R	Wrinkled	r

Table 9.4 Description of genes and alleles

Dominant allele		Recessive allele	
Definition	**Example**	**Definition**	**Example**
The gene corresponding to the trait that expresses itself even in the presence of the gene for the contrasting trait as it masks and hides the other trait	• Purple colour of flowers is the dominant trait • P represents dominant allele	The gene corresponding to the trait that fails to express itself in the presence of the gene representing its contrasting dominant trait	• White colour of flowers is the recessive trait • p represents the recessive allele
Homozygous		**Heterozygous**	
Definition	**Example**	**Definition**	**Example**
An organism having the same alleles that represent either both dominant traits or both recessive traits	RR, rr	An organism having contrasting factors or alleles representing contrasting traits (one dominant allele and one recessive allele)	Rr

Terminology Related to Genetics in Mendel's Experiments

Alleles: The genes (factors) representing a particular character having their contrasting forms are called alleles. The alternative forms of a character are called contrasting traits.

Pure breed: The variety of individuals in which a particular character remains unchanged in large number of successive generations.

Cross: A mating between two individuals leading to the fusion of gametes.

Table 9.5 Description of cross

Monohybrid cross		Dihybrid cross	
Definition	**Example**	**Definition**	**Example**
The crossing of plants considering one pair of contrasting characters	**TT × tt**	The crossing of plants with two pairs of contrasting characters	**TTRR × ttrr**

Phenotype: It is the expressed or observable characteristics of an organism. For example, plant with purple flowers with both genes for purple; one gene with purple and one gene for white flowers.

Genotype: The actual genetic constitution of an organism is its genotype. For example, PP type purple flowers; Pp type purple flowers

Mendel performed experiments in three stages:

1. Selection of pure or true breeding parents (Parental [P1] generation) obtaining first generation plants (First filial or F1 generation)
2. Self-pollination of F1 plants to get subsequent generations (F2, F3, etc.)
3. Hybridization to produce hybrid which is the offspring produced by a cross between the individuals of same species that differ from each other at least in one character.

Mendel's Monohybrid Cross

Pea plants with one pair of contrasting features are chosen and allowed to undergo self-pollination between them. This constitutes P1 parental generation). Since the plants of P1 generation are produced by self-pollination, they possess factors (genes) for either dominant or recessive traits.

For example, **P1** generation—Plant with purple flowers (PP) and plant with white flowers (pp). Purple colour of flower is a dominant trait. White colour of flower is a recessive trait.

F1 generation—Cross-pollination between purple-flowered plant and white-flowered plant resulted in all purple-flowered plants. But these are hybrid plants with one factor for dominant trait and one factor for recessive trait (Pp).

F2 generation—Self-breeding of F1 hybrid plants resulted in some purple-flowered plants and some white-flowered plants.

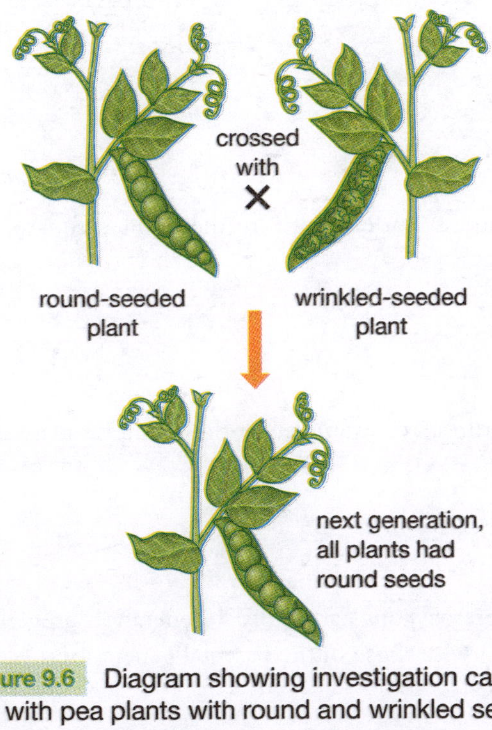

Figure 9.6 Diagram showing investigation carried out with pea plants with round and wrinkled seeds

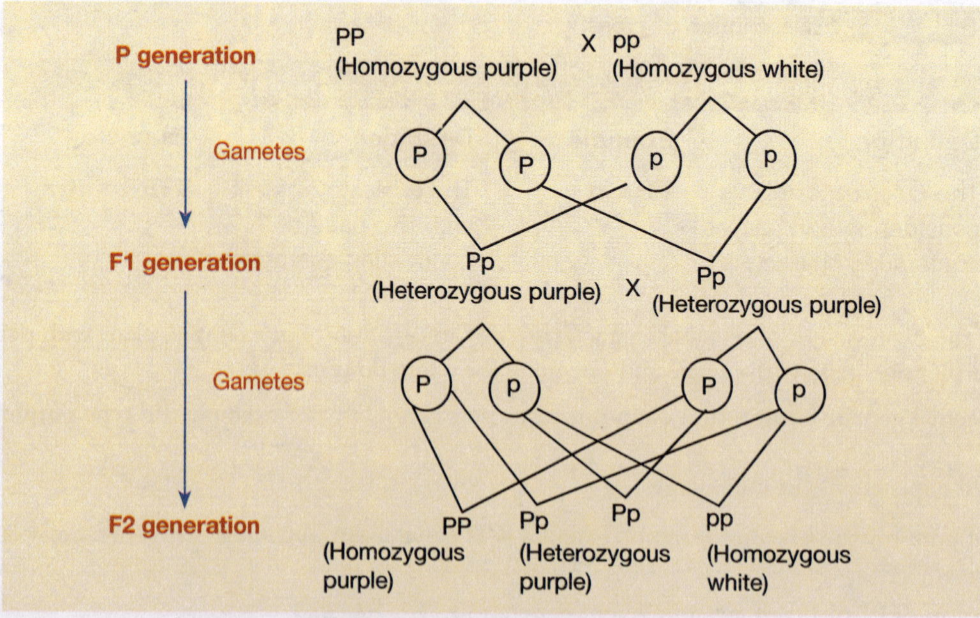

Figure 9.7 Monohybrid cross

Representation of Mendel's Monohybrid Cross by Checker Board (Punnett Square)

A Punnett square is a diagram that represents gametes of the concerned traits. Gametes of one parent are placed along one side and those of another parent are placed on the other side. In the sub-squares, possible combinations of genotypes are mentioned. The resulting phenotypes are mentioned under the respective genotype.

Table 9.6 Representation of a monohybrid cross

X	P (Dominant)	p (Recessive)
P	PP (Purple)	Pp (Purple)
p	Pp (Purple)	pp (White)

Phenotypic Ratio

Phenotypic ratio is the ratio of visible features. For example, for the Punnett square drawn above, phenotypic ratio is 3:1.

- 3 plants with purple flowers
- 1 plant with white flowers

Genotypic Ratio

Genotypic ratio is the ratio of genetic features. For example, for the Punnett square drawn above, genotypic ratio is 1:2:1.

- 1 homozygous purple-flowered plant
- 2 heterozygous purple-flowered plants
- 1 homozygous white-flowered plant

In order to test the homozygous or heterozygous nature of F1 generation progenies, Mendel performed experiments involving the crossing of the progeny (F1) with those of the parental generation.

Verification of Genetic Constitution of Progenies of F1 Generation

Back cross: The cross between the individual of F1 generation with either of the parents is known as back cross.

Test cross: The cross between the individual of F1 generation with the recessive parent is known as test cross.

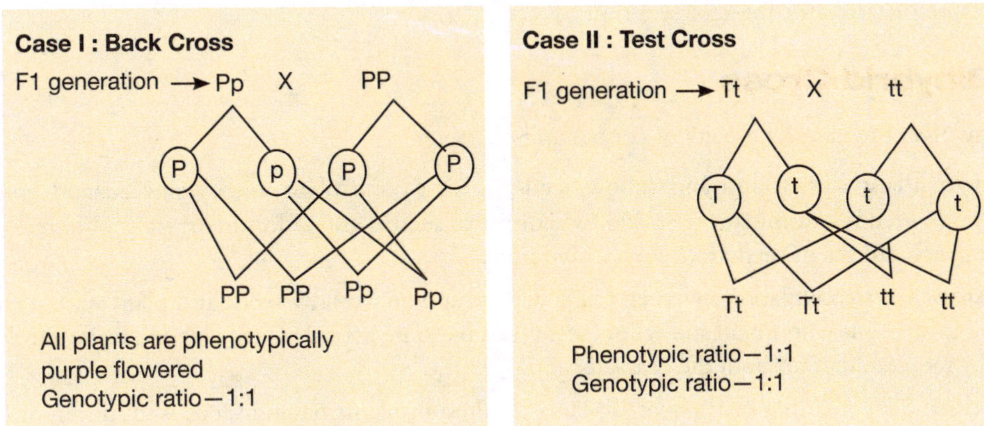

Figure 9.8 Back cross and Test cross

		Back Cross	
		Parental gametes	
F1 Gametes		P (Dominant)	P
	P	PP (Purple)	PP (Purple)
	p	Pp (Purple)	Pp (Purple)

		Test Cross	
		Parental gametes	
F1 Gametes		t (Recessive)	t (Recessive)
	T	Tt (Tall)	Tt (Tall)
	t	tt (Dwarf)	tt (Dwarf)

Reciprocal Cross

A second cross of the same genotypes in which the sex of the individuals is reversed is known as a reciprocal cross.

	Male	Female	Offspring
Original cross	Tall (TT)	Dwarf (tt)	Tt
Reciprocal cross	Dwarf (tt)	Tall (TT)	Tt

Conclusions Drawn by Mendel on the Basis of Monohybrid Cross

On the basis of the results obtained for monohybrid cross, Mendel proposed three postulates. The latter two postulates are popularly known as Mendel's laws of inheritance.

Principle of paired factors: The inheritance of each character in an organism is controlled by two factors (genes) that lie on two homologous chromosomes and represent the same or alternative form of the same character (alleles).

Principle of dominance: When two contrasting factors are present in an organism, one of them may mask the presence of the other. The factor that expresses itself in the hybrid is called dominant allele and the factor that fails to express itself in the presence of dominant factor is called recessive allel.

Principle of segregation or purity of gametes: The two alternative factors of pair representing a character are separated from each other at the time of gamete formation, and hence, a gamete contains only one factor for the character.

Illustration

- P generation plants have same factors, and hence produce gametes with same factors (P or p).
- All F1 generation plants have purple flowers even though one of the parent plants has white flowers. That means, the factor or gene for the dominant trait is expressed out, and hence white colour is masked. However, all the plants possess the gene or factor for the recessive trait.

Mendel's Dihybrid Cross

A dihybrid cross involves breeding two pairs of contrasting characters.

- **P generation**: Plant with round and yellow seeds (RRYY) and plant with wrinkled and green seeds (rryy). Round shape of seed is a dominant trait. Yellow colour of seed is also a dominant trait. Whereas, wrinkled shape of seed and green colour of seed are the recessive traits.
- **F1 generation**: Cross-pollination between plant with round and yellow seeds and plant with wrinkled and green seeds resulted in all plants with round and yellow seeds. But these are hybrid plants with one factor for dominant trait and one factor for recessive trait for both the characters.
- **F2 generation**: Self-breeding of F1 hybrid plants resulted in plants having seeds with different combinations of traits.

Representation of Mendel's dihybrid cross by Checker Board (Punnett Square)

Phenotypic Ratio

Phenotypic ratio for dihybrid cross in F2 generation—9:3:3:1

9 Plants	Round and Yellow seeds
3 Plants	Round and Green seeds
3 Plants	Wrinkled and Yellow seeds
1 Plant	Wrinkled and Green seeds

Info Bytes!

Mendel carried out his experiments on nearly 30,000 pea plants over seven years, meticulously tracking each generation's traits.

Genotypic Ratio

Genotypic ratio for dihybrid cross in F2 generation—1:2:1:2:4:2:1:2:1

1 Plant	Homozygous Round and Homozygous Yellow
2 Plants	Homozygous Round and Heterozygous Yellow
2 Plants	Heterozygous Round and Homozygous Yellow
4 Plants	Heterozygous Round and Heterozygous Yellow
1 Plant	Homozygous Round and Homozygous Green
2 Plants	Heterozygous Round and Homozygous Green
1 Plant	Homozygous Wrinkled and Homozygous Yellow
2 Plants	Homozygous Wrinkled and Heterozygous Yellow
1 Plant	Homozygous Wrinkled and Homozygous Green

Conclusion Drawn by Mendel on the Basis of Dihybrid cross

Principle of independent assortment: If inheritance of two or more allele pairs at a time is considered, their distribution in the gametes and in the subsequent generations takes place independent of each other.

Illustration

- All the plants of F1 generation produced Round and Yellow seeds since they are the dominant traits. But they were hybrid plants and possessed factors or genes for recessive traits also.
- In F2 generation, the plants obtained on self-pollination have different combinations, which proved that both the traits of the two characters are assorted independently, and hence plants with different kinds of seeds are produced.

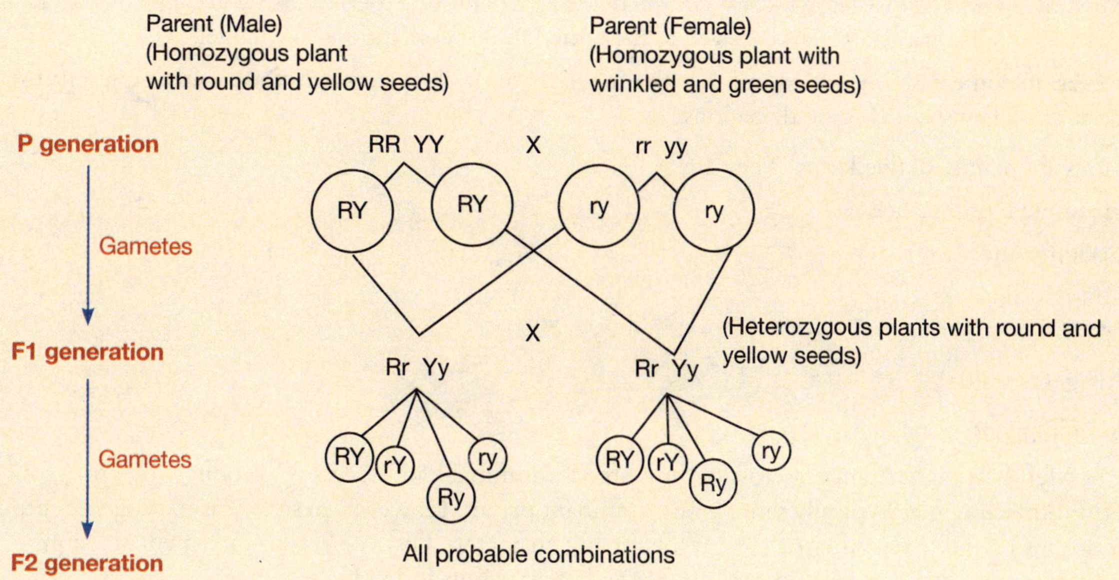

All probable combinations

RY	X	RY	→	RRYY	Ry	X	RY	→	RRYy
RY	X	rY	→	RrYY	Ry	X	rY	→	RrYy
RY	X	Ry	→	RRYy	Ry	X	Ry	→	RRyy
RY	X	ry	→	RrYy	Ry	X	ry	→	Rryy
rY	X	RY	→	RrYY	ry	X	RY	→	RyYy
rY	X	rY	→	rrYY	ry	X	rY	→	rrYy
rY	X	Ry	→	RrYy	ry	X	Ry	→	RrYy
rY	X	rY	→	rrYy	ry	X	ry	→	rryy

	Female gametes				
	X	**RY**	**rY**	**Ry**	**ry**
Male gametes	RY	RR YY	Rr YY	RR Yy	Rr Yy
	rY	Rr YY	rrYY	Rr Yy	rr Yy
	Ry	RR Yy	RrYy	RR yy	Rr yy
	ry	Rr Yy	rr Yy	Rr yy	rr yy

Figure 9.9 Dihybrid cross

Applications of Mendel's Laws of Inheritance

Mendel's Laws of Inheritance find applications in understanding various concepts of genetics. Some of them are as listed below:

- New ideas regarding the new combination of hybrids could be generated.
- Innovation of techniques of plant breeding and animal breeding for producing new breeds with desired traits.
- Production of new varieties of plants with new combinations.

Deviations from Mendel's Laws

Following are some of the demerits of Mendel's Laws of Inheritance:

- Mendel's laws were postulated much before the discovery of gene and DNA as the basis of inheritance. However, they were rediscovered by some scientists such as Hugo de Vries and others in the later period and then republished in a book called Flora.

- Scientist by name Thomas Morgan also conducted similar kind of experiments by taking fruit fly (*D. melanogaster*) instead of Mendel's garden pea and arrived at the same kind of conclusions as Mendel.
- However, in some cases, it was found that the inheritance of characters did not exactly represent the Mendelian inheritance. They showed some deviations.

The deviations are mainly of five kinds. They are as follows.

1. Incomplete dominance
2. Codominance
3. Multiple allele series
4. Pleiotropy
5. Polygenic traits

Incomplete Dominance

According to Mendelian inheritance, a cross of pure breeds (dominant and recessive) produces heterozygous individuals (F1 generation) that are phenotypically same as the dominant parent. However, in some cases, progenies produced in F1 generation do not resemble to either of the parents in any character. That means, an intermediate expression between the dominant and recessive traits is expressed out in the heterozygous individuals.

For example, Snapdragon and 4 o'clock plant : Two types of pure breeds – Red flowers
White flowers

P generation	————	Red flowered RR	**X**	White flowered (Cross-pollination) rr
F1 generation	————	Pink flowered Rr	**X**	Pink flowered (self-pollination) Rr
F2 generation	————	RR Red flowered	Rr Pink flowered	rr White flowered

Figure 9.10 Cross for incomplete dominance

Figure 9.11 Illustration of incomplete dominance

A cross of pure breeds of red-flowered (dominant) and white-flowered (recessive) plants produces all heterozygous progenies with pink-coloured flowers. Pink colour of flower is an intermediate expression between red colour and white colour of flower. The white colour of flower, which is a recessive trait, is expressed out in F2 generation just as in case of Mendelian monohybrid cross. However, the phenotypic ratio in this case is same as the genotypic ratio, that is, 1:2:1. The homozygous individuals possess red colour flowers as in P generation. But the heterozygous individual possesses pink colour as in F1 generation hybrids. The above results indicate that the dominant gene corresponding to red colour of flower shows incomplete dominance resulting in an intermediate expression of character.

Codominance

According to Mendelian inheritance, F1 generation individual resembles the dominant parent phenotypically and contains a recessive gene that is not expressed out. However, in some cases, the F1 generation individual resembles both the parents. That means, in heterozygous condition, the recessive gene also expresses itself along with the dominant gene. Such a phenomenon is called codominance. For example, presence of A; B; O blood groups in humans. The type of the blood group is controlled by the gene 'I' that has three allelic forms, namely I^A; I^B; i. Alleles I^A and I^B produce different types of sugars and allele 'i' does not produce any sugar. I^A and I^B are completely dominant and 'i' is totally recessive and does not express itself in the presence of either I^A or I^B. When both I^A and I^B are present together, they both express their own type of sugars and hence, these are codominant to each other. Since three different alleles are there, six types of genotypes and four types of phenotypes are possible.

Table 9.7 Codominance in ABO blood groups

Allelic combination from parents	Genetic constitution of offspring (genoptype)	Blood group of offspring
I^A; I^A	I^AI^A	A
I^A; I^B	I^AI^B	AB
I^A; i	I^Ai	A
I^B; I^A	I^AI^B	AB
I^B; I^B	I^BI^B	B
I^B; i	I^Bi	B
i; i	ii	O

Multiple Allele Series

A single character is usually controlled by a pair of alleles that are contrasting traits. However, if a single character is controlled by more than two allelic genes, such a condition is known as multiple alleles.

Pleiotropy

According to Mendel, one allelic gene pair controls one specific character. The gene pair that controls height of the plant controls only that character. However, in some cases, one allelic gene pair may influence more than one character. Such a phenomenon is called pleiotropy.

Examples: **1. Plants:** One allelic gene pair →
- → Colour of flower
- → Presence of red spots on leaf axils
- → Colour of seed

2. **Animals:** *Drosophila*—Gene responsible for white eye colour causes depigmentation in many parts of the body.
3. **Humans:** Sickle cell anaemia—Gene causes anemia and other problems such as muscle cramps, jaundice and kidney failure.

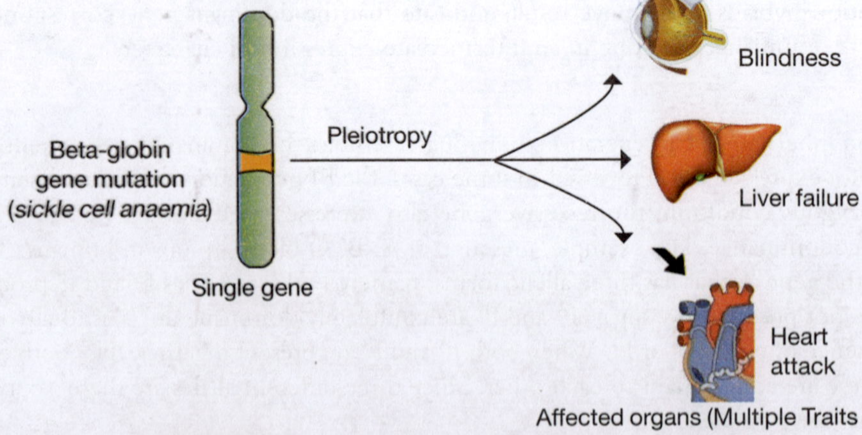

Figure 9.12 Pleiotropic effects in sickle cell anaemia

Polygenic Traits

According to Mendel, the alternative forms of a single character are controlled by a single gene pair. The intermediate forms of the dominant and recessive traits were not considered. Such kind of traits are called monogenic traits or qualitative traits. However, on observation of different characters in various organisms, it is found that there are several traits that exhibit continuous gradation of the two alternative forms of the character, under consideration. Such kind of traits are called polygenic traits or quantitative traits. These polygenic traits are controlled by more than one pair of genes and their additive effect results in individuals with a spectrum of phenotypes in contrast to monogenic traits that show clear and distinct phenotypes with contrasting traits.

Table 9.8 Some examples of polygenic traits

Plants	Animals
• Height of plant	• Skin colour in humans
• Seed size of beans	• Controlled by three pairs of genes
• Grain colour in wheat	• Human skin colour has a number of intermediate shades from dark black to white.

Applications of Genetics

Genetics not only deals with the transmission of characters and inheritance but also it has lot of practical applications in various fields such as plant breeding and animal breeding. Human genetics is a vast area that makes us understand the various genetic traits and diseases. The first and foremost application of genetics is in the determination of sex in different organisms.

Sex Determination

The sex of the progenies is determined on the basis of the inheritance or transmission of sex chromosomes to the progenies during gametic fusion. Different organisms show different kinds of sex determination mechanism depending on the nature of sex chromosomes in male and female organisms.

Types of Sex Determination

There are different types of sex determination methods depending upon the kind of organisms. Some of them are discussed below.

XX–XY Type Sex Determination

Most of the mammals and insects such as *Drosophila* show XX–XY type of sex determination. This mechanism of sex determination is called male heterogamety. The nucleus in human cell contains 46 chromosomes (23 pairs). Among these, 44 (22 pairs) are called autosomes. One pair of chromosomes is called sex chromosomes. Males possess one longer X chromosome and one shorter Y chromosome. Females possess two longer X chromosomes. During the formation of gametes, meiotic cell division takes place, and hence, the gametes thus formed possess 23 chromosomes (half the original number). Two types of gametes are formed in males, one carrying X chromosome and the other carrying Y chromosome. In females, only same type of gametes are formed that carry only one X chromosome each. During the process of fertilization, male and female gametes fuse to form a zygote that is diploid in nature. This restores the chromosome number. If male gamete with X chromosome fuses with any one of the female gametes, the zygote formed possesses both X chromosomes. If a male gamete with Y chromosome fuses with any one of the female gametes, the resultant zygote formed possesses one X and one Y chromosomes. The zygote with two X chromosomes (XX) develops into female, whereas the zygote with one X and one Y chromosome develops into a male. All the offspring invariably receive X chromosome from their mother. The offspring that inherits X chromosome from father will be a daughter. The offspring that inherits Y chromosome from father will be a son.

The characters that are linked to X chromosome or Y chromosome are transmitted to the next generation. Consequently, certain abnormal features are found in some persons. To a large extent, these are present in pairs.

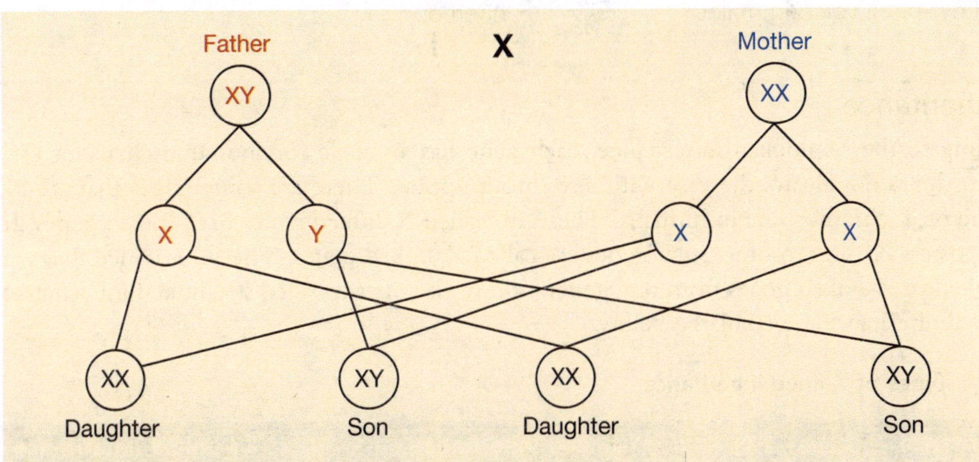

Figure 9.13 Schematic representation—sex determination in humans (XX–XY type)

Table 9.9 Example of certain deviating traits found in humans

Trait	Dominant	Recessive
Hair	Presence	Absence
Ear lobes	Free	Attached
Tongue	Rolled	Not rolled
Tongue	Folding	Not folding

XX–XO Type Sex Determination

Insects such as grasshopper have XO type mechanism of sex determination because the female has a pair of X chromosomes, whereas the male has a single X chromosome, and hence is represented as XO.

ZW–ZZ Type Sex Determination

In certain classes of organisms such as birds, the females possess two different types of sex chromosomes (ZW) and males possess two same types of sex chromosomes (ZZ). In these cases, the mechanism of sex determination is based on female heterogamety.

> **Info Bytes!**
> Organisms such as wasps and bees do not have sex chromosomes.

Aspects of genetics related to gender/sex of an organism

Though most of the characters of an individual are passed on to the next generations without any relevance to the sex of the organism, there are certain traits that are exclusive to either male or female sex of an individual. Such traits that are related to the sex of an individual organism are categorized into three types which are given in the table.

Table 9.10 Traits related to the gender of an individual organism

Sex-limited traits	Sex-linked traits	Sex-influenced traits
These characters are not directly due to particular genes but are due to the sex hormones specific to male or female. For example: • Secretion of milk in female mammals • Development of beard and mustache in human males • Low-pitch voice in males	These are the traits that are determined by the genes present on the sex chromosomes. For example: • Red-green colour blindness, haemophilia	These genes occur in both the sexes. But they are expressed in a particular sex. For example: • Baldness in males

Sex-Linked Inheritance

Generally, according to the Mendelian inheritance, each gene has an allele for the same character on the homologous chromosome. But, this is not always the case with sex chromosomes. There are some genes that are located exclusively on X chromosome or Y chromosome in humans. These are called X-linked genes or Y-linked genes. In birds and other such species that possess Z chromosome, such genes are called Z-linked genes. The inheritance that exclusively involves X-linked or Y-linked or Z-linked genes from one generation to the next is called sex-linked inheritance.
Types of sex-linked inheritance are tabulated below.

Table 9.11 Types of X-lined inheritance

X-linked inheritance	Y-linked inheritance	XY-linked inheritance
Localized on non-homologous sections of X chromosome.	Localized on Y chromosome.	The genes that are located on the homologous part of X or Y chromosome are XY-linked genes.
No corresponding allele on Y chromosome.	Since males are heterozygous, no allele on the other chromosome. Such condition is called hemizygous.	These behave like autosomal genes.
X chromosome is common to male and female, and hence, the genes are called sex-linked genes.	Y-linked traits are less common and are transmitted to only male children.	
The characters controlled by these genes are known as sex-linked characters.	These genes are called holandric genes.	
The transmission of these sex-linked traits is known as sex-linked inheritance.	This inheritance is known as holandric inheritance.	

Sex-Linked Inheritance in *Drosophila*

A mutant gene for producing white eye is found to be located on the X chromosome in Drosophila. This is recessive to dominant gene for red eye. The mutant recessive gene for white eye is represented as w and the dominant gene for red eye is represented as w^+. If both the X chromosomes in female possess alleles for white eye or red eye as the case may be, such a female is said to be homozygous for that trait (eye colour). If one X chromosome possesses allele for white eye and another X chromosome possesses allele for red eye, such a female is said to be hemizygous. However, in this condition, female does not phenotypically exhibit white eye as it is a recessive allele. Mother therefore, acts as a carrier for that trait. Male possesses only one X chromosome and if it possesses allele for white eye, it is hemizygous and phenotypically exhibits white eye.

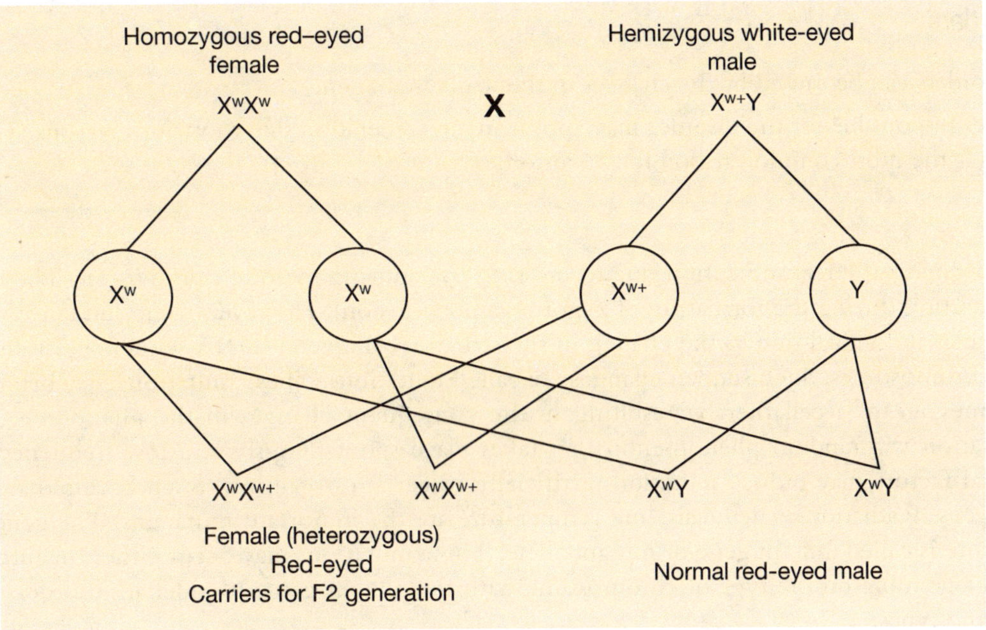

Figure 9.14 Illustration of sex-lined inheritance

Characteristics of Sex-Linked Inheritance

Major features of sex-linked inheritance are as listed below.

- The Y chromosome being confined only to one sex and being smaller with less number of genes, generally the inheritance of traits controlled by the genes located on the X chromosome of either male or female is only considered as sex-linked inheritance.
- This is a criss-cross inheritance. That means, fathers pass the trait to their grandsons through their daughters, whereas mothers pass the trait to both sons and daughters. In other words, sons receive these genes only from mother, whereas daughters receive these genes from both mother and father.
- The phenotypic expression of the respective trait depends on whether it is X-linked dominant gene or X-linked recessive gene in case of females. In case of males, the presence of allele on X chromosome itself is sufficient to express the trait phenotypically irrespective of whether the gene is dominant or recessive. In case of females, if the gene is recessive, they act as carriers for that trait or disease.

Genetic Disorders

Certain diseases are passed on from one generation to the next generation because of the sex-linked inheritance. These are called sex-linked diseases or disorders. The presence of a gene with the disease on the homologous chromosome of mother or father may lead to an abnormality or disorder that can be passed on to the offspring. Such kind of disorders are called genetic disorders.

Types of Genetic Disorders in Humans

Depending on the nature, genetic disorders are broadly classified into two types. These are:

1. Chromosomal disorders
2. Mendelian disorders

Chromosomal Disorders

- These disorders are caused by the change in the structure or number of chromosomes.
- The chromosomes involved can be autosomes or allosomes (sex chromosomes).

Mendelian Disorders

- These disorders can be caused by the changes in the structure of gene.
- Such genes responsible for the disorder may appear in any generation due to various reasons. The occurrence of mutations is the most common reason for the disorder.

Mutations

Variations occur due to the recombination due to crossing over during meiotic cell division. These are transmitted to the next generation during the formation of zygote (gametic fusion). However, some sudden variations may take place in a particular individual due to the change in the structure of a gene (DNA sequence) or chromosome or in the number of chromosomes. Such sudden changes are called mutations. These mutations may bring about a change in the genetic message of a cell thereby resulting in the consequent changes in the phenotype of the respective organisms. Mutation is a random phenomenon that takes place spontaneously at a low frequency. Some external or environmental factors may induce mutations artificially in certain organisms. Such agents that cause mutations are called mutagens. Radiations, chemicals, and temperature are the important mutagens. The gene that undergoes change in structure is called mutant gene or mutant allele. These mutations may occur either on autosomes or on sex chromosomes. Depending on the type of chromosome with the mutant gene, Mendelian disorders can be classified into two following types:

1. Autosomal disorders
2. Sex-linked disorders

If the mutant gene is present on the autosomes, it is called autosomal disorder. It can be autosomal dominant or autosomal recessive depending on whether the gene is dominant or recessive. Autosomal dominant or recessive disorders are heritable in case of both the sexes in equal frequency. That means, they are not sex specific.

If the mutant gene is present on the sex chromosomes, it is called sex-linked disorder. It is highly sex specific. If the mutant gene is present on X chromosome, it is called X-linked disorder. Depending on whether the gene is present on both X chromosomes or not, the disorder can be dominant or recessive. If the mutant gene is present on Y chromosome, it is called Y-linked disorder. Since only one Y chromosome is present, it is always dominant. X-linked recessive inheritance is much more common than X-linked dominant inheritance. Y-linked disorders are very few and are inherited only by sons. Females are not at all affected by such disorders.

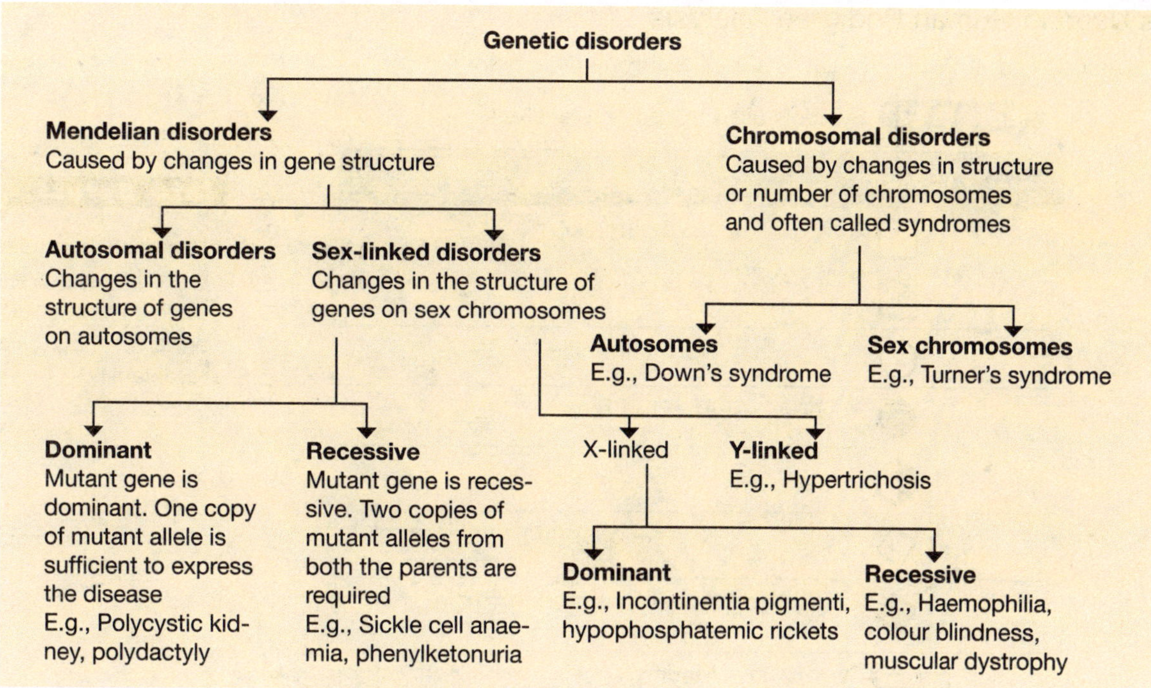

Figure 9.15 Classification of genetic disorders

Illustrations of X-linked disorders

Case I : Mother with X-linked dominant disorder (consider normal father)

1. Daughters with gene on X (not affected by disorder)
2. Sons with gene on X (not affected by disorder by 50%)
3. Daughters with gene on X (affected by disorder)
4. Sons with gene on X^+ (affected by disorder by 50%)

Case II: Mother with X-linked recessive disorder (XX^+) (consider normal father)

1. Daughters with gene on X (no gene for disorder - 25%)
2. Sons with gene on X (no gene for disorder - 25%)
3. Daughters with gene on X^+ (recessive gene for disorder—carrier)
4. Sons with gene on X^+ (gene for disorder—affected by disease - 25%)

Case III: Father with X-linked disoreder (X^+Y) (consider normal mother)

1. Daughter with X+ gene (affected by disorder by 100%)
2. Sons with gene on Y chromosome (not affected by disorder by 100%)

Pedigree Analysis

Pedigree is a family tree that describes the mode of inheritance of certain characteristics or diseases across the generations in that family. This analysis helps us to understand the family history and also predict the future of the family for that abnormal trait or disease as the case may be.

Symbols Used in Human Pedigree Analysis

Common symbols used in Pedigree analysis are given in the table below.

Table 9.12 Symbols used in pedigree analysis

Symbol	Representation
□	Normal male
■	Affected male
○	Normal female
●	Affected female
◐	Carrier female
◇	Normal offspring (male/female)
◆	Affected offspring (male/ female)
□—○	Mating
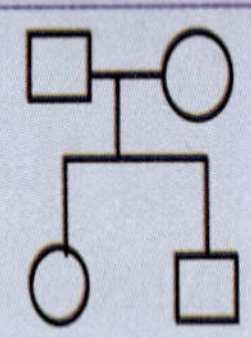	Parents Offspring

> **Info Bytes!**
>
> Haemophilia is referred to as the royal disease since it has been prevalent in European royal families.

For example, three generation pedigree chart for the trait-tongue rolling.

Tongue rolling is an autosomal dominant disorder. Affected male or female is a non-roller, whereas normal male or female is a roller. There are no carriers for this trait. This is because presence of single mutant gene is sufficient to express this trait in an individual.

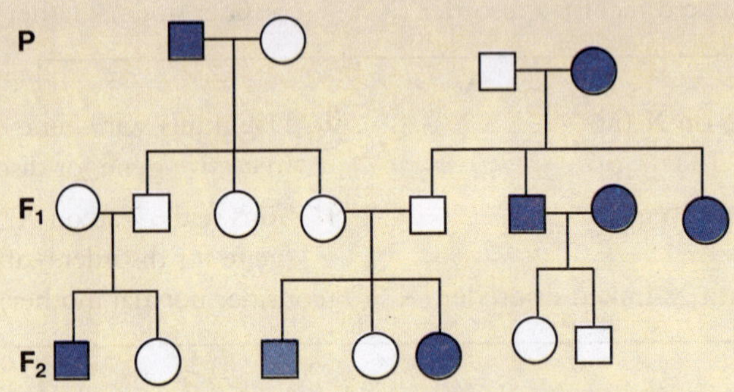

Figure 9.16 Pedigree analysis of trait–tongue rolling

Illustrative examples of some commonly occurring sex-linked diseases in humans are given below.

Haemophilia (X-linked Recessive Disorder)

This disease occurs due to the absence of a factor (gene) for clotting of blood and is called bleeder's disease. The patient continues to bleed even from a minor injury as the factor responsible for the synthesis of the substance required for clotting of blood is absent. This is caused by the presence of a recessive gene on the X chromosome. A woman is affected by the disease only in homozygous condition where both the X chromosomes possess gene for haemophilia. Generally, this condition does not sustain life and likely to end up in foetal stage. In heterozygous condition, the affected gene is masked and the woman acts as a carrier [XX^h]. A man is affected by the disease if he possesses X chromosome with gene for haemophilia (X^hY). Otherwise, he is normal (XY).

F1 generation—Carrier daughters; Normal sons

Colour Blindness (X-Linked Recessive Disorder)

In this disease, the eyes fail to distinguish red and green colours. This condition is caused by a recessive gene present on the X chromosome. Females are affected by the disease only in homozygous condition when the mutant genes are present in both the X chromosomes. If they are in heterozygous condition, they act as carriers and are not affected by the disease. Males are affected by the disease if the lone X chromosome possesses the mutant gene for colour blindness.

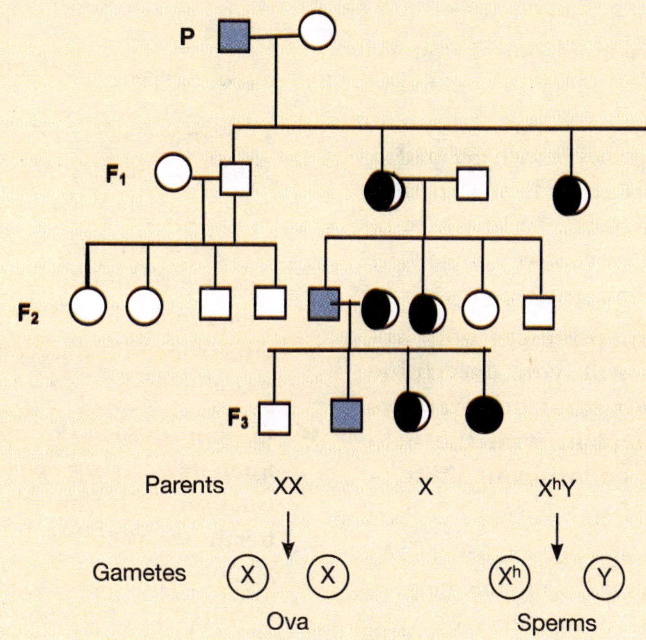

	X^h	Y
X	XX^h	XY
X	XX^h	XY

Figure 9.17 Cross for depicting colour blindness

For example, cross between a normal man and a carrier woman

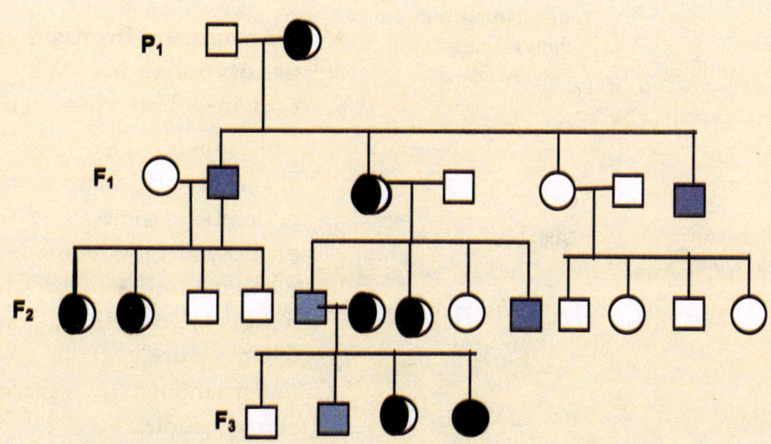

Figure 9.18 Pedigree analysis of colour blindness

Quick Recap

✔ **Variations are produced in each generation in sexual mode of reproduction. Give reasons.**

- Meiotic cell division involves exchange of genetic material between the homologous chromosomes.
- The variations occurring during meiotic cell division are transmitted to the next generation through gametic fusion.
- The variations produced during mitotic cell division may not be transmitted to the next generation.
- Consequently, progenies of each generation show some resemblances and some heritable and some non-heritable variations with those of next generation as well as with the individuals of the same generation.

✔ **A garden pea plant produces only axial flowers. How will you determine whether it is homozygous or heterozygous dominant? Explain with the help of crosses. How is codominance different from the above?**

Usually, the unknown genotype of an individual is determined with the help of test cross. Test cross is the cross between individual with unknown genotype and its homozygous recessive parent. Genotype of a pea plant with axial flower can be either AA (homozygous dominant) or Aa (heterozygous dominant). There are two possibilities for a test cross as given below:

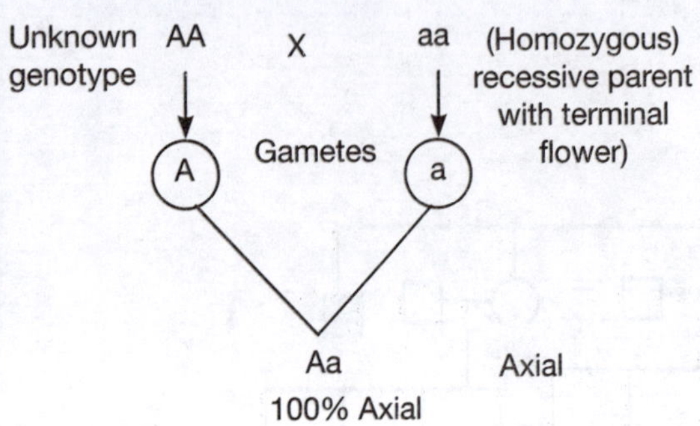

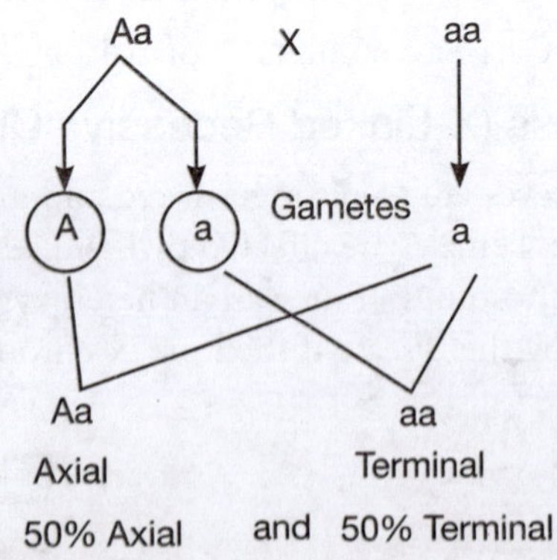

So from the above cross, it is clear that if pea plant with axial flower produces only axial flower, then the plant is homozygous dominant.

When the two alleles neither show dominant recessive relationship nor show intermediate condition but both of them express themselves simultaneously, this condition is known as codominance.

✔ **Explain the role of chromosomes in the nucleus of living cells in character transmission. Why are they regarded as inheritance vehicles?**

Genes, which are physical units of heredity, are carried by chromosomes in the nucleus of living cells. These genes are responsible for the inherited characteristics. Each chromosome is made up of DNA that contains unique genetic information. Chromosomes are passed down from parents to offspring during reproduction, ensuring the transmission of hereditary traits. As a result, they are regarded as inheritance vehicles.

✔ **Distinguish between phenotypic and genotypic ratios. Why are they important in genetic research?**

The phenotypic ratio represents visible characteristics, whereas the genotypic ratio represents genetic characteristics. The phenotypic ratio represents the trait's external manifestation, whereas the genotypic ratio reflects the underlying genetic combinations. These ratios aid in the prediction and understanding of inheritance patterns in genetic studies.

✔ **What distinguishes chromosomal disorders from Mendelian disorders? Make a key distinction between them based on their causes.**

Changes in chromosome structure or number cause chromosomal disorders, whereas changes in gene structure cause Mendelian disorders. Chromosome segment deletions or duplications cause chromosomal disorders. Mendelian disorders, on the other hand, are caused by mutations within specific genes, in accordance with Mendel's principles.

✔ **Human males are heterogametic. Justify.**

In human male, cells contain one X and one Y as their sex chromosomes, that is, their cells have XY pair of sex chromosomes.

During gamete formation, male parent produces two types of sperms, that is, sperm having either 'X' as the sex chromosome or 'Y' as the sex chromosome. Hence, male is said to be heterogametic in nature (producing different types of gamete).

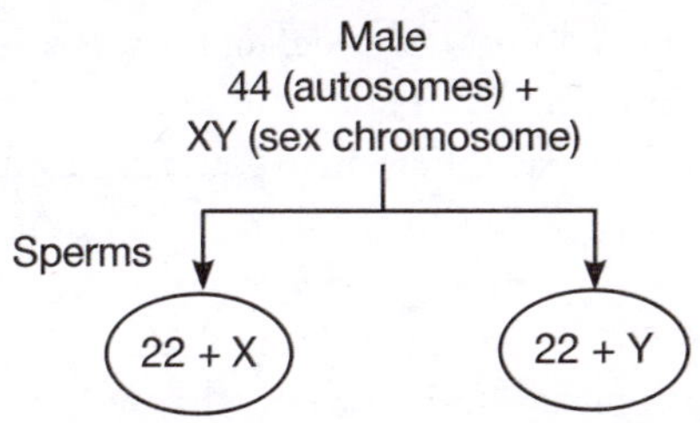

✔ **Explain how it is possible to have four children with different blood groups in one family.**

Genotype of father can be either I^Ai or $I^A I^A$

Genotype of mother—I^Bi

Cross can be represented as below:

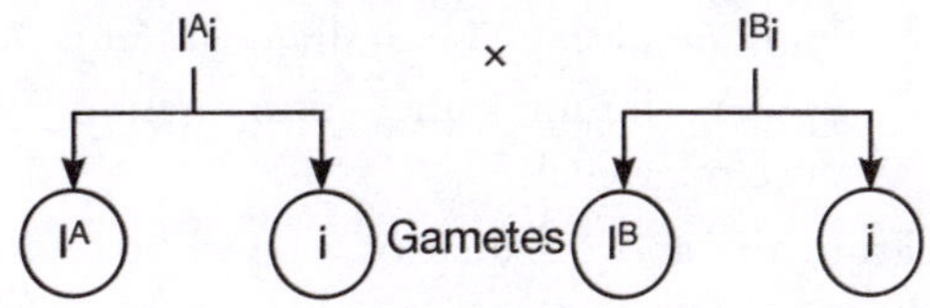

	I^A	i
I^Bi	I^AI^B AB blood	I^BI^O B blood
i	I^Ai A blood	ii O blood

Blood groups of offspring can be A, B, AB, or O

✔ **Explain mechanism of sex determination in birds**

Sex determination in birds can be explained by ZW–ZZ mechanism. Here females are heterogametic (ZW) and males are homogametic. Females produce two types of gametes; one with sex chromosome 'Z' and one with sex chromosome 'W.' Males produce single type of gamete with Z as sex chromosome.

Gamete formation can be represented as below:

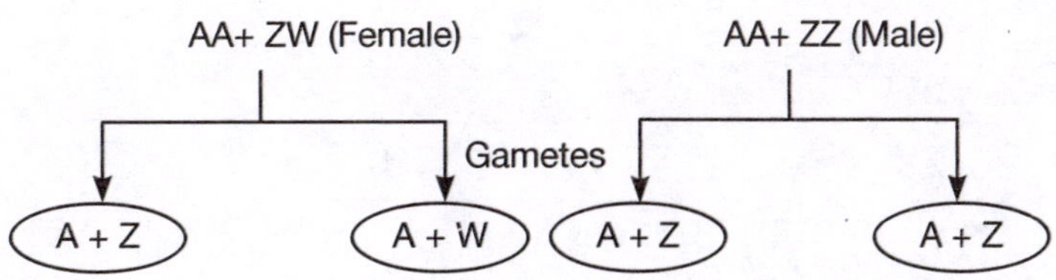

✔ **Women are often blamed for giving birth to female babies. What is your opinion and how will you justify your statement?**

Blaming women for giving birth to female children is wrong as in humans, sex of the baby is determined by father. More specifically, the sex of the baby is decided by the type of male gamete (sperm) fusing with female gamete (ovum). In humans, males are heterogametic producing two types of gametes, that is, gamete with X chromosome and gamete with Y chromosome. Females are homogametic producing only one type of gamete. During fertilization, there is equal chance for the female gamete to fuse with either of the male gametes. According to this, sex of the baby is decided.

The two possible scenarios are given below:

(a) A + X (male) fuses with A + X (female) to give zygotes with AA + XX configuration. The individual with AA + XX chromosome will develop as female.

(b) A + Y (male) fuses with A + X (female) to give zygote with AA + XY configuration. The individual with AA + XY chromosome configuration will develop as male.

From the above scenarios, it is clear that in human beings, sex of the baby is determined by father.

✔ **A normal man and a normal woman got married. One female child was found to be colour blind and did not survive long, while all the rest of the children were normal.**

(a) What conclusion can you draw from the above observation?

(b) Give justification for the conclusion.

(c) In F2 generation, if the colour blind woman marries a normal man, what is the probability of her daughters and sons being colour blind?

(a) The colour blindness of the female child may be because of mutation.

(b) Colour blindness is an X-linked disorder. Females exhibit the disease or trait only in homozygous condition. Even if the mother is a carrier for the gene, daughter should get only one X chromosome with the gene for the disease. In that case, she can be a carrier. She cannot be affected by the disease. Since one daughter is affected by the disease, it can be presumed that the condition would have been due to mutation in that particular individual.

(c) The colour blind woman should have mutant genes on both the X chromosomes. All sons would be colour blind as they get any one of the X chromosomes from mother. Since the father has normal genes on X chromosome, the daughters get only one X chromosome with mutant gene from mother. As a result, all the daughters will be carriers. None of the daughters are colour blind or normal.

✔ **How do Mendelian disorders, which result from changes in gene structure, differ in their inheritance patterns from chromosomal disorders?**

Mendelian disorders adhere strictly to Mendel's principles, whereas chromosomal disorders do not. Mendelian disorders, which are caused by gene mutations, typically exhibit classic inheritance patterns (dominant, recessive, co-dominant). Chromosomal disorders, on the other hand, can result from more complex chromosomal alterations that do not always follow Mendelian inheritance.

POINTS TO REMEMBER

- The branch of biology that deals with the study of heredity and variations is called genetics.
- This transmission of characters and variations along the forthcoming generations is known as inheritance.
- The inheritance of characters from the parents to the offspring is known as heredity.
- The chromosomes present in the nucleus of living cells serve as the vehicles of transmission of characters.
- Genes are the physical units of heredity and DNA is the molecular or chemical unit of heredity.
- The genes (factors) representing a particular character have their contrasting forms that are called alleles.
- Phenotypic ratio is the ratio of visible features.
- Genotypic ratio is the ratio of genetic features.
- The cross between the individual of F1 generation with the recessive parent is known as test cross.
- One allelic gene pair may influence more than one character and this phenomenon is called pleiotropy.
- Chromosomal disorders are caused by the change in the structure or number of chromosomes.
- Mendelian disorders are caused by the changes in the structure of gene.

DW

PRACTICE QUESTIONS CLASSROOM WING

Very Short Answer Type Questions

Directions for questions from 1 to 23.
Fill in the blanks.

1. The branch of biology that studies how the characters of parents are transmitted to the offspring is called_______.
2. The _______ is the molecular or chemical basis of heredity.
3. The phenomenon in which certain genes present on a chromosome are carried on to the daughter cell during meiotic cell division is called _______.
4. Mendel chose the pea plant for his experiments primarily because of its easy cultivation and the fact that it is an ______ plant.
5. If a plant is homozygous for a trait, it means it has ______ alleles for that trait.
6. A _______ cross involves breeding plants with two pairs of contrasting characters.
7. Phenotypic ratio for incomplete dominance is _______.
8. Gene controlling starch synthesis in pea plant is an example for _______.
9. The scientific name of the plant on which Mendel worked is _______.
10. In human cell, there are _______ autosomes and _______ sex chromosomes.
11. The cross of an F1 plant with any one of its parents is called _______.
12. Mendel's monohybrid test cross ratio was _______.
13. In ABO blood group system allele I^A is _______with I^B allele.
14. The type of inheritance associated with the homologous part of the sex chromosomes is called _______.
15. The genes located on Y chromosomes are called _______.
16. Genetic disorders occurring due to the change in the structure or number of chromosomes are called _______.
17. _______ gives the analysis of future of the family with respect to the particular sex-linked trait.
18. Muscular dystrophy is caused due to the mutant _______ gene on _______ chromosome.
19. The traits that are not due to specific genes, but are affected by sex hormones are called _______traits.
20. Males are said to be _______ for genes on the X chromosome.
21. In colour blindness, the affected person fails to distinguish between _______ and _______ colours.
22. *Drosophila* shows _______ type of sex determination.
23. Non-stop bleeding is the characteristic symptom for the disease _______.

Directions for questions from 24 to 30.

For each of the following questions, four choices have been provided. Select the correct alternatives.

24. In honeybee, males are
    (a) Haploid (b) Diploid
    (c) Triploid (d) None of the above
25. In grasshopper, total number of chromosomes in male is
    (a) Equal to female
    (b) Less than female
    (c) Double than female
    (d) More than female
26. In which of the following organisms, female heterogamety is observed?
    (A) Peacock (B) Crocodile
    (C) Butterfly (D) Rabbit
    (E) Fish
    (a) A, B, C (b) B, C, D
    (c) A, B, E (d) B, C, E

27. Identify the feature for which genes are present in both the sexes, but is predominantly sex specific in humans.
(A) Bald head
(B) Secretion of milk
(C) Skin colour
(D) Colour blindness
(E) Development of mustache
(a) A, B (b) A, D
(c) A, B, E (d) B, C, E

28. Identify the diseases that are not sex specific.
(A) Hypertrichiosis
(B) Haemophilia
(C) Phenylketonuria
(D) Pentadactyly
(E) Muscular dystrophy
(a) A, B, E (b) C, D
(c) C, D, E (d) A, E

29. Which of the following type of sex determination involves organisms with different number of chromosomes in males and females?
(a) XX–XY (b) XX–XO
(c) ZZ–ZW (d) None of these

30. Albinism is a genetic disorder but it affects both eye sight as well as hearing. Which of the following term can describe this condition?
(a) Codominance
(b) Polygenic traits
(c) Incomplete dominance
(d) Pleiotropy

Directions for questions 31 and 32.

Match the entries of Column 1 with those of Column 2.

31.

Column 1	Column 2
A. A single gene affecting number of characters	(i) Polygenic inheritance
B. Spectrum of phenotypes	(ii) Codominance
C. Intermediate phenotypic expression	(iii) Pleiotropy
D. ABO blood groups	(iv) Incomplete dominance

(a) A → (iii), B → (i), C → (iv), D → (ii)
(b) A → (ii), B → (i), C → (iv), D → (iii)
(c) A → (i), B → (iii), C → (iv), D → (ii)
(d) A → (iv), → (i), C → (iii), D → (ii)

32.

Column 1	Column 2
A. Birds	(i) One gene controls more than one character
B. True bugs	(ii) ZW–ZZ sex determination
C. Pleiotropy	(iii) More than two alleles for a gene
D. Multiple allelism	(iv) XX–XO type

(a) A → (iii), B → (i), C → (iv), D → (ii)
(a) A → (ii), B → (i), C → (iv), D → (iii)
(a) A → (i), B → (iii), C → (iv), D → (ii)
(a) A → (iv), B → (i), C → (iii), D → (ii)

Short Answer Type Questions

33. What are homologous chromosomes alleles? Give examples.

34. Define the following terms:
(a) Inheritance
(b) Heredity
(c) Trait
(d) Gene
(e) Variations

35. Distinguish between linkage and crossing over.

36. What is meant by recombination? Explain its significance.

37. Distinguish between dominant trait and recessive trait.

38. Distinguish between homozygous and heterozygous.

39. Distinguish between monohybrid cross and dihybrid cross.

40. Describe the importance of the study of genetics.

41. What are alleles and how do they relate to the height of an organism?

42. Why was the pea plant an ideal choice for Mendel's experiments?

43. Explain the principle of dominance as proposed by Mendel.

44. Mention the pairs of contrasting characters chosen by Mendel related to seed in pea plant.

45. Mention the pairs of contrasting characters chosen by Mendel related to flower in pea plant.

46. What is test cross and what is its significance?

47. Differentiate between dominance and codominance.

48. RRYY with rryy plants in P generation are crossed and the plants produced in F1 generation are allowed to self-pollinate.
   (a) Mention the gametes formed by each parent in both the generations?
   (b) What do they represent?
   (c) Mention the two types of gametic combinations possible.

49. Distinguish between autosomal genetic disorders and allosomal genetic disorders.

50. In pea plants, axial position of flowers is considered as dominant trait and terminal position of flower is considered as recessive trait. Heterozygous plant with terminal flower is not possible.

Essay Type Questions

51. How does the combination of linkage and crossing over during meiotic cell division ensure the survival and evolution of a species?

52. Taking seed colour of pea plant as the trait (yellow as dominant and green as recessive), design a test cross to show the nature of P1 generation plants.

53. The sex of a child is determined by the father and not mother. Give reason.

54. Y-linked traits are very less common than X-linked traits. Give reason.

PRACTICE QUESTIONS COMPETITION WING

Level 1: Apply your Concepts

Directions for questions from 1 to 5.
Fill in the blanks in each question.

1. The zygote with two X chromosomes (XX) develops into a _______, whereas the zygote with one X and one Y chromosome develops into a _______.
2. _______ is a random phenomenon that results in changes in the genetic message of a cell.
3. Genetic disorders can be broadly classified into _______ disorders and _______ disorders.
4. A fragment of DNA that provides complete information about one protein is referred as _______ for that protein.
5. _______ is the degree of differences between parents and offspring.

Directions for questions from 6 to 18.
Choose the correct option.

(a) Both A and R are true and R is the correct explanation for A.
(b) Both A and R are true, but R is not the correct explanation for A.
(c) A is true and R is false.
(d) A is false and R is true.

6. **Assertion (A):** Sexual reproduction brings about appreciable variations in the offspring
Reason (R): Sexual reproduction involves cell division in which DNA replication takes place.
7. **Assertion (A):** The DNA of the child will be the same as the DNA of the parent.
Reason (R): The two DNA strands are complementary to each other.
8. **Assertion (A):** Heterozygous recessive progenies are not found in Mendelian inheritance.
Reason (R): Formation of gametes is associated with the segregation of alleles.
9. **Assertion (A):** Red-flowered plants of F1 generation are same as red-flowered plants of P generation.
Reason (R): All the offspring obtained in F1 generation are phenotypically and genotypically same.
10. **Assertion (A):** F1 generation progenies can show an intermediate expression between dominant and recessive characters.
Reason (R): The cross involves the phenomenon of codominance.
11. **Assertion (A):** Children necessarily possess the same blood group as either of the parents.
Reason (R): The gene corresponding to the blood group has three alleles.
12. **Assertion (A):** A cross between tall plants with round seeds can also produce dwarf plants with wrinkled seeds.
Reason (R): Each progeny inherits one homologous chromosome each from male and female.
13. **Assertion (A):** In grasshopper, male individual determines the sex of the offspring.
Reason (R): All organisms show male heterogamety.
14. **Assertion (A):** Genes on the X chromosome are called sex-linked genes.
Reason (R): X chromosome is present in both the sexes.
15. **Assertion (A):** Males cannot act as carriers for genetic disorders.
Reason (R): Males cannot transmit the X-linked genes to their sons.
16. **Assertion (A):** Hypertrichosis is a disease found only in males.
Reason (R): Y-linked traits cannot be transmitted to daughters.
17. **Assertion (A):** For sickle cell anemia, males also can be carriers.
Reason (R): Autosomal recessive traits are not sex specific.
18. **Assertion (A):** Mendel's dihybrid cross resulted in a phenotypic ratio of 9:3:3:1 in the F2 generation.
Reason (R): The two traits in a dihybrid cross sort out independently during gamete formation.

Directions for questions from 19 to 22.
For each of the following questions, four choices have been provided. Select the correct alternative.

19. Which organism displays the XX-XO type of sex determination?
(a) Drosophila (b) Human
(c) Grasshopper (d) Bird
20. Which chromosome combination represents the female sex in birds?

(a) XX (b) XY
(c) ZW (d) ZZ

21. Which trait is an example of sex-linked traits?
(a) Secretion of milk in female mammals
(b) Development of beard in human males
(c) Red-green colour blindness
(d) Low-pitch voice in males

22. Which of the following is an abnormal trait in human beings?
(a) Attached ear lobes (b) Tongue rolling
(c) Presence of hair (d) Folding tongue

Directions for questions from 23 to 27:
Correct the following statements.

23. The number of chromosomes in a particular species is variable.

24. The proportion of plants heterozygous with respect to both the traits in F2 generation of Mendel's dihybrid cross is 3/16.

25. The probability of birth of male child in humans is 25 per cent.

26. Human Y chromosome is longer than X chromosome.

27. Autosomes are responsible for the transmission of characters from parents to the offspring.

Directions for questions from 28 to 35:
Write the missing correlated terms.

28. Gregor Johann Mendel: Genetics:: Thomas Hunt Morgan: ________.

29. Stem height: Tall:: Flower colour: ?

30. Daughter: X chromosome from Father:: Son : ?

31. ______ : Dominant :: Wrinkled seed : recessive

32. Phenotypic ratio : 3 : 1 :: Genotypic ratio : ______

33. XX : female :: ______ : male

34. Homozygous dominant : ______ :: Homozygous recessive : 1

35. TTPP : Parental combination :: ______ : Recombination

Directions for questions from 36 to 41.
Find the Odd one.

36. Chromosome; DNA; Gene; Nucleus

37. PR; pr; RY; Ry

38. R; r; Yy; T

39. RRyy; RrYy; RrYY; RRYY

40. Polycystic kidney; Polydactyly; Phenylketonuria; Haemophilia

41. Crow; *Drosophila*; Whale; Man

Level 2: Review your Concepts

42. Show that in incomplete dominance, the phenotypic and genotypic ratio is same.

43. What would be the possible blood groups of the progeny, if mother is O blood group and father is AB blood group?

44. What would be the blood groups of the progeny of father with blood group 'A' and mother heterozygous B? Explain the cross.

45. With the help of a Punnett square, explain Mendelian experiment where a plant bearing green pods (dominant) is crossed with a plant bearing yellow pods. Write both the phenotypic and genotypic ratios for F2 generation.

46. An experiment is conducted with two sets of plants with red flowers. One set of plants gave rise to progenies with only red flowers in all successive generations. Another set of plants when crossed gave rise to few plants with white flowers also in F2 generation. What conclusions can you draw regarding the plants of P1 generation?

47. Tallness of plant and purple colour of flower are the dominant traits. Dwarfness of plant and white colour of flower are the recessive characters. These two plants are crossed.
(a) What percentage of dwarf plants are produced with purple flowers and white flowers in F2 generation?
(b) Which type of plants are produced in maximum numbers? Predict their percentage.
(c) Subdivide the above category of plants on the basis of their genotypes.
(d) Explain by using Punnett square.

48. Plant with round seeds is crossed with plant with wrinkled seeds. All F1 generation progenies are with round seeds.
(a) What is the percentage of plants with wrinkled seeds in F2 generation?

(b) What is the percentage of hybrid plants in F2 generation?

(c) Justify the above results by drawing Punnett square.

49. Plant with full green pod is said to be homozygous dominant. Plant with constricted yellow pod is said to be homozygous recessive. Crossing of these two plants can also give rise to plants with full yellow pod. Plants with constricted green pod are also produced.

(a) What conclusion could Mendel draw from this observation?

(b) Explain with the help of appropriate diagram.

50. Mendel produced 556 pea plants in his dihybrid cross. What are the various types of plants produced in F2 generation? What are their respective numbers? Justify.

51. Mendel produced 929 pea plants in his experiment for monohybrid cross considering red and white colours. How many red-coloured plants are produced in F2 generation? Are all of them same? Justify.

52. Red-flowered plants of F1 generation plants are different from the red-flowered plants of P1 generation. Give reason.

53. Human beings are found to possess variable skin complexion. Give reason.

54. A person affected by sickle cell anemia may experience problems in multiple organs. Give reason.

55. Study the following pedigree chart and answer the following questions:

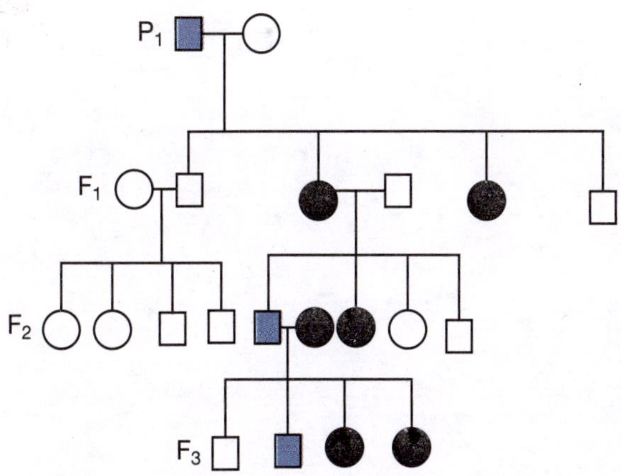

(a) If the disease is expressed in mother, predict the type of genetic disorder represented by the given pedigree chart.

(b) What is the status of sons in F1 generation with respect to the disease? Justify.

(c) In which cases, the successive generations will be totally free of the diseased genes?

(d) Continue the given pedigree chart for F2 generation of B.

(e) Which sex is more affected by the disease? Give justification.

56. How is it possible to conclude whether a particular trait is X-linked or Y-linked?

57. A man suffers from muscular dystrophy. The woman is normal and had no family history for the disease.

(a) Can all her daughters be normal?

(b) Will the successive generations be free of the disease? Discuss different cases considering mating with normal men or women in the later generations.

(c) Draw pedigree chart for three generations and justify the type of inheritance of the disease.

58. Distinguish between Down's syndrome and Turner's syndrome and explain the nature of these diseases with respect to the concept of genetics.

59. Explain the process of sex determination in humans.

60. What are mutagens and their significance?

61. Explain law of dominance with an example.

62. Explain test cross and back cross.

63. What is pleiotropy? Give one example.

64. When a cross is made between tall plant with green pod (TtGg) and a tall plant with yellow pod (Ttgg), what proportion of phenotype in an offspring could be

(a) Tall green?

(b) Dwarf green?

65. Analyze the progenies of F1 generation in the following cases:

(a) Homozygous tall and homozygous dwarfs

(b) Homozygous tall (dominant) and heterozygous tall

(c) Heterozygous tall and heterozygous tall

(d) Heterozygous tall and homozygous dwarf

66. Distinguish between allosomes and autosomes.

67. What are mutagens? Name some mutagens.

68. Give the suitable term for the following:

(a) Condition in which one X chromosome has a gene for particular trait and the other one has no allele for the trait.

(b) A fragment of DNA helix that determines a particular character of an individual.

(c) The gene present in an individual but not expressed out.

(d) A pair of chromosomes having contrasting alleles on each.

(e) The condition in which one gene affects more than one trait.

(f) The traits that are not sex specific.

(g) The condition in which both traits are expressed in heterozygous condition.

(h) The progenies formed due to asexual reproduction.

69. Fill in the blanks in the following flow chart with appropriate terms. (yellow—dominant; green—recessive)

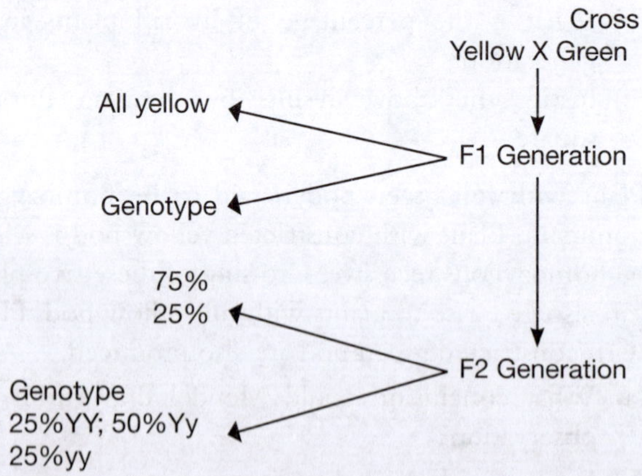

70. Consanguineous marriages are not suggestible from the point of view of genetics. Justify by using pedigree analysis.

Level 3: Assess Your Concepts

71. Mendel's laws laid the foundation for modern genetics. However, there were some deviations observed later on. How do you think these deviations affect our understanding of inheritance, and how does the rediscovery of Mendel's work help address these gaps?

72. Sickle cell anemia and haemophilia are disorders of blood and are found to be genetically transmitted. However, sickle cell anemia is found in both the sexes, whereas haemophilia is usually rare in females. Justify by using pedigree analysis.

73. A child possesses some characteristic resemblances with both father and mother. However, the child is not an exact copy of either of the parents. Give reason.

74. Secretion of milk is the characteristic feature of only female mammals. Give reason.

75. In *Drosophila*, presence of white eye is more predominant in males than in females. Justify with respect to the concept of genetics.

PRACTICE QUESTIONS NEET SPECIAL WING

Multiple-Answer Type Questions

Questions number 1 to 5 are multiple-choice questions. Each question has FOUR options (a), (b), (c), and (d). ONE OR MORE THAN ONE of these four option(s) is/are the correct answer(s).

1. Which of the following is a type of sex determination?
   (a) XX-XY
   (b) XX-ZO
   (c) XX-XO
   (d) ZW-ZZ
2. Which of the following examples show deviations from Mendelian genetics?
   (a) Pink coloured flowers of Snapdragon
   (b) Pea colour in pea plant
   (c) A, B, O blood group
   (d) Sickle cell anaemia
3. Which are the recessive factors that are present in a pea plant?
   (a) Dwarf height
   (b) White flowers
   (c) Axial flower position
   (d) Constricted pod shape
4. Which of the following is true regarding test cross?
   (a) The cross involves individual of F_1 generation
   (b) The genotypic ratio is 1 : 1
   (c) Recessive parents are used for the cross
   (d) Either dominant or recessive parents are used for the cross
5. Which of the following are conclusions drawn by Mendel on the basis of Monohybrid cross?
   (a) Principle of paired factors
   (b) Principle of dominance
   (c) Principle of purity of gametes
   (d) Principle of independent assortment

Comprehension-Based Questions

A. Read the paragraph given below and answer the questions number 6 to 11:

The below given chart is a pedigree chart of a family with history of Colour blindness which is an X- linked recessive disorder. In colour blindness the eyes fail to differentiate between two colours. 1 is a carrier woman who is married to the person having the defect. Answer the below given questions on the basis of the information given in the chart.

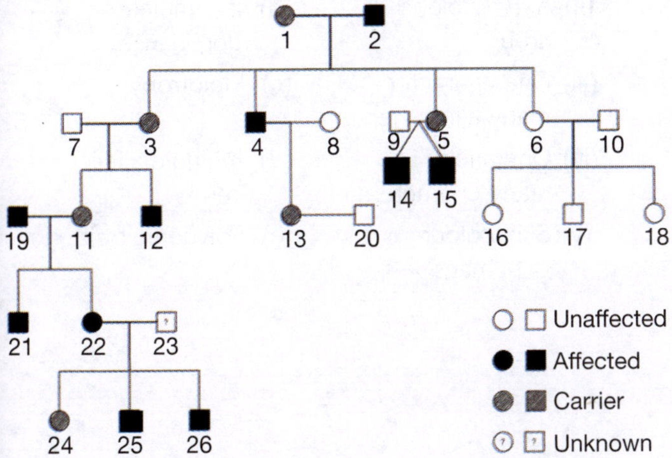

6. What percentage of the male population of 11 and 19 will not have the defect?
   (a) 0% (b) 50%
   (c) 75% (d) 100%
7. What are the chances of 5 and 9 giving birth to a child who does not have a defect?
   (a) 0% (b) 50%
   (c) 75% (d) 100%
8. What is the possible genotype of 23, considering their progeny?
   (a) XY (b) X^cY
   (c) X^cY^c (d) X^cX^c
9. What percentage of a child between 11 and 19 will be a carrier?
   (a) 0% (b) 25%
   (c) 50% (d) 100%
10. What are the chances of 6 and 10 to have children with colour blindness?
    (a) 0% (b) 25%
    (c) 50% (d) 100%

11. Match the column:

Genetic disorders are divided into two main categories- Mendelian disorders and chromosomal disorders. Mendelian disorders are caused due to change in the structure of the gene whereas chromosomal disorders are caused due to change in autosomes or Allosomes. In Mendelian autosomal disorders there is change on autosomes wherein mutation can either be on the dominant gene or recessive gene. The sex linked mendelian disorder can be X linked or Y linked. The mutation on the X linked gene can be either dominant or recessive. Some of the examples of different disorders are given below, match them with the appropriate type of genetic disorder.

Column – A	Column – B
(i) Polydactyly	(a) Autosomal recessive disorder
(ii) Phenylketonuria	(b) Y linked disorder
(iii) Hypertrichosis	(c) X linked dominant disorder
(iv) Hypophosphatemic rickets	(d) Autosomal dominant disorder
(v) Haemophilia	(e) X linked recessive disorder

B. Read the paragraph given below and answer the questions number 12 to 17:

Tongue rolling is an autosomal dominant disorder. Affected male and female is a non-roller. Normal males and females can roll their tongues. Affected males are shown by dark squares and affected females are shown by dark circles. On the other hand, plain square and circle represents males and females who can roll their tongues.

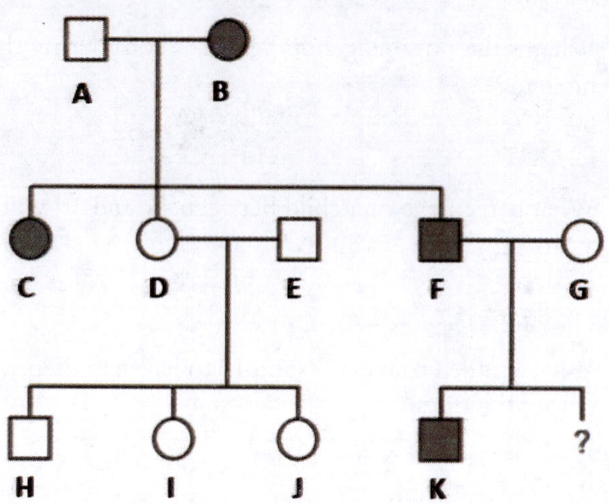

12. What are the chances of the fourth child of D and E to have a non- roller child?
(a) 0%
(b) 25%
(c) 50%
(d) 100%

13. What is the genotype and phenotype of B?
(a) Homozygous, roller
(b) Heterozygous, non-roller
(c) Homozygous, non-roller
(d) Heterozygous, roller

14. What is the chance of the second child of F and G to be roller?
(a) 1 in 1 (b) 1 in 2
(c) 1 in 3 (d) 1 in 4

15. If H marries a person who can roll their tongues, what present of their children will be tongue rollers?
(a) 0% (b) 25%
(c) 50% (d) 100%

16. What if non-tongue rolling was an autosomal recessive defect, and a non-roller marries a person who can roll their tongues with no family history of non-rollers , what percent of their children will be non-rollers?
(a) 0% (b) 25%
(c) 50% (d) 100%

17. Match the column:

Mendel's laws came way before genes and DNA were discovered. However, a lot was learnt by the experiments carried out by Morgan on Drosophila. However, it was found that the characters did not follow Mendelian inheritance. Below given are few of the examples of deviations, match them correctly.

Column – A	Column – B
(i) 4 o'clock plant	(a) Codominance
(ii) A, B, O blood group	(b) Incomplete dominance
(iii) One character many allelic genes	(c) Pleiotropy
(iv) One allele many characters	(d) Multiple allelic series
(v) Skin colour in humans	(e) Polygenic trait

ANSWER KEYS

Crossword

Across

2. Pleiotropy 7. Alleles 9. Inheritance 11. Genes

Down

1. Genetics 3. Phenotypic 4. Test 5. Chromosomes 6. Genotypic
8. Heredity 10. DNA

Classroom Wing

Very Short Answer Type Questions

1. Genetics 2. DNA 3. Linkage 4. Annual 5. Same
6. Dihybrid 7. 1 : 2 : 1. 8. Pleiotropy 9. *Pisum sativum*
10. 22 pairs of, One pair of 11. Back cross 12. 1 : 1 13. Codominant
14. XY-linked inheritance 15. Holandric genes 16. Syndromes
17. Pedigree analysis 18. Recessive, X 19. Sex-influenced 20. Hemizygous 21. Red, Green
22. XX–XY 23. Haemophilia 24. (a) 25. (b) 26. (c)
27. (a) 28. (b) 29. (b) 30. (d)
31. A → (iii), B → (i), C → (iv), D → (ii) 32. A → (ii), B → (iii), C → (i), D → (iv)

Competition Wing

Level 1: Apply Your Concepts

1. Female, Male 2. Mutation 3. Chromosomal, Mendelian 4. Gene
5. Variation 6. (c) 7. (c) 8. (b) 9. (d)
10. (c) 11. (d) 12. (b) 13. (c) 14. (a)
15. (b) 16. (a) 17. (a) 18. (a) 19. (c)
20. (c) 21. (c) 22. (a) 28. Experimental genetics
29. Purple. 30. Y chromosome from father. 31. Round seed 32. 1:2:1
33. XY 34. 9 35. TtPp or TTPp or TtPP 36. Nucleus
37. Ry 38. Yy 39. Rryy 40. Haemophilia 41. Crow

NEET Special Wing

Multiple-Answer Type Questions

1. (a, c, d) **2.** (a, c) **3.** (a, b, d) **4.** (a, b, c) **5.** (a, b, c)

Comprehension-Based Questions

6. (b) **7.** (c) **8.** (a) **9.** (b) **10.** (a)

11. (i) → (d); (ii) → (a); (iii) → (b); (iv) → (c); (v) → (e)

12. (a) **13.** (b) **14.** (b) **15.** (d) **16.** (a)

17. (i) → (b); (ii) → (a); (iii) → (d); (iv) → (c); (v) → (e)

Hints and Explanations

CLASSROOM WING

Short Answer Type Questions

33. The chromosomes occur in pairs in each cell. The two chromosomes of the pair are similar in structure (gene position) and are derived one from each parent. Such pairs of chromosomes are known as homologous chromosomes.

Alleles: The genes (factors) representing a particular character as contrasting traits are called alleles. The alternative forms of a character are called contrasting traits.

34. (a) **Inheritance:** The transmission of characters and variations along the forthcoming generations.

(b) **Heredity:** The inheritance of characters from the parents to the offspring.

(c) **Gene:** The fragment or region of DNA that is made up of specific sequence of nucleotides is called gene, which is the molecular unit of heredity.

(d) **Trait:** The character or feature that is carried by a gene such as height of plant.

(e) **Variations:** The differences existing among the individuals of a species and also among the offspring of the same parents.

35.

Linkage	Crossing over
Tendency of genes on a chromosome to remain together and pass as such to the next generation.	Exchange of genes to establish a new linkage.
Helps to preserve the parental gene combinations.	Helps to bring about recombinations.
Generally more favorable among the genes that are closely placed on a chromosome.	Generally favorable among the genes that are distantly placed on the chromosomes.
The probability of linkage increases with increase in age.	The probability of crossing over decreases with increase in age.

36. The phenomenon of the exchange of segments of non-sister chromatids (genes) of homologous chromosomes is known as crossing over. Crossing over is followed by recombination during the meiotic cell division. The reproductive cells (diploid germ cells) undergo meiotic cell division producing haploid (n) male and female gametes. That means, meiotic cell division involves genetic combination that results in the exchange of some genes and forms the main basis for the variations among the organisms of same species. Due to genetic recombination taking place in meiotic cell division, the exchange of genetic material takes place between the chromosomes. This results in variations that are inherited because the union of male and female gametes results in the formation of diploid zygote.

37.

Dominant Trait	Recessive Trait
The trait that expresses itself even in the presence of its contrasting trait as it masks and hides the other trait. For example: Purple colour of flowers	The trait that fails to express itself in the presence of its contrasting dominant trait. For example: White colour of flowers

38.

Homozygous	Heterozygous
An organism having the traits that carry either both dominant or recessive factors. For example: RR	An organism having contrasting factors (one dominant factor and one recessive factor). For example: Rr

39.

Monohybrid cross	Dihybrid cross
The crossing of plants with one pair of contrasting characters. For example: TT tt	The crossing of plants with two pairs of contrasting characters. For example: TTRR ttrr

40. Genetics plays a crucial role in understanding how characters from parents are transmitted to the offspring and the reasons for variations within a species. It has led to major advancements in fields like agriculture, medicine, and forensic science, transforming society significantly.

41. Alleles are genes that represent contrasting traits of a character. When considering the height of an organism, there are three possible combinations of gene pairs: both corresponding to tallness, one for tallness and the other for dwarfness, or both for dwarfness. These alleles determine the inherited height trait of the organism.

42. The pea plant was an ideal choice for Mendel's experiments because of its ease of cultivation. Pea plants are annual, yielding results within a year. They are normally self-pollinated, but can also be cross-pollinated if required. Moreover, a large number of varieties with observable alternative forms for traits are available, offering a range of contrasting traits for study.

43. The principle of dominance states that when two contrasting factors (now known as alleles) are present in an organism, one may mask the presence of the other. The factor that expresses itself in the hybrid is termed the dominant allele, while the factor that remains hidden or unexpressed in the presence of the dominant allele is termed the recessive allele.

44.

Seed colour	Yellow	Y	Green	y
Seed shape	Round	R	Wrinkled	r

45. Contrasting characters chosen by Mendel

(a)	Flower colour	Purple	P	White	p
(b)	Flower position	Axial	A	Terminal	a

46. The cross between the individual of F1 generation with the recessive parent is known as test cross.

Taking seed colour of pea plant as the trait (yellow as dominant and green as recessive), design a test cross to show the nature of P1 generation plants.

47. According to Mendelian inheritance, F1 generation individual resembles the dominant parent phenotypically and contains a recessive gene that is not expressed out.

However, in some cases, the F1 generation individual resembles both the parents. That means, in heterozygous condition, the recessive gene also expresses itself along with the dominant gene. Such a phenomenon is called codominance.

48. (a) The gametes formed by one parent are RY and RY and those formed by the other parent are ry and ry in P1 generation.

(b) The gametes formed by all F1 generation progenies are Ry type. During the formation of gametes, the characteristics get segregated out.

Parental combination–For example, Ry × Ry

Recombination–For example, Ry × RY; rY × RY

49. Autosomal genetic disorders are those diseases arising due to the mutations occurring in the structure or number of genes or non-sex chromosomes. Allosomal genetic disorders arise due to the mutations occurring in the structure or number of genes in sex chromosomes.

50. Heterozygous condition represents the presence of one gene for axial position and one gene for terminal position. Since axial position of flower is a dominant trait, the gene for terminal position of flower is not expressed out. Therefore, heterozygous recessive condition does not exist.

Essay Type Questions

51. Linkage and crossing over are essential processes in meiotic cell division that determine how traits are inherited in offspring. While linkage helps in preserving certain traits from the parent generation, crossing over introduces genetic variability by allowing non-sister chromatids of homologous chromosomes to exchange segments. This combination ensures that while some traits remain consistent across generations, there's also room for genetic diversity, which is essential for the survival and adaptability of a species. Genetic diversity provides a broader gene pool, allowing organisms to adapt to changing environments over time, ensuring the survival of the species in the face of challenges and facilitating evolution.

52. The cross between the individual of F1 generation with the recessive parent is known as test cross.

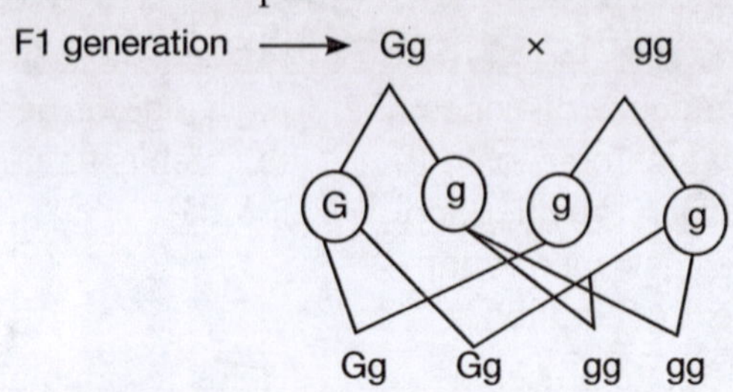

Phenotypic ratio: 1:1

Genotypic ratio: 1:1

F1 Gametes		g (recessive)	g (recessive)
	G	Gg (Tall)	Gg (Tall)

53. In human males, two dissimilar sex chromosomes are present, that is, one X chromosome and one Y chromosome. In human females, two X chromosomes are present.

- The males produce two types of gametes; one with X chromosome and the other one with Y chromosome. The females produce only one type of gametes both containing X chromosomes.
- If the female gamete fuses with the male gamete with X chromosome, the zygote formed has both X chromosomes. If the female gamete fuses with the male gamete with Y chromosome, the zygote has one X chromosome and one Y chromosome. The former develops into a female child whereas the latter develops into a male child.
- Since the child inherits different chromosomes from father and same chromosomes from mother, the chromosome inherited from father only determines the sex of the child.

54. Y chromosome is smaller in size and contains less number of genes when compared to X chromosome. Therefore, Y-linked traits are very less common than X-linked traits.

COMPETITION WING

Level 1: Apply your Concepts

6. Sexual reproduction brings about variations in the offspring because it involves the fusion of gametes produced by meiotic cell division. This is because meiotic cell division involves exchange of genetic material due to crossing over of homologous chromosomes. Crossing over does not take place during mitotic cell division. That is why mitotic cell division does not result in variations in the offspring.

   On the other hand, DNA replication is a part of both mitotic cell division and meiotic cell division. As the new strand formed is always complementary to the original strand, DNA replication serves to preserve the DNA sequence across the generations. Therefore, assertion is correct and reason is wrong.
   Hence, the correct option is (c)

7. The DNA of the child will not be same as that of either of the parents. The DNA replication results in the formation of DNA with the same nucleotide sequence as that of the parent cell because the two strands are complementary to each other. Thus, the nucleotide sequence is preserved in the daughter cell. However, gamete formation involves meiotic cell division, which involves the important phenomena of linkage and crossing over. Linkage passes on the same genes (DNA sequence) whereas crossing over results in the exchange of genetic material between the homologous chromosomes. As a result, the gametes formed will have some part of DNA same as the parent while some part of DNA different from the parent. During gametic fusion, the zygote formed will have a DNA sequence that is a combination of mother and father. Therefore, the DNA of the child resembles that of the parents, but not exactly same as the parent.
   Hence, the correct option is (c)

8. According to Mendelian inheritance, every character is represented by two alternative traits.

   Each character is controlled by a pair of genes called alleles that are located on the homologous chromosomes. One is a dominant allele and the other is a recessive allele. The trait controlled by the recessive allele is always masked by the dominant allele, and hence not expressed out in the presence of its dominant gene. Heterozygous condition represents one dominant and one recessive trait of the same character. Therefore, heterozygous recessive progenies are not possible in Mendelian inheritance. During the formation of gametes, the alleles get segregated independently, which explains the purity of gametes. But this is not the reason for the assertion given.
   Hence, the correct option is (b).

9. Red-flowered plants of P generation are pure breeds (homozygous dominant and homozygous recessive white flowered plant). The cross between these two plants produces all red-flowered plants in F1 generation. But, these plants are heterozygous as they possess a recessive gene for white flower. Since all the plants of F1 generation are heterozygous red-flowered plants, the genotypic ratio and the phenotypic ratio are same.
   Hence, the correct option is (d).

10. When the dominant gene shows incomplete dominance, the flowers of the plants of F1 generation show an intermediate expression between the dominant trait and the recessive trait.
    Hence, the correct option is (c).

11. The gene corresponding to blood group has three alleles instead of usual three alleles. They are represented as I^A; I^B; i. Both I^A and I^B are codominant and hence both are expressed in heterozygous condition. The gene 'I' is recessive, and hence is not expressed in the presence of either of the dominant genes. It is expressed only in homozygous condition. When both the parents have same blood group, then the children necessarily possess the same blood group. But when the parents have different blood groups, the children need not possess the same blood group. For example, if one parent has blood group 'A' and another parent has blood group 'B,' the child will get 'AB' blood group.
    Hence, the correct option is (d).

12. In case of a dihybrid cross, two different traits are considered. The two alternative forms of each trait are assorted independently during the formation of gametes. As a result, the trait for tallness of plant can be combined with that for wrinkled shape of the seeds and the trait for dwarfness of the plant can be combined with that for round shape of the seed. This is because of the independent assortment of the traits. Each progeny gets a homologous chromosome from male and female. But only when these chromosomes possess contrasting alleles, the progenies may inherit the recessive genes. Parental generation plants should be hybrid varieties.
    Hence, the correct option is (b).

13. In grasshopper, male individual determines the sex of the offspring as female has two X chromosomes and males have only one X chromosome. This is called XX–XO type of sex determination. But all organisms do not show male heterogamity. Some organisms such as birds show female heterogamity as females have one Z chromosome and one W chromosome whereas males have two Z chromosomes.
Hence, the correct option is (c)

14. Since X chromosome is present in both the sexes, genes on the X chromosome are called sex-linked genes.
Hence, the correct option is (a)

15. Males possess only one X chromosome. So, if any mutant allele is present on X chromosome, it is phenotypically expressed out. It is no more a recessive gene. Most of the genetic disorders are X-linked diseases. Even in Y-linked traits also, since males only possess Y chromosome, the traits are obviously expressed out. Therefore, males cannot act as carriers for sex-linked traits due to the heterozygous nature of sex chromosomes. Males cannot transmit the X-linked genes to their sons as sons get Y chromosome from father and X chromosome from mother. But this is not the reason for the given assertion.
Hence, the correct option is (b)

16. Hypertrichosis is a disease found only in males because it is a Y-linked trait. Since Y chromosome is transmitted only to sons from fathers, Y-linked traits are passed on to sons. Since females do not possess Y chromosome at all, all Y-linked traits are found only in males.
Hence, the correct option is (a)

17. Sickle cell anemia is a genetic disorder due to the presence of a recessive mutant allele on one of the chromosomes other than sex chromosomes. It is an autosomal recessive disorder. As it does not involve sex chromosomes, it is not sex specific. It can be found in either males or females in equal frequency.
Hence, the correct option is (a)

18. Mendel's dihybrid cross does give a phenotypic ratio of 9:3:3:1, and this is because of the independent assortment of the two traits during gamete formation.
Hence, the correct option is (a)

23. The number of chromosomes in a particular species is constant.

24. The proportion of plants heterozygous with respect to both the traits are in F2 generation of Mendel's dihybrid cross is 4/16.

25. The probability of birth of male child in humans is 50 per cent.

26. Human Y chromosome is shorter than X chromosome.

27. Allosomes or sex chromosomes are responsible for the transmission of characters from parents to the offspring.

28. Monohybrid cross: 3:1::Dihybrid cross: 9:3:3:1

29. Tall : dominant :: Dwarf : recessive

30. RR : homozygous :: Rr : heterozygous

31. Round seed : Dominant :: Wrinkled seed : recessive

32. Phenotypic ratio : 3:1 :: Genotypic ratio : 1:2:1

33. XX : female :: XY : male

34. Homozygous dominant : 9 :: Homozygous recessive : 1

35. TTPP : Parental combination :: TtPp or TTPp or TtPP : Recombination

36. Nucleus is present in cytoplasm whereas others are present in nucleus.

37. Ry represents heterozygous condition whereas others represent homozygous condition.

38. Yy represents a pair of alleles for contrasting traits whereas others represent a single allele for a particular trait.

39. Rryy represents a phenotypically different combination whereas others are all phenotypically similar.

40. Haemophilia is sex-linked genetic disorder whereas others are autosomal genetic disorders.

41. Crow show female heterogamety or ZZ–ZW type of sex determination whereas others show male heterogamity or XX–XY type of sex determination.

Level 2: Review your Concepts

42. Incomplete dominance is the phenomenon where when two alleles of a gene are brought together, none of them is dominant over each other, instead a new phenotype is formed. New phenotype is intermediate between the independent expressions of the two alleles.
In monohybrid cross of snapdragon flower plant (dog flower) (*Antirrhinum majus*), F_1 generation plants showed a blend of parental characters.
The cross can be summarized as follows.

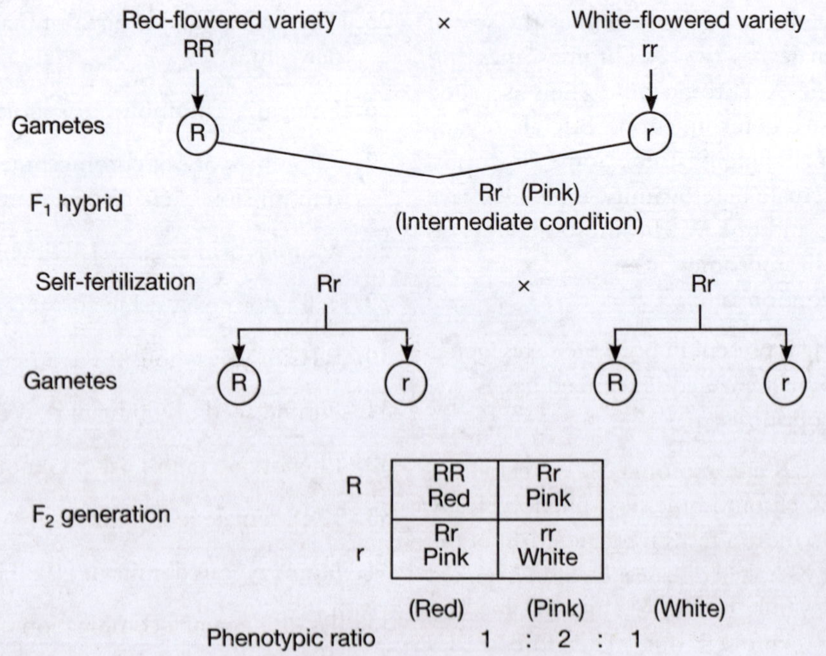

Genotypic ratio 1:2:1

43. Genotype of mother—ii
Genotype of father—I^AI^B

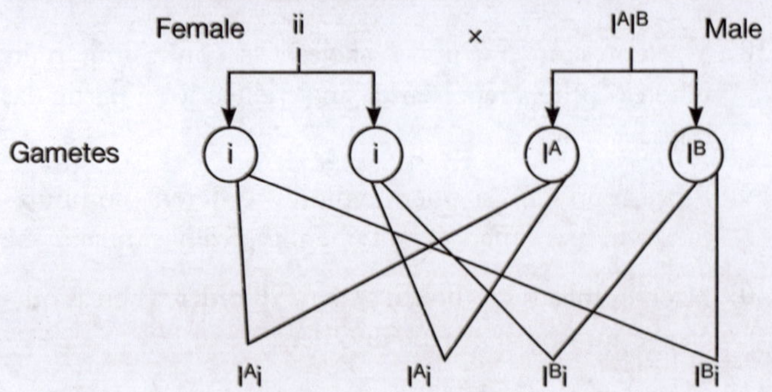

The possible blood groups of the progeny are blood group A and B.

44. Genotype of father can be either I^Ai or I^AI^A
Genotype of mother—I^Bi
Cross can be represented as below:

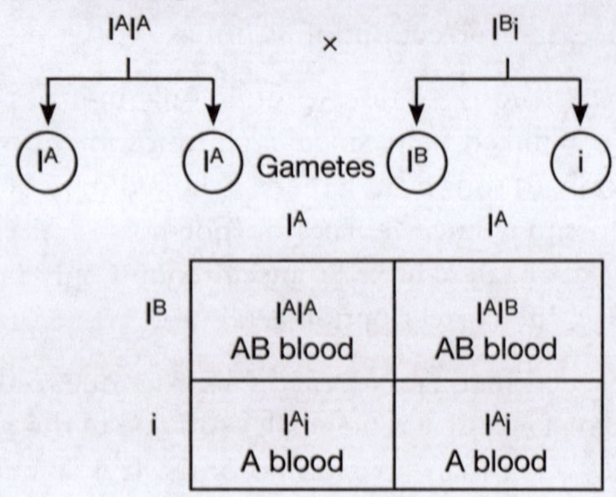

45.

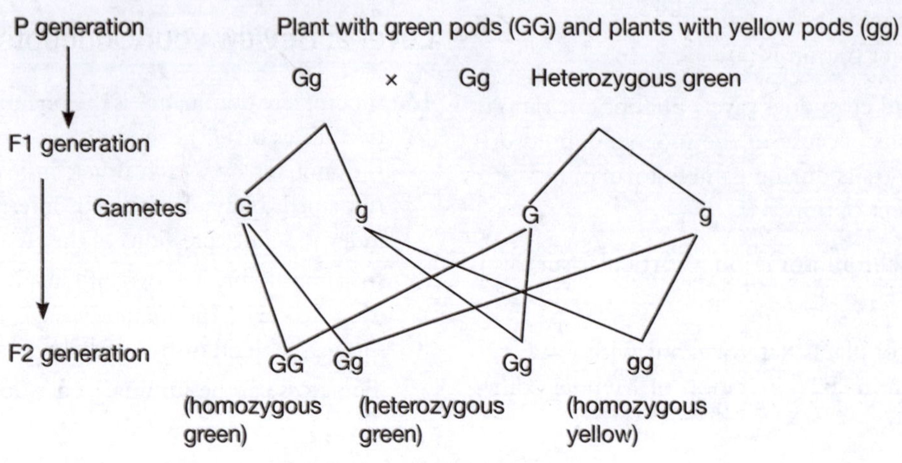

Representation of Mendel's monohybrid cross by Checker Board (Punnett Square)

	G (dominant)	g (recessive)
G	GG (Green)	Gg (Green)
g	Gg (Green)	gg (Yellow)

Phenotypic ratio—3 : 1 (3 plants with green pods; 1 plant with yellow pods)

Genotypic ratio—1 : 2 : 1 (1 homozygous plant with green pods; 2 heterozygous plants with green pods;1 homozygous plant with yellow pods)

46. **Case I:** The plants of P generation in first case would have been homozygous dominant red plants. It would be a cross between two homozygous red plants. Since there is no gene for the recessive trait, all the plants of successive generations would be homozygous dominant red plants.

Case II: The plants of P generation would have been homozygous dominant red-flowered plant and homozygous recessive white-flowered plant. The cross between these two results in heterozygous red-flowered plants in F1 generation. Since they carry the gene for the recessive trait (white flower), one of the next F2 generation progenies would have white flowers.

47. (a) Around 19 per cent of plants are dwarf plants with red flowers.

3 plants out of 16 plants = 18.77 per cent

Around 6 per cent of plants are dwarf with white flowers.

1 plant out of 16 plants = 6.25 per cent

(b) Tall plants with purple flowers are produced in maximum numbers. Around 56 per cent plants are of this type.

(c) 1 plant is homozygous tall with red flowers.

2 plants are homozygous with respect to colour of flower.

(d)

	Female gametes				
	X	TP	tP	Tp	tp
Male gametes	TP	TT PP	Tt PP	TTPp	TtPp
	tP	Tt PP	ttPP	TtPp	ttPp
	Tp	TT Pp	TtPp	TTpp	Ttpp
	tp	Tt Pp	ttPp	Ttpp	ttpp

48. (a) 25 per cent of plants are with wrinkled seeds in F2 generation.

(b) 50 per cent of plants are hybrid plants (heterozygous) as they contain the genes for both round seed and wrinkled seed.

(c) Punnett square for the above experiment

X	R (dominant)	r (recessive)
R	RR (Round)	Rr (Round)
r	Rr (Round)	rr (Wrinkled seeds)

49. (a) The plants obtained on crossing the above plants can have different combination as gametic fusion can take place in any manner (both parental combination and recombination) are possible, which proved that both the traits of the two characters are assorted independently, and hence, plants with different kinds of pods are produced.

(b)

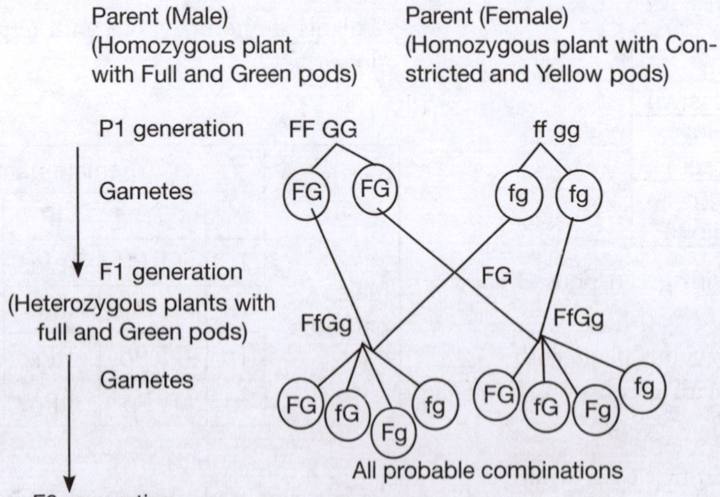

F2 generation

FG	×	FG	⟶	FFGG	Fg	×	FG	⟶ FfGg
FG	×	fG	⟶	FfGG	Fg	×	fG	⟶ FfGg
FG	×	Fg	⟶	FFGg	Fg	×	Fg	⟶ FFgg
FG	×	fg	⟶	FfGg	Fg	×	fg	⟶ Ffgg
fG	×	FG	⟶	FfGG	fg	×	FG	⟶ FfGg
fG	×	fG	⟶	ffGG	fg	×	fG	⟶ ffGg
fG	×	Fg	⟶	FfGg	fg	×	Fg	⟶ Ffgg
fG	×	fg	⟶	ffGg	fg	×	fg	⟶ ffgg

50. Homozygous and heterozygous dominant—556 × 9/16 = 313

Dominant with respect to only first trait—556 × 3/16 = 104

Dominant with respect to only second trait—556 × 3/16 = 104

Recessive with respect to both traits—556 × 1/16 = 35

51. Number of red-flowered plants in F2 generation—929 × 3/4 = 697

All red-flowered plants are not genotypically same. They may be homozygous red or heterozygous red. A total of 232 plants are homozygous red with both dominant genes; 465 plants are heterozygous red.

52. In Mendel's monohybrid cross, one plant of P1 generation is homozygous with both the genes for the red colour, which is a dominant trait. The other parent is homozygous recessive with both the genes for yellow colour.

- The gametes produced by dominant (RR) parent contain both R genes. The gametes produced by recessive (rr) parent contain both r genes.
- During recombination, one gene from each parent gets paired up, and hence, the plants produced have one R gene and one r gene. That means, the plants are heterozygous (Rr) with one dominant gene for red colour and one recessive gene for yellow colour. Since the dominant trait is expressed out, the plants bear red-coloured flowers.
- The plants of F1 generation are phenotypically similar to the homozygous dominant plants of P1 generation (red-coloured flowers). But they are genotypically dissimilar as they are heterozygous with a gene for the recessive trait.

53. Skin complexion is a character that is affected by more than one pair of genes. Such traits are called polygenic traits. These polygenic traits are controlled by more than one pair of genes and their additive effect results individuals with a spectrum of phenotypes in contrast to monogenic traits that show clear and distinct phenotypes with contrasting traits. Due to this reason, human beings are found to possess variable skin complexion.

54. Sickle cell anemia is an autosomal recessive disorder that arises due to a mutant allele. But this gene affects various other organs also. This comes under the condition of pleiotropy where a single gene has effect on various characters.

55.

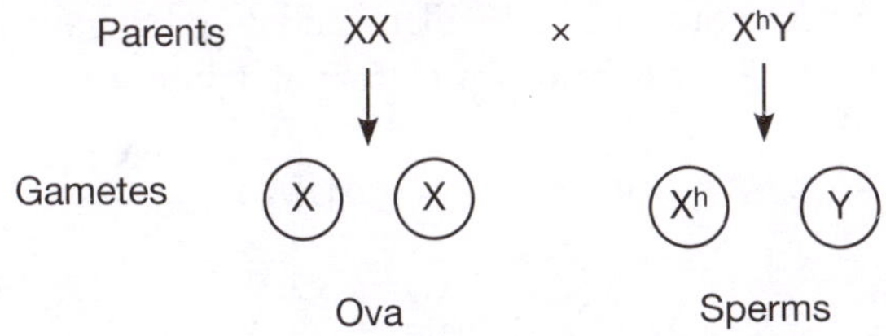

	X^h	Y
X	XX^h	XY
X	XX^h	XY

(a) Since the presence of one X chromosome with the mutant allele is sufficient to express the disease, it should be X-linked dominant disorder.

(b) Fifty per cent of sons are affected by the disease, whereas 50 per cent of sons are normal in F1 generation. 'A' is normal son and 'B' is affected son. The son who inherits X chromosome mutant gene from mother is affected by the disease. The son who inherits normal X chromosome from mother is not affected by the disease.

(c) Since A and C are son and daughter without any mutant genes, the successive generation are totally free of the diseased genes.

(d) As far as F_2 generation is concerned, E and F are normal sons as the mother is normal and sons do not inherit X chromosomes from father. G and H are affected daughters as they inherit the only X chromosome with mutant gene from their father.

(e) Females are more affected by the disease than males. If father is affected, 100 per cent daughters are affected by the diseases as they inherit the single X chromosome from father. If mother is affected, 50 per cent daughters are affected by the disease as they inherit at least one X chromosome from mother. Fifty percent of daughters are not affected by the disease. Therefore, females are predominantly affected by the disease in case of X-linked dominant disorders.

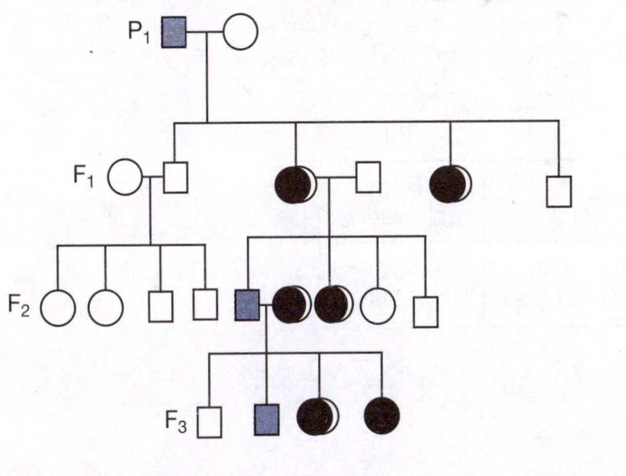

56. X-linked traits show criss-cross inheritance in which the gene corresponding to a trait or disease is passed on from father to daughter. This is because daughters get one X chromosome from father and one X chromosome from mother. Therefore, the genes corresponding to X-linked traits are passed on to daughters, and hence, they act as carriers if they are recessive traits. Sons are normal as they do not get any genes on the X chromosome of father as sons get only Y chromosome from father. Since sons get X chromosome from mother, in F2 generation, if the sons get X chromosome with the recessive gene for the trait or disease, they will be affected by the disease. Y-linked traits are inherited to sons from fathers. They do not show criss-cross inheritance.

57. (a) A man suffering from muscular dystrophy should have a mutant allele on the X chromosome. Since daughters necessarily get one X chromosome from father, they inherit the gene for the disease. Since it is a recessive gene, the daughters act as carriers. Since mother has no gene for the disease, they are not affected by the disease.

(b) The sons receive normal X chromosome from mother, and hence do not possess any mutant gene for the disease. If they marry normal women without any family history for muscular dystrophy, the disease is not at all passed on to the successive generations. If only sons are born in the first generation, the successive generations will be free of the disease. If daughters are born, they act as carriers and can pass on the genes to their sons as well as daughters. Since one X chromosome only possesses the mutant allele, the daughters who get normal X chromosome will be normal and they do not carry the gene. The sons who get normal X chromosome will be normal. In these two cases, the successive generations will be free of the disease.

(c) Pedigree chart for the disease:

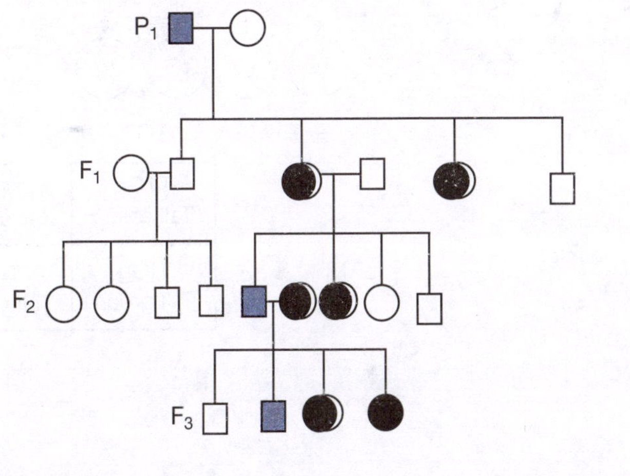

58. Both Down's syndrome and Turner's syndrome are chromosomal disorders. Down's syndrome results due to the presence of extra chromosome. The extra copy of chromosome is autosome and not sex chromosome. Turner's syndrome results due to the absence of an X chromosome in females. In Down's syndrome, the affected individuals are characterized by abnormal physical features and impaired psychomotor functions coupled with mental retardation. In Turner's syndrome, the females are characterized by sterility with rudimentary ovaries and also underdeveloped secondary sexual characters.

59. In humans, sex determination is based on the XX-XY type mechanism. Males have one X and one Y chromosome, while females have two X chromosomes. During gametic fusion, the type of male gamete (X or Y) that fuses with the female's X chromosome determines the sex of the offspring. If the offspring receives an X from both parents, it's a female (XX). If it gets an X from the mother and a Y from the father, it's a male (XY).

60. Mutagens are agents that cause mutations. These can be factors like radiation, chemicals, and temperature. Mutations result in changes in the genetic message of a cell, leading to consequent variations in the phenotype of organisms. Mutagens can induce mutations artificially in certain organisms, influencing their genetic makeup.

61. Law of dominance states that "When a pair of contrasting alleles or traits are brought together in F1 hybrid, then only one of them will express itself, and other will be suppressed. The trait which is expressed is called dominant and the one which is suppressed is called recessive trait." For example, in a cross between homozygous tall (TT) plant and homozygous dwarf plant (tt), F1 hybrid plants were all tall.

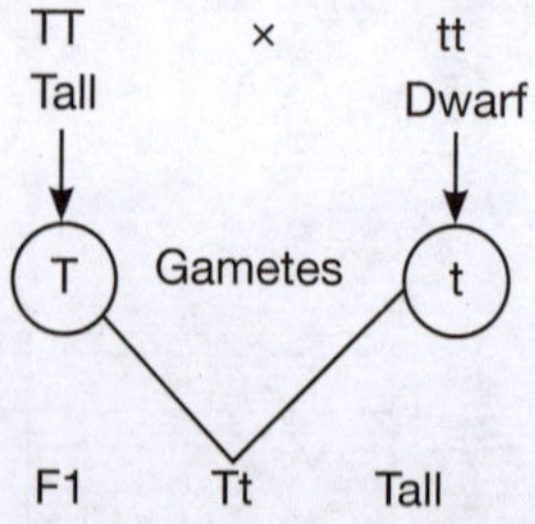

62. The cross of an F_1 hybrid with one of the two parents is called back cross. In plant breeding, back cross is performed a few times in order to increase the traits of that parent. There are two possibilities for back cross. In one possibility, there is a cross between F_1 hybrid (Tt) and dominant parent (TT). In such a cross, plants will be 100 per cent tall. In second possibility, there is a cross between F1 hybrid (Tt) and recessive parent (tt). In such cross, plants will be 50 per cent tall and 50 per cent dwarf.

63. One gene influences two or more seemingly unrelated phenotypic traits. This phenomenon is known as pleiotropism and the gene responsible for pleiotropism is known as pleiotropic gene.

In pea plant, starch synthesis, size of starch grains, and seed shape are controlled by one gene. The gene can be represented as 'B', which has two allelic forms 'B' and 'b'. The homozygous pea plants with BB genotype are efficient in starch synthesis, and hence, the starch grains are large and seeds at maturity are round. The heterozygous Bb plants produce round seeds indicating B is the dominant allele, but the starch grains are intermediate in size, that is, for the starch grain size, alleles show incomplete dominance. Homozygous pea plants with 'bb' phenotype are less efficient in starch synthesis, and they have small starch grains and the seeds are wrinkled.

64.

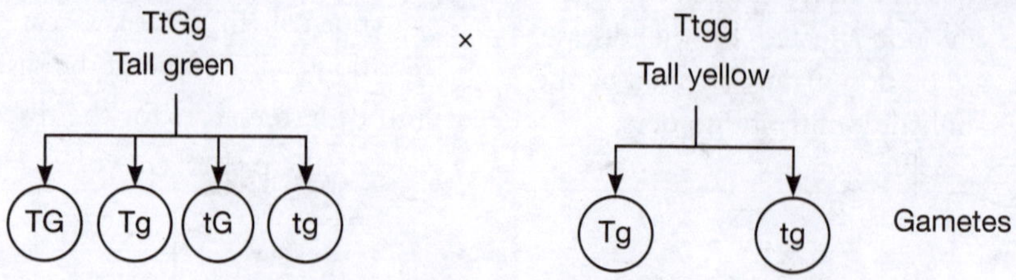

	TG	Tg	tG	tg
Tg	TTGg Tall green	TTgg Tall yellow	TtGg tall green	Ttgg Tall yellow
tg	TtGg Tall green	Ttgg Tall yellow	ttGg Dwarf green	ttgg Dwarf yellow

65. (a) Homozygous tall and homozygous dwarf

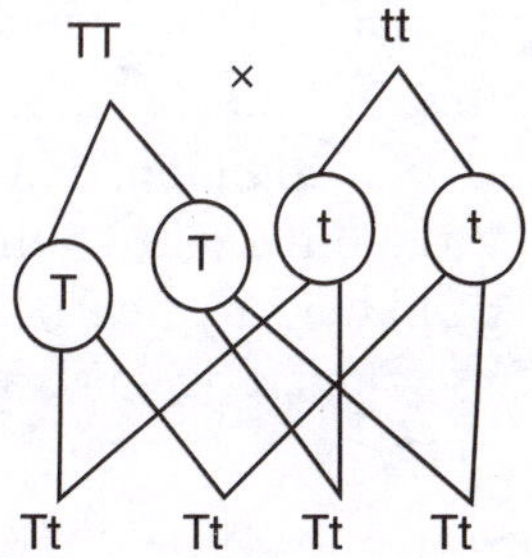

- A homozygous tall plant produces gametes with genes for tall trait. A homozygous dwarf plant produces gametes with genes for dwarf trait.
- The cross between the above plants results in the fusion of gametes produced by them in different combinations, which gives rise to all heterozygous plants with genes for both the contrasting traits (Tt) in the F1 generation. However, all the progenies are phenotypically tall as the recessive dwarf trait is masked.

(b) Homozygous tall (dominant) and heterozygous tall

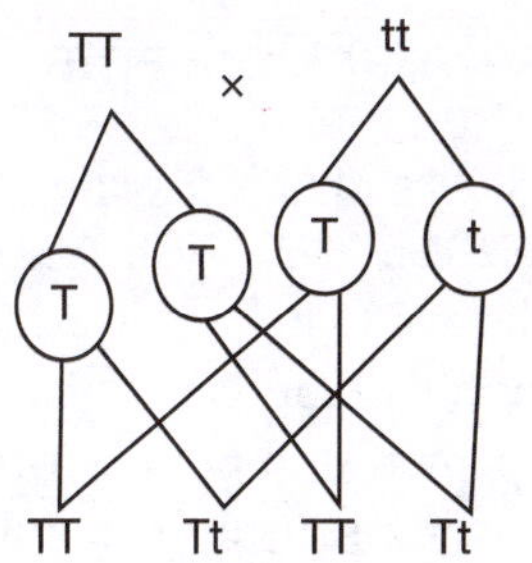

- A homozygous tall plant produces gametes with genes for tall trait. A heterozygous tall plant produces one gamete with gene for tall trait and another gamete with gene for dwarf trait.
- The cross between the above plants results in the fusion of gametes produced by them in different combinations, which gives rise to two homozygous tall plants with both the genes for tall trait and two heterozygous plants with genes for both the contrasting traits (Tt) in the F1 generation. However, all the progenies are phenotypically tall as the recessive dwarf trait is masked in the heterozygous.

(c) Heterozygous tall and heterozygous tall

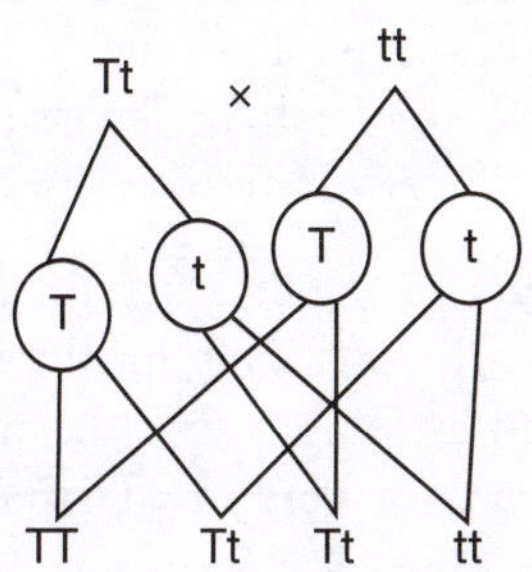

- A heterozygous tall plant produces one gamete with gene for tall trait and another gamete with gene for dwarf trait.
- The cross between the above plants results in the fusion of gametes produced by them in different combinations, which gives rise to one homozygous tall plant with both the genes for tall trait, two heterozygous plants with genes for both the contrasting traits (Tt), and one homozygous dwarf plant with both genes for dwarf traits in the F1 generation. However, three progenies are phenotypically tall as the recessive dwarf trait is masked in the heterozygous plant. Only homozygous dwarf plant is phenotypically dwarf.

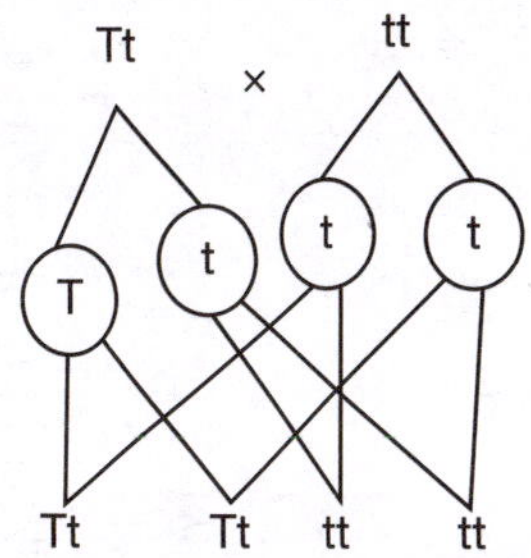

- A heterozygous tall plant produces one gamete with gene for tall trait and another gamete with gene for dwarf trait. A homozygous dwarf plant produces gametes with genes for dwarf trait.
- The cross between the above plants results in the fusion of gametes produced by them in different combinations, which gives rise to two heterozygous plants with genes for both the contrasting traits (Tt) and two dwarf plants with both the genes for dwarf traits in the F1 generation. However, the two heterozygous progenies are phenotypically tall as the recessive dwarf trait is masked.

66. • Allosomes are sex chromosomes that are responsible for the determination of sex. These are responsible for the transmission of hereditary characters in organisms.

- Autosomes are the chromosomes other than sex chromosomes.

67. Sudden variations may take place in a particular individual due to the change in the structure of a gene (DNA sequence) or chromosome or in the number of chromosomes. Such sudden changes are called mutations. These mutations may bring about a change in the genetic message of a cell thereby resulting in the consequent change in the phenotype of the respective organisms.

- Mutation is a random phenomenon that takes place spontaneously at a low frequency. Some external or environmental factors may induce mutations artificially in certain organisms. Such agents that cause mutations are called mutagens. Radiations, chemicals, and temperature are the important mutagens.

68. (a) Heterozygous
(b) Gene
(c) Recessive allele
(d) Homologous chromosomes
(e) Pleiotropy
(f) Autosomal traits
(g) Codominance
(h) Clones

69.

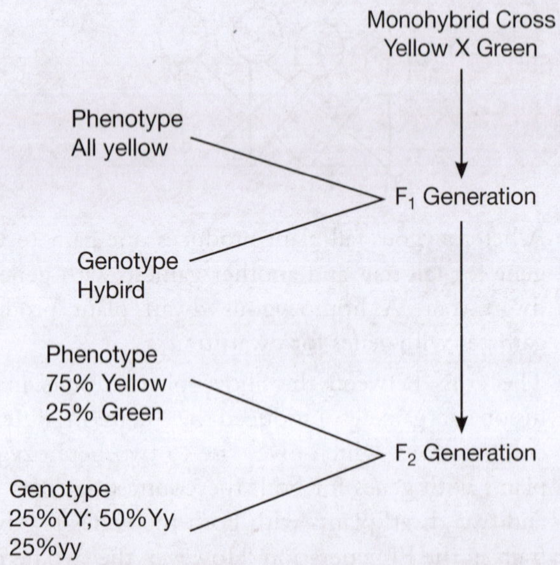

70. Consanguineous marriages are the marriages between close relatives; such marriages are not suggestible due to the following reasons:

- Any gene carrying a particular abnormality or disorder present in the homologous chromosomes is passed onto the next generation. All the offspring necessarily need not be affected by the disease. Sometimes, if the gene is recessive allele, it may be present in the offspring but the child is normal. However, such persons can act as carriers for the disease.
- If the carrier male or female marries a normal female or male, the probability of progenies suffering from the disease is very less. At the most, some of the progenies may become carriers.
- In case of mating between close relatives, there is a chance that both male and female may act as carriers due to their common ancestry. In such a case, the probability of the offspring suffering from the disease is much higher than in the previous case.
- A part from this, the closely related individuals have some part of DNA common, and hence, the variation is less. Variations lead to genetic diversity and heritance of good traits in the family. This scope also is limited in case of marriages between close relatives.

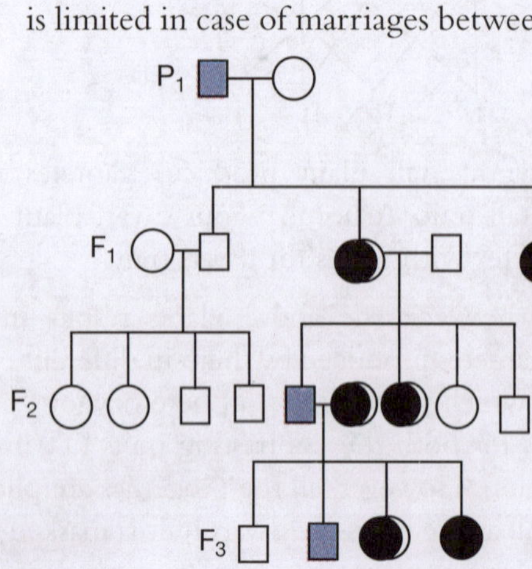

Level 3: Assess Your Concepts

71. Mendel's laws provided a baseline understanding of inheritance patterns in organisms. The subsequent deviations observed in real-world scenarios indicate the complexity of genetic inheritance beyond Mendel's experiments on pea plants. These deviations, like incomplete dominance, co-dominance, and linked genes, showcased that inheritance isn't always straightforward. However, the rediscovery of Mendel's work serves as a foundational pillar, allowing geneticists to build upon it and delve deeper into the intricate details of genetics. By understanding.

72. Sikle cell anemia is an autosomal recessive disorder whereas haemophilia is an X-linked disorder. Autosomal genetic disorders are not sex specific as they do not involve sex chromosomes. Haemophilia is an X-linked recessive disorder. For X-linked recessive traits, females generally act as carriers of the affected gene whereas males are affected by the disease. Females can be affected by the disease only when both the X chromosomes contain mutant genes for the disease. But this condition usually is not viable and the babies are susceptible to death in fetal stage itself. Hence, haemophilia is very rare in females.

73. Male and female gametes are formed by means of meiotic cell division. This involves the phenomena of linkage and crossing over of homologous chromosomes. A group of genes that is normally inherited together is termed as linkage group and the genes are called linked genes. This phenomenon in which certain genes present on a chromosome are together carried on to daughter cell is called linkage. Linkage is responsible for the inheritance of characters to the successive generations. If all the genes on a chromosome are transferred, it is called complete linkage. If some of the genes are transferred, it is called incomplete linkage. Generally, incomplete linkage takes place during meiotic cell division. As some genes are passed on to the daughter cell (gamete) together, the corresponding traits are passed on from the respective parent. The phenomenon of the exchange of segments of non-sister chromatids (genes) of homologous chromosomes is known as crossing over. Crossing over is followed by recombination. Due to the exchange of some genes between the homologous chromosomes, the pairing of chromosomes may give rise to a new combination of genes, which is called recombination. This results in variations (new traits) that are not there in the parents. These are inherited to the next generation because the fusion of these gametes results in the formation of diploid zygote. Therefore, the variations occurring in the chromosomes are transmitted to the children. A child, thus possesses some characteristic resembling with both father and mother. However, the child is not an exact copy of either of the parents.

74. The genes controlling the secretion of milk are found in both males and females. But, they are in recessive condition in males. Hence, the character is not expressed in males. It is expressed in females as the gene is in dominant condition. Such traits are called sex-limited traits.

75. In *Drosophila*, the gene controlling the colour of the eye is present on the X chromosome. The gene for red colour of eye is a dominant allele whereas the gene for the white colour of eye is a recessive allele. That means, white eye colour in *Drosophila* is an X-linked recessive trait. Since it is a recessive trait, it is phenotypically expressed out only in homozygous condition. In females, since two X chromosomes are present, both the chromosomes possessing the diseased genes is a very rare condition and may not be viable. In heterozygous condition, they express only red colour of eye and act as carriers for the gene for white eye. In males, since only one X chromosome is present, the disease is expressed out and the person suffers from the disease.

NEET SPECIAL WING

Multiple-Answer Type Questions

1. Most of the mammals and insects such as *Drosophila* show XX–XY type of sex determination. Insects such as grasshopper have XO type mechanism of sex determination because the female has a pair of X chromosomes, whereas the male has a single X chromosome, and hence is represented as XO. In certain classes of organisms such as birds, the females possess two different types of sex chromosomes (ZW) and males possess two same types of sex chromosomes (ZZ).

2. The pink coloured flowers are produced due to incomplete dominance of both red and white alleles. The codominance of both I^A and I^B alleles produces AB blood group. Sickle cell anaemia is a genetic disorder which follows recessive mendelian inheritance.

3. Dwarf height, white flowers and constricted pod shape are all recessive traits in a pea plant and will get expressed only when present in both the chromosomes.

4. The cross between the individual of F1 generation with the recessive parent is known as test cross. The phenotypic as well as genotypic ratio is 1:1.

5. On the basis of Monohybrid cross Mendel –
   i. The inheritance of each character in an organism is controlled by two factors (genes) that lie on two homologous chromosomes.
   ii. When two contrasting factors are present in an organism, one of them may mask the presence of the other. The factor that expresses itself in the hybrid is called dominant allele.
   iii. The two alternative factors of pair representing a character are separated from each other at the time of gamete formation, and hence, a gamete contains only one factor for the character.

Comprehension-Based Questions

A.

6. 11 is a female carrier so genotype is X^cX and 19 is affected male with genotype is X^cY. So, the male children will have either genotype XY or X^cY. Thus, there is a 50% chance that the male will not have defect.

X^cY \ X^cX	X^c	X
X^c	X^cX^c	X^cX
Y	X^cY	XY

7. The parents are X^cX (5) and XY (9). The Punnett square will be as follows:

XY \ X^cX	X^c	X
X	X^cX	XX
Y	X^cY	XY

3 out of 4 children will not have the defect. Thus 75% of the kids will not have the defect, some of them can be carriers like in the case of X^cX.

8. Since the girl child is a carrier with the genotype X^cX, the X gene without the defect will come from the male parent considering the female parent has the disorder. So the male parent cannot have the defective X chromosome and the genotype will be XY.

9. The punnett square between 11 and 19 will be as follows:

X^cY \ X^cX	X^c	X
X^c	X^cX^c	X^cX
Y	X^cY	XY

Only 1 in 4 is a carrier, so 25% of the progeny will be a carrier.

10. Since both the parents are neither carrier for the gene nor have the defect, there is no chance that they will have children with colour blindness.

11. Match the following:

Polydactyly- Autosomal dominant disorder
(i) (d)

Phenylketonuria- Autosomal recessive disorder
(ii) (a)

Hypertrichosis- Y linked disorder
(iii) (b)

Hypophosphatemic rickets- X linked dominant disorder
(iv) (c)

Haemophilia- X linked recessive disorder
(v) (e)

B.

12. Since non-tongue rolling is an autosomal recessive condition and since both the parents are tongue rollers and all their children also will be tongue rollers. So, there is zero percent chance of them having non tongue roller children as both the parents are homozygous for the gene of tongue rolling.

13. B has the defect but is married to a person who can roll their tongue. Since they have kids both with defects and without, B has to be heterozygous for the defect. Only then can a tongue roller be born, since the defect is autosomal dominant. So, the genotype of B (RR^0) is heterozygous and phenotype is non-roller.

14. Since F is a son of heterozygous mother (RR^0) and homozygous father (RR), his genotype will be also heterozygous (RR^0). His partner is G with homozygous genotype (RR). So, there is one in two chances of having a child who can roll the tongue (RR). Their Punnett square is as follows-

Rr / RR	R	r
R	RR	Rr
R	RR	Rr

15. Both the parents are tongue rollers and have the genotype-RR and thus all their children will be tongue rollers.

16. If the defect is autosomal recessive defect, then it will be phenotypically expressed only when both the genes are recessive so the genotype of the parent with defect will be -rr. Since the other parent is tongue roller and has no family history, will be homozygous with genotype RR. All the progeny will as a result will have genotype Rr. So all the progeny will be tongue rollers and none with the defect.

17. Match the following:
4 o'clock plant- Incomplete dominance
(i) (b)

A, B, O blood group- Codominance
(ii) (a)

One character many allelic genes- Multiple allelic series
(iii) (d)

One allele many characters- Pleiotropy
(iv) (c)

Skin colour in humans- Polygenic trait
(v) (e)

CHAPTER
10

Evolution

Remember

Before beginning this chapter, you should be able to:

- Recall basis of classification of living organisms
- Remember basic characteristics of different plant and animal kingdoms

Key Ideas

After completing this chapter, you should be able to:

- Understand major evidences of evolution
- Explain Lamarckism and Darwinism
- Discuss modern theory of evolution

A Tribute to Charles Darwin (1809–1882)

Charles Darwin (1809–1882), widely regarded as the architect of evolutionary biology, profoundly altered our understanding of the origin and development of life. Darwin set out on a voyage aboard the ship 'HMS Beagle,' where his encounters with the Galapagos Islands' diverse species laid the groundwork for his seminal theory of evolution by natural selection. His monumental work, 'On the Origin of Species,' published in 1859, shook the scientific and religious communities of his time by proposing that species evolve over generations through natural selection.

Darwin's meticulous observations and analyses provided a unifying explanation for the dazzling diversity and complexity of life on Earth, dispelling popular notions of a static world in favour of a dynamic, ever-evolving panorama of life.

FUN TIME

CROSSWORD

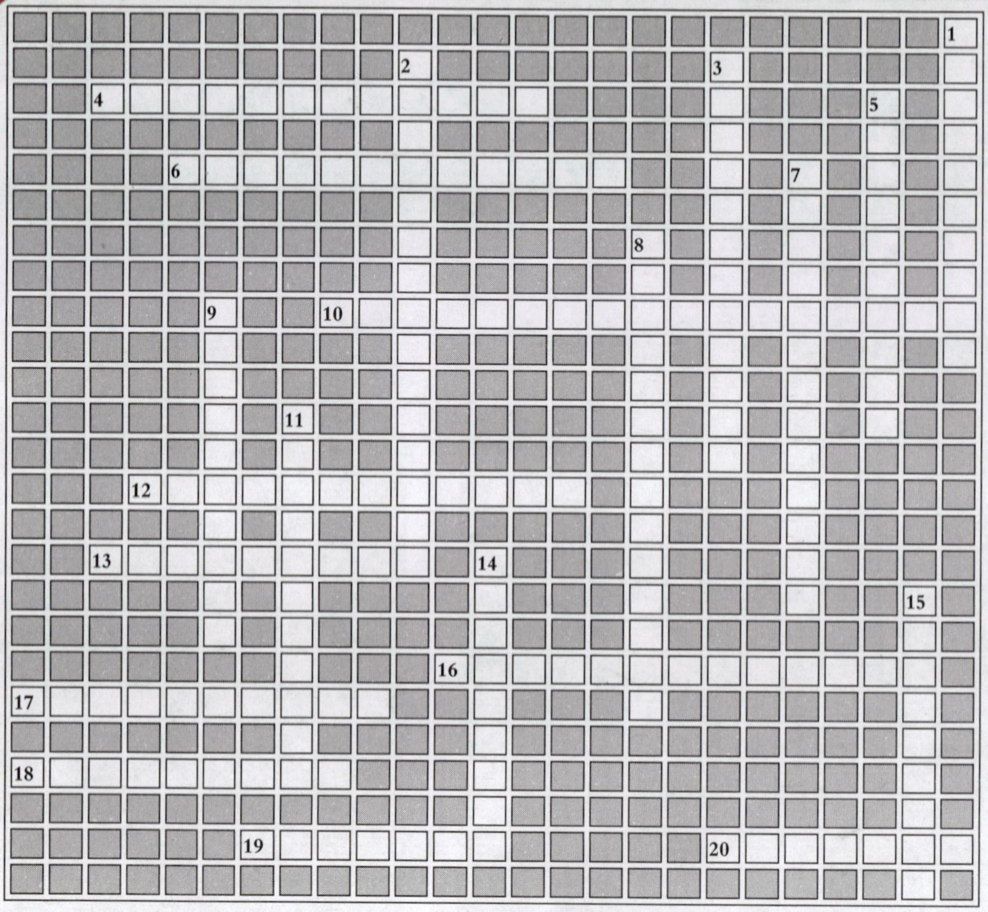

Across

4. The common ancestor of man and apes
6. The first ancestral man
10. The other name for divergent evolution
12. Self-replicating molecules which formed the first living cell and resulted in the origin of life
13. ______ dominated earth during Jurassic period
16. The study of fossils
17. Origin of new species from an existing species
18. Sudden variation in chromosome no. and structure
19. Darwin studied ____ birds on his Galapagos voyage.
20. The connecting link between reptiles and mammals

Down

1. Features exhibited by same species organisms
2. Organ dysfunctions over time in a specific species
3. Elimination of certain genes in the small isolated population of species due to natural calamities
5. The pouched mammals in Australia
7. The missing link between reptiles and birds
8. The period considered as the age of reptiles
9. In ______ period dinosaurs disappeared
11. _____era associated with the earths origin
14. Islands associated with Darwin evolution theory
15. Organisms develop from one group to another over time.

INTRODUCTION

The Earth is the only planet that has been known to be inhabited by a wide variety of flora and fauna. This variety of living beings is called biodiversity. We find many similarities and variations among the wide variety of living organisms. However, even apparently different organisms share some common basic characteristics. For example, all the living organisms are made up of basic units of life called cells. Various scientists believe that the simplest forms of life originated on Earth, which in course of time evolved into complex life forms. This origin of life and the gradual and slow changes brought about in these life forms resulted in enormous biodiversity that formed the basis for evolution. The origin of life is in a way related to the origin of Earth which is in turn related to the origin of universe.

Origin of Universe

How and when did the universe begin? This is the most fundamental question that has led to many active and vigorous discussions amongst scientists and researchers. There were many theories and propositions put forward by various scientists to explain the origin of universe. The most widely accepted theory regarding the origin of universe and hence earth is the Big Bang Theory.

Big Bang Theory

According to the Big Bang theory, a huge explosion of cosmic material resulted in the formation of hydrogen and other nuclei which organized to form galaxies. The universe in the beginning used to be nothing. It started as a little spot of a hot and massive ball. About 13.8 billion years ago, an aggressive explosion threw the material within that ball into all directions of space.

The universe started to expand after the Big Bang and it continues to expand till today. In the course of time, the universe expanded and cooled. As a result, things started to form, from sub-atomic particles such as neutrons, protons to atoms, stars, etc. Everything that exists today developed from that ball that expanded about 13.8 billion years ago. Solar system including our Earth is a part of the milkyway galaxy formed in the above manner. A galaxy is a complex organization of millions or billions of stars along with gas and dust, held together by gravitational attraction. The Origin of Life is intimately associated with the origin of Earth. There were various ideas and beliefs as to how the life originated on Earth. But, they lacked experimental proofs. However, the modern theory of Origin of Life is widely accepted all over the world.

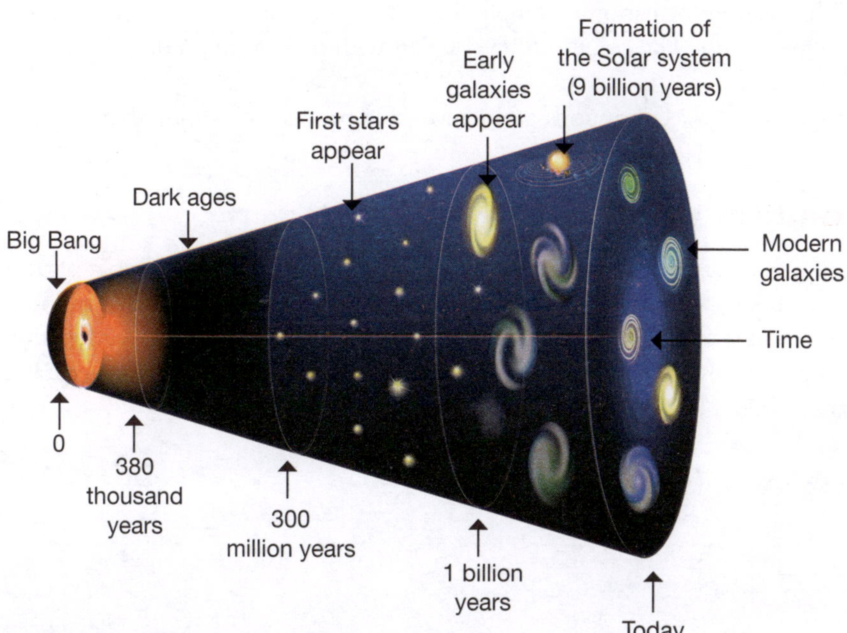

Info Bytes!

The name 'Big Bang' came from the theory's most intense critic, Fred Hoyle.

Figure 10.1 Cosmic Timeline and evolution of stars, galaxy and Universe after Big Bang

Figure 10.2 Milky way galaxy

Origin of Life

Earth was initially assumed to be a hot gaseous mass. As this mass cooled down, the heavy elements such as metals and silica sank to the bottom and formed the Earth's crust. The lighter elements such as hydrogen, nitrogen, oxygen, carbon, etc., formed the early atmosphere. As the cooling of Earth continued, these gaseous elements combined at random to form simple molecules such as water, carbon dioxide, ammonia, methane, etc. Further cooling resulted in the formation of oceans. The ocean water contained various inorganic salts along with ammonia and methane brought by rain water. These simple molecules, in course of time, under suitable conditions, got converted to simple organic molecules such as sugars, amino acids, etc. Since there was no much free oxygen in the early atmosphere, these organic molecules accumulated in water. At some point of time, under suitable conditions, these simple organic molecules underwent transformation to form the various building blocks of life. The most important among them are nucleic acids, proteins, carbohydrates, etc. All these changes were presumed to have derived the required energy from the electric discharges, lightning, solar energy, etc. Nucleic acids being the self-replicating molecules gave rise to the first primitive cells. The gradual increase in complexity in the organization of the living cells over a long period of time resulted in the origin of more complex and diverse forms of life. The various changes associated with this transformation of simple life forms into complex living organisms forms the basis for biological evolution or organic evolution. The origin of life coupled with the evolution of life constitutes the history of life.

Info Bytes!

The term 'milky' in the name 'milky way' is derived from the appearance of the galaxy from the earth.

Biological or organic evolution is defined as a slow, continuous and irreversible process of change that resulted in an orderly change from one form to another.

Biological or Organic Evolution

The orderly changes in the characteristics of groups of organisms over the course of generations lead to biological or organic evolution. This involves the progressive development of animals and plants from ancestors of different forms and functions. There are many evidences provided by scientists in support of the ladder such as gradation in the structure and functioning of plants and animals. These evidences reveal the relationships and gradations across the generations. Based on the characteristics taken as basis, the various evidences are categorized into different types. They are:

- Biogeographical evidences
- Palaeontological evidences
- Morphological evidences
- Anatomical evidences
- Embryological evidences

Biogeographical Evidences

The study of patterns of distribution of animals and plants in different parts of Earth is known as biogeography. The different geographical regions had different environmental conditions. Hence, plants and animals evolved independently in the respective geographical regions. The evidences showing the relationship between biodiversity and the geography can be studied under three categories:

1. Discontinuous distribution
2. Adaptive radiation
3. Convergent evolution

Figure 10.3 The walrus is a large flippered marine mammal with a discontinuous distribution about the North Pole in the Arctic Ocean and subarctic seas of the Northern Hemisphere.

Discontinuous Distribution

It is found that closely related species of plants and animals inhabit the far distant geographical regions. The regions lying in between these territories are not inhabited by any closely related plants or animals. Such kind of discontinuous distribution of organisms shows the common ancestry of those organisms. For example, existence of alligators in south eastern part of the USA and eastern China

Adaptive Radiation

Darwin in his voyage to famous Galápagos islands found many varieties of plants and animals that were unique to that area. He made detailed studies regarding the birds of that area called finches. Hence, these birds are popularly known as Darwin's finches. Initially, these birds were seed eating, as their beaks were suitable for eating seeds. Later, they changed the feeding habit to insect eating. The finches of different islands evolved different adaptations in the their beaks according to the type of food of the particular islands. This kind of evolutionary trend that gave rise to new species of birds to make them suitable for the new habitats and new way of life is called adaptive radiation. The occurrence of pouched mammals called marsupials in Australia showed close resemblances with the placental mammals in the rest of the world. This also shows adaptive radiation indicating common ancestry for the marsupials and various placental mammals.

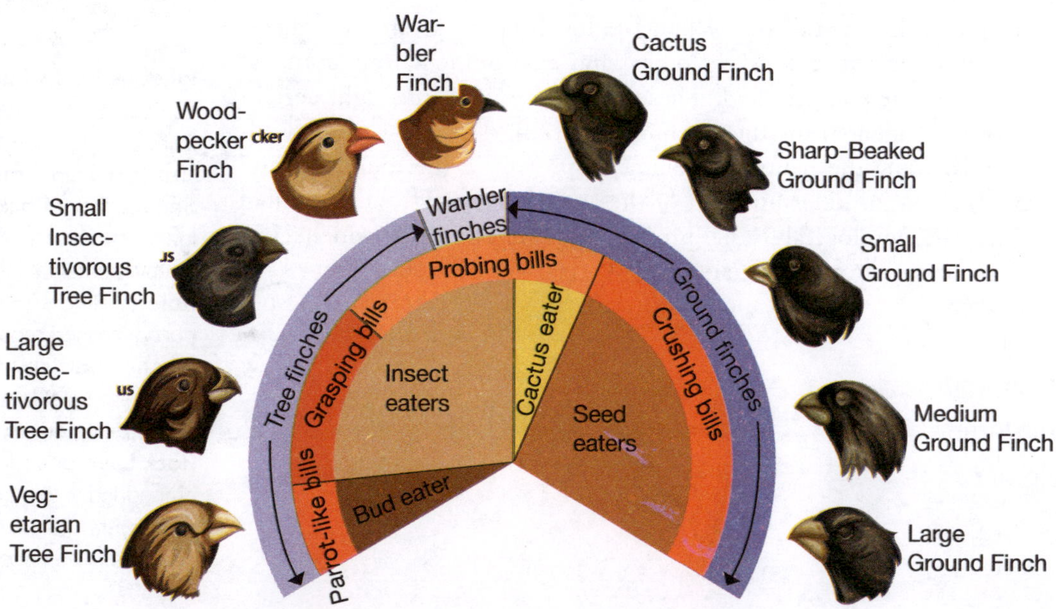

Figure 10.4 Adaptive radiation of Galápagos finches

Convergent Evolution

It is also found that evolution brought about similar kinds of changes or adaptations in the animals living in different regions having similar habitats. This is called adaptive convergence or convergent evolution. This is a parallel evolution. For example, some Australian marsupials closely resemble placental mammals in other regions with the similar environmental conditions.

Figure 10.5 Spiny ant eater—found in Australia (left) and Pangolin—found Southeast Asia (right)

Palaeontological Evidences

The fossils are the preserved remains or traces of animals or plants or any other organisms from the remote past. The formation of fossils is closely associated with the formation of rocks. Igneous rocks are the oldest rocks that are formed by the solidification of the molten material in the Earth's crust. In course of time, these rocks are acted upon by the various agents and get transformed into sedimentary rocks. The dead animals and plants that are carried to the sea by the flowing rivers sink to the bottom of the seas and get buried in the sedimentary rocks. The absence of adequate supply of oxygen prevents the decomposition of these dead living organisms. Thus, these dead organisms that remain buried in the rocks form fossils. When the fossilized rocks are brought to the surface of sea by means of various geological and environmental phenomena, the fossils could be collected and studied. These studies brought into light certain facts that form strong evidences for the organic evolution. The age of the fossils can be determined by using the radioactive elements present in the rocks. Usually radioactive carbon is used for determination of the age of the fossils. This is called carbon dating. The palaeontological studies provided different kinds of evidences in support of the organic evolution. These are:

- Geological time scale
- Mass extinctions
- Ancestral forms
- Transitional forms

Info Bytes!

Palaeontology is the branch of biology concerned with the study of fossils.

Konnect

Igneous Rocks Formation (Oldest rocks formed from solidified molten material in Earth's crust) → **Transformation to Sedimentary Rocks** (Over time, igneous rocks transform due to environmental factors.) → **Role of Rivers** (Rivers transport deceased organisms to the seas) → **Settlement in Seabed** (Organisms settle to the seabed.) → **Embedment in Sedimentary Rock Layers** (Organisms become embedded within sedimentary rock layers. Note: Limited oxygen prevents decomposition.)

Figure 10.6 Fossils embedded in a rock

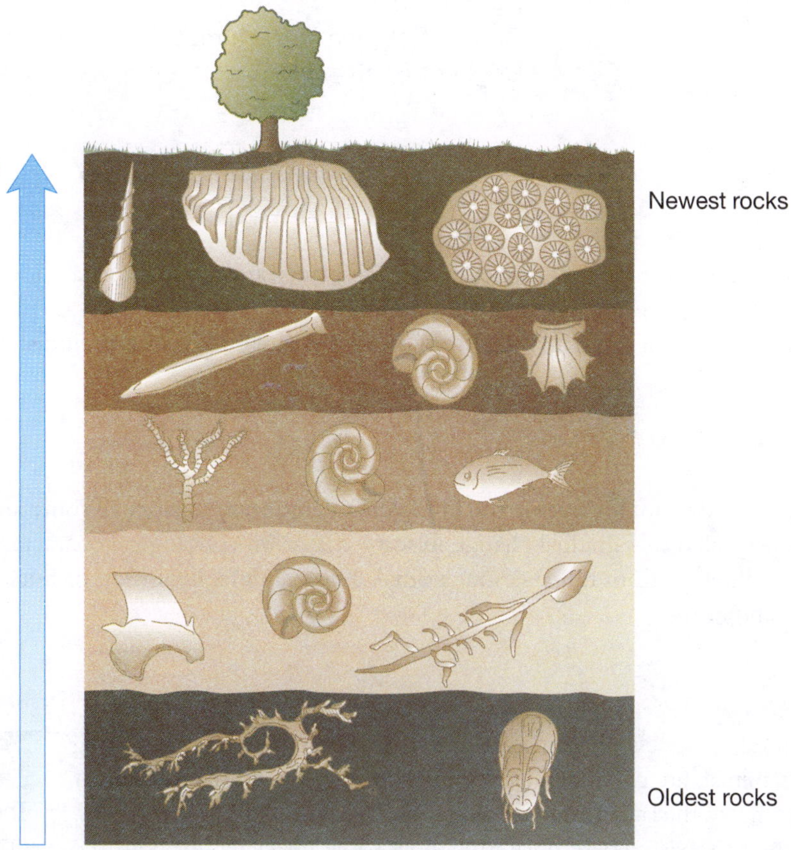

Figure 10.7 Pictorial diagram showing fossils in layers of rock over period of time

Geological Time Scale

The fossils of animals collected from layers of Earth at different depths in a way indicate the chronological order in which the animals were evolved. The animals can be arranged according to the order of geological eras in which they were evolved. This is called geological time scale.

Table 10.1 Geological time scale

Era	Period	Important organisms evolved
Coenozoic	Quarternary	Modern mammals, birds, fish. Modern man
	Tertiary	First mammals, angiosperms, ape-like ancestors of modern man
Mesozoic	Cretaceous	Extinction of dinosaurs and toothed birds Evolution of first flowering plants
	Jurassic (age of reptiles)	Dinosaurs domination Evolution of toothed birds
Palaeozoic	Carboniferous	Origin of reptiles Amphibians dominant First seeded plants
	Devonian	Origin of amphibians Bony fish Gymnosperms
	Cambrian	Origin of invertebrates
Precambrian		Oldest fossils Diverse algae Origin of oxygen in the atmosphere Origin of Earth

Mass Extinctions

The sudden and large-scale extinction of some species of plants and animals in a short span of time is called mass extinction. The fossils of such species indicate the resemblance of existing species of plants or animals to the extinct species. For example, extinction of dinosaurs that dominated the earth in Jurassic period shows some similarities with the living reptiles.

Ancestral Forms

The studies of fossils provided proof for tracing the complete evolutionary history of some animals such as horse, elephant, camel, etc. The studies revealed that gradual change in some major morphological characteristics resulted in the origin of an animal that is totally different from the ancestral animal. For example, evolution of horse from a small fox-like animal with short head, neck and toes.

Transitional Forms

Some organisms are found to possess the characteristics of two different groups of living plants or animals. Such animals are called connecting links. It is presumed that the earlier group of organisms gave rise to the latter group of organisms. In between these two groups, some organisms are found to exist. These organisms show some characters of both the groups.

Konnect

The oldest known fossil of a modern human (Homo sapiens) is about 300,000 years old and was discovered in Jebel Irhoud, Morocco.

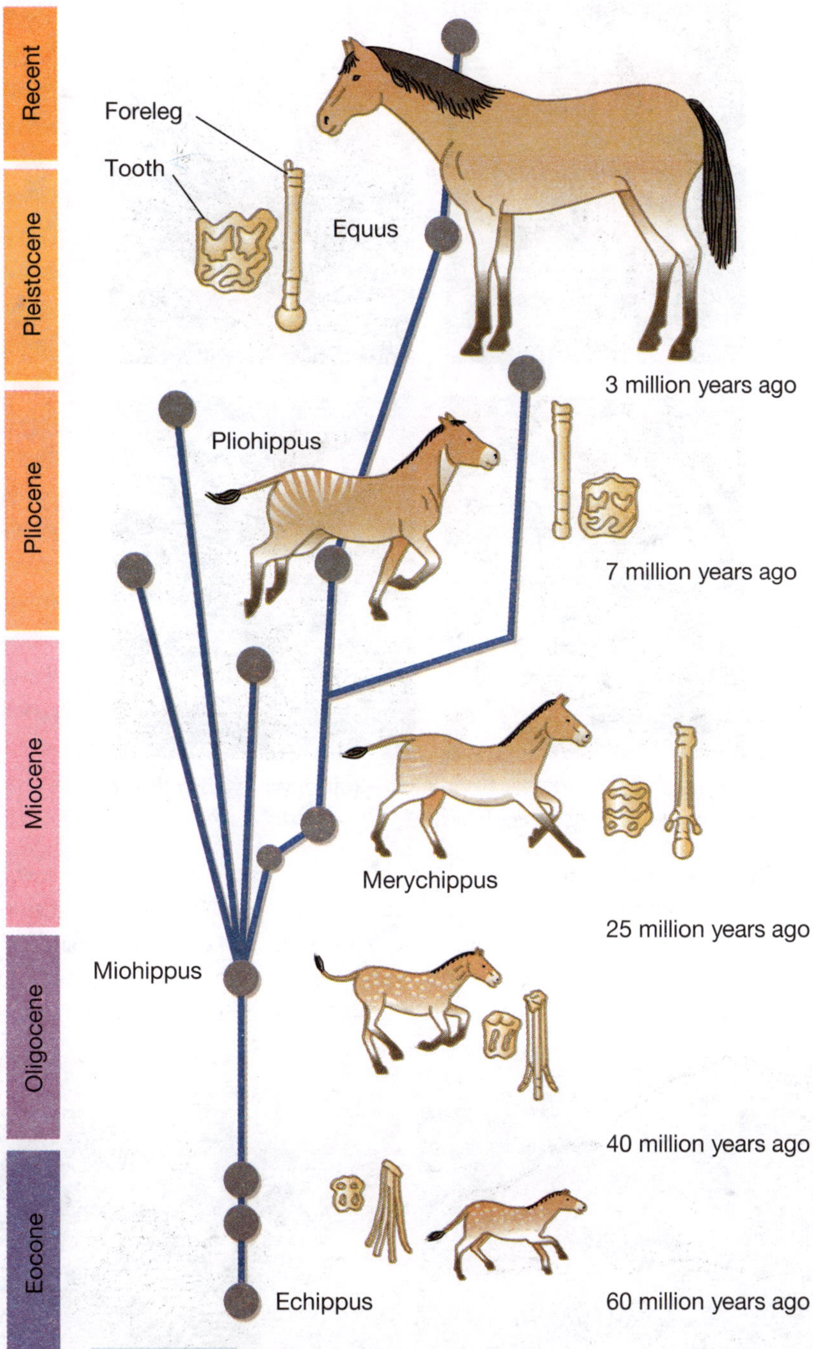

Figure 10.8 Pictorial diagram showing evolution of the horse

The organisms that share some characteristic features of two adjacent taxonomic groups are called connecting links.

Table 10.2 Examples of some connecting links

Animal/plant	Earlier taxonomic unit	Later taxonomic unit
Peripatus	Arthropods	Annelids
Duck-billed platypus and *Echidna*	Reptiles	Mammals
Latimeria	Fish	Amphibians
Cycas	Pteridophytes	Gymnosperms
Euglena	Plants	Animals

Figure 10.9 Connecting links— (clockwise from the top left) *Peripatus, Echidna, Cycas and Euglena*

Some groups of animals that showed a wide distinction in their characteristics did not have any animals or plants that showed transition in characteristics. Some fossil remains of organisms have been found that showed the transitional features. It is presumed that the organisms that evolved from some groups of organisms that existed in the past are still living today. Unlike the connecting links, the group of organisms which have no living representatives now as all of them should have become extinct. Such organisms are called missing links. For example, *Archaeopteryx* is a missing link between reptiles and birds.

Figure 10.10 Fossilized *Archaeopteryx* imprint in stone (on left), *Seymouria* from the Early Permian Period found as fossil in North America (on right)

Table 10.3 Examples of some missing links

Animal/plant	Earlier taxonomic unit	Later taxonomic unit
Archaeopteryx	Reptiles	Birds
Seymouria	Amphibians	Reptiles
Balanoglossus	Fish	Amphibians
Homo habilis (handy man)	Apes	Man
Cooksonia	Non-vascular plants	Vascular plants

The organisms that are presumed to have existed and shared some characteristics features of two adjacent taxonomic groups and are now extinct are called missing links.

Morphological Evidences

Morphology means external appearance of an organism. Almost all the plants possess same structural organization with roots, stem and leaves. Although, the types of leaves may be different in different plants, their main function in all the green plants is photosynthesis.

Anatomical Evidences

These evidences include comparison of anatomical (internal) features of organs of different organisms. Depending upon the structural and functional similarities and variations, these are studied under various categories. Three of the major anatomical evidences are:

1. Homologous organs
2. Analogous organs
3. Vestigial organs

Homologous Organs (Divergent Evolution or Adaptive Radiation)

The different organs in different organisms may have similar basic anatomical structure even though they have different morphology and different functions. This indicates that these organs must have evolved from a common ancestry which in course of time developed into organs with different structural features adapted to the respective environments. Such organs are called homologous organs. Homology means common ancestry. The evolution that gives rise to this kind of homology is called divergent evolution.

Thus, we can say the organs of different animals or plants that are characterized by similar structure, same developmental origin and different functions are called homologous organs.

Table 10.4 Examples of homology in animals

Animal	Organ	Function
Whales	Flukes	Swimming
Bats	Wings	Flying
Bulls	Front foot	Walking
Humans	Arms	Holding

All these organs have same basic structural plan. They are expected to have originated from the ancestral form with five digited limbs. These limbs of ancestral forms became modified according to the special needs of the subsequent generations for performing varied functions. This means, in these organs, homology in structural features indicates common ancestry from pentadactyl limbs.

Another example is of thorns and tendrils of some plants (different appearance and different functions). Thorns in plants like *Bougainvillea* are modified leaves. They perform the function of protection. Tendrils in *Cucurbita* or cucumber are also modified leaves. They perform the function of climbing.

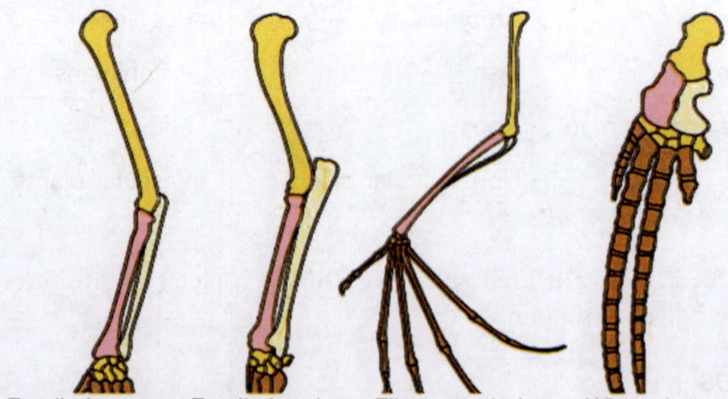

Figure 10.11 Example of homology in animals

Analogous Organs (Convergent Evolution)

Some organs have totally different structural organization in different organisms, but perform similar functions in various organisms. Such organs are called analogous organs, due to the analogy in function. They also do not share common origin. The evolution giving rise to this kind of analogy is called convergent evolution.

The organs of different animals or plants that are characterized by different structure, and different developmental origin but perform similar function are called analogous organs.

For example, different animals possess different organs for flying or swimming or vision. All these organs have different structural features that indicate that they have different origin.

For example, modified stem in potato and modified root in sweet potato perform the same function of storage of food.

Table 10.5 Some examples of analogous organs in various animals/plants

Function	Organism/Plant part	Organ
Vision	Arthropods	Eyes
	Vertebrates	Eyes
Flying	Butterflies	Wings
	Birds	Wings
Swimming	Lobster	Tail fin
	Whale	Flukes
Photosynthesis	Leaf	Mesophytes (all land plants)
	Flattened stem (Phylloclades)	Xerophytes (desert plants)
Storage of food	Stem	Potato
	Root	Sweet potato

Figure 10.12 Leaves of a mesophyte (left) and xerophyte (right)

Vestigial Organs

Some organs are present in rudimentary form and do not perform any significant function in certain organisms. These organs that correspond to fully developed functional organs of other closely related organisms are called vestigial organs.

These organs were complete and functional in the ancestral forms, but became rudimentary in the present living forms because of change in their mode of life. For example, presence of rudimentary tail in humans.

- Monkey possesses tail due to its arboreal habit. Ancestral man also possessed tail.
- Present man does not possess a fully developed tail. But, the rudimentary form of tail is there in the form of a tail bone (coccyx) composed of four fused caudal vertebrae and some muscles.
- The presence of this rudimentary tail in man indicates the common ancestry of man and monkey.

Table 10.6 Some vestigial organs in various organisms

Organism	Vestigial organ
Humans	Tail; Appendix; Hair
Whale	Pelvic bone
Ostrich	Wings
Grasses	Flowers
Indian pipe plant	Scale leaves
Hundred root plant	Gynoecium

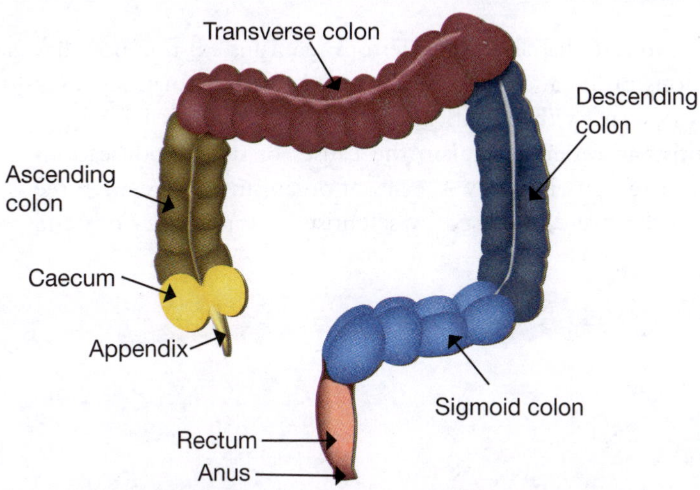

Figure 10.13 Location of appendix in humans

Embryological Evidences

The study of the process of development of an organism from an embryo and the related aspects is called embryology. The embryos of various classes of organisms show a great deal of similarity in their early stages of development. But during the later stages of development, the embryos of various classes of animals differ considerably. The similarities in the early embryonic stages of the organisms belonging to different classes indicate the common ancestry of all these organisms though in the adult stage they do not possess any similarities in the morphological or anatomical features.

Embryological Evidences

- Animals such as dogs, cows and rabbits belong to different categories of placental mammals just like humans.
- All these organisms have a wide range of variations in their structural features.
- However, the embryos of all these animals show close resemblances with the human embryo.
- Animals such as chick, tortoise, salamander and fish belong to different classes of vertebrates namely birds, reptiles, amphibians and pisces, respectively. However, they resemble the embryos of placental mammals to a great extent in the early embryonic stages.

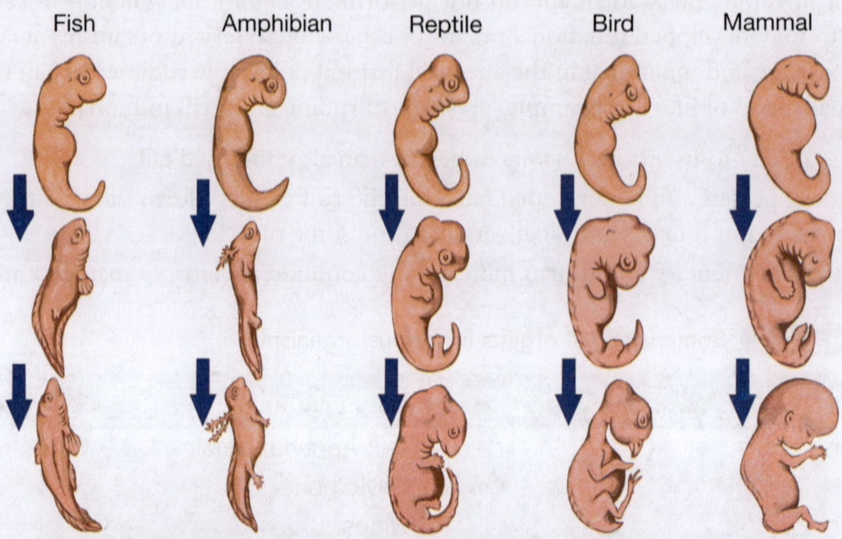

Figure 10.14 Illustration of different stages in early embryonic development of vertebrates—fish, amphibian, reptile, bird and mammal

Theories of Evolution

All different kinds of evidences indicate that all the species of organisms existing now have a common ancestry. In course of time, small and large variations in the ancestral organisms led to the enormous diversity of life. This means that the biological evolution envisages descent with modifications. Various theories have been put forward by different scientists in order to explain the causes of such modifications and the way in which they gave rise to various new species of organisms. There are three important theories of evolution that were proposed by scientists in various periods and are listed as follows.

> **Info Bytes!**
> Lamarckism theory was proposed by Jean Baptist Lamarck in his book `Philosphic Zoologique'.

1. Theory of Lamarckism followed by Neo-Lamarckism
2. Theory of Darwinism
3. Modern theory

Lamarckism

Theory of Lamarckism is also called Theory of Inheritance of Acquired Characters. The major principles of this theory are described below.

New Needs of Organisms

Due to some changes in the environmental conditions, new needs arise for the organisms. In order to fulfil the new needs, some variations are developed in the organisms of that species. These variations may be morphological or anatomical. They lead to variation in functioning also. Such variations are called acquired characters.

Use and Disuse of Organs

Continuous use of a particular organ due to the new needs results in the increase in size of the organ. Similarly, continuous disuse of the organs leads to the degeneration of the organ in course of time in the next generations.

Example for Use and Disuse

For example, Loss of limbs in snakes to suit creeping habit, Development of webbed feet and loss of wings in the aquatic birds due to use and disuse

Inheritance of Acquired Characters

Characters acquired either by new needs or by use and disuse provide better chances of survival of that species and hence, are inherited in the next generations. This is known as soft inheritance. Major examples of inheritance of acquired characters are discussed below.

Origin of Long-Necked Giraffe

- The ancestors of giraffe resembled horse as they possessed small neck and short forelimbs.
- Due to the sudden disappearance of surface vegetation, they had to stretch their neck and forelimbs to reach to the upper foliage of trees.
- This resulted in the elongation of neck and forelimbs which is considered as the acquired character.
- This character acquired in one generation was useful and hence, was transmitted to the later generations. In this way, a new species of long-necked giraffe came into existence

Figure 10.15 Diagram showing origin of long-necked giraffe (Theory of Lamarckism)

Speciation

- The acquired characters so inherited generation after generation get accumulated.
- This gives rise to a new species of organisms after some generations.
- Thus, a single species may result in the development of two or more distinct new species in course of evolution. Such phenomenon is called speciation.
- Species is a class or organisms that are genetically identical and hence, can interbreed among themselves.

The evolutionary process of formation of a new biological species by the division of a single species into two or more genetically distinct species is known as speciation.

Criticism Against Lamarckism

Lamarck's theory was subject to many criticism due to evidences against the theory. Some of them are listed below:

- All the acquired characters need not be inherited to the next generation.
  For example, boring of pinna of ear for women in any number of generations is not carried to the next generations.
- The use and disuse theory also bagged criticism on the basis of certain observations.
  For example, continuous use of eyes or heart did not result in increase in their size.
- The criticism can be viewed in the light of Weismann's germplasm theory.
- According to this theory, the characters corresponding to somatic cells cannot be inherited. The characters corresponding to germ cells can only be inherited. He provided experimental proof for this theory.
  For example, cutting of tails of mice for many successive generations gave rise to only tailed mice.

Neo-Lamarckism

On the basis of germplasm theory and Mendel's studies on inheritance, Lamarckism was modified and was called neo-Lamarckism. According to this theory, Structure, colour, form and functioning of organisms are affected by the environment. They may cause changes in either somatic or germ cells. The characters affecting somatic cells may also be inherited. For example, vegetative propagation in plants.

Theory of Darwinism

This theory was proposed by a famous naturalist, Charles Darwin in his book, 'The Origin of Species'. Since Darwinism mainly focused on the idea of natural selection and resultant survival of fittest, this theory is known as Darwin's theory of natural selection.

Darwin's Theory of Natural Selection

This theory is based on the concept of struggle for existence and survival of the fittest. Darwin undertook a voyage in a famous ship named 'H.M.S. Beagle' and explored many islands around South America and drew certain important conclusions regarding biological evolution.

Darwinism is based on the following principles:

- Overproduction
- Struggle for existence
- Variations
- Natural selection and survival of the fittest
- Inheritance of variations
- Speciation

Konnect

Darwin's book, "On the Origin of Species," was so popular upon its release in 1859 that it sold out on the first

Overproduction

The organisms have much greater reproductive ability than required. Therefore, the organisms produce much larger number of offspring than that can actually survive. This means that there should be some limiting factors that put a natural restriction on the survival of the species.

Struggle for Existence

The major limiting factors for the growing population are the availability of food and space. There is always a competition amongst the organisms for these limited resources. Therefore, the organisms struggle for acquiring the resources. Those organisms that can succeed in this struggle to survive while the others perish. This is called struggle for existence. This keeps the number of organisms stable in the environment. The struggle for existence can be amongst the organisms of various species. This is called interspecific struggle. The competition is more intense between the organisms belonging to the same species. This is called intraspecific struggle. In this case, the organisms compete amongst them selves for mating also in addition for food and space. All the organisms invariably should face the struggle with environmental factors such as adverse climate, drought, famine, natural calamities, etc.

Variations

The environment does not remain constant. It is everchanging. The organisms also should adapt themselves to the changing environmental conditions. Therefore, the organisms of a species undergo some modifications in their colour, form, structure and functioning. These modifications are called variations. In course of time, the organisms that possess these variations stand better chances of being successful in the struggle for existence.

Natural Selection and Survival of the Fittest

This kind of selective survival of the organisms occurs in natural course and is called natural selection. The nature allows these organisms to survive more and contribute to the continuation of the species. This is known as 'survival of the fittest'.

Inheritance of Variations

The useful variations in the fit individuals are passed onto the next generation by the means of inheritance. Consequently, the number of individual organisms with such useful variations increase in number in the population over a period of time.

Speciation

The variations when inherited by the offspring are passed onto the next generations. Number of such variations accumulate generation after generation and at some stage result in the organisms with totally different characters from the original organisms. This eventually leads to origin of new species which is called speciation.

Criticism Against Darwinism

Following are the major points of criticism against Darwinism:

- All the variations in organisms may not be caused as a means of adaptation to the new needs.
- The variations may be caused due to various reasons other than the environmental factors.
- Some variations that are useful may be passed onto the next generations.
- However, the variations that are not useful may also be inherited. For example, inheritance of vestigial organs
- Darwinism could not explain the various causes of variations and the mode of transmission of the variations. There was no distinction between the variations related to somatic and germ cells.
- Natural selection, though an important factor, is not the only factor which is responsible for the evolution.
- Small variations in small groups cannot lead to speciation. Speciation is a macrophenomenon in biological evolution. Darwinism could not take into account the major factors that can cause speciation.
- Genetic basis of inheritance was not taken into consideration.

Modern Theory of Evolution

Hugo de Vries brought the idea of mutation theory. De Vries conducted his work on evening prime rose and brought the idea of mutation. Mutations are sudden changes that occur in genes. New species forms or evolution happens by the inheritance of such genes. In terms of genetics, the characteristics of an organism are attributed to the presence of specific genes. The presence of different alleles in different proportions brings about variations. The various factors that bring about such variations resulting in evolution are called evolutionary agents. The various evolutionary agents are:

- Recombinations
- Mutations
- Gene flow or gene migration
- Genetic drift
- Natural selection

Recombination

The meiotic cell division which is the basis of sexual reproduction involves the important phenomenon of crossing over followed by recombination. This results in independent assortment of chromosomes and genes. As a result, the individuals belonging to the same species including the offspring of same parents show variation in each and every characteristic. These variations increase from one generation to the next.

Mutations

The sudden variations either in the number of chromosomes or in the structure of chromosomes appearing in a particular individual in a generation are called mutations. These mutations sometimes may alter the DNA structure and may lead to the origin of new species.

Gene Flow or Gene Migration

Accidental migration of some individual organisms to far off places may force interbreeding between the migrant species with the closely related species of the new region. This may result in new genetic combinations. It is called gene flow or gene migration. Over a long period, this may result in reproductive isolation of the migrant organisms with the organisms in their original habitat. This becomes obligatory especially when any geographical barrier such as a river or island exists between the two regions. Such reproductive isolation may result in the origin of new species.

Genetic Drift

Sometimes, natural calamities or epidemics or accidents may result in the elimination of certain genes in small, isolated population of a species. This may force interbreeding among the organisms of closely related species in the region which may result in speciation.

Natural Selection

Natural selection leads to progressive changes in gene frequencies from one generation to the other. This means that the frequency of some genes increases from one generation to the next while the frequency of some genes decreases from one generation to the next. Over a long period, such changes in gene frequency may give rise to a new gene pool. This may at some stage result in the origin of new species.

Illustration for the Modern Theory of Evolution

A small population of red beetles living in small bushes with green leaves. Sexual reproduction among the beetles brings about variations.

Variation I

Either recombination or sudden mutation may bring about a change in colour of a particular beetle producing a green beetle. This green beetle produces offspring with green colour. This means that the change in colour is a heritable variation.

Case I (Huge Crow Population)

- Crows feed on beetles.
- In the population of red beetles and green beetles, green beetles have a survival advantage as they cannot be spotted easily by crows in comparison to red beetles.

- Hence, when there is a huge population of crows in that area, the population of green beetles increases considerably while that of red beetles decreases to that extent.
- The mating between the red beetle and green beetle may produce a new genetic combination.
- If this situation continues, at some stage, the original species of red beetles may completely disappear from that area.
- Natural selection and survival of the fittest result in large population of green beetles.

Case II (Limited Crow Population)

- In another area, the crow population is limited due to large eagle population as eagles feed on crows.
- In such a situation, although green colour gives survival advantage, the effect is not appreciable.
- The population of red beetles is also maintained along with green beetles.

Variation-II

The colour variation due to recombination or mutation may result in the production of blue beetle. This blue colour is passed on to the offspring resulting in an increase in the population of blue beetles. But blue colour does not give any survival advantage for the beetles as both red beetles and blue beetles are eaten by crows equally. In case an accident takes place in that area most of the beetles die. If most of the few surviving beetles are blue, the population of blue beetles increases. In this case, the variation which was a rare character in one generation becomes a common trait in the later generation. The increase in gene frequency is because of genetic drift. This provides scope for diversity without any adaptation.

Variation III

A plant disease at some point of time may affect the plants in the bushes. This results in the reduction of leaf material which is food for the beetles. In this situation, beetles start to starve, and they experience reduction in body weight. Once the bushes get rid of the disease, the progeny of the beetles are with normal body weight. This means that the reduction in body weight is not a heritable variation while colour of the beetle is a heritable variation.

Variation IV

If we consider a large population of different kinds of beetles in the bushes spread over a mountain range, each kind of beetles inhabits the bushes in a particular area. This constitutes subpopulation. Usually, sexual reproduction takes place between the male and female beetles in that subpopulation. Sometimes, accidentally or by chance, a beetle from one subpopulation finds its way into another subpopulation which is far off. Such a beetle is forced to interbreed with the beetle of the host population. This may result in the entry of new genes into the population of that region. It is an example of gene flow or gene migration.

Variation V

In the above case, if a geographical barrier such as a river is developed between the two regions, it leads to reproductive isolation. In the long run, the members of these two groups may possess different DNA structures. Then, they become incapable of interbreeding or mating. This results in speciation.

Evolution as the Basis of Classification of Living Organisms

Classification of living organisms is grouping the organisms based on the similarities and differences in their characteristics. The levels of classification will be based on the characteristics shared by them. The various levels of classification depict the increase in complexity of the body organization. This increase in complexity of body organization shows the order in which the organisms evolved. The simplest level of organization is based on the cell structure that is prokaryotic and eukaryotic cells. The organisms with prokaryotic cell structure are supposed to be the most primitive and first evolved ones. The eukaryotes can again be classified into two groups as unicellular and multicellular eukaryotes. The multicellular organisms can be further classified on the basis of nutrition, as autotrophs and heterotrophs. Plants are autotrophic and can be categorized as non-flowering and flowering plants. The further classification of non-flowering plants is on the basis of presence of vascular tissue. The further classification of flowering plants is based on the presence of naked seeds or seeds enclosed in fruits. Heterotrophic organisms basically include all animals. The animals can further be broadly classified on the basis of presence of endoskeleton, i.e., vertebral column. The two groups are invertebrates and vertebrates. Invertebrates are further classified according to the various levels of organization such as tissue level, body symmetry, nature of germ layers, presence of body cavity, etc. Vertebrates can also be categorized on the basis of complexity of organ systems, complexity of metabolism and the mode of reproduction and development.

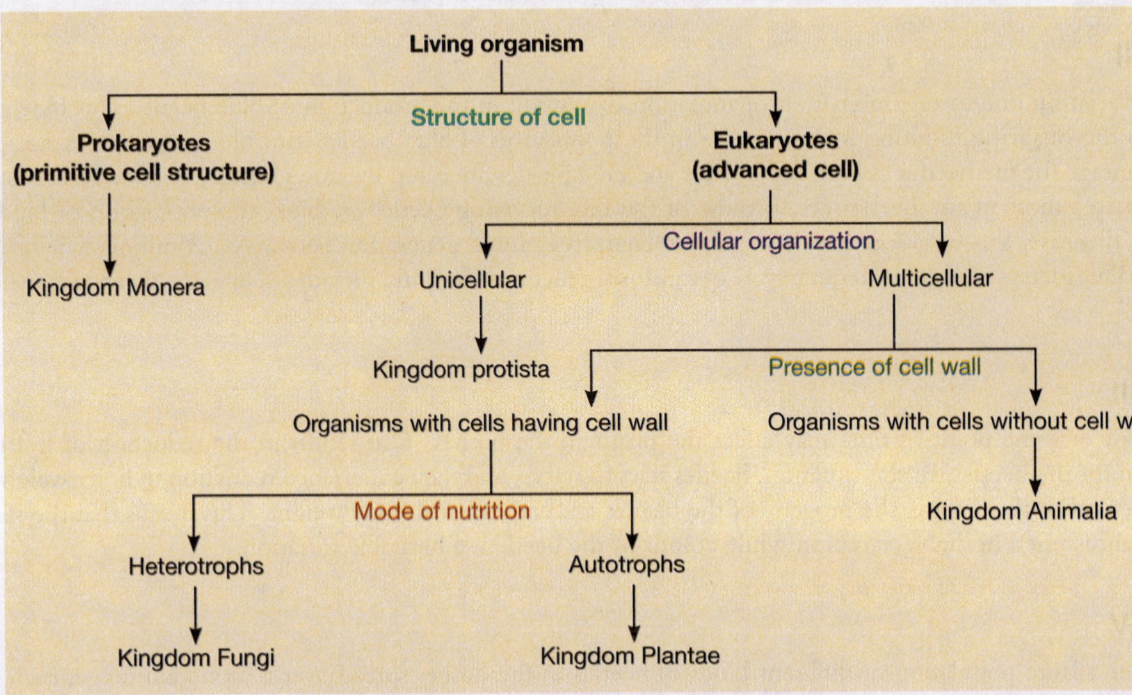

Figure 10.16 Classification of living organisms

The gradual changes in the morphological features and anatomical features observed in various classes of animals indicate the close association between evolution and classification.

Certain organs and organ systems show a gradual change from the primitive to complex organisms and this provides strong evidence for the correlation between evolutionary hierarchy and classification. For example, gradual change in the structure of hearts of vertebrates from fish to mammals.

Evolution of Man

In the evolutionary hierarchy, human beings are considered to be the most evolved living beings and are considered to be at the pinnacle of evolutionary tree. Human evolution is the most important and significant milestones of biological evolution. It can be traced back to fossil records of ancestral organisms. According to palaeontological evidences, it had been concluded that the modern man originated from ancestral apes (*Dryopithecus, Ramapithecus*) that belonged to the order of Primates. These species had close resemblances with gorillas and chimpanzees. For example, bodies were fully covered with thick hair and their walking style also resembled gorillas'. Morphological changes involved in the evolution of man clearly indicate the above ancestry.

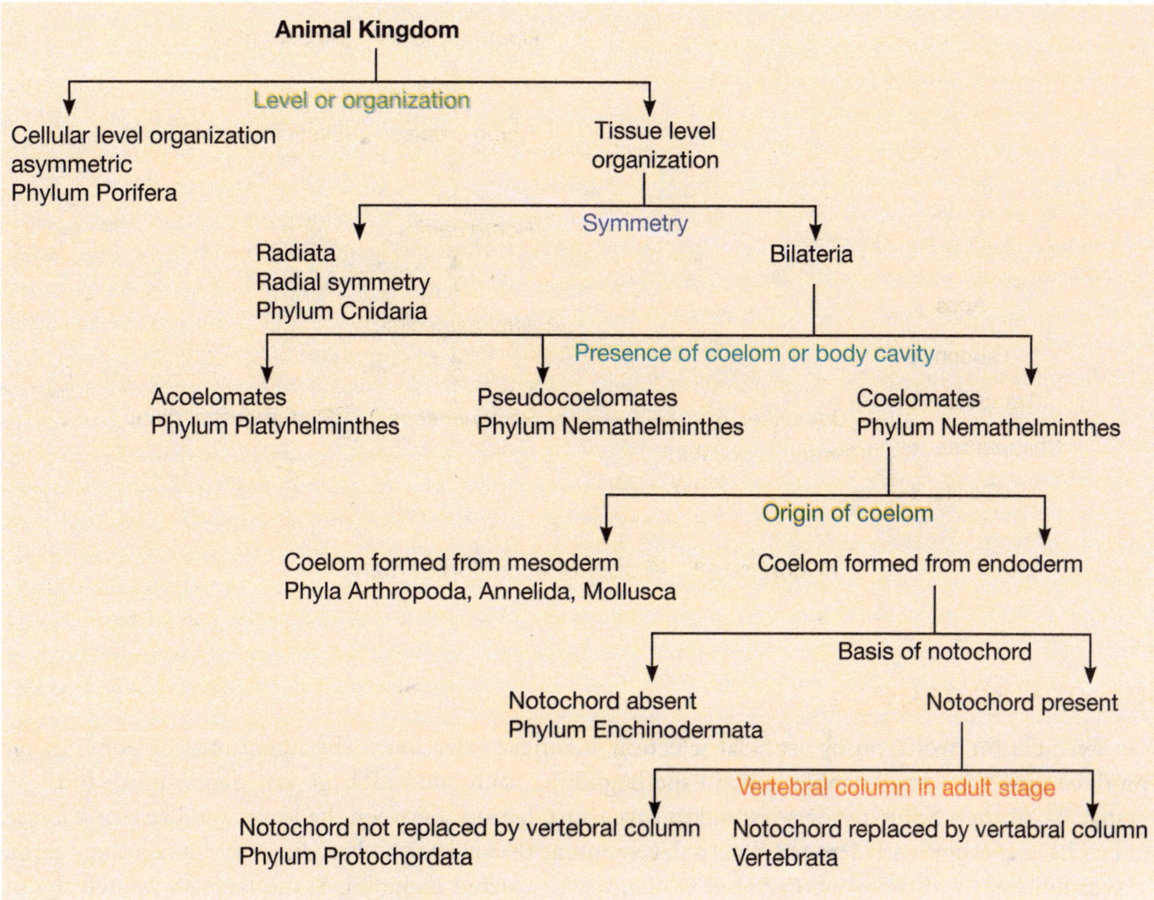

Figure 10.17 Classification—animal kingdom

Table 10.7 Evolution of man—morphological changes

Morphological features	Modifications
Facial features	• Flattening of face • Elevation in nose • Formation of chin
Features related to posture	• Broadening of forehead with vertical elevation • Curves in vertebral column • Erect posture • Bipedal locomotion
Features related to intelligence	• Enlargement of cranium • Increase in brain size
Other features	• Reduction in body hair • Bowl-like pelvic girdle

The evolution of ancestral man and apes from the common ancestor and the evolution of modern man from the ancestral man can be shown in the given schematic diagram.

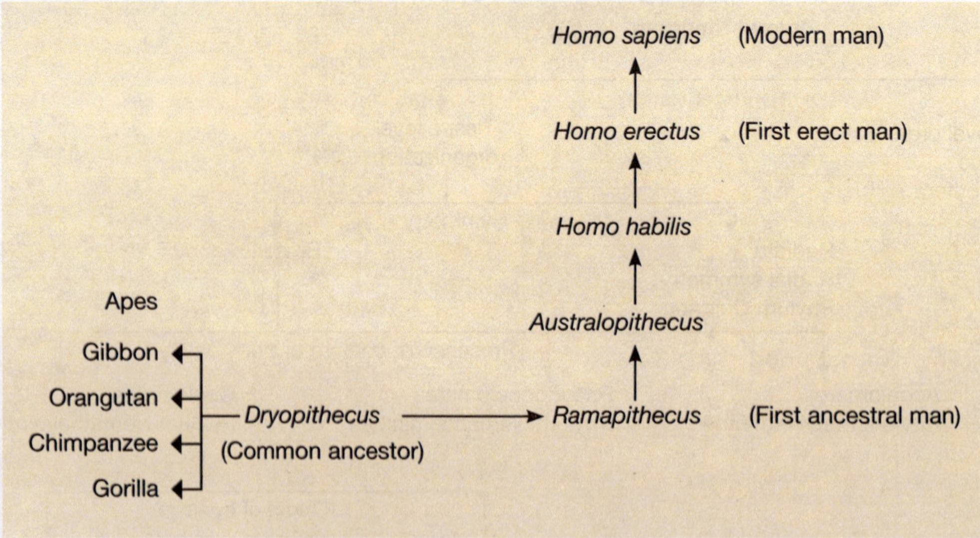

Figure 10.18 History of evolution of man

Evolution of Cabbage

Cabbage is an example for evolution by artificial selection. Artificial selection is the intentional breeding of plants and animals to produce progeny with desirable trait. In the beginning, only wild cabbage was there, unlike today when we have a wide range of cabbage. Some farmers wanted to have short distance between the leaves and bred the cabbage. Some others wanted to have cabbage with arrested flower development that led to the breeding of broccoli. For sterile flower, they made the cauliflower, and those who wanted swollen parts selected Kohlrabi. Some farmers wanted slightly larger leaves, and came up with a leaf vegetable called Kale. Thus, from a single wild cabbage, many varieties have been bred via artificial selection.

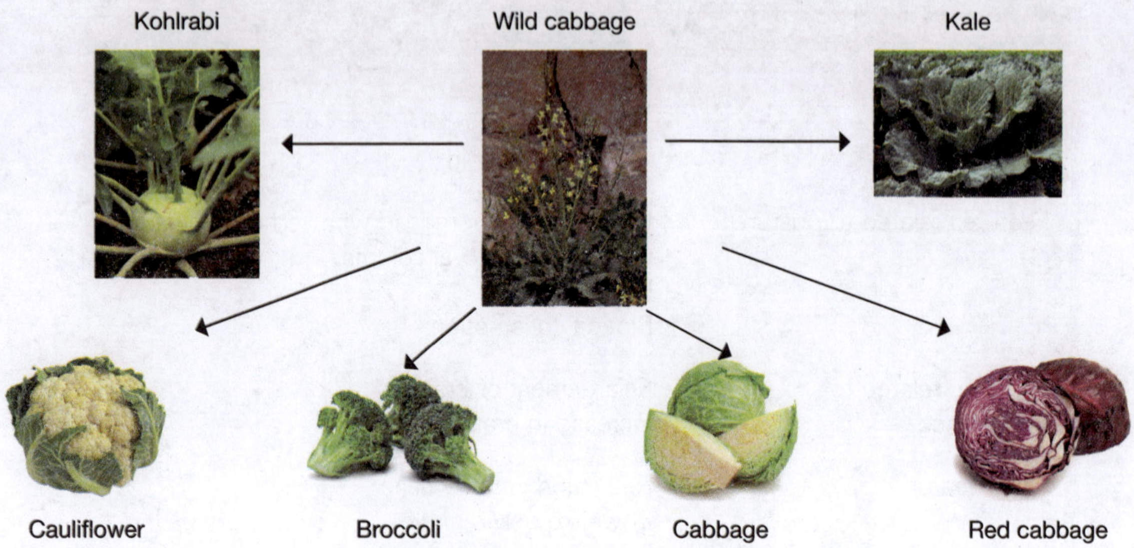

Figure 10.19 Varieties of cabbage

Quick Recap

✔ **Ontogeny repeats phylogeny. Justify.**

Ontogeny refers to the development of an organism from the zygote stage to the adult form which means that the entire lifespan of the organism.

Phylogeny refers to the development of a group of organisms from another group in the course of evolution. This basically gives information as to how different species of organisms are related to each other. In course of evolution, a group of organisms undergoes changes in morphological and anatomical features and also metabolism. This leads to the origin of new species. The organisms of new species undergo the process of development during their lifespan. This is how ontogeny and phylogeny repeat and form the basis for the evolutionary hierarchy.

✔ **How did slow and gradual changes in early life forms lay the groundwork for the vast biodiversity we see today, and what role does this biodiversity play in the evolutionary process?**

Early life forms' slow and gradual changes allowed for adaptations to various environments, resulting in a diverse range of species. This biodiversity creates a large genetic pool, which ensures survival under changing conditions and promotes evolution. Life forms diversify as they adapt to different environmental niches. This diversity results in more genetic variation. Having diverse genes ensures that some species survive, reproduce, and evolve in the face of environmental changes.

✔ **Explain the significance of the Big Bang explosion, which occurred approximately 13.8 billion years ago during the universe's formation and expansion.**

The Big Bang explosion ushered in the universe, with matter spreading out in all directions. This was the beginning of the universe's expansion, which continues to this day. All matter was condensed into a single point before the Big Bang. This matter was scattered by the explosion, resulting in the formation of galaxies, stars, and planets. The universe's ongoing expansion suggests that it is still influenced by the energy of the initial explosion.

✔ **In the context of taxonomy and evolution, distinguish between 'connecting links' and 'missing links.'**

Living organisms that exhibit characteristics of two adjacent taxonomic groups are considered connecting links. Missing links, on the other hand, are presumed extinct organisms that once shared such characteristics but are no longer found. Missing links are theoretical and based on fossil evidence, marking evolutionary paths that are now extinct.

✔ **How do gene mutations influence the formation of new species or the process of evolution?**

Mutations result in genetic variations. When these mutated genes are inherited and provide a survival advantage, they spread, resulting in evolutionary changes and the emergence of new species. Nature's way of introducing genetic diversity is through mutations. Beneficial mutations become more common over time, driving evolution and speciation.

✔ **Organisms show some physiological and biochemical similarities between the different groups. With reference to this statement, justify the following.**

(a) The presence of enzymes trypsin and amylase in the body systems.

(b) Insulin deficiency in humans can be treated by injecting the insulin of other animals.

(a) Trypsin is a proteolytic enzyme that is meant for splitting of proteins. This enzyme is present in all animals from protozoa to mammals. This is therefore referred to as ancient enzyme. The starch-splitting enzyme, amylase is found from sponges to mammals.

(b) The thyroxine and insulin hormones are almost identical in all vertebrates. The deficiency of insulin hormone in man can be made up by giving the insulin of other animals such as pig.

POINTS TO REMEMBER

- ✔ This origin of life and the gradual and slow changes brought about in these life forms resulted in enormous biodiversity that formed the basis for evolution.
- ✔ About 13.8 billion years ago, an aggressive explosion threw the material within the ball of universe into all directions of space.
- ✔ The universe started to expand after the Big Bang and it continues to expand today.
- ✔ Earth was initially assumed to be a hot gaseous mass.
- ✔ The gradual increase in complexity in the organization of the living cells over a long period of time resulted in the origin of more complex and diverse forms of life.
- ✔ The orderly changes in the characteristics of groups of organisms over the course of generations lead to biological or organic evolution.
- ✔ The study of patterns of distribution of animals and plants in different parts of Earth is known as biogeography.
- ✔ The organisms that share some characteristic features of two adjacent taxonomic groups are called connecting links.
- ✔ The organisms that are presumed to have existed and shared some characteristics features of two adjacent taxonomic groups and are now extinct are called missing links.
- ✔ Mutations are sudden changes that occur in genes. New species forms or evolution happens by the inheritance of such genes.

DW

PRACTICE QUESTIONS CLASSROOM WING

Very Short Answer Type Questions

Directions for questions from 1 to 16.
Fill in the blanks.

1. The ________ is the most widely accepted theory regarding the origin of the universe.
2. Earth is a part of the ________ galaxy.
3. Darwin's ________ is an example of adaptive radiation.
4. The ________ organs indicate an evolutionary relationship wherein different structures perform the same function due to evolutionary adaptations in different environments.
5. Organs which have similar basic anatomical structure but may have different morphology and functions are called ________ organs.
6. The ________ in plants like Bougainvillea perform the function of protection.
7. Lamarckism is also called ________.
8. Ancestors of Darwin's finches were ________ eating.
9. The name of the ship in which Darwin undertook his famous voyage is ________.
10. The sudden variations in genetic makeup appearing in a particular generation are called ________.
11. ________ followed by ________ during meiotic cell division bring about variations.
12. Elimination of some genetic traits from an area due to natural calamities or accidents is called ________.
13. The origin of new species from an existing species is called ________.
14. The ancestral ape from which modern man originated belonged to the order of ________.
15. The scientific name of modern man is ________.
16. The simplest living organisms on earth are ________.

Directions for questions from 17 to 29.
For each of the following questions, four choices have been provided. Select the correct alternatives.

17. Which of the following best defines the term 'adaptive radiation'?
    (a) The radiation energy from the sun leads to the adaptation of life.
    (b) The evolution of animals in areas with high radiation.
    (c) The development of new species to fit new habitats or ways of life.
    (d) The movement of species from one radiated area to another.
18. What is the significance of 'missing links' in evolutionary studies?
    (a) They indicate species that are currently living.
    (b) They show the progression of evolution from one species to another.
    (c) They represent species that have never existed.
    (d) They highlight extinct organisms with features shared by two taxonomic groups.
19. What evidence supports the idea of 'Discontinuous Distribution' in biogeography?
    (a) Distribution of alligators in the USA and eastern China.
    (b) Australian marsupials resembling placental mammals.
    (c) Formation of fossils in sedimentary rocks.
    (d) Carbon dating of fossils.
20. Which of the following is an example of divergent evolution?
    (a) Wings of butterflies and birds
    (b) Flippers of whales and dolphins
    (c) Forelimb of a dog and forelimb of a man
    (d) Eyes of arthropods and vertebrates
21. Vestigial organs in organisms indicate:
    (a) Current functional importance
    (b) Future developmental changes
    (c) Past functional significance
    (d) No evolutionary relevance
22. The structural adaptation of certain plants in desert areas to perform photosynthesis is:
    (a) Modified stem called phylloclades
    (b) Modified root for water storage
    (c) Modified leaf tendrils
    (d) Thorns for protection

23. Phylloclades in some plants perform which function?
(a) Food storage
(b) Transpiration
(c) Protection
(d) Photosynthesis

24. Which of the following words mean common ancestry with respect to evolution?
(a) Analogy (b) Homology
(c) Ontogeny (d) Phylogeny

25. Identify the group of organisms that were supposed to have undergone mass extinction.
(a) Marsupials
(b) *Balanoglossus*
(c) Egg laying mammals
(d) Dinosaurs

26. Pelvic bone became rudimentary in which animal?
(a) Human (b) Ostrich
(c) Whale (d) Placental mammals

27. Oldest fossils belonged to which era?
(a) Mesozoic era (b) Palaeozoic era
(c) Precambrian era (d) Coenozoic era

28. The characteristic features of dinosaurs show close resemblance with which of the following organisms living today?
(a) Salamanders (b) Apes
(c) Crocodiles (d) Kangaroos

29. Which of the following evidences suggest the common ancestry of fish and birds?
(A) Presence of fins and wings
(B) Same excretory product in fishes and birds
(C) Same respiratory organs in adult organisms
(D) Similarity in embryonic structure
(a) A; D (b) D only
(c) A only (d) B; C

Direction for Questions 30 and 31.
Match the entries of Column 1 with those of Column 2.

30.

Column 1	Column 2
A. Homologous organs	(i) Convergent evolution
B. Abiogenesis	(ii) Life originated from pre-existing life forms
C. Biogenesis	(iii) Divergent evolution
D. Wings of bat and bird	(iv) Life from non-living matter

31.

Column 1	Column 2
A. Walked on two limbs	(i) Ape like
B. *Homo sapiens*	(ii) *Homo erectus*
C. Java man	(iii) Hugo de Vries
D. *Dryopithecus*	(iv) Modern man

Short Answer Type Questions

32. Explain the difference between connecting links and missing links.

33. What does the Geological Time Scale signify in the context of organic evolution?

34. What are the various types of studies on fossils that could provide evidences for organic evolution?

35. Explain how the study of embryos of vertebrates provide evidence for their common ancestry.

36. What are fossils? How are they formed?

37. State the similarities and differences between connecting links and missing links.

38. Distinguish between homologous organs and analogous organs.

39. What are vestigial organs? Provide an example.

40. What are vestigial organs? Explain with an example in digestive system of human body.

41. List out the morphological changes that took place in the course of evolution of man from other primates.

42. Define the following.
(a) Struggle for existence
(b) Acquired characters

43. Distinguish between gene flow and genetic drift.

44. List out the various evolutionary agents as envisaged by the modern theory of evolution.

Essay Type Questions

45. Explain Lamarckism principle of use and disuse with respect to the origin of giraffe.
46. What are acquired characters? Give an example.
47. Explain the evolution of man.
48. Under what conditions, gene migration lead to speciation?
49. How did Weismann's germplasm theory disprove Lamarckism?
50. Distinguish between the following.
    (a) Prokaryotes and eukaryotes
    (b) Invertebrates and vertebrates
    (c) Gymnosperms and angiosperms
    (d) Protochordates and vertebrates
51. Explain the concept of survival of the fittest.
52. What is meant by struggle for existence and survival of the fittest? Explain with an appropriate example.

PRACTICE QUESTIONS COMPETITION WING

Level 1: Apply your Concepts

Directions for questions from 1 to 11.

Fill in the blanks in each question.

1. _______ period in _______ era was known as the Golden age of reptiles.
2. _______ organs are examples of divergent evolution.
3. Analogous organs are examples of _______ evolution.
4. Fossils are usually formed in the _______ rocks.
5. _______ is a missing link between reptiles and birds.
6. Wisdom teeth in man are considered as _______ organs.
7. The preserved dead remains of the extinct organisms in earth's crust are called _______,
8. The study of fossils is known as _______,
9. The nonfunctional structures in the body of an organism is called _______,
10. The approximate number of vestigial organs in human body is _______,
11. The organs in different animals having similar function and different structure are called _______,

Direction for Questions from 12 to 15.

For each of the following questions four choices have been provided. Select the correct alternatives.

12. Identify the vestigial organ in human body.
    (a) Coccyx
    (b) Nictitating membrane of eye
    (c) Ear muscles
    (d) All the above
13. Which of the following are homologous organs?
    (a) Wings of bird and fly
    (b) Wing of bat and flippers of whale
    (c) Fin of lobster and fluke of whale
    (d) None of these
14. Identify analogous organs among the following.
    (a) Eyes of ant and cat
    (b) Arm in man and leg in bull
    (c) Fluke of whale and limb of man
    (d) Forelimb of bat and forelimb of horse
15. Who proposed the theory of natural selection?
    (a) Jean Baptist Lamarck
    (b) Charles Darwin
    (c) Hugo de Vries
    (d) Johann Mendel

Direction for Questions 16 and 17.

Write the missing correlated terms.

16. Duck-billed platypus: Reptiles :: Euglena: _________?
17. Forelimb of a Man : Holding :: Flukes of a Whale : ?

Direction for Questions 18 and 19.

Correct the following statements.

18. Vestigial organs in the organisms of one species are non-functional in the organisms of all the other species.
19. Growth of algae and fungi on the tree trunk imparts black colour to the tree trunk.

Direction for Questions from 20 to 28.

Choose the correct option.

(a) Both A and R are true and R is the correct explanation for A.

(b) Both A and R are true, but R is not the correct explanation for A.

(c) A is true and R is false.

(d) A is false and R is true.

20. **Assertion (A):** Jurassic period was known as the golden age of dinosaurs.

    Reason (R): Dinosaurs originated in the Jurassic period.
21. **Assertion (A):** Fossils are formed in the rocks in the deep layers of earth's crust.

    Reason (R) : Decomposition of dead organisms is prevented due to lack of oxygen.
22. **Assertion (A):** Thorns of bougainvillea and tendrils of passiflora are said to be homologous organs.

    Reason (R): They both perform the same function.

23. **Assertion (A):** *Euglena* is a connecting link between plants and animals.
Reason (R): *Euglena* is a unicellular eukaryote

24. **Assertion (A):** *Balanoglossus* is a missing link between non-chordates and chordates
Reason (R): *Balanoglossus* possesses a notochord in the adult form.

25. **Assertion (A):** The struggle for existence between two tigers is more intense than that between a tiger and a lion.
Reason (R): Tiger and lion differ widely in their feeding habits.

26. **Assertion (A):** It is presumed that man originated from chimpanzee.
Reason (R): *Dryopithecus* was the ancestor for chimpanzee.

27. **Assertion (A):** Boring the nose or pinna of ear by women is not inherited by their daughters.
Reason (R): Acquired characters cannot be inherited.

28. **Assertion (A):** Sometimes, the variations that are not useful are also inherited.
Reason (R): Vestigial organs are inherited

Level 2: Review your Concepts

29. Define and differentiate between homologous and analogous organs.

30. On what basis it was presumed that dinosaurs were subjected to mass extinctions?

31. The origin of living matter from non-living matter is called abiogenesis. It is accepted in scientific community. However, cell theory always says that life starts from a living cell only. How do you justify this contradiction?

32. Justify that cycas plant as a connecting link between pteridophytes and gymnosperms.

33. Explain the anatomical structure of forelimb of man and relate its homology with any other non-mammalian animal.

34. What is the function of appendix in vertebrates? Why did it become vestigial in modern man?

35. What does the following diagram indicate? Mention the conclusion which can be drawn from the diagram.

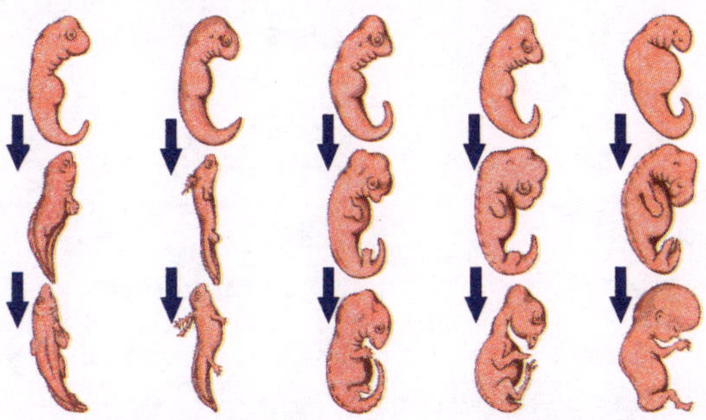

36. What are the similarities and differences found in the early embryonic stages of different classes of vertebrates? How can they support the organic evolution?

37. What does the mode of breathing in lung fish indicate? Explain.

38. Duck-billed platypus is the connecting link between reptiles and mammals. Give reason.

39. Leaves are the food factories of plants. But, in the plant Indian pipe, the leaves are considered as the vestigial structures. Justify.

40. Identify the homologous or analogous pairs of organs among the following by giving proper justification:
(a) Thorn of bougainvillea and tendrils of cucurbita
(b) Flippers of dolphin and penguin

41. The two chambered heart in fish underwent a gradual change to three- and four-chambered heart in the other classes of vertebrates. Justify.

42. With respect to embryology, justify the prediction that vertebrates are evolved from invertebrates.

43. Gymnosperms are evolved from pteridophytes. Give reason.

44. What is the status of duck-billed platypus in the evolutionary lineage?

45. Mule and hinny are produced by hybridization horse and donkey. But they are sterile. Justify.

46. What is the status of duck-billed platypus in the evolutionary lineage?

47. Explain the anatomical structure of forelimb of man and relate its homology with any other non-mammalian animal.

Level 3: Assess Your Concepts

48. How do the studies of adaptive radiation and convergent evolution together offer a comprehensive understanding of the processes that have shaped the unique biodiversity we observe on Earth?

49. Considering the principles of evolution and the presence of vestigial organs, discuss the implications of these vestigial structures in understanding the evolutionary pathway of organisms and their adaptations over time.

50. Explain molecular phylogeny with respect to common ancestry of ape and man.

51. Embryos of birds are found to develop tooth buds. What do we infer from this?

52. Justify the phylogeny of the following.
Mosses and ferns are evolved from algae

53. Site some evidences to show that man is more closely related to apes than to monkeys though they share common ancestry.

AT

PRACTICE QUESTIONS NEET SPECIAL WING

Multiple-Answer Type Questions

Questions number 1 to 5 are multiple-choice questions. Each question has FOUR options (a), (b), (c), and (d). ONE OR MORE THAN ONE of these four option(s) is/are the correct answer(s).

1. Which of the following are examples of homologous organs?
   (a) Wings of a bat and flipper of a whale
   (b) Tail fin of lobster and flukes of whales
   (c) Forelimb of a cat and forelimb of a man
   (d) Leaf of Mesophytes and flattened stem of xerophytes

2. Which of the following is true regarding Mesozoic era during Cretaceous period?
   (a) Extinction of dinosaurs
   (b) Origin of reptiles
   (c) Origin of invertebrates
   (d) Evolution of first flowering plants

3. Which of the following are examples of discontinuous distribution?
   (a) Alligators in south eastern part of the USA and eastern China
   (b) Darwin's finches
   (c) Walrus present in the North Pole in the Arctic Ocean and subarctic seas of the Northern Hemisphere
   (d) Australian marsupials and the placental mammals

4. Which of the following are correctly matched to each other?
   (a) Mass extinctions - Dinosaurs
   (b) Fossils of animals - Geological timescale
   (c) Duck billed platypus - Reptile
   (d) Transitional forms - connecting links

5. The evolutionary agents which bring about evolution are:
   (a) Recombination
   (b) Overproduction
   (c) Genetic drift
   (d) Natural selection

Comprehension-Based Questions

A. Read the paragraph given below and answer the questions number 6 to 11:

Scientists have provided many evidences to support the theory of evolution of how subtle gradations in both structures and functions lead to evolution of new species. Biogeographical evidences depend heavily on the pattern of distribution of the organisms in different parts of the Earth. This includes discontinuous distribution, adaptive radiation and convergent evolution. Paleontological evidences are based on the preserved remains of plants and animals from the remote past. Different types of paleontological evidences have been found like geological time scale, mass extinctions, ancestral forms and transitional forms which support organic evolution. Morphological evidences include homologous organs, analogous organs as well as vestigial organs. Embryological evidences have shown that there is a great deal of similarity in the early stages of development.

6. Which of the following is an example of adaptive radiation?
   (a) Evolution of new species in response to geographical isolation
   (b) Evolution of new species in response to different habitats
   (c) Evolution of new species in response to reproductive evolution
   (d) Evolution of new species in response to different temperatures

7. According to the paleontological evidences Archaeopteryx is considered to be:
   (a) species that underwent mass evolution
   (b) missing link between reptiles and birds
   (c) evolved during the Devonian period
   (d) connecting link to humans

8. Tail, appendix, hair are examples of:
   (a) Homologous organs
   (b) Orthologous organs
   (c) Analogous organs
   (d) Vestigial organs

9. What is the relationship between dogs, cows, rabbits and humans?
   (a) They all belong to different categories of placental mammals
   (b) They all have a non-functional appendix
   (c) They all use front foot for locomotion
   (d) They all use the same vestigial organ

10. The chronological order in which the animals are found at different depths in the earth's crust is based on
   (a) Geological time scale
   (b) Mass extinctions
   (c) Transitional forms
   (d) Discontinuous distribution

11. Match the column:

Column – A	Column – B
(i) Study of pattern of distribution of animals and plants in different parts on earth	(a) Convergent evolution
(ii) Australian marsupial and placental mammals	(b) Mass extinction
(iii) Dinosaurs	(c) Analogous organs
(iv) Flukes of whale and wings of bats	(d) Biogeography
(v) Stem of potato and root of sweet potato	(e) Homologous organs

B. Read the paragraph given below and answer the questions number 12 to 17:

Different kinds of theories have been put forth to explain the course of evolution. Amongst the important theories came Lamarckism which explained evolution on the basis of use and disuse of organs. A little while later on the basis of germplasm theory and Mendel's work Neo-Lamarckism came into being. Darwin's theory of natural selection was based on the following principles- overproduction, struggle for existence, variations, natural selection, survival of the fittest, inheritance of variation and speciation. Hugo de Vries introduced the idea of theory of mutation This gave rise to the modern theory of evolution which talks about evolutionary agents which bring about evolution. The evolutionary agents include- recombination, mutations, gene flow, genetic drift and natural selection.

12. Which among the following is not a feature associated with natural selection and Darwinism?
   (a) Variation
   (b) Artificial selection
   (c) Overproduction of offspring
   (d) Competition for resources

13. Which among the following is an example where changes in somatic or germ cells affect characters which can be inherited according to the Neo Lamarckism theory?
   (a) Height of humans
   (b) Eye colour of humans
   (c) Vegetative propagation in plants
   (d) Number of progeny of human

14. If a natural calamity results in the elimination of certain genes in a small population, then this is called:
   (a) Variation
   (b) Mutation
   (c) Genetic drift
   (d) Natural selection

15. Accidental migration leads to interbreeding between migrant species which eventually gives rise to new species, this is called:
   (a) Recombination
   (b) Mutation
   (c) Gene flow
   (d) Genetic drift

16. Selective survival of organism which are more adaptive to the changing environment in the natural course of events is called:
   (a) Natural selection
   (b) Variation
   (c) Gene flow
   (d) Genetic drift

17. Match the column:

Column – A	Column – B
(i) Use and disuse of organs	(a) Reproductive isolation
(ii) Survival of the fittest	(b) Lamarckism
(iii) Example of artificial selection	(c) Variation
(iv) Speciation due to geographical barrier	(d) Cabbage
(v) Recombination	(e) Darwinism

ANSWER KEYS

Crossword

Across

4. Dryopithecus
6. Ramapithecus
10. Adaptive radiation
12. Nucleic acids
13. Dinosaurs
16. Palaeontology
17. Speciation
18. Mutations
19. Finches
20. Echidna

Down

1. Variations
2. Vestigial organ
3. Genetic drift
5. Marsupials
7. Archaeopteryx
8. Jurassic period
9. Cretaceous
11. Precambrian
14. Galapagos
15. Phylogeny

Classroom Wing

Very Short Answer Type Questions

1. Big Bang Theory
2. Milky Way
3. Finches
4. Analogous
5. Homologous
6. Thorns
7. Soft inheritance or inheritance of acquired characters
8. Seed
9. HMS Beagle
10. Mutations
11. Crossing over, Recombination
12. Genetic drift
13. Speciation
14. Primates
15. *Homo sapiens*
16. Prokaryotes
17. (c)
18. (d)
19. (a)
20. (c)
21. (c)
22. (a)
23. (d)
24. (b)
25. (d)
26. (c)
27. (c)
28. (c)
29. (b)
30. A – iii, B – iv, C – ii, D – i
31. A- ii, B – iv, C – i, D – iii

Competition Wing

Level 1: Apply Your Concepts

1. Jurassic, the Mesozoic
2. Homologous
3. Convergent
4. Sedimentary
5. *Archaeopteryx*
6. Vestigial
7. Fossils
8. Palaeontology
9. Vestigial organs
10. 100
11. Analogous organs
12. (d)
13. (b)
14. (a)
15. (b)
16. Plants
17. Swimming
20. (b)
21. (a)
22. (b)
23. (c)
24. (a)
25. (c)
26. (d)
27. (c)
28. (a)

NEET Special Wing

Multiple-Answer Type Questions

1. (a, c) **2.** (a, d) **3.** (a, c) **4.** (a, b, d) **5.** (a, c, d)

Comprehension-Based Questions

6. (b) **7.** (b) **8.** (d) **9.** (a) **10.** (a)

11. (i) → (d); (ii) → (a); (iii) → (b); (iv) → (e); (v) → (c)

12. (b) **13.** (c) **14.** (c) **15.** (c) **16.** (a)

17. (i) → (b); (ii) → (e); (iii) → (d); (iv) → (a); (v) → (c)

Hints and Explanations

CLASSROOM WING

Short Answer Type Questions

32. Connecting links are organisms that share some characteristic features of two adjacent taxonomic groups and are still living today. Missing links, on the other hand, are presumed to have existed, shared features of two adjacent taxonomic groups, and are now extinct.

33. The Geological Time Scale arranges animals according to the order of geological eras in which they evolved, effectively showcasing a chronological order of their evolution.

34. The various kinds of studies as part of palaeontology provide evidences for organic evolution are:

- Geological time scale
- Mass extinctions
- Ancestral forms
- Transitional forms

35. The study of embryos of various classes of vertebrates revealed the fact that the early embryonic stages of all vertebrates show great deal of similarities with human embryo.

36. The fossils are the preserved remains or traces of plants or animals or any other organisms from the remote past. Usually, the hard parts of the bodies of organisms such as bones and teeth in case of vertebrates and exoskeleton in case of invertebrates undergo partial mineralization during their lifetime and when the organisms are dead, they get deposited on the hard surfaces such as rocks.

37. Similarities based on fossil studies suggests that both are transitional forms that is, show some characters of earlier group and some characters of later group. Both provide strong evidence for the taxonomic hierarchy of the organisms.

Connecting links	Missing links
They are still living Some representatives of the transitional forms are living until today. For example, *Echidna*, *Balanoglossus*	They are not living today. They are extinct forms and are available only in the form of fossils. For example, *Archeopteryx*

38.

Homologous organs	Analogous organs
The different organs in the different organisms may have similar basic anatomical structure even though they have different morphology and different functions.	Some organs have totally different structural organization in different organisms, but perform similar functions in various organisms. Such organs are called analogous organs due to the analogy in function.
This indicates that these organs must have evolved from a common ancestry which in course of time developed into organs with different structural features adopted to the respective environments. Such organs are called homologous organs.	The evolution giving rise to this kind of analogy is called convergent evolution.

39. Vestigial organs are organs that are present in a rudimentary form and no longer serve a significant function in an organism. An example is the human appendix.

40. The organs that are present in the rudimentary form and do not perform any significant function in certain organisms, but correspond to fully developed functional organs of other closely related organisms are called vestigial organs. These organs were well-developed and functional in their ancestors but became nonfunctional and rudimentary in the present living forms because of change in their mode of life. For example, monkey possesses tail due to its arboreal habitat.

Ancestral man also possessed tail.

Present-day man does not possess fully developed tail. But the rudimentary form of tail is there in the form of a tail bone composed of four fused vertebrae and some muscles attached to that.

The presence of this rudimentary tail in man indicates the common ancestry of man and monkey.

41.

Morphological features	Modifications
Facial features	• Flattening of face • Elevation in nose • Formation of chin
Features related to posture	• Increase in height • Broadening of forehead with vertical elevation
	• Curves in vertebral column • Erect posture • Bipedal locomotion
Features related to intelligence	• Enlargement of cranium • Increase in brain size
Other features	• Reduction in body hair • Bowl-like pelvic girdle

42. (a) Due to the limited availability of food and space, the organisms compete among themselves to acquire the resources. This is called struggle for existence. The organisms that adapt themselves to the prevailing environmental conditions are fit to survive and come out successful in their struggle. This is known as survival of the fittest.

(b) Due to some changes in the environmental conditions, new needs arise for the organisms. In order to fulfil the new needs, some variations are developed in the organisms of that species. These variations may be morphological or anatomical. They lead to variation in functioning also. Such variations are called acquired characters.

43.

Gene flow	Genetic drift
Accidental migration of some individual organisms to far off places may force interbreeding of the migrant species with the closely related	Sometimes, natural calamities or epidemics or accidents may result in the elimination of certain genes in small, isolated
species of the new region which may result in new genetic combinations. This is called gene flow or gene migration.	population of a species. This is known as a genetic drift.

44. The various evolutionary agents:

- Recombinations
- Mutations
- Gene flow or gene migration
- Genetic drift
- Natural selection

Essay Type Questions

45. The ancestors of giraffe resembled horse as they possessed small neck and short forelimbs.

- Due to the sudden disappearance of surface vegetation, they had to stretch their neck and forelimbs to reach to the upper foliage of trees.
- This resulted in the elongation of neck and forelimbs which is considered as the acquired character.
- This character acquired in one generation was useful and hence was transmitted to the later generations. In this way, a new species of long-necked giraffe came into existence
- The continuous use of neck by stretching it to reach the upper foliage resulted in the increase in length of neck.

46. Acquired characters are those features which the organisms acquired during their life time as a part of adaptation to the changes in the environmental factors. These are not inherited from the parental generation. But, they may be transmitted to the successive generations for making them more suitable to the environment. They in a way, help in the continuance of the species. For example, long neck of giraffe.

47. In the evolutionary hierarchy, human beings are considered to be the most evolved living beings and are considered to be at the pinnacle of evolutionary tree. Human evolution is one of the most important and significant milestones of biological evolution. It can be traced back to fossil records of ancestral organisms. According to palaeontological evidences, it had been concluded that the modern man originated from ancestral apes (*Dryopithecus: Ramapithecus*) which belonged to the class of Primates. These species had close resemblances with gorillas and chimpanzees. For example, bodies were fully covered with thick hair and their walking style also resembled gorillas. Morphological changes involved in the evolution of man clearly indicate the above ancestry. The evolution of ancestral man and apes from the common ancestor and the evolution of modern man from the ancestral man can be shown in the given schematic diagram.

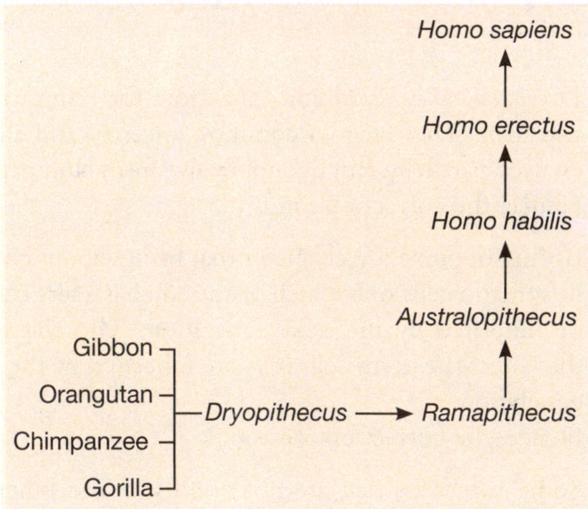

48 Accidental migration of some individual organisms to far off places may force interbreeding of the migrant species with the closely related species of the new region. This may result in new genetic combinations. This is called gene flow or gene migration. Over a long period, this may result in reproductive isolation of the migrant organisms with the organisms in their original habitat. This becomes obligatory, especially when any geographical barrier such as a river or island exists between the two regions. Such reproductive isolation may result in the origin of new species.

49. Lamarckism is mainly based on use and disuse theory. According to this theory, the organs that are used continuously will become more developed and the organs that are not useful in the changed environmental conditions get degenerated in the organisms. These characteristics developed in the organisms as adaptations to the changed mode of life are called acquired characters. These are passed on to the next generations by inheritance. This is the concept of inheritance of acquired characters. According to germplasm theory, the characters corresponding to somatic cells cannot be inherited. The characters corresponding to germ cells can only be inherited.

50. Distinguish between the following.

(a)

Prokaryotes	Eukaryotes
Unicellular organisms having cell with indistinct nucleus	Unicellular and multicellular organisms having cell with indistinct nucleus

(b)

Invertebrates	Vertebrates
Organisms that may possess only exoskeleton and no endoskeleton	Organisms that possess endoskeleton in the form of vertebral column

(c)

Gymnosperms	Angiosperms
Naked seeded flowering plants without fruit formation	Flowering plants forming seeds enclosed in fruits

(d)

Protochordates	Vertebrates
Animals possessing primitive notochord that is retained even in the adult stage	Animals in which notochord is present in the embryonic stage and is replaced by vertebral column in the adult stage

51. The environment does not remain constant. It is ever changing. The organisms should also adapt themselves to the changing environmental conditions. Therefore, the organisms of a species undergo some modifications in their colour, form, structure and functioning. These modifications are called variations. This is known as 'survival of the fittest'.

52. Struggle for existence:

- The organisms living in a particular habitat face competition from the other organisms of same species as well as different species.
- The organisms belonging to the same species compete among themselves to a large extent because they have common basic necessities like food, shelter, breeding etc.
- Members belonging to different species also compete to some extent for food and shelter.
- All the organisms also experience struggle against the environmental factors such as drought, heavy rain, heat waves, cold waves, floods, etc.,
- Due to this struggle for existence faced by the organisms, the number of individuals of any species becomes restricted.
- Individuals of the same species also show lot of differences in the size, shape, colour, behavior etc., These are called variations.

COMPETITION WING

Level 1: Apply your Concepts

16. Fish: Amphibians :: Reptiles: Birds

17. Acquired inheritance : Lamarck :: Natural selection : Darwin

18. Vestigial organs in the organisms of one species may be functional in the organisms of the other species.

19. Growth of algae and fungi on the tree trunk imparts grey colour to the tree trunk.

20. Dinosaurs were the dominant group of animals in Jurassic period. Hence it was called the golden age of reptiles.
Hence, the correct option is (b)

21. The absence of adequate supply of oxygen prevents the decomposition of the dead plants and animals. This leads to the formation of fossils in the deep layers of the earth's crust.
Hence, the correct option is (a)

22. Thorns of *Bougainvillea* and tendrils of passiflora are said to be homologous organs. This is because both thorns and tendrils are modified leaves. But they perform different functions. Thorns help in protection while tendrils help in climbing.
Hence, the correct option is (b)

23. *Euglena* possesses chloroplasts and shows autotrophic mode of nutrition. But it possesses flagella helpful for locomotion. Therefore, this unicellular eukaryote can be considered as the connecting link between plants and animals.
Hence, the correct option is (c)

24. *Balanoglossus* possesses a notochord only in the anterior region . In rest of the chordates, notochord is present in the embryonic stage and is replaced by the vertebral column in the adult stage. However, in *Balanoglossus*, the notochord is retained in the adult stage also. Hence, it is considered as a connecting link between nonchordates and chordates.
Hence, the correct option is (a)

25. Tiger and lion have similar feeding habits. The struggle between them is interspecific struggle. However, the struggle between two tigers is intraspecifc struggle. This is more intense because they struggle for mating also in addition to food and space.
Hence, the correct option is (c)

26. *Dryopithecus* is common ancestor for chimpanzee and man. They share a common ancestry and almost evolved parallelly. But did not evolve from chimpanzee.
Hence, the correct option is (d)

27. Boring of pinna is a character that brings about change in somatic cells only. Such acquired characters cannot be inherited by the next generation. The characters that affect the germ cells only are inherited by the next generation.
Hence, the correct option is (c)

28. Some variations that are not useful are also inherited along with useful variations. Vestigial organs are not useful to the organisms, but are not inherited.
Hence, the correct option is (a)

Level 2: Review your Concepts

29. Homologous organs have a similar basic anatomical structure but may have different functions and indicate common ancestry, e.g., the forelimbs of humans and dogs. Analogous organs have different structures but perform the same function, indicating separate evolutionary origins, e.g., wings of butterflies and birds.

30. Dinosaurs were believed to be the dominant group of organisms in the Jurassic period of Mesozoic era. Mass extinction of these animals took place in the latter period of that era. One factor that might have led to the extinction of dinosaurs could be meteorites.

Basis for this belief is the presence of high concentration of iridium in the Earth's crust. Iridium is not an original component of the earth's crust. These iridium deposits were traced back to the same time period in which dinosaurs became extinct.

31. Before the origin of life on Earth, the atmospheric conditions were totally different from the present atmospheric conditions. The atmosphere was rich in hydrogen and there was no appreciable amount of oxygen. This means it was a reducing atmosphere. Under those conditions, the formation of complex organic molecules from the simple inorganic materials was possible. The same transformation is not possible now as the organic molecules formed might get oxidized as it is oxidizing atmosphere with a large amount of oxygen. Moreover, the microorganisms may also decompose the complex molecules. Therefore, abiogenesis is not possible now. According to the accepted theory of origin of life, life originated by abiogenesis and continued by biogenesis.

32. Characters of *Cycas* resembling pteredophytes:

- Fern-like foliage
- Stem similar to ferns
- Xylem with tracheids and xylem parenchyma and without vessels
- Phloem with sieve tubes and companion cells and without companion cells
- Presence of motile spores

Characters of *Cycas* resembling gymnosperms

- Formation of well-defined seeds
- Presence of ovules on the lateral sides of leaf like megasporophylls
- Ovules with integuments and nucellus

33. The forelimb of human has the following bones:

Upper arm — humerus

Lower arm — radius and ulna

Carpals — wrist

Metacarpals — Palm

Phalanges — fingers

The wing of a bird also possesses similar anatomical features. This means that they possess same bones showing that the wings are modified forelimbs. However, the wings are covered by feathers. But, flying birds mostly possess fused bones that are hollow inside. This is a major flight adaptation of birds.

34. Vermiform appendix was functional in ancestors of humans. The ancestral man was habituated to eat uncooked food available in the forest. The food has considerable amount of cellulose in it. Appendix was associated with the function of digestion of cellulose present in uncooked food. Gradually, as the man became more and more civilized in the course of evolution, he started eating cooked food instead of uncooked food. Cellulose got transformed into simple sugars during the process of cooking. Therefore, the appendix became nonfunctional and became rudimentary. Hence it is considered as a vestigial organ in modern man.

35. The diagram indicates that the different stages of embryonic development of organisms belonging to different classes (fish, reptile and mammal) of the embryos in their early stages of development show very close resemblances though they have striking differences in the later stages of development.

36. The embryonic development shows the following similarities among the various classes of vertebrates:

- The zygote undergoes cleavage and develops into a blastula and then into gastrula which contains three layers namely ectoderm, mesoderm and endoderm. These are called primary germ layers. The condition of presence of three primary germ layers is called triploblastic. This is a common feature of embryos of all vertebrates.
- Embryos of all vertebrates from fish to mammals show the presence of gill clefts and notochord. The notochord is replaced by the vertebral column in all vertebrates.
- The gills are replaced by lungs in all the vertebrates other than fish.

37. Lung fish is a fish and hence is expected to breath by means of gills. But, it breaths by primitive lungs which indicates a transition stage from fish to amphibians and the course of evolution from fish to amphibians.

38. The duck-billed platypus lays eggs like reptiles. At the same time, it possesses hair and mammary glands that are the characteristic features of mammals. Since this organism possesses significant features of both reptiles and mammals, it is supposed to be the connecting link between reptiles and mammals.

39. In Indian pipe plant, scale-like leaves are seen. It is considered that the plant has lost the chlorophyll and transformed from autotrophic mode of nutrition to saprophytic mode of nutrition in the course of evolution. The leaves must have become nonfunctional and are reduced to scales in the successive generations which are considered to be the vestigial structures.

40. (a) Both thorns of *Bougainvillea* and tendrils of cucurbita are leaf modifications. Both of them show similarities in anatomic features. But they differ in morphology and perform different functions. Hence, these are homologous organs.

(b) Flippers of dolphin and penguin possess similar morphological features. But they have different anatomical features as they have different origins. Therefore, they are analogous organs.

41. Fish are aquatic organisms and are the simplest vertebrates. So, their energy requirement is also less. Therefore, they have two-chambered heart with one auricle and one ventricle. Mixed blood is circulated in the body. Amphibians lead partly aquatic and partly terrestrial life. They possess a three-chambered heart. Reptiles are the first totally terrestrial organisms. They also possess a three-chambered heart because of relatively simpler body organization. Birds require much greater amount of energy for their metabolism due to their aerial mode of life. Hence they possess four-chambered heart. Mammals possess the most complicated organ systems and complex metabolism. Hence, they possess four-chambered heart.

42. Invertebrates mostly show external fertilization and oviparity. Some of them show metamorphosis during development. The lower vertebrates show almost the same features. For example, amphibians.

Some reptiles show oviparity and few show ovoviviparity that is a slightly advanced feature. Birds show internal fertilization and oviparity. Mammals are viviparous which is the most advanced feature in the embryonic development.

43. Gymnosperms show some similarities with pteridophytes. These are:

- Alternation of generations with dominant sporophyte and reduced gametophyte.
- Generation of haploid spores with meiotic cell division.
- Absence of vessels in xylem and companion cells in phloem.
- Absence of root hairs.

Differences

Pteridophytes	Gymnosperms
Independent gametophyte	Gametophyte dependent on sporophyte
No seed formation	Seed-bearing plants
Adventitious root system	Tap root system
No formation of secondary xylem	Formation of secondary xylem
Pollination absent	Pollination present
No pollen tube development during fertilization	Pollen tube development during fertilization

In this way, gymnosperms show advancement over pteridophytes. This shows the close phylogenetic relationship leading to the origin of angiosperms.

44. Duckbilled platypus is an egg-laying primitive mammal which shows a transition from Australian marsupials to placental mammals.

45. Hinny is the offspring of the crossbreeding between a male horse and a female donkey. Mule is the progeny of the cross between a male donkey and female horse. A horse has 64 chromosomes and a donkey has 62 chromosomes in their diploid cells. But mule and hinny have 63 chromososmes in their diploid cells. It makes the splitting difficult during cell division. Due to this reason, mule and hinny are sterile.

46. Duckbilled platypus is an egg-laying mammal that shows a transition from ancestral reptiles to placental mammals.

47. The forelimb of human has the following bones.

Upper arm — humerus

Lower arm — radius and ulna

Carpals — wrist

Metacarpals — palm

Phalanges — fingers

The wing of a bird also possesses similar anatomical features. This means that they possess same bones showing that the wings are modified forelimbs. However, the wings are covered by feathers. But, flying birds mostly possess fused bones that are hollow inside. This is a major flight adaptation of birds.

Level 3: Assess Your Concepts

48. Adaptive radiation explains how new species evolve with different adaptations from a common ancestor when exposed to different environments or habitats. It showcases how diversity can arise from a single point of origin. On the other hand, convergent evolution illustrates how completely unrelated species can develop similar features or traits due to experiencing similar environmental pressures. Together, they provide a full picture of evolution – how species can diverge from a common point and how different species can converge in traits, painting a complex tapestry of life's evolutionary journey on Earth.

49. Vestigial organs provide compelling evidence for the theory of evolution. Their presence indicates that organisms have undergone changes over time, adapting to their environment and discarding what's no longer necessary. For instance, the human appendix, once essential for digesting a plant-based diet, is now redundant in our primarily omnivorous diet. Similarly, the coccyx or tailbone, a remnant of our tailed ancestors, signifies our shared lineage. As environments and lifestyles changed, certain organs became obsolete. However, these vestiges remain as silent testimonials to an organism's evolutionary journey. Their existence challenges the notion of a fixed, unchanging blueprint of life, underscoring the dynamic nature of evolution and the intricate pathways that life forms have taken over millennia.

50. Genetic difference between apes and humans is less than 2 per cent. Humans have 23 pairs of chromosomes while apes have 24 pairs. Out of these, 18 pairs are identical. This is molecular phylogeny.

51. The possession of tooth buds by embryos of birds indicates the phylogeny of birds from reptile-like ancestors.

52. Green algae are believed to be the phylogenetic ancestors for land plants. The major similarities between the green algae and land plants is in the basic cell structure. The chloroplasts and mitochondria possess DNA in both the cases. The sperms of these plants possess similar structure. The mode of cell division is mitosis in both the plants. However, mosses and ferns show advancement over green algae in an important feature that mosses and ferns possess multicellular embryos. This shows the phylogenetic relationship between green algae and mosses and ferns.

    Mosses and ferns are evolved from algae.

53. Monkeys have a small posture like other mammals such as cats, dogs, etc., Apes have a larger body posture than monkeys. This is similar to humans. Apes have a larger brain than monkeys. The intelligence, communication skills and cognitive skills are also closer to ancestral humans. Apes do not run from branch to branch on trees. The apes swing from branch to branch by hanging with the help of arms. The blood groups A and B are found in both apes and humans. But these are not found in monkeys. Though monkeys, apes and humans have common ancestry, the presence of common blood groups show that humans are more closely related to apes than to monkeys apart from the morphological and behavioral similarities between apes and humans.

NEET SPECIAL WING

Multiple-Answer Type Questions

1. The different organs in different organisms may have similar basic anatomical structure even though they have different morphology and different functions. This indicates that these organs must have evolved from a common ancestry which in course of time developed into organs with different structural features adapted to the respective environments. Such organs are called homologous organs. Examples include- wings of a bat and flipper of a whale and forelimb of a cat and forelimb of a man

2. The Mesozoic era consisted of the cretaceous era which saw the extinction of dinosaurs and the evolution of first flowering plants.

3. It is found that closely related species of plants and animals inhabit the far distant geographical regions. The regions lying in between these territories are not inhabited by any closely related plants or animals. Such kind of discontinuous distribution of organisms shows the common ancestry of those organisms. For example, existence of alligators in south eastern part of the USA and eastern China and Walrus present in the North Pole in the Arctic Ocean and subarctic seas of the Northern Hemisphere.

4. The correctly matched pairs include- Mass extinctions of Dinosaurs, Fossils of animals which give us the geological timescale and transitional forms which become the connecting links between the organisms. Duck billed platypus is a egg- laying mammal.

5. New species forms or evolution happens by the inheritance of such genes. In terms of genetics, the characteristics of an organism are attributed to the presence of specific genes. The presence of different alleles in different proportions brings about variations. The various factors that bring about such variations resulting in evolution are called evolutionary agents. Some of the various evolutionary agents are: Recombination, genetic drift and natural selection.

Comprehension-Based Questions

A.

6. Adaptive radiation is the kind of evolutionary trend that gives rise to new species to make them suitable for the new habitats and new way of life. For example, the finches of Galapagos islands.

7. Some groups of animals that showed a wide distinction in their characteristics did not have any animals or plants that showed transition in characteristics. Some fossil remains of organisms have been found that showed the transitional features. It is presumed that the organisms that evolved from some groups of organisms that existed in the past are still living today. Unlike the connecting links, the group of organisms which have no living representatives now as all of them should have become extinct. Such organisms are called missing links. For example, *Archaeopteryx* is a missing link between reptiles and birds.

8. Vestigial organs are complete and functional in the ancestral forms, but became rudimentary in the present living forms because of change in their mode of life. For example, presence of rudimentary tail in humans.

9. Cats, animals, cows and humans have a common structure called placenta which is an organ through which a mother is able to nurse the young one. So, they all belong to different categories of placental mammals.

10. The fossils of animals collected from layers of Earth at different depths in a way indicate the chronological order in which the animals were evolved. The animals can be arranged according to the order of geological eras in which they were evolved. This is called geological time scale.

11. Match the following:
The study of patterns of distribution of animals and plants in different parts of Earth is known as biogeography.
(i) (d)

Evolution which brings about similar kinds of changes or adaptations in the animals which are living in different regions having similar habitats. This is called adaptive convergence or convergent evolution. This is a parallel evolution. For example, some Australian marsupials closely resemble placental mammals in other regions with the similar environmental conditions.
(ii) (a)

The sudden and large-scale extinction of some species of plants and animals in a short span of time is called mass extinction. The fossils of such species indicate the resemblance of existing species of plants or animals to the extinct species. For example, extinction of dinosaurs that dominated the earth in Jurassic period shows some similarities with the living reptiles.
(iii) (b)

The different organs in different organisms may have similar basic anatomical structure even though they have different morphology and different functions. These are homologous organs. E.g. Flukes of whale and wings of bats.
(iv) (e)

Some organs have totally different structural organization in different organisms, but perform similar functions in various organisms. Such organs are called analogous organs, due to the analogy in function. They also do not share common origin. The evolution giving rise to this kind of analogy is called convergent evolution. For example, modified stem in potato and modified root in sweet potato perform the same function of storage of food.
(v) (c)

B.

12. According to Darwin's theory of evolution, overproduction, struggle for existence, variations, natural selection, survival of the fittest, inheritance of variation and speciation are the various factors involved in evolution. Artificial selection (a process controlled by humans) is not a process involved in evolution.

13. On the basis of germplasm theory and Mendel's studies on inheritance, Lamarckism was modified and was called neo-Lamarckism. According to this theory, Structure, colour, form and functioning of organisms are affected by the environment. They may cause changes in either somatic or germ cells. The characters affecting somatic cells may also be inherited. For example, vegetative propagation in plants.

14. Sometimes, natural calamities or epidemics or accidents may result in the elimination of certain genes in small, isolated population of a species. This may force interbreeding among the organisms of closely related species in the region which may result in speciation. This is called genetic drift.

15. Accidental migration of some individual organisms to far off places may force interbreeding between the migrant species with the closely related species of the new region. This may result in new genetic combinations. It is called gene flow or gene migration.

16. The kind of selective survival of the organisms occurs in natural course and is called natural selection. The nature allows these organisms to survive more and contribute to the continuation of the species.

17. Match the following:
According to Lamarckism, continuous use of a particular organ due to the new needs results in the increase in size of the organ. Similarly, continuous disuse of the organs leads to the degeneration of the organ in course of time in the next generations.
(i) (b)

The kind of selective survival of the organisms occurs in natural course and is called natural selection. The nature allows these organisms to survive more and contribute to the continuation of the species. This is known as 'survival of the fittest'. This was part of Darwin's theory of evolution.
(ii) (e)

Cabbage is an example for evolution by artificial selection. Artificial selection is the intentional breeding of plants and animals to produce progeny with desirable trait. In the beginning, only wild cabbage was there, unlike today when we have a wide range of cabbage.
(iii) (d)

If a geographical barrier such as a river is developed between the two regions, it leads to reproductive isolation. In the long run, the members of these two groups may possess different DNA structures. Then, they become incapable of interbreeding or mating. This results in speciation.
(iv) (a)

The meiotic cell division which is the basis of sexual reproduction involves the important phenomenon of crossing over followed by recombination. This results in independent assortment of chromosomes and genes. As a result, the individuals belonging to the same species including the offspring of same parents show variation in each and every characteristic.
(v) (c)

CHAPTER 11

Ecology

Remember

Before beginning this chapter, you should be able to:

- Recall basic components of ecosystem
- Remember the concepts of food chain and food web
- List the types of pollution and their basic control measures

Key Ideas

After completing this chapter, you should be able to:

- Understand the major components of an ecosystem and their inter-dependence
- Classify ecosystem on various bases
- Explain the concept of ecological pyramid
- Describe various types, causes, sources, effects and control measures of pollution

A Tribute to Dr. Ramdeo Misra (1924–1998)

Dr. Ramdeo Misra (1924–1998) is a renowned eco-scientist who played a pivotal role in shaping environmental studies in India. Misra, who specialised in plant ecology and environmental sciences, pioneered extensive research that added a new dimension to our understanding of ecological patterns, processes, and principles.

Dr. Misra's lifelong passion for ecology was evident in his efforts to promote environmental awareness and ecological balance. His extensive research in ecosystem dynamics and conservation has shed light on the symbiotic relationship between various species and their habitats, allowing for the development of strategies to preserve biodiversity and ecological integrity.

He was honoured with the Pitamber Pant National Environment Fellowship in recognition of his outstanding contributions to ecology. Misra's profound influence extends beyond his numerous scholarly publications.

FUN TIME

CROSSWORD

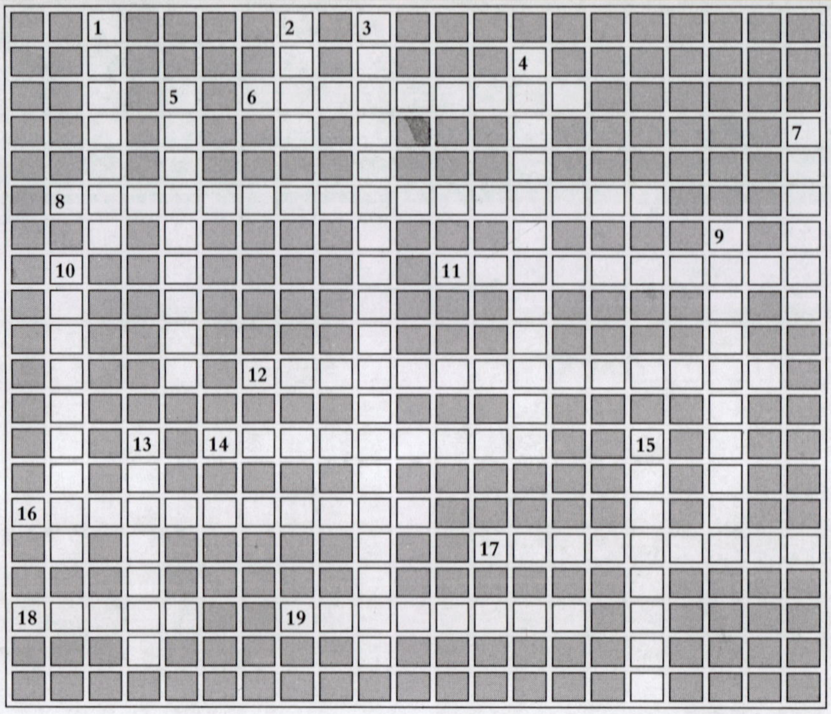

Across

6. The harmful materials introduced into the environment
8. The gas which leaked out during the Bhopal gas tragedy and killed many people
11. The other name for primary consumers
12. Uncontrolled growth of weeds in the water bodies due to the availability of excess minerals
14. The organisms arranged in the order of their dependence on one over the other for food
16. The scavengers which break down the dead plants and animals
17. The component of the ecosystem which can capture solar energy and pass on to various trophic levels
18. The layer of gas which protects the earth from harmful solar radiation
19. The disease caused by consuming water containing mercury as a contaminant

Down

1. The interconnected network of various food chains
2. A pollutant which is a mix of smoke and fog
3. The volatile organic compounds which cause ozone depletion
4. The process of destruction of waste materials by burning
5. The natural source of oxides of nitrogen
7. Finely divided residue formed by the combustion of coal
9. The layer of the atmosphere in which ozone acts as a pollutant
10. The secondary consumers which depend on both primary consumers and producers
13. The transitional region between two neighbouring ecosystems
15. A device installed to neutralise harmful industrial emissions

INTRODUCTION

In our daily life, we use many articles that are composed of either natural or synthetic material. After using them, the remnants of these materials are disposed. The waste generated from these may or may not decompose easily. Some of them do not undergo decomposition at all. They are called non-biodegradable materials. Whereas, materials that decompose in due course of time are called biodegradable materials. Accumulation of such kind of garbage eventually disturbs the nature and a number of natural phenomena. Hence, the development of awareness among people regarding natural environment and its maintenance becomes mandatory. Natural environment comprises living organisms and non-living components such as air, water, etc. around them and the link between them can be understood by studying the ecosystem. Ecology is the branch of biology which deals with the study of interactions between organisms and their environment. The term ecology is derived from Greek words 'oikos' meaning house or dwelling place and 'logia' meaning study of.

Ecosystem

Ecosystem is a community of living organisms and non-living components of the environment, such as air, water, mineral and soil, linked together through the nutrient cycles and energy flows. Living and non-living components of ecosystem are called biotic and abiotic components, respectively.

Let us understand the concept of ecosystem by taking example of a pond. Algae grows in ponds using air, water and solar energy. The other living organisms in it, such as fish, tadpoles, frogs and small fish, feed on algae as well as the leaves, flowers or fruits that fall into the pond from the plants grown beside the pond. The bigger fish and birds depend on these smaller fish for their food. Thus, the ecosystem in pond exists.

Info Bytes!

The term 'ecosystem' was first used by the British ecologist Arthur Tansley in 1935.

Figure 11.1 A pond ecosystem comprising biotic factors, like algae and plants, and abiotic factors like water and sunlight

Info Bytes!

The Pacific Ocean, the world's largest marine ecosystem, spans over 63 million square miles.

Components of Ecosystem

Ecosystem comprises the following two main components:

1. **Biotic components**: The living components in an ecosystem, such as plants, animals, microorganisms and human beings are called biotic components.
2. **Abiotic components**: The non-living components of an ecosystem, such as air, temperature, rainfall, wind, soil and minerals are called abiotic components.

> **Info Bytes!**
> A montane component is the one relating to, or growing in mountainous region

Biotic components interact with each other and with their abiotic components to grow, reproduce and perform other activities. Ecosystems do not have rigid boundaries. They can overlap with each other and the area of transition is called ecotone. For example, ecotone is a transitional area of vegetation between two different plant ecosystems, such as forest and grassland. It has some of the characteristics of each type of ecosystems. The ecotones may be as small as of length 1 km or very wide, extending up to 90 km.

Figure 11.2 Ecotone of Hill Evergreen forest (left) and montane scrub (right)

Classification of Ecosystems

Ecosystems can be classified into various types based on different factors. In this chapter we shall look at three different methods of classifying ecosystem.

Classification on the Basis of Formation

Ecosystems can be classified as natural and artificial ecosystems based on the way they are formed.

1. **Natural ecosystems:** Ecosystems in ponds, lakes, forests, etc., that are formed naturally without the involvement of the human beings are called natural ecosystems.
2. **Artificial ecosystems:** Artificial ecosystems are man-made ecosystems, such as zoos, parks, gardens, fields, etc. They are not formed as a result of any natural phenomenon, instead they have been formed due to human activities.

Figure 11.3 Natural and artificial ecosystems

Classification on the Basis of Region

Another way of classifying ecosystems is based on the region they exist, that is, on land or on water.

1. **Terrestrial ecosystem:** Ecosystems that exist on land are called terrestrial ecosystems. Examples are forests, grasslands, deserts and tundra ecosystems.
2. **Aquatic ecosystem:** Ecosystems that exist in water are called aquatic ecosystems. Examples are fresh water, marine water and river water ecosystem.

Figure 11.4 Terrestrial (left) and aquatic (right) ecosystems

Classification on the Basis of Size

Ecosystems can also be classified based on their sizes. They are:

1. **Micro:** Small-scale ecosystems, such as tree trunk, pond, communities living under a rock, come under this category.
2. **Meso:** These are Medium-scaled ecosystems, such as large lakes.
3. **Macro:** An ecosystem like entire rainforest is considered a large-scale ecosystem and is known as biome.

Figure 11.5 Micro, Meso and Macro-ecosystems

Classification of Biotic Components of Ecosystems

The biotic components of ecosystems can be classified based on their dependence on each other for food. Biotic components can be broadly classified into producers and consumers. Producers are autotrophs and prepare their food from solar energy, carbon dioxide and water. Solar energy is the ultimate source of energy and producers convert solar energy to chemical energy. Thus, solar energy is trapped in the food prepared by producers. Green plants, algae and some bacteria are producers.

Consumers, on the other hand, survive on producers for their food and they are called heterotrophs. Consumers can be of three different types, namely:

1. **Primary consumers:** They are herbivores and completely depend on producers for their food. For example, cow, goats, etc.

2. **Secondary consumers:** They depend on primary consumers for their food. Secondary consumers can be carnivores or omnivores. Carnivores survive only on animals whereas omnivores survive on both plants and animals. Eagles, dogs, cats, etc., are carnivores, and human beings, monkeys, bears, etc., are omnivores.
3. **Tertiary consumers:** They survive on primary and secondary consumers. Large carnivores, such as lion, wolf, tiger, etc., are examples of tertiary consumers.

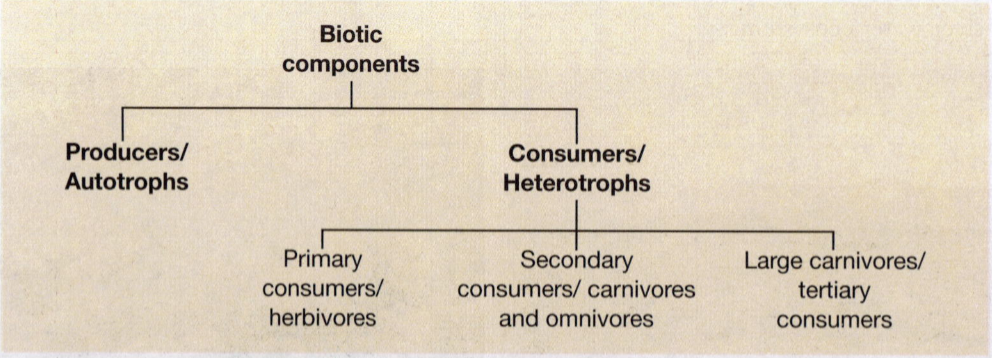

Figure 11.6 Classification of biotic components

Flow of Energy in Ecosystem

When light energy in the form of sunlight falls on the leaves of plants, a part of it is transformed into chemical energy which is stored in the form of various substances like carbohydrates. When herbivores consume plants, they transform this chemical energy into kinetic energy in form of doing work. Also, dissipation of energy will occur in this process. When herbivores are consumed by carnivores, further degradation will occur. In this way, there is flow of energy established in an ecosystem. This flow can be described either through food chains or ecological pyramids.

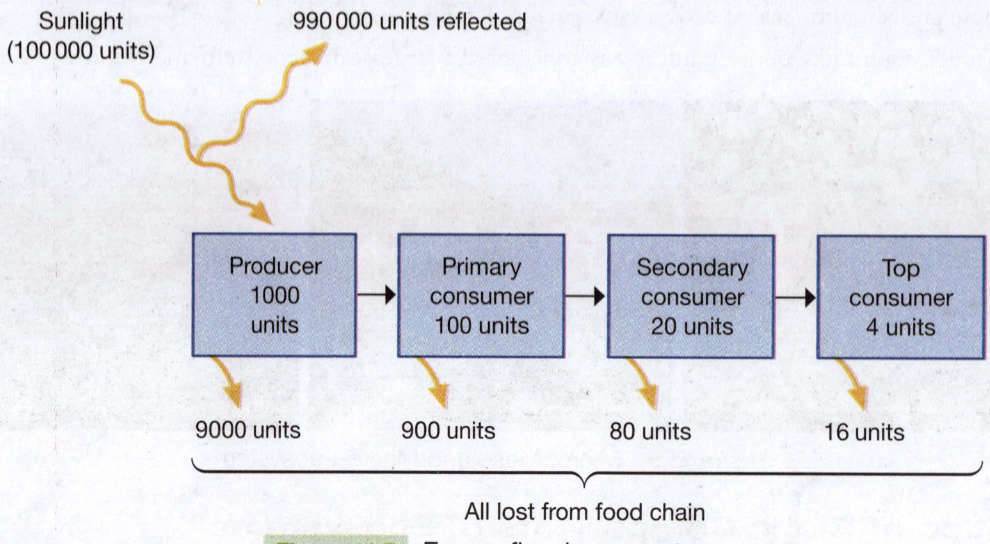

Figure 11.7 Energy flow in ecosystem

Food Chains and Webs

A food chain is the linear flow of energy between various components of the ecosystem. Example: Grassland food chain (Grass → Grasshopper → Frog → Snake → Vulture) Food chains are neither simple nor rigid. A specific food can be consumed by different organisms. For example, aphids (plant lice) suck the juices from plant stems and a deer also consumes the same food. Thus, they belong to the same level of a food chain and form a trophic level in the food chain. In an ecosystem, a trophic level comprises a group of organisms that occupy the same level in a food chain. The interlinking of various food chains is called food web. Ecological pyramids are the other ways of representing the flow of energy from one organism to another.

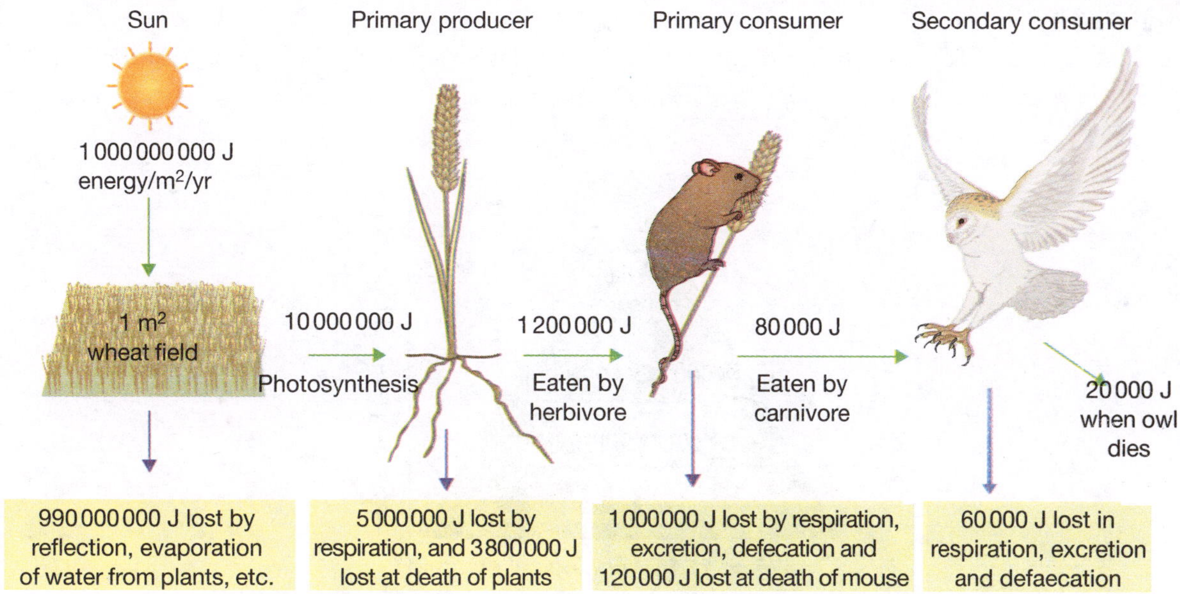

Figure 11.8 Flow of energy in a wheat-field food chain

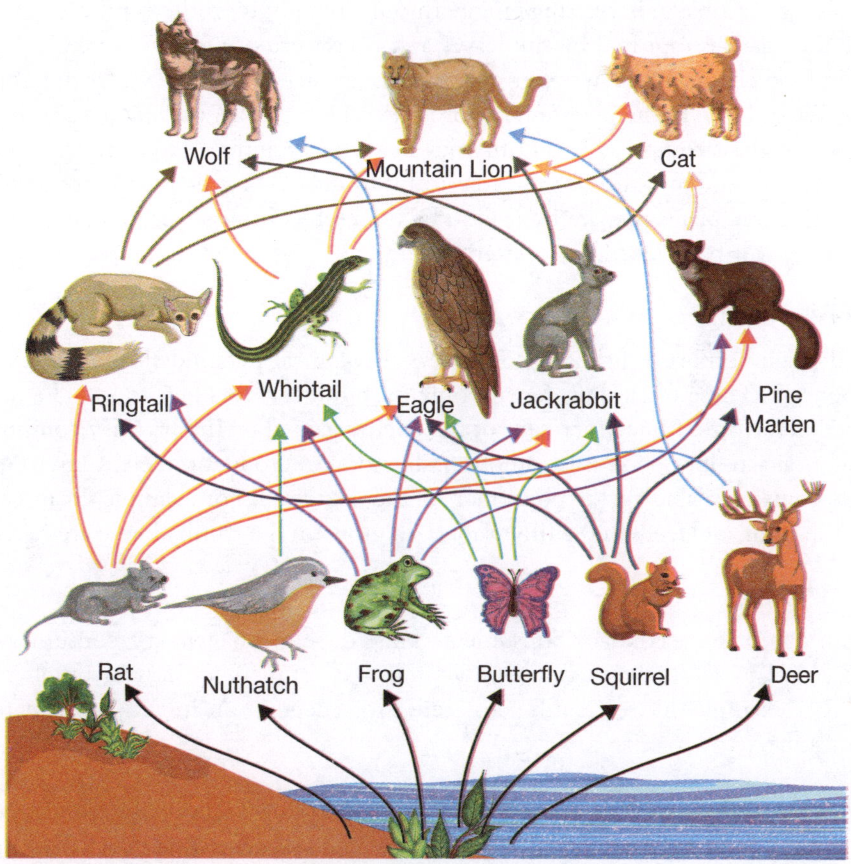

Figure 11.9 Food web

Ecological Pyramid

An ecological pyramid is a diagrammatic representation of food chains by arranging the organisms at the various trophic levels.

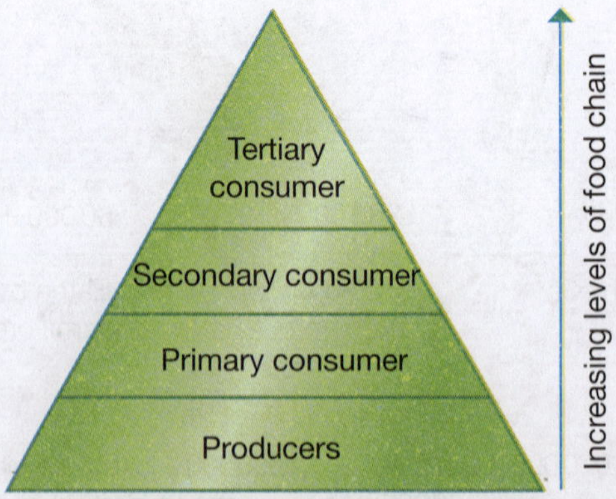

Figure 11.10 Ecological pyramid

First Trophic Level of Food Chain

Solar energy is the basic source of energy for all the trophic levels. The basic level of a food chain of an ecosystem comprises producers. These are capable of harvesting energy through the photosynthesis process. Only 1 per cent of entire solar energy received by the Earth is captured by the leaves and is converted into food energy. The ecological pyramid shows the various levels of food chain and the number of organisms at each level. The wider the trophic level, the more is the number of organisms at that level. In the pyramid, the producers (autotrophs) occupy the first level and the number of organisms in this level is the highest compared to all other levels in the pyramid. For example, in a tree trunk ecosystem, the humidity in atmosphere provides moisture for the tree trunk to decay. This decaying tree trunk acts like ground for the tiny plants to grow. These tiny plants prepare their food by themselves using heat, light, air and humidity. Therefore, they form the first trophic level or basic level of ecosystem.

Second Trophic Level of Food Chain

Second level of the food chain comprises primary consumers. Ecological pyramid shows that they are less in number compared to that of producers. These organisms depend only on producers for their food. The plants are consumed by primary consumers, called herbivores. Ninety per cent of the energy gained by the primary consumers from producers is utilized for different biological activities, such as locomotion, digestion, reproduction, etc. Only 10 per cent of the energy gets stored in them and becomes available for the consumers of the next level. For example, in a tree trunk ecosystem, the bugs, insects live around the trunk and feed on the tiny plants that grow on the trunk. These are called primary consumers.

Third Trophic Level of Food Chain

Third level of food chain comprises secondary consumers. They depend on primary consumers as well as producers for their food. The ecological pyramid shows that the secondary consumers are less in number compared to that of the primary consumers. For example, in tree trunk ecosystem, frogs depend on insects for their food. Hence, frogs are considered secondary consumers.

Fourth Trophic Level of Food Chain

Fourth level of food chain comprises tertiary consumers. These are the organisms that feed on the primary and secondary consumers. The number of tertiary consumers is less than the number of secondary consumers. For example, in tree trunk ecosystem, the frogs are consumed by snakes. Hence, snakes come under the category of tertiary consumers. Decomposers of an ecosystem are the scavengers that break down dead plants, animals and organic wastes. They play an important role in the ecosystem by providing nutrients to the plants. Moreover, the nutrient cycles, such as carbon cycle, nitrogen cycle, etc., are maintained because of the decomposers. Thus, decomposers play a significant role in maintaining ecological balance. The chemical fertilizers and pesticides used for the nourishment and protection of crops also enter various food chains, that is, from soil to plants, plants to herbivores and then to consumers. During the process of energy flow, these chemicals also get transmitted at every level. These chemicals get accumulated at each level of food chains since they are not biodegradable. The concentration of the chemical substances increases from producers to different levels of consumers as the number of organisms in each level reduces gradually. Thus, the concentration of the toxic chemicals is the maximum in tertiary consumers, such as human beings and this phenomenon is called biological magnification. These chemicals cannot be removed from food grains, fruits, vegetables or meat by simply washing them. Hence, usage of chemical fertilizers and pesticides beyond certain limits disturbs the natural ecosystems as well as leads to environmental pollution.

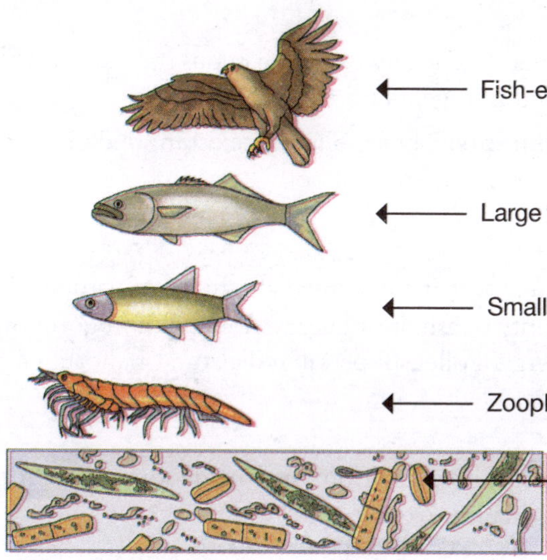

Figure 11.11 Illustration of sequence of biomagnification at various levels of food chain

Environmental Pollution

Contamination of natural environment that has an adverse effect on the ecosystem is called pollution. A pollutant is a substance or an energy introduced into the environment that has undesired effects on the natural ecosystem. A pollutant itself may not be harmful in nature. However, if the intensity or the concentration of it exceeds certain limit, it brings about undesirable changes in the environment. For example, Listening to music with moderate volume is not harmful. If the intensity of the sound goes beyond a certain limit, it can lead to hypertension, hearing impairment, etc. Similarly, CO_2 is useful for photosynthesis. But, If its concentration exceeds certain limit, its toxic effects cause different health hazards, such as dizziness, dim vision, headache, breathing problems, etc.

Types of Pollution

Depending on the nature of the substance polluted or the pollutant causing the pollution, it is classified into following types:

- Air pollution
- Water pollution
- Soil/land pollution
- Noise pollution
- Radioactive pollution

Air Pollution

Introduction of harmful substances to the air that adversely affect the well being of living and certain non-living things is called air pollution. Air pollutants are divided on a number of factors. Some of them are:

Based on Origin

- **Primary pollutants:** These pollutants are directly emitted from the sources and enter the atmosphere. For example, oxides of sulfur and nitrogen, ash, smoke, dust, radioactive compounds, carbon dioxide, etc.
- **Secondary pollutants:** These pollutants are formed by chemical reactions between primary pollutants and the atmosphere. For example, hydrogen cyanide, peroxyacetyl nitrate, ketones, SO_3, O_3, etc.

Based on State of Matter

- **Gaseous air pollutants:** These pollutants generally exist in gaseous state at normal temperature and pressure. For example, CO, CO_2, oxides of sulfur and nitrogen, etc.
- **Particulate or non-gaseous air pollutants:** These pollutants exist in solid or liquid state. For example, suspended particulate matter, suspended droplets or the mixture of both.

Based on Sources

- **Natural sources:** These include pollutants that are formed as a result of natural phenomena.
  Volcanic eruptions give out large quantity of ash, heat energy along with huge amount of greenhouse gases. Forest fire introduces dust, ash and heat energy. Pollen dispersal and natural radioactivity are also natural sources of air pollution.
- **Man-made sources:**
  Smoke and dust particles are the pollutants obtained from man-made sources, such as industries, factories, automobiles, aircrafts, nuclear experiments, agriculture, etc.

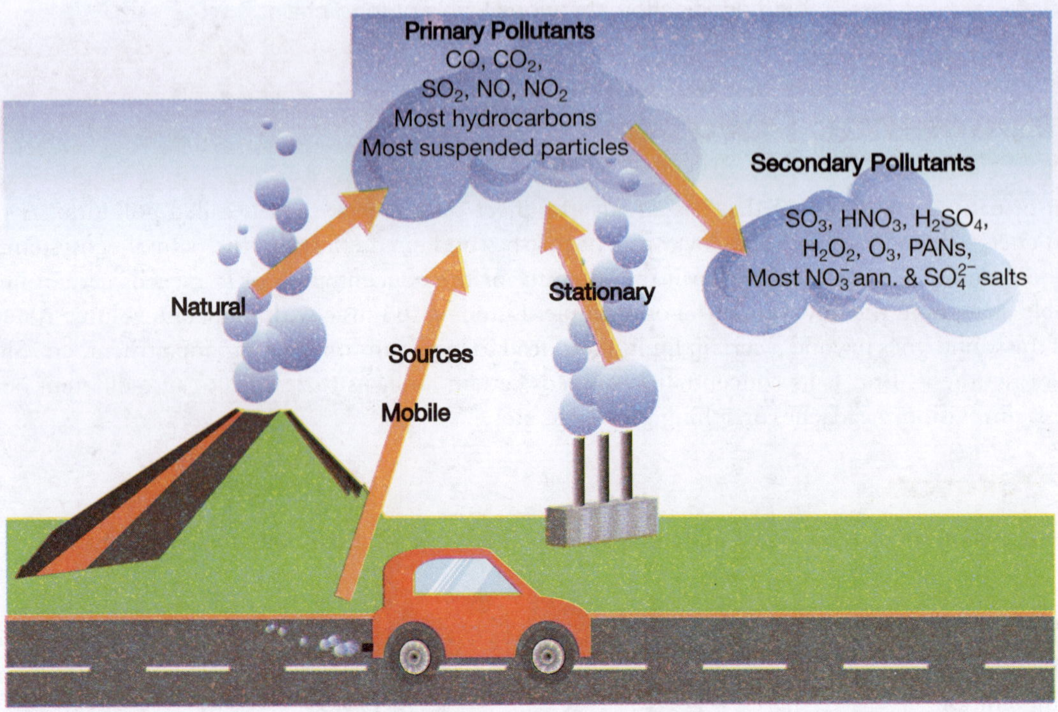

Figure 11.12 Types of air pollutants

Different Sources of Air Pollution

A number of factors are responsible for releasing air pollutants in air. Some of them are:

Transportation

Vehicles or automobiles are the main sources of air pollution. The pollutants released from automobiles are carbon monoxide, unburnt hydrocarbons, carcinogenic organic compounds, particulate matters and nitrogen monoxide. The liberation of automobile exhaust is the maximum in metropolitan cities.

Figure 11.13 Emissions from automobiles polluting the air

> **Info Bytes!**
> According to the World Health Organization, around 90% of the global population breathes polluted air.

Industry

Smoke from factories, petroleum refineries and thermal power stations also causes air pollution. Release of chlorofluorocarbons (CFCs) used in refrigerators, air conditioners and spray cans lead to the depletion of ozone layer. Petroleum industries emit sulfur dioxide and oxides of nitrogen. Dust released from paper and pulp mills, cotton mills, cement plants, stone crushing units causes air pollution. SO_2 is produced from various industrial processes. It undergoes following reactions with rain water and results in acid rains.

$$2\,SO_2 + O_2 \rightarrow 2\,SO_3$$
$$SO_3 + H_2O \rightarrow \underset{\text{Acid Rains}}{H_2SO_3}$$

During winter, the smoke combines with fog and forms smog that causes health hazards and poor visibility leading to traffic congestion and accidents.

Figure 11.14 Emissions from thermal power station polluting the air

> **Info Bytes!**
> Some plants can help reduce indoor air pollution. Spider plants, for example, can absorb carbon monoxide and xylene.

Figure 11.15 Thick smog over the city of Santiago

Agriculture

Greenhouse gases emitted due to decomposition of agricultural wastes, foul odour from agricultural farms, pesticides and other chemicals are the pollutants released by the agricultural sector.

Figure 11.16 Pesticides sprayed in fields add to pollution

Burning of Materials/Garbage

Burning of garbage releases excess CO_2, harmful gases and particulate pollutants. Smoke and ashes are emitted from brick kilns due to the burning of raw moist clay bricks. Forest fires produce NO_2 that reacts with water in the atmosphere and forms nitric acid. Burning of municipal wastes is also responsible for air pollution.

Figure 11.17 Burning of garbage polluting the air

Effects of Air Pollution

Air pollution has adverse effects on living organisms as well as on non-living things.

Human beings

- The following factors of air pollutants affect human beings:
  - o Increase in concentration of air pollutants
  - o Nature of pollutants
  - o Time period of exposure
- Air pollutants entering the human body reduces the transfer of oxygen to blood.
- These pollutants cause few short-term and few long-term diseases to human beings which are discussed in the table below.

Table 11.1 Short- and long-term effects of air pollutants on humans

Short-term effects	Long-term effects
Irritation in eyes, nose, mouth and throat	Chronic pulmonary diseases
Slurring of speech, asthma attacks, headache, nausea, vomiting, dizziness and allergy	Cardiovascular diseases
Respiratory infections, such as acute bronchitis in children and pneumonia	Lung cancer
Affecting the function of lung	Premature death

Plants

- Air pollution reduces plant growth and causes chlorosis (yellowing) of leaf.

Figure 11.18 Chlorosis seen on a tobacco leaf

> **Info Bytes!**
>
> Bhopal gas tragedy was an industrial accident happened in 1984. The plant released about 40 tonnes of toxic methyl isocyanate gas. Thousands have died since then from gas-related diseases.

Animals

- Animals that consume the grass coated with polluted particulate matter get affected by arsenic material.
- They also experience breathing problem.

Environment

- Increase in CO_2 due to deforestation and combustion of fuels, increases the temperature of the atmosphere resulting in melting of glaciers. This is called global warming.

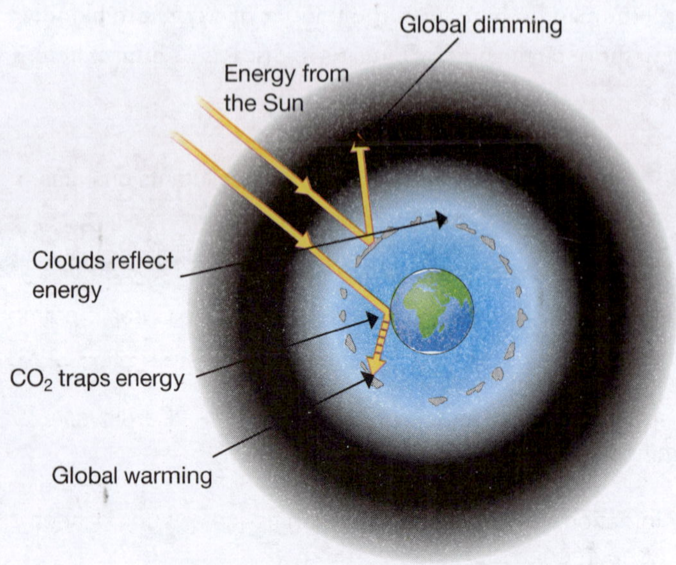

Figure 11.19 Illustration of Global warming

- Pollutants entering the atmosphere undergo various reactions and cause acid rain. Release of CFCs into the atmosphere causes depletion of the ozone layer.
- Agricultural production gets affected due to the change in the weather pattern.

Materials

- Acid rain damages constructions made of marble or lime stone by changing their colour to yellow and corroding their surfaces.
- O_3, SO_2 and NO_2 change the colour and damage the strength of the textiles.
- Acid rain also corrodes metals, such as steel, copper and zinc.

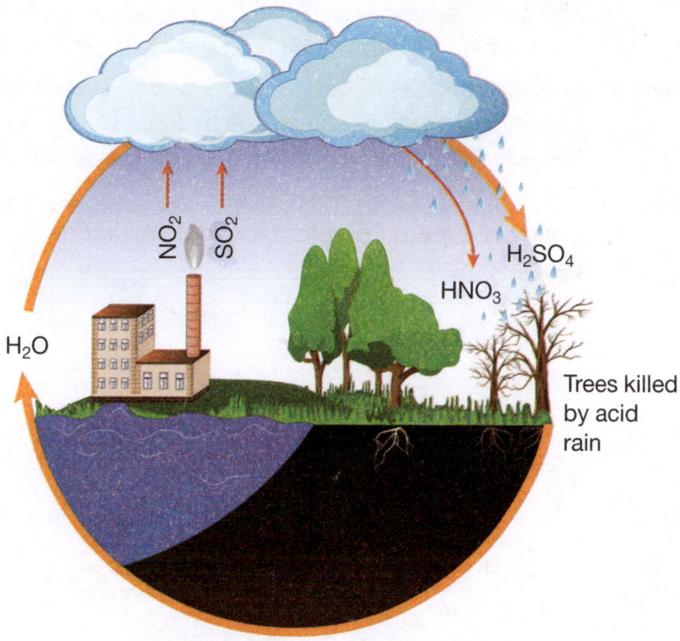

Figure 11.20 Illustration of acid rain

Measures to Control Air Pollution

Air pollution can be controlled effectively by the following methods:

- Source correction method
- Pollution control method

Source Correction Method

Minimizing the emission of air pollutants at the source is called source correction method. In this method, the following tabulated measures are followed to minimize the production of air pollutants.

Info Bytes!

Air around Taj Mahal contains alarming levels of sulfur and nitrogen oxides due to large number of industries around this area which has led to acid rain that has reacted with the marble (calcium carbonate).

Table 11.2 Source correction methods of controlling air pollution

Method	Explanation
Change of raw material	• Raw material should be chosen in such a way that it produces less air pollutants. • LPG or CNG can be chosen instead of coal or diesel to reduce undesirable fumes and particles. • Low-sulfur fuel is preferred over high-sulfur fuel to reduce harmful emissions.
Change of process	• The process of production can be altered to reduce the emission of air pollutants. • Coal is being washed before using in thermal power plants to reduce fly ash.
Modify the existing equipment	• Controlled basic oxygen furnaces can be preferred over open-hearth furnaces. • In petroleum refineries, loss of hydrocarbon vapours from storage tanks can be reduced by designing the storage tanks with floating roof covers.
Maintenance of equipment	• Generally, the badly maintained machines consume more energy and give out more fumes. Therefore, periodic maintenance of the machines should be mandatory.

Pollution Control Methods

Different types of pollution control equipment are available, but the choice of equipment can be made based on the following factors:

- Volume or size of particulates
- Physical and chemical properties of particulates
- Temperature or humidity of gaseous medium
- Toxicity and inflammability
- Concentration of particulate matter in the exhaust gas

Table 11.3 Pollution control equipment

Device	Explanation
Filters	Filters comprise several layers of cloth bags to trap the particles in smoke emitted from electric power plants or any other factories.
Cyclone separators	Polluted gas is made to pass through a cylindrical or conical container called cyclone with a high speed in a helical pattern so that particles fall at the bottom by hitting the walls of the cylinder.
Gravitational settling chamber	This equipment comprises a huge rectangular chamber. The polluted gas is passed through it. The velocity of the gas is sufficiently reduced when it passes through the chamber so that the particulate matter settles down due to gravity and only the smoke escapes from the chamber.
Scrubber	This device sprays water to trap the pollutants. A dry scrubber sprays wet lime powder so that the acidic gases leaving the exhaust pipe interact with it and become neutralized.
Electrostatic precipitators	This device removes chemicals (lime, activated charcoal, ordinary smoke, etc.) and particles of metals (lead, cadmium, nickel) from hot fuel gases.

Figure 11.21 Dust purification by cyclone separator

Water pollution

Water pollution can be defined as alteration in physical, chemical or biological characteristics of water making it unsuitable for designated use in its natural state.

Water Pollutants

Depending upon the nature, water pollutants are divided into following types:

- **Biological pollutants:** Pollutants, such as algae, bacteria, virus and parasites are called biological pollutants.
- **Inorganic pollutants:** Fine sand, clay, soil, dissolved particles, rock and other compounds in the Earth's crust are inorganic water pollutants. Toxic materials, such as arsenic, mercury, cadmium also come under this category.
- **Organic pollutants:** Wastes from industries and excess use of herbicides, pesticides to achieve great yields contaminate water.

Sources of water pollutants

Depending upon the origin, sources of water pollutants are broadly classified into following two types.

1. **Natural sources:** Heavy rains carry minerals from land to water along with dead animal wastes. Sulfur compounds released during an earthquake finally go to water bodies. Presence of these substances in water bodies leads to uncontrolled growth of weeds. This phenomenon is called eutrophication.
2. **Artificial sources:** Wastes produced due to human activities cause water pollution. These wastes are called artificial sources. Different types of artificial sources are described in the table given below.

Info Bytes!

There are rivers that literally catch fire due to pollution. The Cuyahoga River in Ohio has caught fire multiple times since the 1930s.

Table 11.4 Various types of artificial sources of water pollution

Type of artifical source	Explanation
Household detergents and sewage	• The phosphates in these materials enter water bodies and promote rapid growth of algae that further disturbs fishing, navigation and irrigation.
Industrial wastes	• Industrial wastes enter the water bodies through direct discharge or from waste dumps. Industries that use wood, chemicals, paper pulp produce wastes, such as heavy metals. Lead metal from industrial wastes accumulates in the biological system. • Manganese is released into water body by steel industries. Mercury is used in plastic-manufacturing industries. Wastes from these industries are released to water bodies which then accumulate in fish.
Offshore oil drilling and oil spills	• Offshore drilling is a mechanical process where a wellbore is drilled below the seabed for extracting petroleum. The drilling companies dispose the treated wastes to the shore. • Accidents occurring during the transportation of crude oil across the sea result in spilling of oil. This causes damage to the aquatic and marine environment.
Agricultural runoffs	• Intensive crop cultivation using excess pesticides and insecticides contaminating the ground water during rain.
Thermal pollution	• Thermal power plants located near water bodies use water for cooling the machineries and release the hot water back into the water bodies. This affects the aquatic life. The hot water can hold less oxygen compared to normal water. The reduction in the percentage of oxygen in water affects fish like trout. Warm water increases the growth of blue-green algae that produce some toxins. The rise in the temperature of water increases the solubility of salts.

Figure 11.22 Environmental pollution caused by oil spill from cargo ship

Effects of Water Pollution

Water pollution has adverse effects on aquatic life as well as on human beings.

Human beings

- Consumption of polluted water leads to certain waterborne diseases, such as cholera, typhoid, diarrhoea, dysentery, hepatitis, polio and jaundice.
- Mercury dumped into water transforms to methyl mercury due to bacterial action. This accumulates in fish and it further reaches the human beings due to the consumption of fish. Methyl mercury causes numbness in body parts, hearing impairedness and abnormal mental behavior (Minamata disease). Pollution due to heavy metals (cadmium) causes the disease called Itai-itai.

Info Bytes!

Minamata disease was first discovered in Minamata city in Japan, in 1956. It was caused due to release of methyl mercury from the Chisso Corporation's chemical factory.

Aquatic Life

- Chemical changes in water due to pesticides and detergents affect reproduction, growth, respiration (due to reduction of O_2) of fish.
- Oil pollution affects cell division and photosynthesis of algae.
- Traces of NH_3 and cyanide entering water due to various sources cause death of aquatic life.
- Excessive growth of phytoplankton and algae due to the enrichment of plant nutrients in water bodies leads to water pollution. This obstructs the entry of heat, light and air in water. This phenomenon is called eutrophication and affects aquatic life.

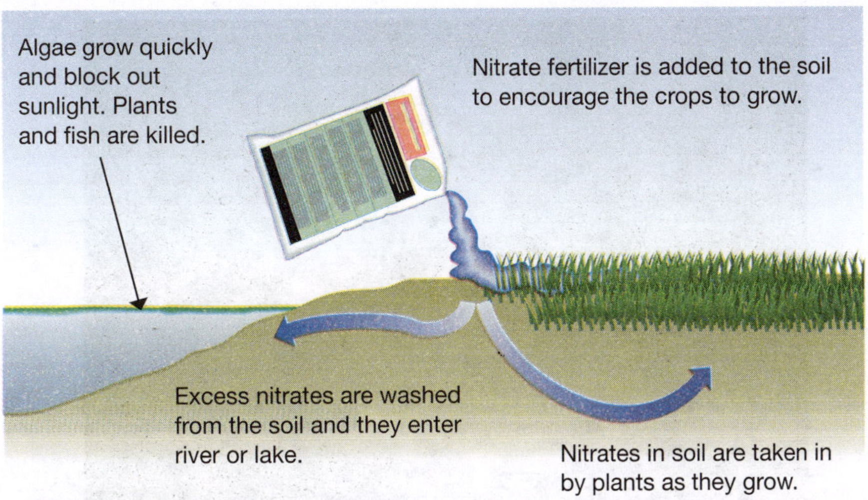

Figure 11.23 Diagram showing fertilizer use leading to eutrophication

Measures to Control Water Pollution

Following preventive measures can help to stop/minimize water pollution in our surroundings.

- Avoiding dropping of litter into water bodies.
- Following reduce, reuse and recycle methods.
- Adopting eco-friendly ways for the disposal of wastes.
- Using environment-friendly substances or products.
- Using natural cleansing products instead of chemical face washes, cosmetics, etc.
- Recycling plastics

- Avoiding overusage of pesticides.
- Treating industrial effluents before their disposal.

Central Pollution Control Board has set few standards to protect water sources from getting polluted due to industries and factories.

Soil/Land Pollution

Soil pollution is defined as the change in physical, chemical and biological conditions of the soil because of the intervention of man, resulting in degradation of quality and productivity of the soil.

> **Info Bytes!**
> On an average, each person in India generates 0.2 kg domestic wastes per day.

Soil Pollutants

Pesticides, inorganic pollutants (Hg, As, Cd, Pb, etc.), radioactive elements, organic wastes, airborne contaminants, etc., are soil pollutants.

Sources

Depending upon the origin, sources of soil pollutants are broadly classified into following two types:

Industrial wastes

Wastes generated in chemicals, paints, paper manufacturing industries are dumped directly into soil. Large quantity of fly ash released by thermal power plants also causes soil pollution.

Figure 11.24 Disposed garbage polluting land

Domestic Wastes

- **Biodegradable substances:** Disposal of biodegradable substances, such as food, paper, etc., causes soil pollution.
- **Non-biodegradable substances:** Either they do not undergo degradation or their degradation takes a long time. Examples are polythene bags, foot wear, plastic, etc.
- **Chemical fertilizers:** Excessive usage of chemical fertilizers containing nutrients, such as nitrogen, phosphorous and potassium, for a better yield of crops contaminate the soil. Then these chemicals sink into the ground water.
- **Biomedical wastes:** Hospital wastes, such as outdated medicines, cytotoxic drugs, soiled dressing, used cotton, body fluids, dissected body organs, tissues, disposable syringes, intravenous fluids, bottles, gloves, needles, blades, etc., contaminate the soil.

- **Pesticides and weedicides**: Pesticides and weedicides are used in agriculture to control weeds and pests. The chemicals in them accumulate in soil and change the chemical properties of the soil. These chemicals also affect natural bacteria in soil. They reach human beings and animals from the soil.

Effects of Soil Pollution

Soil pollution has adverse effects on human beings as well as on other living organisms.

Human beings

- Diseases are caused due to the attack of viruses and bacteria present in sewage sludge.
- Human and animal excreta contain pathogens that pollute soil and vegetable crops.
- Human and animal excreta are used as manure to grow food and commercial crops. The consumption of food grown using this kind of manure leads to various diseases.

Other Organisms

- Radioactive materials or soil contaminants move from soil into various food chains and affect various organisms.
- Pesticides absorbed by plants enter food chains and finally reach animals and human beings.

Environment

- Nitrogenous fertilizers produce toxic concentration of nitrate and nitrite in leaves.
- Chemical wastes percolate through ground and contaminate ground water.

Measures to Control Soil Pollution

Following preventive measures can be taken in order to stop/minimize soil/land pollution in our surroundings.

- Open dumping of waste should be avoided.
- Sanitary landfills can be preferred because the waste gets covered by soil to prevent the entry of rodents and insects in the landfills.
- Composting of organic wastes produces good fertilizers for the plants.
- Incineration process is generally preferred for waste disposal by industries and municipalities. In this process, wastes are burnt at high temperatures. But this process generates lots of fly ash, sulfur dioxide, hydrogen chloride and organic acids. Useful energy and material must be recovered by using proper pollution control equipment.
- Proper cropping pattern can be followed to reduce the growth of weeds. Thus, the usage of weedicides can be reduced.
- Segregation: In this method, different types of wastes are collected in different bins so that they can be reused by the process of recycling.

Noise Pollution

The word 'noise' is taken from Latin word 'nausea' which means unwanted and unpleasant sound. Noise pollution is the propagation of sound that irritates us and acts as a source of stress. The intensity of normal conversation that can be heard by a human being is nearly 20 dB.

Sources of Noise Pollution

Major sources of noise pollution are:

- Industrial sector
- Transport sector
- Household sector

Info Bytes!

Intensity of sound is expressed in terms of decibels (dB).

- Defence sector
- Loud speakers
- Miscellaneous sources including loud music in public space, disturbingly loud conversations, etc.

Table 11.5 Intensity of various sounds

Source	Intensity (dB)
Breathing	10
Soft whisper	20
Ticking clock	20–30
Normal conversation	15–60
Library	30–35
Traffic	50–90
Office noise	60–80
Motor cycle	105
Lion's roar	105–110
Aircraft	110–120
Pneumatic drill	110–120
Jet take off	120
Space rocket	170–180

Effects of Noise Pollution

Effects of noise pollution on human health can be discussed with the help of following points.

- **Auditory effects:** Hearing impairment, auditory fatigue (whistling or buzzing sounds in the ears)
- **Nonauditory effects:** Hypertension, reduction in concentration and working efficiency, develops annoyance, violent behavior, short temperament, mental disorientation, communication interference, sleep interference, etc.
- **Psychological effects:** Causes irritation, anxiety, visual disturbances, insomnia, cardiovascular disease, nausea, fatigue, etc.

Measures to Control Noise Pollution

Following preventive measures can be taken in order to stop/minimize noise pollution in our surroundings:

- Plantation of trees and bushes around noisy areas to block the sound.
- Silence zones should be declared in places where schools, hospitals, religious places are located.
- Servicing of vehicles should be done regularly.
- Industries should use improvised tools and machines to reduce noise pollution.

Radioactive Pollution

The release of high-energy radiations from radioactive substances into air, water and soil due to human activities that results in undesirable effects is called radioactive pollution.

Sources of radioactive pollution

Major sources of noise pollution are listed below.

Info Bytes!

After the bombing of Hiroshima and Nagasaki in 1945, the cities experienced alarming increases in leukemia and cancers due to radiation exposure

Natural sources

- **Natural sources** are the sources of harmful cosmic rays with high energy that reach the Earth from outer space.

Man-made Sources

- **X-ray waste:** X-rays are used for detecting skeletal disorders. Radium and other isotopic radiations are used to treat cancer. These radiations cause gene mutation (permanent alteration of nucleotide sequence of genome of an organism/ virus/DNA).
- **Nuclear weapons:** Radioactive substances, such as uranium 235, plutonium 239 are used in testing nuclear weapons. Atomic explosions generate huge amount of radioactive materials that reach water bodies along with rain water. The radioactive materials accumulate in aquatic animals and then get transferred to human beings through food chains.
- **Atomic reactors and nuclear fuel:** Fuel elements, radioactive wastes from atomic reactors and coolants are the basic sources of radiation pollution.
- **Radioactive isotopes:** The radioactive isotopes used in research laboratories reach rivers through waste water.

Effects of radioactive pollution

Radioactive radiations have harmful effects on human beings and other living organisms. These are:

Genetic Variation

- The damage caused due to radioactive radiations is seen in the offspring and transmitted to many generations.
- Transfer of radioactive substances to plants through polluted soil affects their DNA, growth of plants and the quality of seeds (genetic disorder).

Somatic Variation

- Somatic variation is the damage in the organs caused due to the short-term exposure to radiation. The short-term effects include breast cancer, lung cancer, thyroid cancer and brain cancer. It also damages the reproductive ability of living organisms.
- Its impact on human beings depends on the intensity and the time of exposure to the radiation.
- Radioactive substances react with bio-molecules, such as proteins, carbohydrates, and thus, cells get affected.

Info Bytes!

Chernobyl disaster was a disastrous nuclear accident occurred in 1986 at the Chernobyl Nuclear Power Plant in the northern Ukrainian Soviet Socialist Republic, Soviet Union.

Measures to Control Radioactive Pollution

Following preventive measures can be taken in order to stop/minimize radioactive pollution in our surroundings:

- Avoiding routine x-rays.
- Reducing the time of exposure to the radiations as much as possible.
- Keeping ourselves away from sources of radioactive radiation.
- Wearing appropriate protective clothing while working with radioactive substances.
- Adopting appropriate scientific methods to collect, store and dispose radioactive materials.
- Proper treatment of nuclear wastes before their disposal.
- Proper maintenance of uranium and thorium mines.

Worldwide Implications of Environmental Pollution

Greenhouse Effect

The greenhouse effect is a phenomenon in which the Earth experiences rise in temperature because of the presence of water vapour, carbon dioxide, methane, etc., in the atmosphere which allow incoming sunlight to pass through, but trap the heat radiated from the Earth's surface.

Info Bytes!

The term 'greenhouse effect' was first used by J. Fourier in 1827.

Mechanism of Greenhouse Effect

Complete process of greenhouse effect can be summarized in following four steps.

Step 1: Penetration of high-energy radiations through Earth's atmosphere and absorption of this energy by Earth's surface.

Step 2: Energy of long wavelength radiated back by the Earth.

Step 3: Radiated energy is heat energy which gets, trapped in the atmosphere due to the presence of certain greenhouse gases such as CO_2, CH_4, N_2O, O_3, etc.

Step 4: Greenhouse gases liberate the heat energy to the troposphere. Thus, the temperature required for the sustenance of life on Earth is maintained.

Excess accumulation of few gases, such as carbon dioxide, CFCs, ozone and water vapor block the heat radiated from the earth surface. This results in increase in the temperature of earth's surface. Thus, green house effect causes global warming.

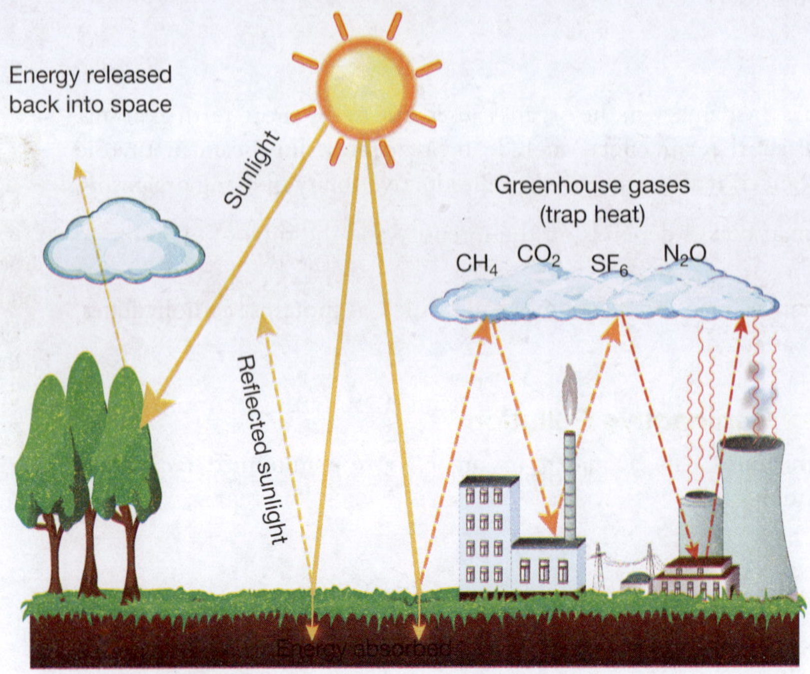

Figure 11.25 Illustration of greenhouse effect

Global Warming

Excess accumulation of greenhouse gases takes place due to following reasons:

Table 11.6 Role of greenhouse gases

Greenhouse gas	Features
Carbon dioxide	• Carbon dioxide is mostly released due to fossil fuel burning. • Concentration of CO_2 is increasing at the rate of 1.8 mg/m^3 per year. • This gas absorbs infrared radiations and increases the temperature of the Earth's atmosphere.
Water vapour	• Rise in the temperature of Earth's atmosphere produces more water vapour by the process of transpiration and evaporation. This further increases global warming.
Chlorofluorocarbons	• When old refrigerators, cars, air conditioners, etc., are not properly disposed, they leak CFCs into the atmosphere. • They are responsible for global warming as well as depletion of ozone layer.
Oxides of nitrogen	• Natural source of oxides of nitrogen is lightning. • The heat absorbing capacity of this gas is 230 times that of carbon dioxide gas.
Methane (CH_4)	• CH_4 is produced during decomposition of forest biomass and peat. • Its capacity of trapping heat energy from the atmosphere is more than that of carbon dioxide.
Ozone	• Ozone in troposphere is liberated by the reaction between volatile hydrocarbon and oxides of nitrogen in presence of UV rays.

Effects of Global Warming

- **On climate:** Increase in concentration of carbon dioxide in the atmosphere increases the temperature of Earth's surface.
- **On forests:** The rapid change in atmospheric temperature is harmful for the temperate forests. Trees lose their ability to complete their life cycles.
- **On agriculture:** The global warming has considerable effect on agriculture. The increase in temperature of soil increases evaporation. Thus, the water content of the soil reduces.
- **On human beings:** Increase in temperature of the Earth's atmosphere results in different diseases in human beings like heart stroke, etc. Rise in temperature and rainfall together are favourable conditions for the insects to grow. Thus, insects like mosquitoes spread diseases, such as malaria, dengue and filariasis.

Measures to Control Global Warming

Following control measures can be taken to reduce global warming:

- Alternative sources of energy should be used instead of using fossil fuels. Examples of such sources are solar energy, hydrogen as a fuel, hydroelectricity, etc.

- Deforestation should be avoided and efforts should be made to develop new forests by encouraging tree planting programs.
- Fertilizers that emit nitrous oxide should be regulated and biofertilizers can be used.
- Smoke from industries should be treated before their expulsion into the atmosphere.
- Automobiles should be serviced regularly.

Acid Rain

Any precipitation or deposition having a pH lower than 5.6 is called acid rain. Acid rain occurs by the emission of sulfur dioxide and oxides of nitrogen that react with rain water and form acids.

Causes of Acid Rain

Smoke emitted from industries and automobiles contains sulfur dioxide and oxides of nitrogen. This smoke reacts with other gases and water present in the atmosphere and form sulfuric and nitric acids. The acids thus formed reach the Earth in the form of rain called acid rain. Acid rain has many adverse effects.

Effects of Acid Rain

Following are some of the major adverse effects of acid rain:

- **On buildings and monuments:** Acid rains have corroding effect on buildings, metal monuments and rock structures.
- **On living beings:** Acid rain causes irritation in eyes and skin. It reduces visibility, and creates disorder in the respiratory system. Trees in forests die due to acidification of soil and water.
- **On environment:** Acid rain causes acidification of lakes and streams. These acidified water bodies become unsuitable for aquatic life.
- **On agriculture:** Acidified soil does not yield healthy crops. The acids react with soil and release toxic metals that are absorbed by plants. Acids enter various food chains from soil to plants, and from plants to animals and eventually, human beings.
- **On microorganisms:** Acidified soil reduces the population of certain useful micro-organisms.

Measure to Control Acid Rain

Following measures can be taken to prevent and control acid rain.

- Acid rain is mainly caused due to air pollution. Air pollution can be reduced by using pollution-controlling equipment, such as scrubber.
- Other sources for the generation of electricity, such as nuclear fuel or solar power can be used instead of using fossil fuel to reduce the release of oxides of nitrogen and sulfur.
- Cleaner fuels, such as LPG, CNG, etc., could be used in automobiles.
- Addition of neutralizing agents: Powdered lime stone can be sprayed over areas that are prone to acid rain.

Ozone Layer Depletion

Our atmosphere contains five layers—troposphere, stratosphere, mesosphere, thermosphere and exosphere. Ozone is a colourless gas present in the second layer of our atmosphere called stratosphere. Ozone molecule contains three oxygen atoms and is represented as O_3. This layer protects us from the harmful ultraviolet (UV) rays coming from the sun. Ozone gas has pungent smell and is deadly poisonous.

Formation of Ozone Layer

The UV rays coming from the sun act on oxygen molecules (O_2) and split them into free oxygen atoms (O). These free oxygen atoms combine with O_2 molecules and thus, ozone (O_3) is formed.

$$O_2 \xrightarrow{\text{UV Rays}} O + O$$
$$O + O_2 \longrightarrow O_3$$

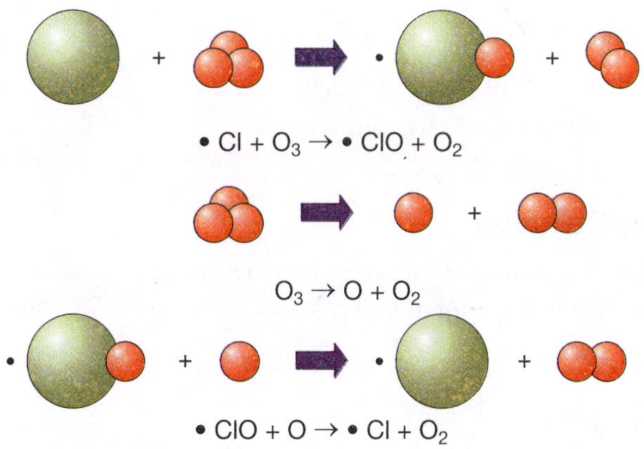

Figure 11.26 Splitting up of ozone molecules by UV rays

Causes of Ozone Layer Depletion

Following are some of the causes of ozone layer depletion:

- Ozone hole or depleted ozone layer does not indicate a hole in the ozone layer but it indicates a region of ozone layer that has become thinner.
- Destruction of ozone layer is mainly due to chlorine atoms of CFC molecules. CFCs are very stable compounds and hence, they accumulate in the upper atmosphere.
- Nitrogen monoxide also leads to ozone layer depletion.
- The other substances that cause ozone depletion are hydrochlorofluorocarbons (HCFCs), carbon tetrachloride (CCl_4), methyl chloroform and volatile organic compounds (VOC). They are found in smoke emitted by vehicles, industries, aerosols, refrigerants, etc.

Effects of Ozone Layer Depletion

Following are the adverse effects of ozone layer depletion:

- Due to the depletion of ozone layer, UV rays from the sun are incident directly on the living beings.
- Ozone layer depletion leads to many health disorders, such as skin cancer (malignant melanoma, squamous cell carcinoma, etc.), eye damage (cataract) and weakening of the immune system. Difficulty in breathing, throat irritation, etc., are also the hazards of ozone depletion.
- Plant growth and the time of flowering of few plant species change due to ozone layer depletion.

Measures to Control Ozone Layer Depletion

Following measures can be taken to control ozone layer depletion:

- Every individual can contribute to reduction in ozone layer depletion by using public transport and recycled products, and thus saving energy:
- Air conditioners and refrigerators in which CFCs are not used as refrigerant should be used.
- Preference should be given to those aerosols that do not contain CFCs or HCFCs.
- During the repair of ACs or refrigerators, proper care should be taken by shifting the refrigerant to recycling machine instead of exposing it to the atmosphere.
- Spreading awareness in the society about the causes, effects and controlling measures of ozone layer depletion.
- Since this is not the problem related to a specific country, international agreements can be established to reduce industrial emissions of CFCs.

Measures Taken by Government of India for Prevention, Control and Abatement of Pollution

Following acts have been made by the Government of India to control environmental pollution

- Act 1974 — Water act (Prevention and control of pollution)
- Act 1981 — Air act (Prevention and control of pollution)
- Act 1986 — Environment act (Protection of environment).

Role of Citizens in Controlling Pollution

Citizens of a country play the utmost important role in keeping surroundings clean for themselves as well as for others. Following are some ste‸ ‸nd habits that can be implemented by us for a clean environment:

- Keeping our suııoundings clean
- Regular servicing of vehicles
- Using non-conventional sources of energy, like solar and wind energy.
- Using public transport instead of private vehicles
- Reducing the usage of polythene or plastic goods
- Recycling plastics instead of simply disposing them
- Planting trees and developing gardens in our localities
- Avoiding burning of plastic or polythene materials.

Table 11.7 Environment-related important days

Day	Date
World Forest day	21 March
World Water & Sanitation day	22 March
Earth Day	22 April
World Biodiversity Day	22 May
World Pollution Day	11 July
World Wildlife Day	8 October

Quick Recap

✔ **Differentiate between food chain and food web.**

Food chain	Food web
Food chain is a straight single path of transfer of food energy in the ecosystem.	It comprises several inter-connected food chains through which food and energy pass in the ecosystem.
Members of higher trophic level feed upon single type of organisms of the lower trophic level.	Members of higher trophic level can feed on a variety of organisms of the lower trophic level.
Separate and isolated food chains increase instability to the ecosystem.	Food web increases the stability of the ecosystem.

✔ **How does the interaction of biotic and abiotic components contribute to an ecosystem's stability?**

In an ecosystem, the interaction of biotic (living) and abiotic (non-living) components ensures resource availability and regulation. Air, water, and sunlight, for example, provide the necessary conditions and resources for biotic components to thrive. In turn, living organisms modify and maintain these abiotic conditions through their activities and metabolic processes.

✔ **Distinguish between natural and artificial ecosystems. Please provide an example of each.**

Natural ecosystems, such as forests or oceans, form without human intervention, whereas artificial ecosystems, such as gardens or aquariums, are created by humans. Natural ecosystems evolve over time as a result of natural processes and events, whereas artificial ecosystems are purpose-built and managed by humans.

✔ **Explain the primary difference in energy sources between autotrophs and heterotrophs.**

Autotrophs derive energy from inorganic sources, primarily sunlight, whereas heterotrophs derive energy from the consumption of other organisms. Producers or autotrophs, such as plants, prepare their food through photosynthesis, which involves the use of sunlight, carbon dioxide, and water. Consumers or heterotrophs, on the other hand, like animals, rely on consuming producers or other consumers for energy.

✔ **What are the effects of introducing a pollutant on the balance of biotic and abiotic components in an ecosystem?**

Pollutants can change the properties of the environment and have a negative impact on organisms' health and survival. When a pollutant is introduced, it can alter the chemical composition of water or soil, as well as the quality of the air. This can reduce producers' ability to perform photosynthesis or make the environment toxic for certain species, disrupting the natural balance.

POINTS TO REMEMBER

- ✔ Natural environment comprises living organisms and non-living components, such as air, water, etc., around them and the link between them can be understood by studying the ecosystem.
- ✔ Ecosystem is a community of living organisms and non-living components of the environment.
- ✔ Living and non-living components of ecosystem are called biotic and abiotic components, respectively.
- ✔ Ecosystems can be classified as natural and artificial ecosystems based on the way they are formed.
- ✔ Biotic components can be broadly classified into producers and consumers.
- ✔ Producers are autotrophs and prepare their food from solar energy, carbon dioxide and water.
- ✔ Consumers survive on producers for their food and they are called heterotrophs.
- ✔ There is flow of energy established in an ecosystem.
- ✔ In an ecosystem, a trophic level comprises a group of organisms that occupy the same level in a food chain.
- ✔ A pollutant is a substance or an energy introduced into the environment that has undesired effects on the natural ecosystem.

PRACTICE QUESTIONS CLASSROOM WING

Very Short Answer Type Questions

Directions for questions from 1 to 10.

Fill in the blanks.

1. Materials that do not decompose are called ___________.
2. The term 'ecology' is derived from the Greek words 'oikos' meaning _________ and 'logia' meaning ________.
3. ___________ components interact with abiotic components to grow, reproduce and perform other activities.
4. An area of transition where ecosystems overlap is called ___________.
5. The concentration of toxic chemicals is the maximum in tertiary consumers, and this phenomenon is called ____________.
6. A ___________ is a substance or energy introduced into the environment that has undesired effects on the natural ecosystem.
7. In a food chain, green plants, algae, and some bacteria are termed as ___________.
8. The pollutant that results from the chemical reactions between primary pollutants and the atmosphere is termed as ________ pollutants.
9. The Earth absorbs the energy from the sun and gives out _______.
10. Controlling of water pollution due to the industrial wastes is done by establishing _______ plant in industries.

Directions for questions from 11 to 15.

For each of the following questions, four choices have been provided. Select the correct alternatives.

11. What is the community of living organisms and non-living components linked through nutrient cycles and energy flows?
    (a) Biome (b) Ecotone
    (c) Ecosystem (d) Habitat
12. What are the non-living components in an ecosystem called?
    (a) Biotic components
    (b) Trophic components
    (c) Abiotic components
    (d) Decomposers
13. Which is NOT a method of classifying ecosystems?
    (a) On the basis of colour
    (b) On the basis of formation
    (c) On the basis of size
    (d) On the basis of region
14. Which consumer is at the top of the food chain?
    (a) Primary consumers
    (b) Secondary consumers
    (c) Tertiary consumers
    (d) Producers
15. In an ecological pyramid, which level has the highest number of organisms?
    (a) Producers
    (b) Primary consumers
    (c) Secondary consumers
    (d) Tertiary consumers

Directions for question 16.

Match the entries of Column 1 with those of Column 2.

16.

Column 1	Column 2
A. Biome	(i) Fresh water ecosystem
B. Micro ecosystem	(ii) Garden
C. Artificial ecosystem	(iii) Ecosystem under a rock
D. Aquatic ecosystem	(iv) Rain forest

(a) A → (iv), B → (iii), C → (ii), D → (i)

(b) A → (i), B → (ii), C → (iii), D → (iv)

(c) A → (iv), B → (ii), C → (iii), D → (i)

(d) A → (iv), B → (iii), C → (i), D → (ii)

Short Answer Type Questions

17. Differentiate between biotic and abiotic components.
18. What is an ecosystem?
19. Why is biodiversity crucial for the health of an ecosystem?
20. How do invasive species impact native species in an ecosystem?
21. How does the burning of municipal wastes contribute to air pollution?
22. Define the following:
    (a) Autotrophs
    (b) Decomposers
    (c) Heterotrophs
23. Construct the food web with the following living organisms.
    plant, cow, lion, hen, frog, snake, honey bee, hawk
24. Decomposers play a major role in the ecosystem. Explain.
25. Does recycling process have any impact on environment? Justify your answer.
26. Write a short note on the effect of human beings on ecosystem.
27. Construct food web with the following organisms.
    carrots, grass, groundnuts, rabbit, deer, squirrel, fox snake, hawk
28. What is the difference between primary and secondary pollutants?
29. Mention the factors of air pollutants that affect human body.
30. How does agriculture lead to pollution? Explain.
31. What are the various methods to control air pollution from industries?
32. What is the role of citizens in controlling pollution?
33. Give few examples of natural air pollution.
34. What are the short-term and long-term effects of air pollution on human beings?
35. Mention various man-made sources of water pollution.
36. Name few inorganic water pollutants.
37. Identify the layer of atmosphere responsible for all weather phenomena.
38. How does CO harm us?
39. Carbon dioxide is required for the sustenance of life, but it is considered as a pollutant. Justify your statement.
40. What are the devices used in the industry for reducing suspended particulate matter?

Essay Type Questions

41. How do radioactive pollutants affect plants?
42. How are oxides of nitrogen formed in the air naturally?
43. (i) As refrigerants, hydrochloroflurocarbons and hydrofluorocarbons are preferred over CFCs. Give reason.
    (ii) What is the role of nitrogen monoxide in depletion of ozone layer?
    (iii) How can acid rain be neutralized?

PRACTICE QUESTIONS COMPETITION WING

Level 1: Apply your Concepts

Directions for questions from 1 to 13.

Fill in the blanks.

1. Pollutants that exist in solid or liquid state are termed as ________ air pollutants.
2. One of the natural sources of air pollutants includes ________ dispersal.
3. Smoke from ________, petroleum refineries, and thermal power stations causes air pollution.
4. When smoke combines with fog, it forms ________ that can lead to poor visibility and health hazards.
5. Greenhouse gases emitted due to decomposition of agricultural wastes and pesticides are pollutants released by the ________ sector.
6. ________ rain damages constructions made of marble or limestone by corroding their surfaces.
7. Broad categories of ecosystems are called _______.
8. In ecosystems, _______ and _______ are conserved.
9. Savannas and deserts are the examples of _______ ecosystems.
10. Filters arrest _______ from the exhaust gases.
11. Usage of _______ in refrigeration system leads to the ozone layer depletion.
12. _______ radiation emitted by the Earth is absorbed by CO_2, CH_4 and water vapors in the atmosphere and sent back toward the earth surface as heat energy causing Greenhouse effect
13. Diseases, such as cholera, typhoid and jaundice are _______ borne diseases

Direction for Questions from 14 to 18.

For each of the following questions, four choices have been provided. Select the correct alternatives.

14. Which of the following is not an abiotic component of an ecosystem?
    (a) Sunlight (b) Air
    (c) Temperature (d) Decomposers
15. Which of the following is not a functional aspect of an ecosystem?
    (a) Productivity (b) Nutrient cycle
    (c) Energy flow (d) None of these
16. Ozone layer is found in —
    (a) Stratosphere (b) Troposphere
    (c) Thermosphere (d) Mesosphere
17. Which of the following is not a water pollutant?
    (a) Fine sand (b) Algae
    (c) Fertilizers (d) CFCs
18. Identify the non-biodegradable waste among the following.
    (a) Peels of vegetables (b) Rubber (organic)
    (c) Plastic (d) Excreta of animals

Direction for Questions from 19 to 21.

Write the missing correlated terms.

19. Biodegradable: Decomposes :: Non-biodegradable: _________.
20. Ecology: Interaction between organisms and environment :: Zoology: ________.
21. Ecosystem: Community of Living Organisms :: ________ : Community of Plants and Animals.

Direction for Questions from 22 to 28.

Choose the correct option.

(a) Both A and R are true and R is the correct explanation for A.

(b) Both A and R are true, but R is not the correct explanation for A.

(c) A is true and R is false.

(d) A is false and R is true.

22. **Assertion (A)**: Decomposers are the scavengers in the ecosystem.

Reason (R): A food chain starts with decomposers.

23. **Assertion (A)**: Producers are known as autotrophs in the ecosystem.

Reason (R): Solar energy is the basic source of energy for all tropic levels.

24. **Assertion (A)**: In any food chain, the number of organisms in any trophic level should always be less than that in its previous trophic level.

Reason (R): Only 10 per cent of total energy present in a trophic level is transferred to the next trophic level in any food chain.

25. **Assertion (A)**: Powdered limestone can be sprayed over areas which are prone to acid rain.

Reason (R): Major component of limestone is calcium carbonate.

26. **Assertion (A)**: Ozone protects us from UV rays present in sun's radiation.

Reason (R): Ozone is a greenhouse gas.

27. **Assertion (A)**: Electrostatic precipitator prevents air pollution.

Reason (R): Acidic gases like oxides of sulfur and nitrogen are neutralized in electrostatic precipitator.

28. **Assertion (A)**: Concentration of toxic chemicals is maximum in producers.

Reason (R): Producers are directly in contact with the toxic chemicals present in the soil.

Level 2: Review your Concepts

29. What are the basic requirements for the survival of animals in the ecosystem? Explain.
30. How do biomedical wastes affect our environment?
31. What is auditory fatigue? How does it occur?
32. Define the following:
    (a) Biomass
    (b) Ecosystem
    (c) Food web
    (d) Bio-accumulation
33. Is greenhouse effect necessary for life? If so, give reason.
34. What is ozone layer depletion? What are the causes and effects of it?
35. What is eutrophication?
36. How do pollutants released from the automobiles affect the environment?
37. How can the pollution due to transportation be reduced?
38. How does household detergents and sewage lead to water pollution?
39. Explain thermal pollution and its effect on aquatic life.
40. What are the effects of water pollution on human being?
41. Mention the gases other than chlorofluorocarbons that cause ozone depletion.
42. How does acid rain affect human beings and plants?
43. How can an individual contribute to reduction in ozone depletion?

Level 3: Assess Your Concepts

44. Answer the following based on the given food web:
    (a) Name the producers in the food web shown in the figure.
    (b) Name the primary consumers in the given food web.
    (c) Name the secondary consumers in the given food web.
    (d) Name the organisms that share food with rabbit.
    (e) Where does the food web end?
    (f) Where does the food web start?

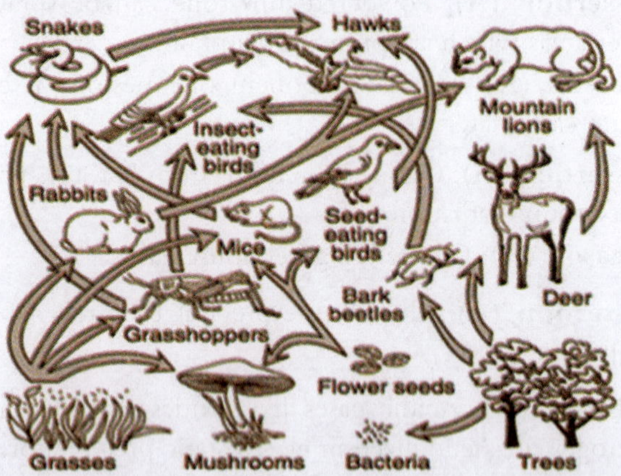

45. Keystone species have a disproportionately large impact on their ecosystems relative to their abundance. Discuss the significance of keystone species in maintaining ecosystem balance and what happens when such species are removed or introduced.

46. How does radioactive pollution cause somatic variation?

47. Discuss the long-term consequences of thermal pollution on aquatic ecosystems.

48. How do the types of fuels we use in our daily lives influence air pollution?

AT

PRACTICE QUESTIONS NEET SPECIAL WING

Multiple-Answer Type Questions

Questions number 1 to 5 are multiple-choice questions. Each question has FOUR options (a), (b), (c), and (d). ONE OR MORE THAN ONE of these four option(s) is/are the correct answer(s).

1. Which of the following terms describe ecosystems on the basis of size?
   (a) Micro (b) Macro
   (c) Endo (d) Meso

2. Which of the following organisms do not undergo natural processes which helps to remove carbon dioxide from the atmosphere?
   (a) Herbivores
   (b) Producers
   (c) Carnivores
   (d) Secondary consumers

3. Which of the following are caused due to long term effects of air pollution?
   (a) Alteration of DNA
   (b) Chronic pulmonary diseases
   (c) Lung cancer
   (d) Cardiovascular diseases

4. Identify the effects of acid rain from the following:
   (a) Irritation in eyes and skin
   (b) Corrosion of metal monuments
   (c) Acidification of lakes and streams
   (d) Reduces population of useful micro-organisms

5. Which of the following are the correct steps of the process of Greenhouse effect?
   (a) Penetration and absorption of the high energy rays by the earth's surface.
   (b) Radiation of short wavelength energy back by the Earth.
   (c) Trapping of the radiated energy by the greenhouse gases.
   (d) Liberation of heat energy by the greenhouse gases.

Comprehension-Based Questions

A. Read the paragraph given below and answer the questions number 6 to 11:

The continuous interaction that occurs between the living and non-living components of the environment make the ecosystem. Ecosystem can be natural or artificial or can be also classified as terrestrial or aquatic based on the regions where they exist. Based on the sizes also ecosystem can be classified. The consumers of the ecosystem are also classified into primary, secondary and tertiary based on the type of food they consume. If we consider the energy flow of the ecosystem, only 1% of the solar energy trapped by the green plants is used to make food. From the second trophic level only 10 % of the energy is passed on to the next trophic levels and it successively decreases as we move to higher trophic levels. This flow of energy is unidirectional. The linear flow of energy which takes place between the different components of the ecosystem is called food chain. The interconnectedness between the different food chains forms a web and is called as food web. Another method of showing the flow of energy is ecological pyramid. They are diagrammatic representation of food cains which arrange organisms at various trophic levels.

6. In the food chain Grass → Grasshopper → Frog → Snake → Vulture, snake is a
   (a) Primary consumer
   (b) Secondary consumer
   (c) Tertiary consumer
   (d) Apex consumer

7. If in a small ecosystem, green plants receive 10,000 kJ of solar energy, what percentage of this energy is converted into food?
   (a) 1 kJ (b) 10 kJ
   (c) 100 kJ (d) 1000 kJ

8. In an aquatic ecosystem which of the following is a primary consumer?
   (a) Phytoplankton (b) Small fish
   (c) Large fish (d) Zooplankton

9. Find the odd one out of the following based on the type of ecosystems.
(a) Ponds (b) Lakes
(c) Forest (d) Zoo

10. Which of the following is not an example of terrestrial ecosystem?
(a) Forest (b) Grassland
(c) Taiga (d) None of the above

11. Match the column:

Match the trophic levels of the organisms as part of the ecological pyramid:

Column – A	Column – B
(i) Green grass	(a) Third trophic level
(ii) Grasshopper	(b) Second trophic level
(iii) Frog	(c) First trophic level
(iv) Hawk	(d) Fourth trophic level
(v) Snake	(e) Fifth trophic level

B. Read the paragraph given below and answer the questions number 12 to 17:

Environmental pollution is one of the major problems in the 21st century. Depending on the nature of the substance polluted or the pollutant causing the pollution, it is classified into following types: Air pollution, Water pollution, Soil/land pollution, Noise pollution and Radioactive pollution. Increase in CO_2 due to deforestation and combustion of fuels, increases the temperature of the atmosphere resulting in melting of glaciers. This is called global warming. Different types of pollution control equipment are available, but the choice of equipment can be made based on the following factors: volume or size of particulates, physical and chemical properties of particulates, temperature or humidity of gaseous medium, toxicity and inflammability and concentration of particulate matter in the exhaust gas. Water pollutants can be either organic, inorganic or biological in nature. Some ill effects of water pollution include spread of infectious diseases and eutrophication. Pesticides and Industrial wastes lead to water pollution. Noise pollution can cause auditory, non-auditory and psychological effects. Radioactive pollution can cause genetic and somatic variation.

12. Reducing the emission of air pollutants at their origin is called:
(a) Pioneer emission method
(b) Source correction method
(c) Direct reduction at source method
(d) Direct control of emission method

13. What is sprayed by the dry scrubber so that acidic gases in the exhaust pipes can get neutralised?
(a) Lemon juice
(b) Solid NaOH powder
(c) Wet lime powder
(d) Activated charcoal

14. Depletion of which gas in the atmosphere leads to increased incidences of skin cancer, cataracts and more people with impaired immune systems?
(a) CO (b) CO_2
(c) H_2O (d) O_3

15. Which of the following is not an effect of global warming?
(a) Increase in temperature of the earth's surface
(b) Trees lose their ability to complete life cycles
(c) Acidification of lakes and streams occurs
(d) Water content of the soil reduces

16. Which of the following is not a greenhouse gas?
(a) Carbon dioxide
(b) Chloro fluoro carbons
(c) Methane
(d) Carbon mono oxide

17. Match the column:

Column – A	Column – B
(i) Minamata disease	(a) Eutrophication
(ii) Nitrate fertilizers in fields	(b) Radioactive radiation
(iii) Hospital waste	(c) Non auditory effect of noise pollution
(iv) Hypertension	(d) Biomedical waste
(v) Genetic variation	(e) Mercury effluents in water

ANSWER KEYS

Crossword

Across

6. Pollutant 8. Methylisocyanate 11. Herbivores 12. Eutrophication 14. Food chain
16. Decomposers 17. Producers 18. Ozone 19. Minamata

Down

1. Food web 2. Smog 3. Chlorofluorocarbons 4. Incineration
5. Lightning 6. Pollutant 7. Flyash 8. Methylisocyanate 9. Troposphere
10. Omnivores 13. Ecotone 15. Scrubbers

Classroom Wing

Very Short Answer Type Questions

1. Non-biodegradable materials 2. Environment, Study of 3. Biotic
4. Ecotone 5. Biomagnification 6. Pollutant 7. Producers 8. Secondary
9. Infrared radiation 10. Sewage treatment 11. (c) 12. (c) 13. (a)
14. (c) 15. (a) 16. (a)

Competition Wing

Level 1: Apply Your Concepts

1. Particulate 2. Wind 3. Vehicles 4. Smog 5. Agricultural
6. Acid 7. Biomes 8. Matter, Energy 9. Terrestrial
10. Suspended particulate matter 11. Chlorofluorocarbons 12. Infrared
13. Water 14. (d) 15. (a) 16. (a) 17. (d)
18. (c) 19. Does not decompose 20. Study of animals 21. Biome
22. (c) 23. (b) 24. (a) 25. (a) 26. (b)
27. (c) 28. (d)

NEET Special Wing

Multiple-Answer Type Questions

1. (a, b, d) 2. (a, c, d) 3. (b, c, d) 4. (a, b, c, d) 5. (a, c, d)

Comprehension-Based Questions

6. (c) 7. (c) 8. (d) 9. (d) 10. (d)
11. (i) → (c); (ii) → (b); (iii) → (a); (iv) → (e); (v) → (d)
12. (b) 13. (c) 14. (d) 15. (c) 16. (d)
17. (i) → (e); (ii) → (a); (iii) → (d); (iv) → (c); (v) → (b)

Hints and Explanations

CLASSROOM WING

Short Answer Type Questions

17.

Biotic components	Abiotic components
The living components in an ecosystem are known as biotic components. For example: plants, animals, etc.	The non-living components of an ecosystem are known as abiotic components. For example: air, water, etc.

18. Ecosystem is a community of living organisms and non-living components of the environment linked together through nutrient cycles and energy flow.

19. Biodiversity increases the stability and resilience of an ecosystem, allowing it to recover from disturbances. A diverse ecosystem has multiple species performing similar roles, ensuring that if one species is eliminated or decreases in number, others can compensate and maintain ecosystem functions.

20. Invasive species, when introduced to a new ecosystem, can outcompete, prey on, or bring diseases to native species, often leading to a decline or extinction of native populations. Since invasive species lack natural predators in the new environment, their populations can explode, further stressing the native species and the ecosystem's balance.

21. Burning of municipal wastes, especially when done without proper control measures, releases a cocktail of harmful gases and particulate pollutants into the air. These include carbon monoxide, dioxins, furans, heavy metals, and volatile organic compounds. When plastics, rubber, or treated wood are burned, the combustion releases especially toxic compounds.

22. (1) **Autotrophs:** The organisms that feed themselves by preparing food with the help of sunlight are known as autotrophs.

(2) **Decomposers:** The organisms that break down the dead plants and animals are known as decomposers.

(3) **Heterotrophs:** The organisms that depend upon autotrophs for their food are known as heterotrophs.

23.

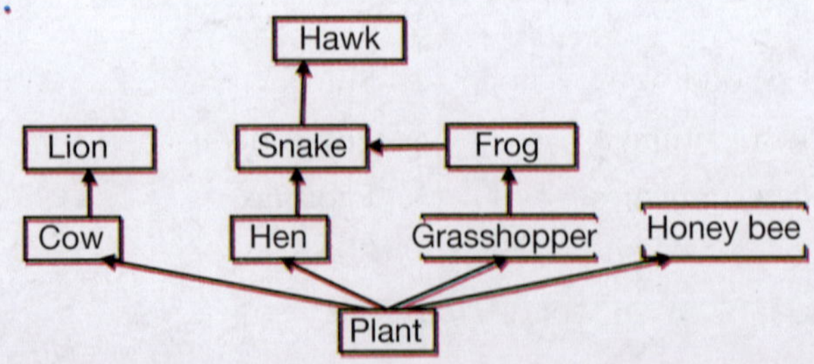

24. Role of decomposers in ecosystem: Decomposers are the scavengers that break down dead plants, animals and waste. These play an important role in providing nutrients to the plants, thereby keeping the environment clean from piling up of dead matter and waste.

25. Recycling reduces the need for mining and refining raw materials for various purposes. The process of refining raw materials causes different types of pollutions. Recycling is certainly a good method for reducing pollution.

26. Effect of human beings on ecosystem: Human activities such as urbanization and deforestation disturb various ecosystems or biomes, such as forest ecosystems, aquatic ecosystems, etc.

27. Carrots, grass, groundnuts, rabbit, deer, squirrel, fox snake, owl, etc.

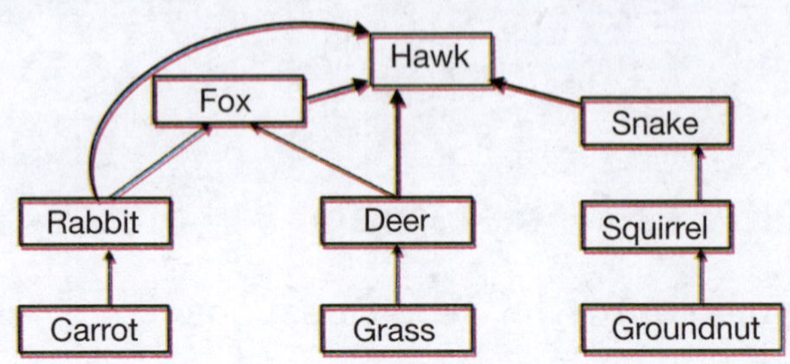

28. Primary pollutants are added directly into the air whereas the secondary pollutants are formed due to the various chemical reactions of the primary pollutants with other components of the atmosphere.

29. Factors of air pollutants that affect human body are
   (a) Concentration of air pollutants,
   (b) Nature of the pollutants,
   (c) Time of exposure

30. (i) Open field burning produces large amount of ash, CO_2, methane, etc.

(ii) Different toxic chemicals from pesticides, manure decomposition produce greenhouse gases.

(iii) Industrial farms emit foul odour.

(iv) Extensive usage of fertilizers leads to air pollution and also eutrophication.

31. Various methods to control air pollution from industries are as follows:

- Dilution of source discharge by tall chimneys
- Changing to raw materials that produce less air pollutants
- Using effective pollution control equipment, like dust collectors, electrostatic precipitators, etc.

32. Role of citizens in controlling pollution:

- Keep our surroundings clean.
- Regular servicing of vehicles.
- Using unconventional sources of energy, such as solar, wind, etc., wherever possible.
- Use public transport instead of private vehicles.
- Reduce usage of polythene or plastic goods and if used discharge them properly for recycling.
- Plant trees and develop gardens in our localities.
- Avoid burning of plastic or polythene materials.

33. Volcanoes, forest fires and pollen are few examples of natural ways of air pollution.

34. Effects on human beings due to air pollution can be classified into two types. They are:

(a) Short-term effects—asthma, bronchitis, pneumonia, etc.

(b) Long-term effects—cardiovascular disease, chronic pulmonary disease and lung cancer, etc.

35. Various man-made sources of air pollution are domestic sewage, industrial wastes, radioactive wastes, agricultural run-offs, oil spills and thermal pollution.

36. Inorganic water pollutants are arsenic, cadmium, lead, mercury, silver, precipitated salts, etc.

37. Troposphere is the layer where all weather phenomena take place.

38. CO combines with haemoglobin present in our blood and reduces the transport of oxygen in our body. Thus, different organs fail to work due to lack of oxygen.

39. Carbon dioxide is required for photosynthesis as well as it is useful for the maintenance of the temperature of earth. But higher concentration of carbon dioxide leads to global warming.

If its concentration exceeds certain limits, its toxic effects cause different health hazards, such as dizziness, dim vision, headache, breathing problems, etc.

40. Filters, gravitational settling chamber, cyclone separator and electrostatic precipitator prevent the release of suspended particulate matter in the atmosphere.

Essay Type Questions

41. Transfer of radioactive substances to plants through polluted soil affects their DNA, growth of plants and the quality of seeds (genetic disorder).

42. A natural source of nitrogen oxides occurs from a lightning stroke. The very high temperature in the vicinity of a lightning bolt causes the gases, oxygen and nitrogen, in the air to react to form nitric oxide. The nitric oxide very quickly reacts with more oxygen to form nitrogen dioxide.

43. (i.) Hydrochlorofluorocarbons and hydrofluorocarbons are less stable and more reactive than CFCs because of the presence of hydrogen atoms. Hence, they break down in the troposphere before reaching stratosphere and attack the ozone layer.

(ii.) Nitrous oxides are stable when emitted at the ground level, but break down when they reach the stratosphere to form other gases, called nitrogen oxides, that trigger ozone-destroying reactions.

(iii.) Powdered limestone can be sprayed over areas that are prone to acid rain.

COMPETITION WING

Level 1: Apply your Concepts

19. Electrostatic precipitators : Air pollution :: Sewage treatment : Water pollution

20. Carbon dioxide : global warming:: CFCs : Ozone depletion.

21. Desert: Terrestrial ecosystem :: Freshwater lake: Aquatic ecosystem.

22. Decomposers are the scavengers in the ecosystem. Food chain starts with producers and ends up with decomposers.
Hence, the correct option is (c)

23. Producers prepare their own food with the help of sunlight, water and air. Hence, are known as autotrophs (where sun is the major source of energy)
Hence, the correct option is (b)

24. In any food chain, the number of organisms in any trophic level should always be less than that in its previous trophic level since only 10 per cent of total energy present in a trophic level is transferred to the next trophic level in any food chain. The members in first trophic level should be greater than the next trophic level.
Hence, the correct option is (a)

25. Calcium carbonate reacts with acid present in acid rain and neutralizes it to prevent the damages caused by acid rain.
Hence, the correct option is (a)

26. Ozone absorbs ultraviolet rays and thus protects us from the harmful effect of them. Ozone is called greenhouse gas since it absorbs the heat energy radiated by Earth's crust.
Hence, the correct option is (b)

27. Electrostatic precipitator prevents air pollution by arresting suspended particulate matter. Neutralization of acidic gases does not take place in electrostatic precipitator.
Hence, the correct option is (c)

28. The concentration of a toxic chemical increases in the tissues of organisms at successively higher levels in a food chain because the number of organisms gradually decreases at successively higher levels. Although the entry of toxic chemicals in a food chain takes place through the producer, but concentration of toxic substance in producers is the least due to their large number.
Hence, the correct option is (d)

Level 2: Review your Concepts

29. In any ecosystem, the survival of any species depends on the abiotic and biotic factors. There should not be any drastic changes in the weather conditions. The ratio between any two successive trophic levels should be maintained properly because only 10 per cent of energy flows from one trophic level to another.

30. Biomedical wastes contain potentially harmful microorganisms, which enter and remain in the air in the form of spores or simply as pathogens themselves.

Biomedical wastes also contain harmful chemicals, such as acid, bleach or oil that should be disposed in approved, correctly labelled containers.

Pollution may also come from burning wastes, such as paper, plastics and other medical containers and materials. Such chemicals can build up in the ozone layer over time. Some garbage also releases harmful gases, such as methane, which significantly contribute to global warming.

31. Auditory fatigue is a phenomenon that occurs when our ears get overexposed to an audio-stimulus such as a mixing track for a long period of time or a sound of high volume.
When our ears are overexposed to a sound of high volume, the blood vessels in the ears become constricted. Therefore, less amount of blood reaches hair follicles inside the ear and our audibility becomes slightly muffled. As a result, we experience temporary and short-term hearing loss.

32. (a) **Biomass:** The total quantity or weight of organisms in an area or volume is called biomass.

(b) **Ecosystem:** Ecosystem is a community of living organisms and non-living components of their environment (air, water and mineral soil) linked together through nutrient cycles and energy flow.

(c) **Food web:** A network of food chains or feeding relationships by which energy and nutrients are passed from one species of living organisms to another.

(d) **Bio-accumulation:** Accumulation of substances such as pesticides or other chemical in an organism is called bio-accumulation.

33. Yes, greenhouse effect is necessary for life to keep the surface of the Earth warmer and thus, life can be sustained.

34. Ozone layer depletion and its causes:
Destruction of ozone layer mainly due to chlorine atoms of CFC molecules.

The other substances that cause this depletion are hydrochlorofluorocarbon carbons (HCFC) and volatile organic compounds (VOC). These are found in smoke from vehicles, industries, aerosols, refrigerants, etc.

Effects of ozone layer depletion:

- Causes skin cancer. For example, malignant melanoma, squamous cell carcinoma, etc.
- Climatic changes.
- Eye damage. For example, cataract.
- Weakens response of immune system.
- Affects plant growth and the time of flowering of few plant species.
- Excessive exposure to ultraviolet rays of the sun causes difficulty in breathing, throat irritation, etc.

35. Eutrophication: Excessive growth of phytoplankton and algae due to the enrichment of plant nutrients in water bodies leads to water pollution. This obstructs the entry of heat, light and air in water. This phenomenon is called eutrophication and affects aquatic life.

36. Carbon dioxide, oxides of sulfur and nitrogen are the gases released from automobiles. Excess carbon dioxide leads to global warming and different health hazards. Oxides of nitrogen and sulfur cause acid rain. Suspended particulate matter causes respiratory diseases.

37. Fossil fuels such as petrol and diesel release different toxic gases. Use of CNG and LPG in automobiles reduces pollution since their combustion does not release toxic gases.

38. The phosphates in these materials enter water bodies. They promote rapid growth of algae that disturbs fishing, navigation and irrigation.

39. Thermal power plants located near water bodies use water for cooling the machineries and release the hot water back into the water bodies. This affects the aquatic life. The hot water can hold less oxygen compared to normal water. The reduction in the percentage of oxygen in water affects fish like trout. Warm water increases the growth of blue-green algae that produce some toxins. The rise in the temperature of water increases the solubility of salts.

40. Consumption of polluted water leads to certain waterborne diseases, such as cholera, typhoid, diarrhoea, dysentery, hepatitis, polio and jaundice. Mercury dumped into water transforms to methyl mercury due to bacterial action. This accumulates in fish and it further reaches the human beings due to the consumption of fish. Methyl mercury causes numbness in body parts, hearing impairment and abnormal mental behavior (Minamata disease). Pollution due to heavy metals (cadmium) causes a disease called Itai-itai.

41. Hydrochlorofluorocarbons (HCFCs), carbon tetrachloride (CCl_4), methyl chloroform and volatile organic compounds (VOC) are the gases other than chlorofluorocarbons that cause ozone depletion.

42. Acid rain causes irritation in eyes and skin. It reduces visibility, develops disorders of the respiratory system. Trees in forests die due to acidification of soil and water.

43. Every individual can contribute to reduction in ozone layer depletion by using public transport and recycled products, saving energy, etc.

Level 3: Assess Your Concepts

44. (a) Producers: grasses and trees

(b) Primary consumers: rabbit, grasshoppers, bark beetles, deer, mice and seed-eating birds.

(c) Secondary consumers: mountain lion, hawk, insect-eating birds and snake.

(d) Organisms that share food with rabbit are mice and grasshopper.

(e) Food web ended at hawk and mountain lion, that is, secondary consumers.

(f) Food web starts with producers.

45. **Keystone Species and Their Importance:** A keystone species has a disproportionately large impact on its environment relative to its abundance or biomass. The term ‘keystone’ is derived from architecture, where the keystone is the central stone at the top of an arch that holds all the other stones in place. In an ecological context, if a keystone species is removed from an ecosystem, the ecosystem would undergo drastic changes.

Implications of Removing or Introducing Keystone Species: The removal or introduction of a keystone species can have cascading effects on an ecosystem. Removing a keystone predator, for example, can lead to an overabundance of its prey, which can in turn overconsume their food sources, leading to ecosystem degradation. Conversely, introducing a keystone species where it was once extirpated can help restore balance to an ecosystem, as seen with the reintroduction of wolves in Yellowstone National Park. The return of wolves altered the behaviour of elk, leading to the recovery of riparian vegetation and benefiting various other species.

46. The functions of living tissue are carried out by molecules, that is, combinations of different types of atoms united by chemical bonds. Some of these molecules can be quite large. The proper functioning of these molecules depends upon their composition and also their structure (shape). Altering chemical bonds may change composition or structure. Radioactive radiation is powerful enough to do this.

47. Thermal pollution, primarily due to industries discharging hot water into water bodies, can have severe long-term effects on aquatic ecosystems. Increased water temperatures can reduce dissolved oxygen levels, which is vital for aquatic life. It can disrupt the life-cycle of many aquatic organisms, especially those that require specific temperatures for breeding. Additionally, warmer waters can favour harmful algal blooms, which produce toxins affecting marine life and the humans consuming them. The altered temperatures can also lead to migration or death of temperature-sensitive species, leading to a potential reduction in biodiversity.

48. The type of fuel used directly correlates to the kind and number of pollutants emitted. For instance:

- Burning coal releases sulphur dioxide, leading to acid rain and respiratory issues.
- Diesel engines emit more particulates than gasoline engines, causing respiratory problems.
- Clean fuels like natural gas produce fewer emissions compared to coal or oil.
- Using biofuels can be more sustainable and may produce fewer greenhouse gases, but the cultivation might lead to other environmental issues like deforestation or excessive water usage.
- Electric vehicles, if charged by renewable sources, can significantly reduce local air pollutants.

NEET SPECIAL WING

Multiple-Answer Type Questions

1. Ecosystems can also be classified based on their sizes. They are: Micro: Small-scale ecosystems, such as tree trunk, pond, etc; Meso: These are Medium-scaled ecosystems, such as large lakes; Macro: An ecosystem like entire rainforest is considered a large-scale ecosystem.
2. Producers undergo photosynthesis which uses the atmospheric carbon dioxide in order to prepare food. The rest of the components of the ecosystem cannot perform photosynthesis, they can only respire which adds carbon dioxide gas to the atmosphere.
3. Some of the major impact of air pollution on humans include- Chronic pulmonary or lung diseases, cardiovascular diseases, lung cancer and even premature death.
4. Following are some of the major adverse effects of acid rain:

   Acid rains have corroding effect on buildings, metal monuments. It causes irritation in eyes and skin. It causes acidification of lakes and streams. Acidified soil reduces the population of certain useful micro-organisms.
5. Complete process of greenhouse effect takes place in the following four steps.
   Step 1: Penetration of high-energy radiations through Earth's atmosphere and absorption of by Earth's surface.
   Step 2: Energy of long wavelength radiated back by the Earth.
   Step 3: Radiated energy gets, trapped in the atmosphere due to the presence of certain greenhouse gases such as CO_2, CH_4, N_2O, O_3, etc.
   Step 4: Greenhouse gases liberate the heat energy to the troposphere.

Comprehension-Based Questions

A.

6. In this food chain, grass is the producer, grasshopper is the primary consumer followed by frog which is a secondary consumer. So, snake is the tertiary consumer and vulture which feeds on it becomes the apex consumer.
7. Only 1% of the solar energy received by the green plants is used by them to convert into food. So, 1% of 10,000 kJ is $(1/100) \times 10000 = 100$ kJ.
8. In an aquatic ecosystem, phytoplankton and algae are the producers. The zooplanktons are the primary consumers which feed on them.
9. Artificial ecosystem are man-made ecosystems, such as zoos, parks, gardens, fields, etc. They are not formed as a result of any natural phenomenon, instead they have been formed due to human activities.
10. Ecosystems that exist on land are called terrestrial ecosystems. Examples are forests, grasslands, deserts, taiga and tundra ecosystems.
11. Match the following:

    Green grasses are the producers of the food chain which trap solar energy and are part of the first trophic level.
    (i) (c)

    Grasshoppers are herbivores and occupy the second trophic level in the ecological pyramid.
    (ii) (b)

    Frogs feed on grasshoppers and occupy the third trophic level.
    (iii) (a)

    Hawk are the apex consumers in this food chain and occupy the fifth trophic level.
    (iv) (e)

    Snakes occupy the fourth trophic level in the food chain which feed on frogs.
    (v) (d)

B.

12. Minimizing the emission of air pollutants at the source is called source correction method.
13. A scrubber sprays water to trap the pollutants. A dry scrubber sprays wet lime powder so that the acidic gases leaving the exhaust pipe interact with it and become neutralized.
14. Ozone in troposphere is liberated by the reaction between volatile hydrocarbon and oxides of nitrogen in presence of UV rays. It continuously breaks down and forms back and this reversible reaction uses a lot of energy of the UV rays, thus decreasing their impact when they finally reach the surface of the earth. So, if ozone gets depleted the UV rays will come down on the earth's surface unfiltered and this will lead to increased cases of skin cancer, cataract, etc.

15. The effects of global warming include- Increase in concentration of carbon dioxide in the atmosphere increases the temperature of Earth's surface. The rapid change in atmospheric temperature is harmful for the temperate forests. Trees lose their ability to complete their life cycles. The global warming has considerable effect on agriculture. The increase in temperature of soil increases evaporation. Thus, the water content of the soil reduces. Increase in temperature of the Earth's atmosphere results in different diseases in human beings like heart stroke, etc. Acidification of water bodies and soil is an effect of acid rain.

16. Green house gases help to maintain the temperature on the earth. Methane, carbon dioxide, nitrogen dioxide, ozone and water vapour gases are the greenhouse gases. Carbon monoxide is not a greenhouse gas among the options given.

17. Match the following:

Minamata disease was first discovered in Minamata city in Japan, in 1956. It was caused due to release of methyl mercury from the Chisso Corporation's chemical factory.

(i) (e)

Excessive use of nitrate fertilisers leads to the nitrates entering the water bodies. This in turn leads to the growth of phytoplankton and algae due to the enrichment of plant nutrients in water bodies which causes water pollution. This obstructs the entry of heat, light and air in water. This phenomenon is called eutrophication and affects aquatic life.

(ii) (a)

Hospital wastes, such as outdated medicines, cytotoxic drugs, soiled dressing, used cotton, body fluids, dissected body organs, tissues, disposable syringes, intravenous fluids, bottles, gloves, needles, blades, etc., contaminate the soil. This is a type of biomedical waste.

(iii) (d)

Nonauditory effects of noise pollution include Hypertension, reduction in concentration and working efficiency, develops annoyance, violent behaviour, short temperament, mental disorientation, communication interference, sleep interference, etc.

(iv) (c)

Genetic variation is the damage caused due to radioactive radiations is seen in the offspring and transmitted to many generations. Transfer of radioactive substances to plants through polluted soil affects their DNA, growth of plants and the quality of seeds (genetic disorder).

(v) (b)

CHAPTER

12

Management of Natural Resources

Remember

Before beginning this chapter, you should be able to:

- Recall natural resources
- List abiotic and biotic aspects of nature
- Understand the importance of conservation of resources

Key Ideas

After completing this chapter, you should be able to:

- Classify resources into renewable and nonrenewable resources and biotic and abiotic resources.
- Discuss various disruption to environment caused by human interference in consumption of resources.
- Explain the importance of sustainable development and conservation of environment.
- Understand the principles of conservation of resources, such as reuse, reduce and recycle, etc.
- Discuss various sustainable steps to preserve forest and wildlife community.
- Understand the importance of conservation of resources

A Tribute to Thomas Alva Edison (1847–1931)

Thomas Alva Edison (1847–1931), a name synonymous with innovation, demonstrated remarkable foresight in natural resource management. Edison's prolific inventions enlightened the world on prudent resource utilisation and long-term solutions. His invention of the incandescent light bulb was a game changer, changing how we harness and consume energy. It served as a sustainable alternative to traditional gas lights, allowing for resource conservation and pollution reduction.

Edison's 1,093 US patents were not limited to lighting. His invention of the phonograph paved the way for uncharted territory in sound recording and playback. His pioneering work in motion pictures established the film industry, and his invention of the alkaline storage battery demonstrated his diverse brilliance in resource management.

Edison's perseverance in pushing the boundaries of knowledge and technology earned him awards such as the Legion of Honour.

FUN TIME

CROSSWORD

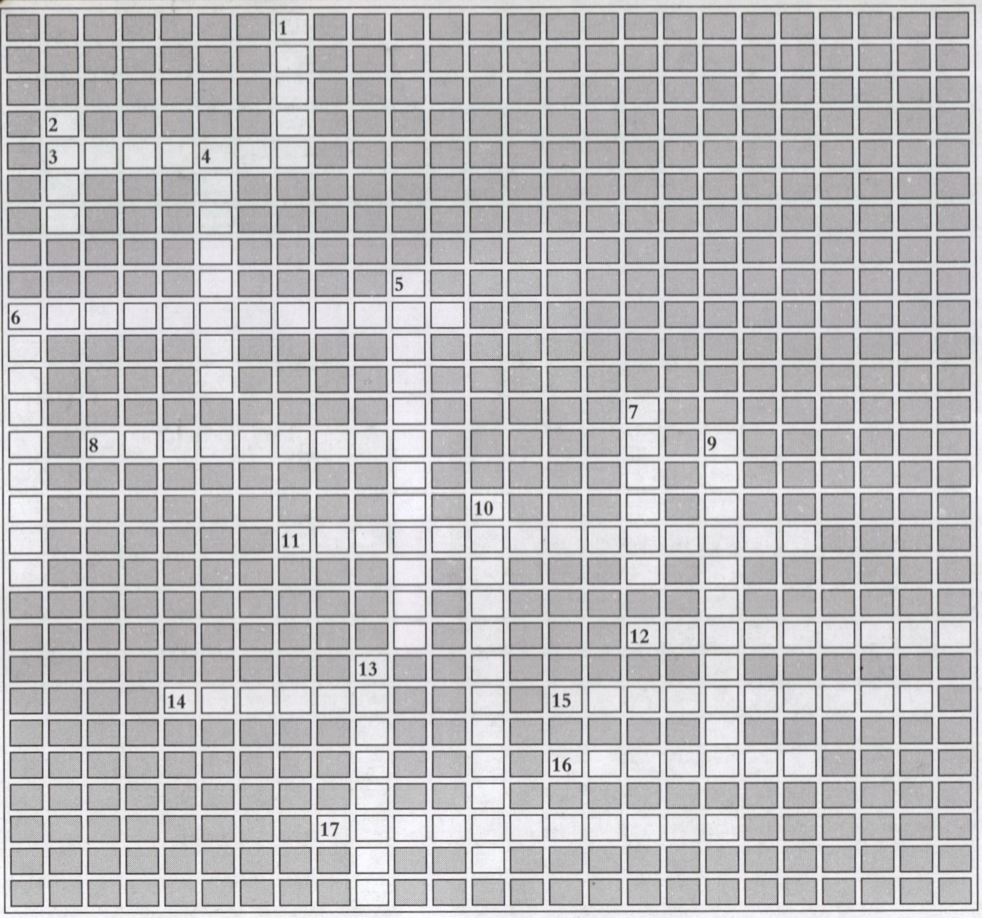

Across

3. Upcycling waste to prevent wastage.
6. Water distribution network in water harvesting
8. Irrigation technique that mimics rain, conserves water.
11. The ability to maintain or conserve something over time; often linked with environmental conservation
12. Resource that are replenishable and reusable.
14. Environmental conservation step: using fewer resources
15. Technique replenishing the groundwater table.
16. Non-living; the other classification of resources based on the source of origin
17. An agricultural method that conserves moisture and reduces soil erosion

Down

1. Reusing items to conserve resources
2. Precise irrigation technique for water delivery to roots.
4. Crop fields benefiting from water harvesting techniques.
5. Act of preserving biodiversity or natural resources
6. Water-diverting dam in water harvesting.
7. Life-related; one resource classification based on origin.
9. The surroundings in which an organism lives, which must maintain three basic functions for sustainability
10. The variety of life in all its forms on Earth; crucial for maintaining healthy ecosystems
13. Planting trees to replace those that have been cut down; an essential step to save the environment

INTRODUCTION

Natural resources are a gift of the environment to mankind which facilitates their daily life. They include air, water, soil, mineral, climate and solar energy that forms the non-living part of nature. The living parts of nature consist of plants and animals including microbes. Ecosystems of various kinds are formed due to the connection between the abiotic (non-living) aspects of nature and specific living organisms together.

Natural Resources

The resources that the nature provides for life support or for sustenance of life on earth for plants, animals and human beings are known as 'Natural resources'. There are different ways to classify the natural resources and they are (a) the source of origin, (b) the state of development and (c) the renewability of the resources.

Info Bytes!

Costa Rica holds the record for producing 98% of its electricity from renewable sources for over four consecutive years.

Examples: Water, air, soil, forests, minerals, crops, etc.

The major natural resources that are currently used are as follows.

- Forest resources
- Mineral resources
- Energy resources
- Water resources
- Food resources
- Land resources

As per the source of origin, the resources can be classified as follows:

1. **Biotic:** The natural resources that are obtained from living organisms, such as plants, animals and human beings as well and organic materials are known as biotic resources.

   Examples: Forests and animals, fossil fuels, such as coal and petroleum is a product of decayed organic matter.

2. **Abiotic:** The natural resources which are derived from non-living and non-organic material are known as abiotic resources.

   Examples: Land, fresh water, air and heavy metals (gold, iron, copper, silver, etc.).

The natural resources is divided on the basis of their stage of development:

1. **Potential resources:** These types of resources as the name suggests is kept for future use, as they exist in a particular region.

   Example: If a country has petroleum in sedimentary rocks, then it is a potential resource until it is actually drilled out of the rock and put to use.

2. **Actual resources:** The resources that are surveyed, their quantity and quality has been determined, and are in current use are known as actual resources. Their development is technology dependent.
3. **Reserve resources:** These resources are a part of an actual resource and it can be developed profitably in the future.
4. **Stock resources:** These resources cannot be utilized due to lack of technology.

Natural resources can be classified on the basis of their renewability as discussed below:

1. **Renewable resources:** These types of resources can be recycled and regenerated within a given period of time.

   Examples: Forests, wind energy, solar energy, biomass energy, hydropower, etc.

2. **Non-renewable resources:** These types of resources cannot be regenerated and hence, with time they will be exhausted with increasing consumption.

   Examples: Fossil fuels such as coal, petroleum, minerals, etc.

Managing Resources: The Need

The recent concern about the natural resources has increased due to its finite nature. The natural resources which seemed abundant are depleting due to the growing demand, population and limitless exploitation. This stands like a huge problem in front of the future generations.

With the advancement of industrial and technological aspect in human's life span, the population has increased by a large amount. This leads to a high demand of natural resources. Natural resources do not regenerate at this high pace which leads greater depletion of resources. Non-renewable resources on the other hand are in the endangered zone.

This exploitation of natural resources is not only depleting them but also causing damage to the environment. For example, the rivers like Ganga and Yamuna has become polluted due to the industrial waste ejected in them (Fig. 12.1). Soil contamination is taking place due to over use of chemical fertilizers and pesticides. Due to the pressurizing demand of more food crops, more and more deforestation is taking place. This is leading to soil erosion and climate change drastically. Automobiles are adding onto the air pollution and industrial emissions are causing greenhouse gases to rise and cause global warming. All these together are a lethal combination to deplete the natural resources.

Figure 12.1 Polluted river

It is essential for the environment to be conserved by having a proper waste disposal in a more scientific and sustainable manner with a long-term perspective rather than for short term gains. It should also be maintained by the government that the resources should be equally distributed.

National Mission for Clean Ganga

National Mission for Clean Ganga (NMCG) was registered as a society on 12th August 2011 under the Societies Registration Act 1860 (Fig. 12.2). It acted as implementation arm of National Ganga River Basin Authority (NGRBA) which was constituted under the provisions of the Environment (Protection) Act (EPA), 1986. The aims and objectives of NMCG is to accomplish the mandate of National Ganga River Basin Authority (NGRBA):

1. To ensure effective abatement of pollution and rejuvenation of the river Ganga by adopting a river basin approach to promote inter-sectoral co-ordination for comprehensive planning and management and
2. To maintain minimum ecological flows in the river Ganga with the aim of ensuring water quality and environmentally sustainable development.

CLEAN GANGA PROJECT: EVOLUTION

1986

The Congress Government launched the first phase of Ganga Action Plan (GAP) along selected stretches of 25 cities in U.P, Bihar and West Bengal.

1993

GAP-II was initiated which included the tributaries-Damodar, Gomati and Mahanadi.

2009

The government re-launched GAP, giving ganga the status of a national river. It reconstituted GAP with National Ganga River Basin Authority (NGRBA) which included the cleaning of the entire river basin.

2014

The Modi government launched the Namami Gange project with massive fund allocation for rejuvenation of the river.

2016

The National Ganga Council was set up under the under the River Ganga (Rejuvenation, Protection and Management) Authorities order 2016. The order dissolved the NGRBA. National Mission for Clean Ganga was set up as the implementation wing.

Figure 12.2 Clean Ganga mission

Sustainable Development and Conservation of Environment

The commonly accepted definition of sustainable development is a process whereby the present generation uses the resources on earth for development in such a way that the needs of today are met without compromising the requirements of the future generations. Due to over exploitation of natural resources by growing countries, the life support base is on the verge of collapse.

The concept of sustainable development is directly connected to the intergenerational equity which explains that the future and present generations have same rights. **Intergenerational equity** means people of same generation belonging to different genres have the same rights.

From this it is deduced that development is a continuous process that includes integration of three aspects of development as listed below (Fig. 12.3).

1. Environmental
2. Economic
3. Social dimension

Konnect

The United Nations 2030 Agenda for Sustainable Development has 17 Sustainable Development Goals, many of which focus on the preservation and sustainable use of our natural resources.

Environmental Sustainability

It is the ability to conserve over time the three basic functions of the environment as stated below.

1. The resource supply function.
2. The waste receiver function.
3. Direct usefulness.

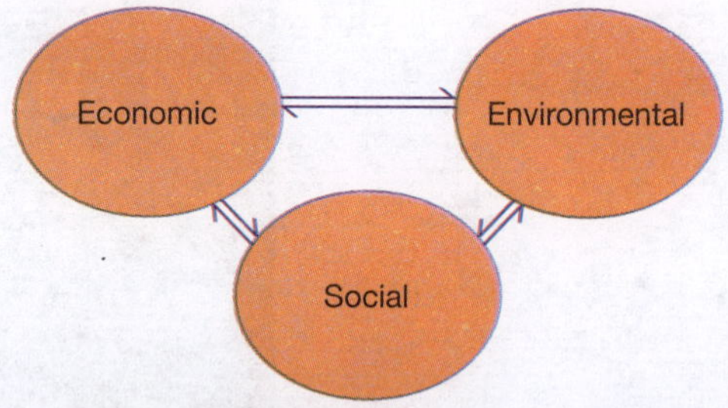

Figure 12.3 Steps for sustainable development

Sustainability means the ability within an area to build the value of environment and its aspects while confirming the protection and the renewal of natural resources and the environmental patrimony.

1. **Economic sustainability:** It is the ability of an economic system to create a constant and improving growth of its economic indicators. In other words, generating employment and income to sustain the growing population is called economic sustainability. Within an area, it means the ability to create and sustain highest added value through the most efficient mix of resources in order to improve the specificity of territorial products and services.
2. **Social sustainability:** It is the capability to guarantee welfare, equitably distributed among social classes and gender. As per an area it means, the ability of social stakeholders to communicate effectively and focus on the same goals, encouraged by the close communication of the institutions at all levels.

To conclude political and ethical principles are the basis of sustainable development. It means that both the social and economic aspects of modern economy are in sync with the improving life condition as well as the ability of natural resources to regenerate in an indefinite manner.

Forest and Wildlife

Biodiversity conservation is the preservation of life in all its forms on Earth and keeping the natural ecosystems functioning and healthy (Fig. 12.4). Biodiversity conservation raises ecosystem productivity, where each of the species, irrespective of size has an important role to play. For example, a larger number of plant species means a greater variety of crops. Greater diversity of species ensures natural sustainability for all life forms. The various major functions of forest resources has been discussed below.

Figure 12.4 Forest and wildlife

1. **Watershed protection**
   (a) Decreases the rate of surface run-off of water.
   (b) Avoids flash floods and soil erosion.

(c) During rainy season, it cuts down the speed of run-off by thus increasing percolation (which results in increase in water table) and reducing erosion.

2. **Atmospheric regulation**
   (a) Heat absorption.
   (b) Maintaining carbon dioxide levels in atmosphere.
   (c) Maintaining the local climatic conditions.
3. **Erosion control**
   (a) Preventing physical wash away of soil with water streams.
4. **Soil conservator**
   (a) Maintenance of soil nutrients and structure.

Use

Forest is one of the natural resource in which the livelihood of people depends upon (Fig. 12.5). People do not benefit directly from it and derive benefits out of this resource. Some of the uses of forest resources are as follows.

1. Water used by the population is dependent upon the existence of forests around the river channels.
2. Furniture and paper used in homes are derived out of the woods from forests.
3. Many medicines are organic based and derived from forests.
4. Oxygen that humans are dependent upon is generated by plants and the carbon dioxide is absorbed by them as well.

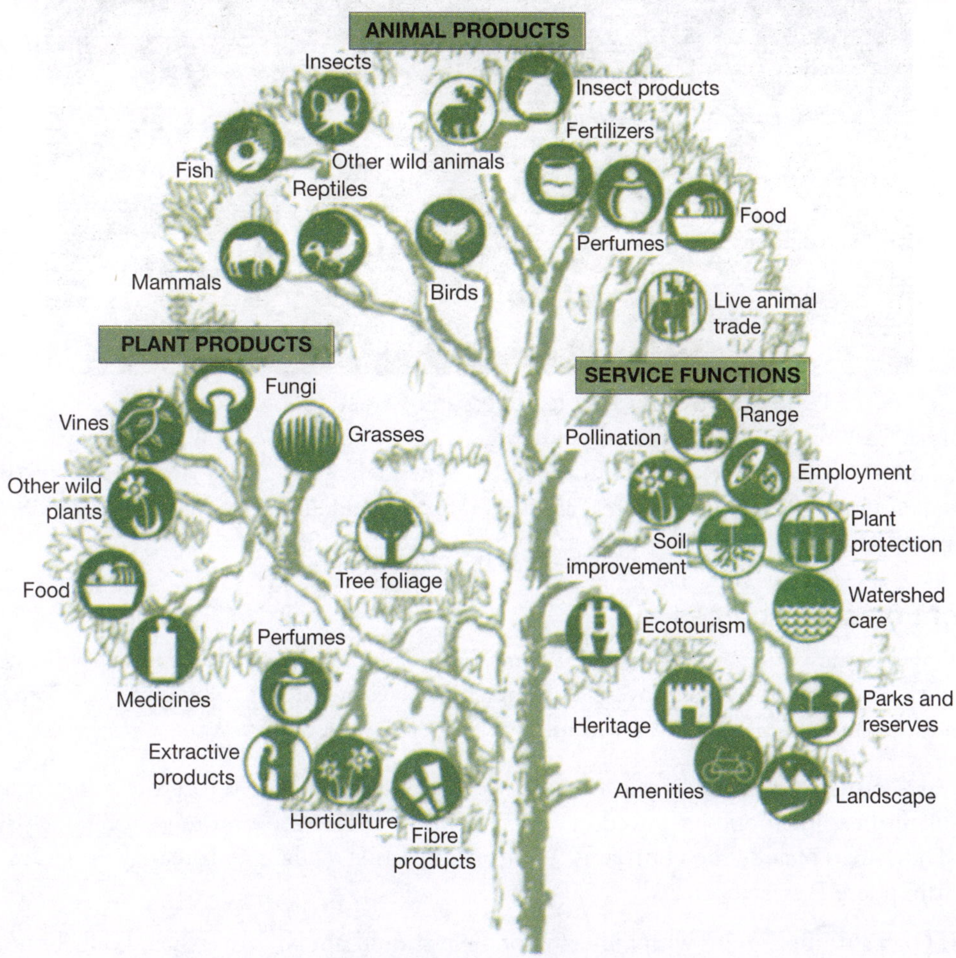

Figure 12.5 Forest Resources

Exploitation of Forest Resources

1. People have survived on forests and its resources for a long period of time. With the expansion of agriculture, forests were reduced slowly and controlled by the tribal people who were solely dependent on the forest resources. Deforestation became a threat when the British extracted wood for their ships and these factors lead them to create scientific forestry in India. They estranged the local people by creating reserved and protected forests so people had a deficient access to the resources. This caused a loss of stake in the conservation of the forests which degraded and fragmented forests across the country.

2. Another period of exploitation of forest took place when the British left after independence and people felt they can use the forest as per their whims and fancies. **Timber extraction** was the main concern till 1970's.

3. **Deforestation:** The civilization which used their forest resources thought provokingly flourished through the years and vice versa happened to those people who were reckless about deforestation. Logging and mining has become a sole reason for deforestation all over the world. Construction of dams have submerged the forests and put all the lives of tribal people into stake who were solely dependent on those forests.

Figure 12.6 Deforestation and Forest degradation

4. Forest degradation due to timber extraction and the dependency on fuel wood is one of the main causes of environmental problems. People in rural areas are still highly dependent on wood for cooking of meals. Not enough trees are planted to support the need of timber and fuel wood.

Conservation of Forest Resources

According to the Forest Policy (1952), one-third (33 per cent) of the land should be under forest cover. However, in reality, only around 21 per cent is the forest coverage in the country which needs to be remedied before its late. Some of the measures for forest resource improvement are as follows.

1. **Reserve forests conservation:** The most eminent conservation strategy is to protect the major water resources and no commercial exploitation be allowed in the areas where India's most prominent reserves of natural resources are located. These areas include the Himalayas, Western and Eastern Ghats and areas like reservoirs, National Parks, Sanctuaries, Biosphere Reserves, etc.

2. **Hill forests:** High altitude regions with hilly environment should not be damaged and only limited harvesting with utmost care be allowed.

3. **Forests of plains:** Productivity of plain forest should be increased by proper management.
4. **Social/Commercial forestry:** Social forestry is a concept where the forests are grown in non-natural forest region so as to ensure the continuous supply of minor forest produces like firewood, fodder and timber, etc., without jeopardizing the natural forests. This is essentially a cooperative system based on the participation of farmers, forest dwellers, gram panchayats and civil societies along with the government agencies. It is based on the utilization of marginal and barren lands which aren't the priority agriculture regions. It should be mentioned here that this type of forestry combines the social and commercial forestry in a way that the plantation provides sufficient food and fodder for the dependents and will also provide sufficient timber for industrial purposes.

Info Bytes!

The Chipko movement, or Chipko Andolan

It was a forest conservation movement in India. It began when in 1970 in Reni village of Chamoli district, Uttarakhand. The movement aimed at protecting trees and forests slated for government-backed logging.

Konnect

Bishnoi Community in Rajasthan

The Bishnoi religion is the one based on care towards nature and Bishnois are also called tree-huggers. Amrita Devi, was a young girl that sacrificed her life in order to save the Khejri trees (the state tree of Rajasthan and also the famous Bishnoi tree). When she saw that the soldiers wanted to cut the trees, she went and hugged a tree. Until there was an order to stop the cutting of trees, Along with Amrita Devi, 363 Bishnois lost their lives. The Government of India has instituted an 'Amrita Devi Bishnoi National Award for Wildlife Conservation' in memory of her.

Sustainable Management

In a developing country, the management of forests and the economic viability of utilization of natural resources as most of the resource regions like mines and queries are covered with the forests. Similarly, the creation of large infrastructure projects like dams and roads also crumbles on the forest land. So, it becomes very important that the policies are made and executed in a way that a balance is achieved between the development of goals and preservation of forests.

Water Resources

Through hydrological systems which are formed due to the water cycle through evaporation and precipitation, form rivers (Fig. 12.7) and lakes and support in an assortment of aquatic ecosystems.

Wetlands are the bridges between terrestrial and aquatic ecosystems and it consists of varying plant species and animals that are highly moisture dependent. For the daily needs, people use all aquatic ecosystems such as drinking water for the purpose of washing, cooking, watering animals and irrigating fields. There is a limited quantity of fresh water on which the world is dependent upon. Water covers 70% of the earth's surface.

Figure 12.7 Hydrological cycle

1. Only 3% of this is fresh water.
2. Of this, 2% is in polar ice caps.
3. Only 1% is usable water in rivers, lakes and subsoil aquifers.

Only a fraction of this can be actually used.

1. At a global level, 70% of water is used for agriculture.
2. About 25% for industry.
3. Only 5% for domestic use.

Water for Agriculture and Power Generation

For agriculture and electricity, the demand of water has increased. The consumption in urban areas is met by building dams (Fig. 12.8).

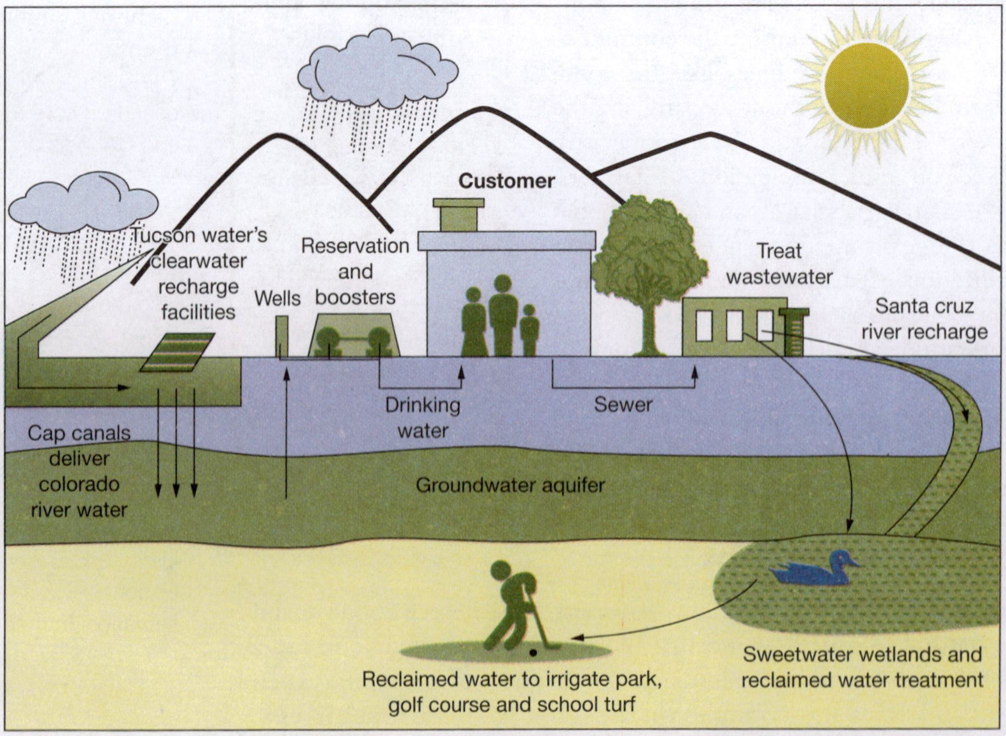

Figure 12.8 Process of urban water usage

Exploitation of Water Resources

1. Due to the growing population, the management of water resources is the greatest challenge. It is estimated that around the world, a billion people have no access to clean water.
2. It has been estimated that by 2050, four billion people will be seriously affected by water shortages. This will result in multiple conflicts between countries over sharing of water. **Example:** India and Bangladesh negotiation agreement on the water use of the Ganges.
3. **Overexploitation and pollution of surface and groundwater:** With the growing population, the demand of water has increased to fulfil the daily needs. In most of the regions, it is difficult to fulfil these needs. Overexploitation of water is seen at various stages. People waste more water than they need. **For example:** People waste water during showers or washing clothes.
4. Many agriculturists use unnecessary water to grow crops. There are many ways in which farmers can use less water without reducing yields. **Example:** Use of drip irrigation systems.
5. Due to the excessive use of chemical fertilizers and pesticides, surface water and underground water stores get polluted.
6. The ever expanding demand of water in households due to the increasing population is also a very potent cause of exploitation.
7. Due to irrigation, unequal distribution of water takes place. **For example:** For cash crops like sugarcane, irrigation produces an unequal distribution of water. Big landlords get major share of water, while poor farmers get affected.

Global Climate Change

1. Air pollution is a serious threat to the climate. Global warming and the El Nino winds create storms that lead to long droughts. Due to atmospheric pollution, the greenhouse effect is causing unpredictable climatic effects. This affects the regional hydrological conditions gravely.

2. **Floods:** Floods are another environmental hazard that disrupts life. The safety net that mankind was dependent upon at such havoc time have been damaged by them. Deforestation and the intensified use of river flood plains have removed all safety nets.
3. **Deforestation:** Deforestation causes floods in the hills making the rivers change their course resulting in the loss of valuable soil to the sea. With degraded forests, no rainwater percolates slowly into the subsoil but runs off down the mountainside taking with it large amount of topsoil. This becomes a bigger problem as it blocks the rivers temporarily creating a large pressure leading large quantities of water to burst down the plain below destroying the lives of people, their farms and homes as well.
4. **Drought:** Drought prone areas go through irregular periods of famine due to unpredictable rains. The agriculturists are in constant fear of drought as there is no steady income due to lack of crops in drought.

Info Bytes!

Wetlands in flood plains are nature's flood control systems into which overfilled rivers could spill and act like a temporary sponge holding the water, and preventing fast flowing water from the damaging surrounding land.

Conservation

1. An effective environmental management reduces the ill effect of the monsoon failure.
2. Preventive measures have to be taken if the monsoon fails to make its impact in the lives of local people. The 'Drought Prone Areas Development Programs' is put to use in such areas to shield the effects of droughts. As per the schemes, people are given wages to build roads, minor irrigation works and plantation programs.
3. In years when the monsoon is adequate, we use up the good supply of water without trying to conserve it and use the water judiciously. Thus, during a year when the rains are poor, there is no water even for drinking in the drought area.
4. Deforestation worsens the effect of drought. Forest cover allows the water to be held in the area permitting it to seep into the ground. This fills the underground stores of water in natural aquifers. This can be put to use in drought years if the stores have been filled during a good monsoon. This **soil** and **water management** and **afforestation** are long-term measures that reduce the impact of droughts.
5. To reduce the agriculture pollution, the surface and ground water methods like use of biomass as a fertilizer and non-toxic pesticides, such as neem products and the use of integrated pest management systems can be applied.

Sustainable Management

1. Industrial waste is released into the water stream to maximize the short term gains. But in the long run, the increasing demand for green products has created an awareness among people for not to use polluter's products. This public awareness has in turn pressurized the industries to produce only eco-friendly products.
2. Public awareness can also pressurize farmers to use more eco-friendly pesticides that are not injurious to health.
3. Campaigns like 'Save Water' are eminent for public awareness on water scarcity and its effects. Measures are needed to be taken for better management of the world's water resources and few measures are listed in the following points.
4. Opting for several small reservoirs rather than few mega projects. Build small catchment dams and protect wetlands.
5. Recharging underground aquifers by soil management, microcatchment development and afforestation by thus decreasing the need for large dams.
6. For agriculture use, treating and recycling of municipal waste water. Leakage prevention from dams and canals.
7. Preventing loss in municipal pipes.
8. For urban environment, effective rain water harvesting is required.
9. Drip irrigation like methods are to be used for water conservation.
10. Reforestation in affected areas with local species ensures better soil and environmental conservation.

Dams

In today's world, dams have an eminent role in communities and economies to connect these water resources for their economic development Fig. 12.9. Around 30–40% of irrigated land worldwide depends on dams.

Problems

1. Fragmentation and change of course rivers.
2. Degradation of riverine ecosystems in downstream.
3. Heavy social cost due to displacement of people and animals.
4. Stabilization and creation of marshy lands in the nearby areas.
5. Methane emission in large reservoirs.

Figure 12.9 Dams

In recent times, the conflict due to dams has increased. The reason for this increase is the increasing socio-economic impact that forces people to relocate and the alteration of local ecology. In India, the protests against the large projects have increased due to environmental concerns like landslides and seismic activities. The scientists have also started accepting that the small flow of the river dams are more suitable for Himalayas than large dams.

Water Harvesting

Water harvesting refers to the techniques which are used to catch the rain water in the catchment area or the run-off downstream by a storage method so that the water gradually percolates and recharges the ground water table rather than wasted.

Water harvesting can take place in a number of ways. Water harvesting techniques can be categorized as follows.

1. Microcatchments
2. Macrocatchments
3. Floodwater harvesting
4. Storage Ponds

Water Harvesting Techniques

1. **Floodwater harvesting system:** This is the oldest technique in the book. In this technique, water runs through dry riverbeds at the time of heavy rains and it helps in natural irrigation in the adjacent cultivating fields. The features of water harvesting techniques are as follows.

   (a) Diversion dam

   (b) Distribution network

   (c) Cropping fields

   The diversion dam is made for emergencies in case when the flood water is not under control, the diversion dam can be broken then to control the water flow. The distribution network is made up of open canals with soft slopes. To prevent the silting, slopes are not given in partition points.

   Cropping fields are flat areas constructed in rectangular shape which can hold 1 m of water.

2. **Recharge wells:** This technique is used to recharge the groundwater table (Fig. 12.10). Here, casting tubes are drilled into the underlying bedrock when the permeability is low to increase the rate of penetration of run-off water to ground water table.

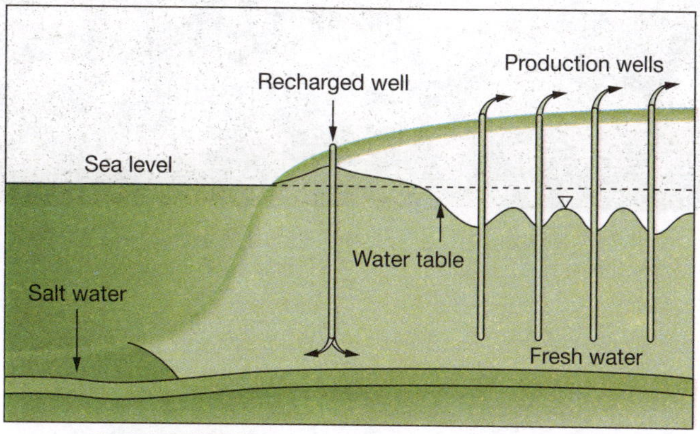

Figure 12.10 Functions of recharge wells

3. **Terraces:** This technique is used to control erosion (Fig. 12.11). It is mainly practiced in hilly areas where retention of water is an issue. Terrace is built on steep slopes and at the end of these terraces, small wall of stones are created to slow down the flow of water.

Figure 12.11 Terrace formation

Water Saving Techniques

1. **Sprinkler irrigation:** As the name suggests, the irrigation is done by sprinklers. Sprinklers are spread all across the land to spread the water at a larger space with minimum water (Fig. 12.12). With this method, the water is spread in a larger area instead of wastage of water in traditional gully and canal system. It also prevents washing of soil as there is no surface water movement.

Figure 12.12 Sprinkler irrigation

2. **Drip irrigation:** In this system, overhead water lines are fitted along the plantation of crops (Fig. 12.13). From the pipelines, water drips from very small holes directly on the plant. It helps in minimizing the wastage of water. This technique is suitable for arid/semi-arid regions in India.

Figure 12.13 Drip irrigation

3. **Zero tillage:** In this method, the soil is not tilled so as to prevent the soil moisture from evaporating (Fig. 12.14). The seed is sown directly in the soil without removing the stubble of the harvested crop.

Figure 12.14 Zero tillage

> **Activity 1**
> Plant a sapling in the lawn or a big pot and arrange a bottle over it. Make a tiny hole in bottle and fill water in it. The water drops should fall on the sapling at a very slow rate. Observe its growth comparing to the normally irrigated plants in the lawn.

These techniques provide the following water usage parameters.

(a) Drinking water

(b) Irrigation water

(c) Increase groundwater recharge.

(d) Reduce storm water expulsions, urban floods and overloading of sewage treatment plants.

(e) Reduce seawater access in coastal areas.

Coal and Petroleum Resources

Minerals are natural substances with specific physical and chemical properties that are found on or inside the earth's surface in various forms. These minerals can be found in a pure ready–to–use form or in the form of ores, i.e., the raw material from which the useful mineral can be extracted after some processing (Table 12.1). For example, bauxite is the ore from which aluminium is extracted. Bauxite is of no direct use but aluminium is a useful metal.

> **Info Bytes!**
> Jharia in Jharkhand is one of India's richest coal fields but has been burning continuously for over 100 years, causing environmental and health hazards.

Table 12.1 Different minerals and their ores

S. No.	Mineral	Ore/s
1.	Aluminium (Al)	Bauxite, Gibbsite, Boehmite
2.	Beryllium (Be)	Beryl
3.	Chromium (Cr)	Chromites
4.	Copper (Cu)	Malachite, Turquoise, Azurite,
5.	Lead (Pb)	Galena, Calcite
6.	Gold (Au)	Calaverite, Sylvanite
7.	Iron (Fe)	Magnetite, Hematite, Goethite, Limonite or Siderite
8.	Manganese (Mn)	Pyrolusite
9.	Silver (Ag)	Argentite, Tetrahedrite
10.	Mercury (Hg)	Cinnabar
11.	Nickel (Ni)	Pentlandite
12.	Tin (Sn)	Cassiterite
13.	Titanium (Ti)	Rutile, Ilmenite
14.	Uranium (U)	Carnotite
15.	Zinc (Zn)	Sphalerite

Uses

1. Eminent raw materials like iron, aluminium, zinc, manganese and copper are used for industrial purposes.
2. Imperative non-metal resources include **coal, salt, clay, cement and silica**.
3. Stones are used for building material. For example, granite, marble and limestone constitute another category of minerals.
4. Minerals with aesthetic and ornamental value are gems, such as **diamonds, emeralds and rubies**. Gold, silver and platinum is used by humans for ornaments.
5. Minerals in the form of oil, gas and coal are used as different kinds of fuels.

Mining

Mineral extracted from below the surface of the earth for various purposes is known as mining. Mining takes place in the following four stages.

1. **Prospecting:** Locating minerals.
2. **Exploration:** Determining the size, quantity, quality and feasibility of the deposits.
3. **Development:** Preparation of the mine for extraction.
4. **Exploitation:** Extracting the minerals from the mines.

Exploitation

1. Mining is the main cause of environmental degradation. The extraction of all the minerals from the lithosphere has a variety of side effects and few of them are listed in the subsequent points.
2. Industrial waste.

3. Conversion of agricultural land into industrial or mining region leads to the wastage of that land and accumulates pollution in its nearby area due to industrial waste.
4. Coal is a hazardous fuel which emits sulphur dioxide on burning which in turn forms sulphuric acid in air and causes acid rain in faraway places.
5. Soil depression takes place on excavation of coal from mines which are a threat to the residential areas above the coal mines.
6. Environmental problems takes place on combustion of coal as the flash generated by it gives out solid waste.
7. Coal is less convenient to handle than petroleum or natural gas due to its solid nature.

Conservation and Sustainable Management

1. To overcome this problem, less polluting forms of coal should be used by transforming it into gaseous, liquid or low sulphur, low-ash solid fuel.
2. Mining should be reduced and the dependence on the minerals should be restricted.
3. Renewable source of energy should be used instead.
4. Alternative fuels should be looked into which are more eco-friendly.

Renewable Energy Resources

As discussed, the petroleum resources that run the world today in terms of energy requirements are not everlasting or infinite. Besides, the indiscriminate use of these resources is putting a lot of pressure on the planet. To overcome the problem of finite and polluting natural resources of energy, there have been considerable research and advancement in the field of alternative fuels which are less polluting and have unlimited supply. These are called unconventional or renewable energy resources. Some of the most prominent renewable resources are hydroelectricity, wind, solar, geothermal, and tidal, etc.

1. **Hydroelectric energy:** Hydroelectric energy is the most popular renewable source of energy resource. Across the world, dams have been constructed to generate electricity. It is a simple non-polluting technique with basic science of converting kinetic energy into electric energy.

   Despite the obvious advantages of hydroelectricity, there are certain concerns that prevent it from being the ultimate solution for the energy quest of the world.

   (a) It requires a large land for the construction of reservoir.
   (b) The water stored in reservoir also leads to methane generation.
   (c) It leads to alteration of local ecology.
   (d) It leads to displacement of people.
   (e) Large dams may also increase seismicity.

2. **Solar energy:** Using the solar photovoltaic cells to produce electricity is also a very potent source of energy generation. The viability lies in the fact that the solar energy is clean and in abundance. However, it does not come without limitations. Firstly, it requires a huge space for SPV cells to produce electricity. The conversion rate is quite low. Secondly, the SPV cell uses silicon which is obtained through mining.
   Despite the limitations of the solar electricity, various other methods like solar cooker, solar geyser, etc., have been increasingly used now.
3. **Wind energy:** Wind turbines are also a viable option and it is increasing at a fast rate in India. The only limitation of wind energy is that it requires a large space to setup windmills to produce electricity at mass level. However, due to the negligible environment, it has a great scope. India currently stands third in terms of wind energy production.
4. **Biogas energy:** Biogas is mix of many gases including carbon dioxide and methane. It is obtained from animal and human waste and industrial and plant waste. The methane burns easily. Once it is burnt, the residue is used as a fertilizer.
5. **Tidal energy:** With constant rising and falling of the tide, sufficient potential for hydroelectric energy is present. In many countries including India, tidal energy is already produced.

6. **Geothermal energy:** The geothermal energy is produced from the hot steam originating from hot water springs and geysers. It is extensively used in countries, like Iceland, New Zealand and Japan, etc., and also in India geothermal energy is being produced in Himalayan states that have hot water springs.

Saving Environment-Reduce, Recycle, Reuse and Reforest

With the depletion of the natural resources at a faster rate than expected, it is very eminent that public awareness needs to rise to the situation for conserving and managing these resources. At this rate, the renewable resources are not able to regenerate and are depleting and on the other hand, the non-renewable sources are in the endangered zone. So it is very essential for all to conserve our resources before the fight for survival begins. There are few words to live by in this situation and they are as follows (Fig. 12.14).

1. Reduce
2. Recycle
3. Reuse
4. Reforest

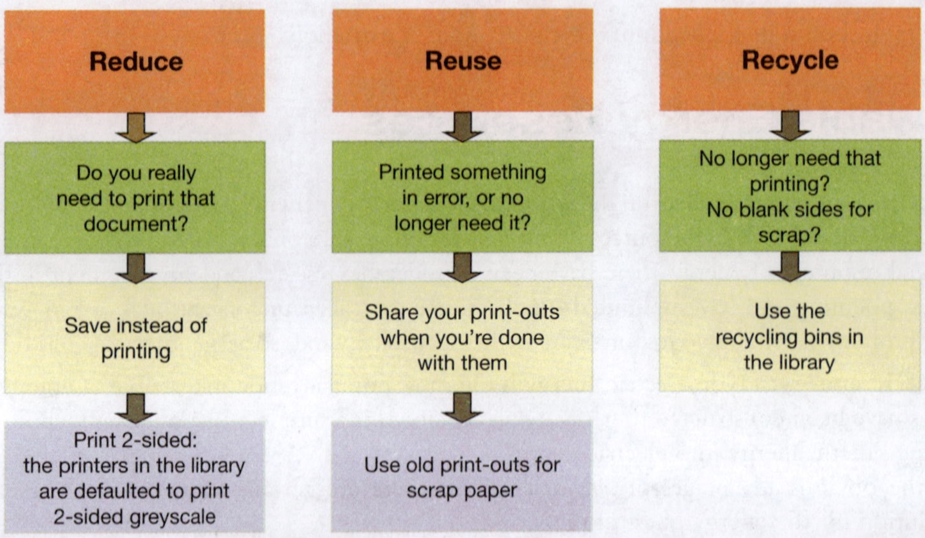

Figure 12.15 Reduce, reuse and re-cycle

1. **Reduce:** The required amount of resources should be used and not wasted. Resources saved in the present are resources earned for the future.
   For example: Save water by switching off leaky taps and use limited water for bathing. Save energy by switching off electrical appliances when a room is not in use, more use of public transport. Save food by sharing extra food to the less unfortunate.
2. **Recycle:** Cycle should be put into practice in daily lives. Any material that can be recycled in any form should not be thrown away. **Example:** Plastic and glass. This leads to the reduced volume of discarded material and also aids the conservation of natural resources.
3. **Reuse:** Things that can be reused should not be discarded. It brings down waste pollution. Things can be used at a domestic level. **Example:** Paper, plastic bags and glass containers.
4. **Reforest:** Deforestation is one of the major problems of environment in present times. Living beings are dependent on the natural resource for abundant things. So it is essential for mankind to take care of this resource and regenerate it. Trees should be planted during rainy season. Strict punishment should be awarded on cutting of trees. On cutting of one tree, plenty more should be planted instead. This helps the habitat as well as to control soil erosion.

Konnect

Refuse: This means to say No to things people offer you that you don't need. Refuse to buy products that can harm you and the environment, say No to single-use plastic carry bags.

Repurpose: This means when a product can no more be used for the original purpose, think carefully and use it for some other useful purpose. For example, cracked crockery, or cups with broken handles can be used to grow small plants and as feeding vessels for birds.

Quick Recap

✔ **Why do you think there should be equitable distribution of resources? What forces would be working against an equitable distribution of our resources?**

Equitable distribution of resources is a fair system and will help the resources reach every individual in convenient and easier way.

✔ **Distinguish between renewable and non-renewable resources. What are the long-term consequences of excessive use of non-renewable resources?**

Renewable resources regenerate and can be replenished naturally, whereas non-renewable resources are finite. Overuse of non-renewable resources may result in their depletion, posing environmental and economic challenges because these resources cannot be easily replaced.

✔ **Explain the three basic environmental functions that must be preserved for environmental sustainability. Why are they so important to the environment?**

The three primary functions are to support life, maintain ecological balance, and accommodate human activities. The preservation of these functions ensures a sustainable environment, allowing ecosystems to thrive and meet human needs.

✔ **Discuss why wildlife conservation is important?**

Wildlife conservation is important due to the following factors.

- It maintains ecological balance in nature.
- It also maintains the forests by facilitating the growth of plants in different places by dispersing seeds.
- By grazing grass, it also maintains the soil fertility.
- It also helps in cleaning of forest.

✔ **Find out about the traditional systems of water harvesting/management in your region.**

The traditional systems of water harvesting management are as follows.

- Bandharas and talc in Maharashtra.
- Bundhis in Madhya Pradesh and Uttar Pradesh.
- Kulhs in Himachal Pradesh.
- Khadins, tanks and nadir in Rajasthan.
- Ahars and pynes in Bihar.

✔ **Explain what water harvesting is and why it is important in modern ecology. What role does it play in replenishing the groundwater table?**

Water harvesting is the process of collecting rainwater or runoff for storage and later use. Groundwater tables are replenished by capturing and allowing water to percolate, reducing water scarcity and ensuring long-term water supplies.

✔ **Identify and explain the three main characteristics of the water harvesting techniques listed. How do they ensure that harvested water is used efficiently?**

The three main features are the diversion dam, the distribution network, and the cropping fields. Water is diverted by the dam, distributed by the network, and used by the fields. This methodical approach ensures that water is used efficiently.

✔ **What is mining?**

A mineral extracted from below the surface of the earth for various purposes is known as mining.

✔ **Define deforestation.**

Deforestation is one of the major problems of environment in present times. Living beings are dependent on the natural resources for abundant things. So, it is essential for mankind to take care of this resource and regenerate it.

✔ **What do you understand by biogas energy?**

Biogas is a mix of many gases including carbon dioxide and methane. It is obtained from animal and human waste and industrial and plant waste.

✔ **List and explain the four steps for environmental conservation that have been mentioned. What role do they play in combating the global ecological crisis?**

The four steps are as follows: Reduce, Recycle, Reuse, and Reforest. These actions combat environmental crises by reducing waste, promoting sustainable consumption, and restoring natural habitats, resulting in a more balanced environment.

POINTS TO REMEMBER

- ✔ As per the source of origin, the resources can be classified as Biotic and Abiotic.
- ✔ Natural resources can be classified on the basis of their renewability into renewable and non-renewable resources.
- ✔ Intergenerational equity means people of same generation belonging to different genres have the same rights.
- ✔ Environmental sustainability is the ability to conserve over time the three basic functions of the environment.
- ✔ Biodiversity conservation is the preservation of life in all its forms on Earth and keeping the natural ecosystems functioning healthy.
- ✔ Water harvesting refers to the techniques which are used to catch the rain water in the catchment area or the run-off downstream by a storage method so that the water gradually percolates and recharges the ground water table rather than wasted.
- ✔ The features of water harvesting techniques are as follows. (a) Diversion dam (b) Distribution network (c) Cropping fields
- ✔ Sprinkler irrigation, drip irrigation, zero tillage are water saving techniques.
- ✔ Reduce, recycle, reuse, and reforest are a few essential steps to save the environment.

DW

PRACTICE QUESTIONS CLASSROOM WING

Very Short Answer Type Questions

Directions for questions from 1 to 24.

For each of the following questions, four choices have been provided. Select the correct alternatives.

1. Which of the following best defines the term 'Biotic'?
(a) Derived from non-living matter
(b) Pertaining to renewable resources
(c) Originating from living organisms
(d) Associated with water saving techniques

2. What is the major distinction between renewable and non-renewable resources?
(a) One is biotic, the other is abiotic.
(b) One regenerates quickly, while the other takes a very long time.
(c) One leads to intergenerational equity, the other does not.
(d) One is associated with water harvesting, the other is not.

3. Environmental sustainability primarily focuses on conserving which of the following?
(a) Only Biodiversity
(b) Only Water harvesting techniques
(c) The three fundamental functions of the environment
(d) Intergenerational equity

4. Which of the following techniques primarily focuses on using water efficiently in agriculture?
(a) Water harvesting (b) Reforest
(c) Sprinkler irrigation (d) Diversion dam

5. To achieve a sustainable environment, which of the following steps should NOT be prioritized?
(a) Reduce (b) Recycle
(c) Reforest (d) Reject

6. The pH range most conducive for life of fresh water plants and animals is
(a) 6.5–7.5 (b) 2.0–3.5
(c) 3.5–5.0 (d) 9.0–10.5

7. The three R's that will help us to conserve natural resources for long term use are
(a) recycle, regenerate and reuse.
(b) reduce, regenerate and reuse.
(c) reduce, reuse and redistribute.
(d) reduce, recycle and reuse.

8. Given below are a few statements related to biodiversity. Pick those that correctly describe the concept of biodiversity.
(i) Biodiversity refers to the different species of flora and fauna present in an area.
(ii) Biodiversity refers to only the flora of a given area.
(iii) Biodiversity is greater in a forest.
(iv) Biodiversity refers to the total number of individuals of a particular species living in an area.
(a) (i) and (ii) (b) (ii) and (iv)
(c) (i) and (iii) (d) (ii) and (iii)

9. Among the statements given below, select the ones that correctly describes the concept of sustainable development.
(i) Planned growth with minimum damage to the environment.
(ii) Growth irrespective of the extent of damage caused to the environment.
(iii) Stopping all developmental work to conserve the environment.
(iv) Growth that is acceptable to all the stakeholders.
(a) (i) and (iv) (b) (ii) and (iii)
(c) (ii) and (iv) (d) (iii) only

10. In our country, vast tracts of forests are cleared and a single species of plant is cultivated. This practice promotes
(a) biodiversity in the area.
(b) monoculture in the area.
(c) growth of natural forest.
(d) preserves the natural ecosystem in the area.

11. A successful forest conservation strategy should involve
(a) protection of animals at the highest trophic level.
(b) protection of only consumers.
(c) protection of only herbivores.

(d) comprehensive programme to protect all the physical and biological components.

12. The important message conveyed by the 'Chipko movement' is

(a) to involve the community in forest conservation efforts.
(b) to ignore the community in forest conservation efforts.
(c) to cut down forest trees for developmental activities.
(d) government agencies have the unquestionable right to order destruction of trees in forests.

13. In our country, there are attempts to increase the height of several existing dams like Tehri and Almati, dams across Narmada. Choose the correct statements among the following that are a consequence of raising the height of dams.

(i) Terrestrial flora and fauna of the area is destroyed completely.
(ii) Dislocation of people and domestic animals living in the area.
(iii) Valuable agricultural land may be permanently lost.
(iv) It will generate permanent employment for people.

(a) (i) and (ii) (b) (i), (ii) and (iii)
(c) (ii) and (iv) (d) (i), (iii) and (iv)

14. Expand the abbreviation GAP.

(a) Governmental Agency for Pollution Control
(b) Gross Assimilation by Photosynthesis
(c) Ganga Action Plan
(d) Governmental Agency for Animal Protection

15. Select the incorrect statement from the following.

(a) Economic development is linked to environmental conservation.
(b) Sustainable development encourages development for current generation and conservation of resources for future generations.
(c) Sustainable development does not consider the view points of stakeholders.
(d) Sustainable development is a long planned and persistent development.

16. Which of the following is not a natural resource?

(a) Mango tree (b) Snake
(c) Wind (d) Wooden house

17. Select the wrong statement from the following.

(a) Forests provide variety of products.
(b) Forests have greater plant diversity.
(c) Forests do not conserve soil.
(d) Forests conserve water.

18. Arabari forests of Bengal is dominated by

(a) Teak (b) Sal
(c) Bamboo (d) Mangrove

19. Ground water will not be depleted due to

(a) afforestation
(b) thermal power plants.
(c) loss of forest and decreased rainfall.
(d) cropping of high water demanding crops.

20. Opposition to the construction of large dams is due to

(a) social reasons
(b) economic reasons
(c) environmental reasons
(d) all the above

21. Khadins, Bundhis, Ahars and Kattas are ancient structures that are examples for

(a) grain storage (b) wood storage
(c) water harvesting (d) soil conservation

22. Pick the right combination of terms which has no fossil fuel.

(a) Wind, ocean and coal.
(b) Kerosene, wind and tide.
(c) Wind, wood and sun.
(d) Petroleum, wood and sun.

23. Select the eco-friendly activity among the following.

(a) Using car for transportation.
(b) Using poly bags for shopping.
(c) Using dyes for colouring clothes.
(d) Using windmills to generate power for irrigation.

24. It is important to make small check dams across the flooded gullies because they

(i) hold water for irrigation.
(ii) hold water and prevent soil erosion.
(iii) recharge ground water.
(iv) hold water permanently.

(a) (i) and (iv) (b) (ii) and (iii)
(c) (iii) and (iv) (d) (ii) and (iv)

Direction for Questions from 25 to 34:
Fill in the blanks in each question.

25. ______ is a greenhouse gas.

26. Floods can be prevented by ______.

27. Narmada Bachao Andolan was to ______.

28. Synthetic material/ chemical which depleted ozone layer is ______.

29. Water harvesting is a method which ______.

30. The full form of UV rays is ______.

31. The other name given for replenishment of forest is______.

32. ______ is produced from the hot steam originating from hot water springs and geysers.

33. ______ is a simple non-polluting technique with basic science of converting kinetic energy into electric energy.

34. ______ are spread across the land to spread water at a larger space with minimum water.

Short Answer Type Questions

35. What changes can you make in your habits to become more eco-friendly?

36. How would these advantages differ from the advantages of using a long-term perspective in managing our resources?

37. Why do you think there should be equitable distribution of resources? What forces would be working against an equitable distribution of our resources?

38. What can you do as an individual to reduce your consumption of the various natural resources?

39. Every one of us can do something to reduce our consumption of various natural resources. List four such activities based on the 3-R approach.

40. The construction of large dams leads to social and environmental problems. List two problems of each category.

Essay Type Questions

41. Discuss how drip irrigation is suitable for minimizing the wastage of water.

42. Discuss the different uses of minerals.

43. Describe how mining is the major cause of environmental degradation.

44. Describe how solar energy is considered a major renewable energy resource.

45. Discuss the benefits of reduce, reuse and recycle.

46. Discuss various sustainable management in conserving water resources.

PRACTICE QUESTIONS COMPETITION WING

Level 1: Apply your Concepts

Direction for Questions from 1 to 80:

For each of the following questions four choices have been provided. Select the correct alternatives.

1. If an ecosystem's functionality deteriorates, but no species are lost, what aspect of environmental health is still at risk?

(a) Biotic classification
(b) Intergenerational equity
(c) Biodiversity conservation
(d) Renewable resources status

2. The 'Limits to growth' concept was introduced in:

(a) 1859 (b) 1948
(c) 1947 (d) 1970

3. Which of the following scenarios best depicts the violation of the concept of intergenerational equity?

(a) A country importing resources from another country.
(b) Overuse of non-renewable resources by the present generation.
(c) Different species competing for the same resource in an ecosystem.
(d) Seasonal variation in the availability of a renewable resource.

4. What underlines the difference between sprinkler irrigation and traditional flood irrigation in the context of environmental sustainability?

(a) Source of water
(b) Volume of water used
(c) Type of crops grown
(d) Depth of water table

5. In the context of preserving the environment, which action reflects the principle of 'Reduce'?

(a) Planting more trees in urban areas.
(b) Using a refillable water bottle instead of disposable ones.
(c) Transforming waste paper into new paper products.
(d) Selling second-hand items.

6. Which of the following is NOT a feature specific to water harvesting techniques?

(a) Diversion dam
(b) Distribution network
(c) Aquatic biodiversity preservation
(d) Cropping fields

7. The resources that are surveyed, their quantity and quality has been determined, and are in current use are known as

(a) potential resources (b) actual resources
(c) reserve resources (d) renewable resources

8. The resources which are a part of an actual resource that can be developed profitably in the future is called

(a) potential resources (b) actual resources
(c) reserve resources (d) renewable resources

9. The resources that cannot be utilized due to lack of technology is called

(a) stock resources
(b) potential resources
(c) actual resources
(d) non-renewable resources

10. These types of resources cannot be regenerated and hence, with time they will be exhausted with the increasing consumption.

(a) Stock resources
(b) Non-renewable resources
(c) Potential resources
(d) Actual resources

11. Resources do not regenerate at this high pace leading to their depletion and resources on the other hand are in the endangered zone.

(a) Stock, Actual
(b) Natural, Artificial
(c) Renewable, Non-Renewable
(d) Actual, Reserve

12. Over use of chemical fertilizers and pesticides are creating

(a) Contamination
(b) Soil contamination
(c) Pollution
(d) Deficiency

13. Automobiles are adding onto air pollution and industrial emissions that are causing the greenhouse gases to rise and cause

(a) globalization (b) contamination
(c) pollution (d) global warming

14. A process whereby the present generation uses these resources on earth for development in such a way that the needs of today are met without compromising the requirements of the future generations is known as

(a) global warming
(b) sustainable development
(c) liberalization
(d) globalization

15. People of same generation belonging to different genres have same rights means, it is called

(a) generational development
(b) sustainable development
(c) intergenerational equity
(d) global warming

16. It is the ability of an economic system to create a constant and improving growth of its economic indicators.

(a) Economic sustainability
(b) Social sustainability
(c) Environmental sustainability
(d) Sustainable development

17. It is the capability to guarantee welfare, equitably distributed among social classes and gender.

(a) Economic sustainability
(b) Social sustainability
(c) Environmental sustainability
(d) Sustainable development

18. Fossil fuels are an example of which of the following type of resources?

(a) Renewable (b) Biotic
(c) Abiotic (d) Biomass

19. The natural resources classified on the basis of their stage of development includes all except

(a) potential (b) reserved
(c) recognized (d) actual

20. The three dimensions of sustainable development do not include

(a) economic (b) anthropological
(c) social (d) economic

21. Preventing physical wash away of soil with water streams is called

(a) watershed protection
(b) atmospheric regulation
(c) erosion control
(d) soil conservator

22. It is one of the natural resource in which people's livelihood depends upon.

(a) Forest (b) Erosion
(c) Soil (d) Atmosphere

23. It is a concept where the forests are grown in non-natural forest regions so as to ensure the continuous supply of minor forest produces, like firewood, fodder and timber, etc., without jeopardizing the natural forests.

(a) Social forestry
(b) Deforestation
(c) Sustainable management
(d) Erosion control

24. What amount of fresh water on earth is readily available to use?

(a) 1% (b) 2%
(c) 3% (d) 70%

25. Which of the following is not true about the limitations of a dam?

(a) Fragmentation and change of course rivers.
(b) Degradation of riverine ecosystems in downstream.
(c) Heavy social cost due to displacement of people and animals.
(d) Methanol emission in large reservoirs.

26. The techniques which are used to catch rain water in the catchment area or the run-off downstream by a storage method so that the water gradually percolates and recharges the ground water table rather than wasted.

(a) Microcatchments
(b) Macrocatchments
(c) Pits
(d) Water harvesting

27. Which of the following is not a renewable resource?

(a) Wind (b) Geothermal
(c) Tidal (d) Nuclear

28. Which of the following is not a farm water saving technique?

(a) Zero tillage (b) Drip irrigation
(c) Recharge wells (d) Sprinklers

29. Find the odd one out from the following.
(a) Reuse (b) Reproduce
(c) Reduce (d) Recycle

30. Which of the following is not a step of mining?
(a) Prospecting (b) Projecting
(c) Developing (d) Exploiting

31. Which of the following are the different ways to classify natural resources?
(i) The source of origin.
(ii) The state of development.
(iii) Adaptability of resources.
(iv) The renewability of the resources.
Select the correct option.
(a) Only (i) and (ii)
(b) Only (i), (ii) and (iii)
(c) Only (i), (ii), (iii) and (iv)
(d) Only (i), (ii) and (iv)

32. As per the source of origin, the resources can be classified as follows.
(i) Biotic
(ii) Abiotic
(iii) Probiotic
(iv) Antibiotic
Select the correct option.
(a) Only (i) and (ii)
(b) Only (i), (ii) and (iii)
(c) Only (i), (ii), (iii) and (iv)
(d) Only (i), (ii) and (iv)

33. Which of the following are biotic resources?
(i) Forests
(ii) Land
(iii) Animals
(iv) fossil fuels
Select the correct option.
(a) Only (i) and (ii)
(b) Only (i), (ii) and (iii)
(c) Only (i), (ii), (iii) and (iv)
(d) Only (i), (iii) and (iv)

34. Which are abiotic resources?
(i) Land
(ii) Fresh water
(iii) Heavy metals
(iv) Fossil fuels
Select the correct option.
(a) Only (i) and (ii)
(b) Only (i), (ii) and (iii)
(c) Only (i), (ii), (iii) and (iv)
(d) Only (i), (iii) and (iv)

35. What are the types of natural resources on the basis of their stage of development?
(i) Potential resources
(ii) Actual resources
(iii) Reserve resources
(iv) Stock resources
Select the correct option.
(a) Only (i) and (ii)
(b) Only (i), (ii) and (iii)
(c) Only (i), (ii), (iii) and (iv)
(d) Only (i), (iii) and (iv)

36. The major natural resources are
(i) forest resources
(ii) water resources
(iii) mineral resources
(iv) food resources
Select the correct option.
(a) Only (i) and (ii)
(b) Only (i), (ii) and (iii)
(c) Only (i), (ii), (iii) and (iv)
(d) Only (i), (iii) and (iv)

37. What are the three aspects of sustainable development?
(i) Environmental
(ii) Economic
(iii) Social dimension
(iv) Sustainability
Select the correct option.
(a) Only (i) and (ii)
(b) Only (i), (ii) and (iii)
(c) Only (i), (ii), (iii) and (iv)
(d) Only (i), (iii) and (iv)

38. Which are the three basic functions of environment?
(i) The resource supply function.
(ii) Pollution
(iii) The waste receiver function.
(iv) Direct usefulness
Select the correct option.
(a) Only (i) and (ii)
(b) Only (i), (ii) and (iii)
(c) Only (i), (ii), (iii) and (iv)
(d) Only (i), (iii) and (iv)

39. Which of these are the functions of watershed protection
(i) Decreases the rate of surface run-off of water.
(ii) Avoids flash floods and soil erosion.
(iii) During rainy season, it cuts down the speed of run-off by thus increasing percolation (which

results in increase in water table) and reducing erosion.

(iv) None of these

Select the correct option.

(a) Only (i) and (ii)
(b) Only (i), (ii) and (iii)
(c) Only (i), (ii), (iii) and (iv)
(d) Only (i), (iii) and (iv)

40. Which of them are the measures for improvement in conservation?

(i) Reserve forests conservation
(ii) Hill forests
(iii) Forests of plains
(iv) Social/Commercial forestry

Select the correct option.

(a) Only (i) and (ii)
(b) Only (i), (ii) and (iii)
(c) Only (i), (ii), (iii) and (iv)
(d) Only (i), (iii) and (iv)

41. Water harvesting techniques can be categorized as

(i) microcatchments
(ii) catchments
(iii) floodwater harvesting
(iv) storage ponds

Select the correct option.

(a) Only (i) and (ii)
(b) Only (i), (ii) and (iii)
(c) Only (i), (ii), (iii) and (iv)
(d) Only (i), (iii) and (iv)

42. Microcatchment techniques consist of

(i) delineation of natural depression.
(ii) construction of contour and stone bunds.
(iii) terracing
(iv) eyebrow

Select the correct option.

(a) Only (i) and (ii)
(b) Only (i), (ii) and (iii)
(c) Only (i), (ii), (iii) and (iv)
(d) Only (i), (iii) and (iv)

43. Macrocatchment on the other hand consists of techniques like

(i) circular catchment
(ii) large semicircular
(iii) trapezoidal bunds
(iv) hillside conduits

Select the correct option.

(a) Only (ii), (iii) and (iv)
(b) Only (i), (ii) and (iii)
(c) Only (i), (ii), (iii) and (iv)
(d) Only (i), (iii) and (iv)

44. Which of these are water harvesting techniques?

(i) Floodwater harvesting system
(ii) Recharge wells
(iii) Terraces
(iv) Tanker

Select the correct option.

(a) Only (ii), (iii) and (iv)
(b) Only (i), (ii) and (iii)
(c) Only (i), (ii), (iii) and (iv)
(d) Only (i), (iii) and (iv)

45. Which of these are water saving techniques?

(i) Sprinkler irrigation
(ii) Drip irrigation
(iii) Flood water
(iv) Zero tillage

Select the correct option.

(a) Only (ii), (iii) and (iv)
(b) Only (i), (ii) and (iii)
(c) Only (i), (ii), (iii) and (iv)
(d) Only (i), (ii) and (iv)

46. Conservation is

(a) proper use of natural resources.
(b) protection of natural resources.
(c) management of natural resources.
(d) all of these

47. The most appropriate definition of a natural resource is that it is a substance/commodity that is

(a) present only on land.
(b) a gift of nature which is very useful to mankind.
(c) a man-made substance placed in nature.
(d) available only in the forest.

48. Wild life conservation means the production and preservation of

(a) ferocious wild animals only.
(b) wild plant only.
(c) non-cultivated plants and non-domesticated animals.
(d) all the above living in natural habitat.

49. Which of the following bacteria is found in Ganga water?

(a) Coliform bacteria
(b) Streptococcus bacteria
(c) Staphylococcus bacteria
(d) Diplococcus bacteria

50. Which of the following is not done in a wild life sanctuary?

(a) Fauna is conserved.
(b) Flora is conserved.
(c) Soil and flora is utilized.
(d) Hunting is prohibited.

51. Ganga Action Plan was started in

(a) 1973 (b) 1985
(c) 1971 (d) 1983

52. If the Bengal tiger becomes extinct,

(a) hyenas and wolves will become scare.
(b) its gene will be lost forever.
(c) the population of beautiful animals like deer will be stabilized.
(d) the wild area will be safe for man and domestic animals.

53. BOD test or biological oxygen demand test is made for measuring

(a) air pollution (b) water pollution
(c) noise pollution (d) soil pollution

54. The role of forests is

(a) productive (b) protective
(c) regulative (d) all of these

55. Red Data Book is produced by

(a) IBWL (b) ZSI
(c) WWF (d) IUCN

56. Which of the following animals has become extinct in India?

(a) Tiger (b) Rhinoceros
(c) Cheetah (d) Lion

57. Water in a reservoir is

(a) inexhaustible resource
(b) non-renewable resource
(c) renewable resource
(d) both (a) and (b)

58. Water is a

(a) exhaustible resource
(b) inexhaustible resource
(c) national resource
(d) organic resource

59. Chipko movement originated in

(a) Panchmari in Madhya Pradesh.
(b) Silent Valley of Kerala.
(c) Kaziranga in Assam.
(d) Tehri Garhwal in Uttarakhand.

60. Wildlife Protection Act was enacted by the Government of India in

(a) 1952 (b) 1972
(c) 1958 (d) 1973

61. Silent valley is situated in

(a) Kerala (b) Rajasthan
(c) Mumbai (d) Madhya Pradesh

62. Which one of the following is not a biotic natural resource?

(a) Water (b) Milk
(c) Fruits (d) Fish

63. Which one of the following natural resources is inexhaustible?

(a) Air (b) Coal
(c) Ground water (d) Human beings

64. In developing countries, the heaviest demand on forests is for

(a) paper pulp (b) fruits
(c) furniture wood (d) fuel wood

65. Sunderban National Park is situated in

(a) Jharkhand (b) Uttarkhand
(c) West Bengal (d) Orissa

66. Major oil deposits are found in

(a) Persian Gulf (b) USA
(c) India (d) Afghanistan

67. Which layer lies closest to the earth's surface?

(a) Stratosphere (b) Mesosphere
(c) Troposphere (d) Thermosphere

68. Which one of the following is a depleting source of energy?

(a) Fossil fuel (b) Sunlight
(c) Wind energy (d) Water

69. Crocodile sanctuary is located in

(a) Kerala (b) Orissa
(c) Tamil Nadu (d) Andaman and Nicobar

70. Botanical gardens and zoos are meant for conservation of rare and endangered forms of

(a) *Ex situ* (b) *In situ*
(c) bead specimens (d) none of these

71. Sulabh International Organization is famous for generating

(a) solar energy (b) biogas energy
(c) nuclear energy (d) none of these

72. The five main objectives of the Chipko movement were

(a) food, fodder, shelter, fuel and paper.
(b) food, fodder, fibres, fuels and fertilizer.
(c) food, fuel, fibres, fodder and fire.
(d) food, fuel, gums, resins and bamboos.

73. Photovoltaic conversion is useful to trap

(a) solar energy (b) wind energy
(c) nuclear energy (d) none of these

74. Largest amount of fresh water on earth is in the form of

(a) ponds and lakes.
(b) rivers and streams.
(c) ice caps and glaciers.
(d) underground water.

75. Forest cover of India is less than

(a) 15% (b) 20%
(c) 25% (d) 30%

76. Match the entries of Column I with those of Column II and choose the correct alternative.

Column I Mineral	Column II Ore/s
A. Aluminium (Al)	(i) Beryl
B. Beryllium (Be)	(ii) Malachite, Turquoise, Azurite
C. Chromium (Cr)	(iii) Galena, Calcite
D. Copper (Cu)	(iv) Chromites
E. Lead (Pb)	(v) Bauxite, Gibbsite, Boehmite

(a) A-iv, B-i, C-v, D-iv, E-iii
(b) A-iv, B-i, C-iv, D-ii, E-iii
(c) A-v, B-iii, C-iv, D-iv, E-i
(d) A-v, B-i, C-iv, D-ii, E-iii

77. Match the entries of Column I with those of Column II and choose the correct alternative.

Column I	Column II
A. Prospecting	(i) Determining the size, quantity, quality and feasibility of the deposits.
B. Exploration	(ii) Extracting the minerals from mines.
C. Development	(iii) Locating minerals.
D. Exploitation	(iv) Preparation of mine for extraction.

(a) A-iii, B-i, C-iv, D-ii
(b) A-v, B-i, C-iv, D-ii
(c) A-v, B-iii, C-iv, D-iv
(d) A-iv, B-iii, C-v, D-iv

78. Match the entries of Column I with those of Column II and choose the correct alternative.

Column I	Column II
A. Water, air, soil, forests, minerals and crops.	(i) Biotic
B. Forests and animals, fossil fuels.	(ii) Stock resources
C. Fresh water, air, and heavy metals (gold, iron, copper, silver, etc.).	(iii) Abiotic
D. Hydrogen	(iv) Natural resources

(a) A-iv, B-i, C-v, D-iv
(b) A-iv, B-i, C-iii, D-ii
(c) A-v, B-iii, C-iv, D-iv
(d) A-iv, B-iii, C-v, D-iv

79. Match the entries of Column I with those of Column II and choose the correct alternative.

Column I	Column II
A. Forests, wind energy, solar energy, biomass energy, hydropower, etc.	(i) Non-renewable resources
B. Fossil fuels such as coal, petroleum, minerals, etc.	(ii) Water harvesting techniques
C. Microcatchments	(iii) Microcatchment techniques
D. Delineation of natural depression.	(iv) Renewable resources

(a) A-iv, B-i, C-ii, D-iii
(b) A-v, B-i, C-iv, D-ii
(c) A-v, B-iii, C-iv, D-iv
(d) A-iv, B-iii, C-v, D-iv

80. Match the entries of Column I with those of Column II and choose the correct alternative.

Column I	Column II
A. Construction of contour and stone bunds.	(i) Water harvesting techniques
B. Mix of many gases including carbon dioxide and methane.	(ii) Macrocatchment techniques
C. Large semicircular and trapezoidal bunds.	(iii) Biogas energy
D. Macrocatchments	(iv) Microcatchment techniques

(a) A-iv, B-i, C-v, D-iv
(b) A-v, B-i, C-iv, D-ii
(c) A-v, B-iii, C-iv, D-iv
(d) A-iv, B-iii, C-ii, D-i

Level 2: Review your Concepts

81. Discuss about the renewable and non- renewable resources with examples.

82. How can maintaining biodiversity impact the resilience of an ecosystem in the face of environmental changes or threats?

83. Water harvesting is crucial in today's changing climate. How might it play a role in addressing global water scarcity concerns?

Level 3: Assess Your Concepts

84. What is the main constituent of biogas? How is biogas obtained from biomass? Write any two advantages of using this gas.

85. Mention any four limitations in harnessing wind energy on a large scale.

86. Biodiversity conservation is a multifaceted objective, aiming not just at preserving individual species, but also at ensuring that ecosystems continue to function healthily. The integration of concepts like water harvesting and the 4 R's can significantly enhance biodiversity preservation efforts.

AT

PRACTICE QUESTIONS NEET SPECIAL WING

Multiple-Answer Type Questions

Questions number 1 to 5 are multiple-choice questions. Each question has FOUR options (a), (b), (c), and (d). ONE OR MORE THAN ONE of these four option(s) is/are the correct answer(s).

1. What are the main aims and objectives of National Ganga River Basin Authority?
   (a) To ensure effective abatement of pollution and rejuvenation of the river Ganga
   (b) Ensuring water quality and environmentally sustainable development
   (c) To build water-based projects on the river Ganga
   (d) Launching of fishing beds on the river

2. Identify the uses of the forest as a resource.
   (a) Water as a resource is dependent on the existence of forests for its replenishment
   (b) Many organic medicines are derived from forests
   (c) CO amounts are dependent on the forests
   (d) Furniture and chair derived from woods are obtained from forests

3. Which among the following are the major steps for sustainable development?
   (a) Resource sustainability
   (b) Economic sustainability
   (c) Function sustainability
   (d) Social sustainability

4. Identify the types of natural resources on the basis of their stages of development.
   (a) Renewable resources
   (b) Actual resource
   (c) Reserve resources
   (d) Stock resources

5. Identify the water harvesting techniques from the following:
   (a) Flood water harvesting system
   (b) Zero tillage
   (c) Recharge wells
   (d) Terraces

Comprehension-Based Questions

A. Read the paragraph given below and answer the questions number 6 to 11:

Gopal as part of his 10th class science project makes an environmentally friendly project wherein, he uses a renewable source of energy to power his project. The resource he uses is the strongest form of energy which is available to us on a daily basis and if collected properly and used can be used as a sustainable form of energy. He has prepared a device which helps to cook food with the help of the renewable energy. The judges appreciated his efforts on the project and were also impresses with his understanding of the subject. He was asked about the principle and the working of the device; he was also asked questions on renewable and non-renewable sources of energy.

6. Identify the renewable source of energy which was used by Gopal.
   (a) Wind energy (b) Solar energy
   (c) Tidal energy (d) Biogas energy

7. Identify the device made by Gopal for the project.
   (a) Solar heater
   (b) Solar batteries
   (c) Solar cooker
   (d) LED home lighting

8. Which of the following is a non-renewable source of energy?
   (a) Tidal energy
   (b) Wind energy
   (c) Fossil fuels
   (d) Solar energy

9. Which of the following energy can be produced from the hot water springs?
   (a) Geothermal energy
   (b) Tidal energy
   (c) Biogas energy
   (d) Wind energy

10. Which mirror is used to make the device?
(a) Plane
(b) Concave
(c) Convex
(d) Spherical

11. Match the column:

Column – A	Column – B
(i) Hydroelectric energy	(a) Photovoltaic cells
(ii) Solar energy	(b) Wind turbines
(iii) Wind energy	(c) Dams
(iv) Biogas energy	(d) Rise and fall of tides
(v) Tidal energy	(e) Plant and animal waste

B. Read the paragraph given below and answer the questions number 12 to 17:

Sustainable development involves having the right balance between development of goals and preservation of forests. It involves conservation of water resources and Dams which not only help with economic development but also irrigation of the fields. Water harvesting techniques help to conserve water. Drip irrigation, sprinkle irrigation and zero tillage are some of the techniques used to save water. Coal and petroleum resources are limited and have to be used judiciously. Minerals are natural substances with specific physical and chemical properties that are found on or inside the earth's surface in various forms. These minerals can be found in a pure ready–to–use form or in the form of ores, i.e., the raw material from which the useful mineral can be extracted after some processing. Simple efforts on the daily basis can also help to save our environment like reusing, recycling and reducing the wasteful use of resources.

12. Which of the following is not the 'R' which helps to save our environment?
(a) Reduce
(b) Recycle
(c) Reenter
(d) Reuse

13. The technique which is used to recharge the ground water table is:
(a) Diversion dam
(b) Cropping fields
(c) Recharge wells
(d) Terraces

14. Which among the following is NOT a problem caused due to construction of dams?
(a) Change of course of rivers
(b) Methane emission in large reservoirs
(c) Degradation of downstream aquatic ecosystems
(d) Emission of large amounts of carbon dioxide

15. Which of the following step of mining involves locating minerals?
(a) Development
(b) Exploitation
(c) Exploration
(d) Prospecting

16. Which basic principle of saving environment involves planting more trees?
(a) Reforest
(b) Deforest
(c) Reuse
(d) Recycle

17. Match the column:

Column – A (Mineral)	Column – B (Ores)
(i) Iron	(a) Argentite
(ii) Silver	(b) Cinnabar
(iii) Lead	(c) Bauxite
(iv) Mercury	(d) Magnetite
(v) Aluminium	(e) Galena

ANSWER KEYS

Crossword

Across

3. Recycle
6. Diversion
8. Sprinkler
11. Sustainability
12. Renewable
14. Reduce
15. Harvesting
16. Abiotic
17. Zero tillage

Down

1. Reuse
2. Drip
4. Cropping
5. Conservation
6. Distribution
7. Biotic
9. Environment
10. Biodiversity
13. Reforest

Classroom Wing

Very Short Answer Type Questions

1. (c) 2. (b) 3. (c) 4. (c) 5. (d)
6. (a) 7. (d) 8. (c) 9. (a) 10. (b)
11. (d) 12. (a) 13. (b) 14. (c) 15. (c)
16. (d) 17. (c) 18. (b) 19. (a) 20. (d)
21. (c) 22. (c) 23. (d) 24. (b)
25. Nitrogen dioxide 26. Afforestation 27. Save Narmada 28. CFCs
29. Increase ground water level 30. Ultraviolet 31. Afforestation
32. Geothermal energy 33. Hydroelectric energy 34. Sprinklers

Competition Wing

Level 1: Apply Your Concepts

1. (c) 2. (d) 3. (b) 4. (b) 5. (b)
6. (c) 7. (b) 8. (c) 9. (a) 10. (b)
11. (c) 12. (b) 13. (d) 14. (b) 15. (c)
16. (a) 17. (b) 18. (b) 19. (c) 20. (b)
21. (c) 22. (a) 23. (a) 24. (a) 25. (d)
26. (d) 27. (d) 28. (c) 29. (b) 30. (b)
31. (d) 32. (a) 33. (d) 34. (b) 35. (c)
36. (c) 37. (b) 38. (d) 39. (b) 40. (c)
41. (d) 42. (b) 43. (a) 44. (b) 45. (d)
46. (d) 47. (b) 48. (d) 49. (a) 50. (c)
51. (b) 52. (d) 53. (b) 54. (d) 55. (d)
56. (c) 57. (c) 58. (b) 59. (d) 60. (b)
61. (a) 62. (a) 63. (a) 64. (d) 65. (c)
66. (a) 67. (c) 68. (a) 69. (d) 70. (a)
71. (b) 72. (b) 73. (a) 74. (c) 75. (c)
76. (d) 77. (a) 78. (b) 79. (a) 80. (d)

NEET Special Wing

Multiple-Answer Type Questions

1. (a, b) **2.** (a, b, d) **3.** (b, d) **4.** (b, c, d) **5.** (a, c, d)

Comprehension-Based Questions

6. (b) **7.** (c) **8.** (c) **9.** (a) **10.** (b)

11. (i) → (c); (ii) → (a); (iii) → (b); (iv) → (e); (v) → (d)

12. (c) **13.** (c) **14.** (d) **15.** (d) **16.** (a)

17. (i) → (d); (ii) → (a); (iii) → (e); (iv) → (b); (v) → (c)

Hints and Explanations

CLASSROOM WING

Short Answer Type Questions

35. • Stop wastage of water.
    - Switching off unnecessary lights and fans.
    - Don't waste food and take as much as you require.
    - Walking down or use cycle for going to nearby market instead of using vehicle.
    - Separate wastes into recyclable and non-recyclable.
    - Reuse carry bags, packing materials, plastic containers and other reusable material.

36. Short term exploitation of natural resources fulfil the current demand. It is beneficial for the present generation only, whereas management of resources with long-term perspective is aimed to fulfil the needs of future generations. Long-term use of resources can be achieved through its sustainable use.

37. Equitable distribution of resources will ensure benefits to all the sections of the society including rich as well as poor. This is necessary for the growth and development of a country. Money force is the main factor which is working against an equitable distribution of resources as rich people and rich nations try to encroach upon the share of the poor people or poor nations.

38. • Save electricity.
    - Do not waste food.
    - Save water.
    - Use cooking gas instead of wood for cooking.
    - Observe the principle of three R's (Reduce, recycle and reuse).

39. Use of materials such as paper should be preferred as they can be reused and recycled.
    - Materials like glass and some plastics can be recycled on heating and get easily converted into different products like toys, containers which can be reused again.
    - e-wastes such as unused computers, mobiles etc. can be repaired and used again.
    - Household wastes such as vegetable wastes etc. can be used as manure for plants.

40. Construction of dams leads to several environmental problems such as deforestation and loss of biodiversity because large areas of forest land get submerged in water leading to an ecological imbalance

Essay Type Questions

41. In this system, overhead water lines are fitted along the plantation of crops. From the pipelines, water drips from very small holes directly on the plant. It helps in minimizing the wastage of water. This technique is suitable for arid/semi-arid regions in India.

42. • Eminent raw materials like iron, aluminium, zinc, manganese and copper are used for industrial purposes.
    - Imperative non-metal resources include coal, salt, clay, cement and silica.
    - Stones are used for building material. For example, granite, marble and limestone constitute another category of minerals.
    - Minerals with aesthetic and ornamental value are gems, such as diamonds, emeralds and rubies. Gold, silver and platinum is used by humans for ornaments.
    - Minerals in the form of oil, gas and coal are used as different kinds of fuels.

43 Mining is the main cause of environmental degradation. The extraction of all the minerals from the lithosphere has a variety of side effects and a few of them are as follows.
    - Land depletion due to mining.
    - Industrial waste
    - Conversion of agricultural land into industrial or mining region leads to the wastage of that land and accumulates pollution in its nearby area due to industrial waste.

44. Using the solar photovoltaic cells to produce electricity is also a very potent source of energy generation. The viability lies in the fact that the solar energy is clean and in abundance. However, it does not come without limitations. Firstly, it requires a huge space for SPV cells to produce electricity. The conversion rate is quite low.

Secondly, the SPV cell uses silicon which is obtained through mining. Despite the limitations of the solar electricity, various other methods like solar cooker, solar geyser, etc., have been increasingly used now.

45. The benefits of the 3 R's are as follows.

Reducing, reusing and recycling construction materials provide the following benefits.

- Donating or saving materials for reuse is a free alternative to paying disposal fees.
- Recycling fees are generally lower than disposal fees.
- Tax deductions from donating materials to non-profits.
- Helping local governments meet their goal of reducing disposal by 50%.
- Creating business: New business and product opportunities associated with recycled materials add to the growth of our local economy.

46. Public awareness can also pressurize farmers to use more eco-friendly pesticides that are not injurious to health.

- Campaigns like 'Save Water' are eminent for public awareness on water scarcity and its effects. Measures are needed to be taken for better management of the world's water resources and few measures are listed in the following points.
- Opting for several small reservoirs rather than few mega projects. Build small catchment dams and protect wetlands.
- Recharging underground aquifers by soil management, microcatchment development and afforestation by thus decreasing the need for large dams.
- For agriculture use, treating and recycling of municipal waste water. Leakage prevention from dams and canals.
- Preventing loss in municipal pipes.
- For urban environment, effective rain water harvesting is required.

COMPETITION WING

Level 2: Review your Concepts

81. **Renewable Resources:** These types of resources can be recycled and regenerated within a given period of time. **Examples:** Forests, wind energy, solar energy, biomass energy, hydropower, etc.

    Non-renewable Resources: These types of resources cannot be regenerated and hence, with time they will be exhausted with increasing consumption.

    Examples: Fossil fuels such as coal, petroleum, minerals, etc.

82. A diverse ecosystem, supported by biodiversity conservation, has multiple species playing varied roles. This diversity can act as a buffer; if one species is affected or diminishes due to a change or threat, others can potentially step in to fulfil its role, ensuring the ecosystem's resilience and continued functionality.

83. Water harvesting directly counters the effects of water scarcity by storing rainwater for future use. Especially in areas with irregular rainfall or over-exploited groundwater, water harvesting provides an alternate, localized water source, reducing dependency on distant or depleting water bodies.

Level 3: Assess Your Concepts

84. Biogas is obtained by the anaerobic degradation of biomass in the presence of water.

    Two advantages of using biogas are:

    (a) It burns without smoke and hence does not cause air pollution.

    (b) It has a high calorific value.

85. Four limitations in harnessing wind energy on a large scale are:

    (a) Wind energy farms can be established only at those places where wind blows at least with a speed of 15 km/h for the most part of the year.

    (b) There should be some back-up facilities (like storage cells) to take care of the energy needs during a period when there is no wind.

    (c) Establishment of wind energy farms requires large area of land.

    (d) Since the tower and blades are exposed to the vagaries of nature like rain, sun, storm and cyclone, they need a high level of maintenance.

86. (a) **Water Harvesting and Ecosystem Rejuvenation:** Water is the lifeblood of ecosystems. Techniques like water harvesting ensure that groundwater tables are replenished. Healthy water tables lead to thriving wetlands, rivers, and lakes. These water bodies support a vast array of life forms, from aquatic species to terrestrial fauna that depend on them. By promoting water harvesting, we ensure a stable environment for many species, thereby conserving biodiversity.

    (b) **Reduce and Biodiversity Pressure:** The principle of 'Reduce' can directly decrease the strain on biodiversity. By consuming less, there's reduced pressure to exploit habitats and resources, allowing ecosystems to thrive without disruption.

    (c) **Recycle and Natural Resource Conservation:** By recycling, we ensure that fewer raw materials are extracted from the environment. This means fewer habitats are disrupted or destroyed, allowing for a more robust preservation of biodiversity.

    (d) **Reuse and Habitat Preservation:** The more we reuse, the less we need to produce. This principle, when widely adopted, can limit the expansion of agricultural or industrial land, ensuring that natural habitats remain undisturbed.

    (e) **Reforest and Biodiversity Enhancement:** Forests are significant reservoirs of biodiversity. By actively planting trees and restoring forests, we're directly contributing to increasing biodiversity. Forests act as carbon sinks, climatic stabilizers, and habitats for myriad species.

NEET SPECIAL WING

Multiple-Answer Type Questions

1. The aims and objectives of NMCG is to accomplish the mandate of National Ganga River Basin Authority (NGRBA):
   (a) To ensure effective abatement of pollution and rejuvenation of the river Ganga by adopting a river basin approach to promote inter-sectoral co-ordination for comprehensive planning and management and b. To maintain minimum ecological flows in the river Ganga with the aim of ensuring water quality and environmentally sustainable development.

2. The uses of forests as a resource include-Water used by the population is dependent upon the existence of forests around the river channels. Furniture and paper used in homes are derived out of the woods from forests. Many medicines are organic based and derived from forests. Oxygen that humans are dependent upon is generated by plants and the carbon dioxide is absorbed by them as well.

3. Sustainability means the ability within an area to build the value of environment and its aspects while confirming the protection and the renewal of natural resources and the environmental patrimony. It involves economic aspects like generating employment and income to sustain the growing population. Social sustainability is the capability to guarantee welfare, equitably distributed among social classes and gender.

4. The various natural resources on the basis of their stages of development include-
   i. Actual resources- The resources that are surveyed, their quantity and quality has been determined, and are in current use.
   ii. Reserve resources- These resources are a part of an actual resource and it can be developed profitably in the future.
   iii. Stock resources- These resources cannot be utilized due to lack of technology.

5. In Floodwater harvesting system, water runs through dry riverbeds at the time of heavy rains and it helps in natural irrigation in the adjacent cultivating fields. Recharge wells are used to recharge the groundwater table. Here, casting tubes are drilled into the underlying bedrock when the permeability is low to increase the rate of penetration of run-off water to ground water table. Terraces is a technique used to control erosion. It is mainly practiced in hilly areas where retention of water is an issue. Terrace is built on steep slopes and at the end of these terraces, small wall of stones are created to slow down the flow of water.

Comprehension-Based Questions

A.

6. Gopal used solar energy for his device which is solar cooker. Solar energy is abundantly available and is clean.

7. Gopal made a solar cooker. It basically works on the principle that solar energy warms the pot. Concave mirrors reflect the sunlight into a single focal point. The light energy is converted into heat energy and finally the pot is warmed and the food is cooked.

8. Fossil fuels are the non-renewable sources of energy. Fossil fuels will get depleted in the future at the rate at which we are using them today. They are formed by the decomposition of million of years of animals and plants buried deep under the earth's crust.

9. The geothermal energy is produced from the hot steam originating from hot water springs and geysers. It is extensively used in countries, like Iceland, New Zealand and Japan, etc., and also in India geothermal energy is being produced in Himalayan states that have hot water springs.

10. Concave mirrors reflect the sunlight into a single focal point. The light energy is converted into heat energy and finally the pot is warmed and the food is cooked.

11. Match the following:

    Hydroelectric energy is the most popular renewable source of energy resource. Across the world, dams have been constructed to generate electricity. It is a simple non-polluting technique with basic science of converting kinetic energy into electric energy.

    (i) (c)

    Using the solar photovoltaic cells to produce electricity is also a very potent source of energy generation. The viability lies in the fact that the solar energy is clean and in abundance.

    (ii) (a)

    Wind turbines are also a viable option and it is increasing at a fast rate in India. The only limitation of wind energy is that it requires a large space to setup windmills

to produce electricity at mass level. However, due to the negligible environment, it has a great scope. India currently stands third in terms of wind energy production.
(iii) (b)

Biogas is mix of many gases including carbon dioxide and methane. It is obtained from animal and human waste and industrial and plant waste. The methane burns easily. Once it is burnt, the residue is used as a fertilizer.
(iv) (e)

With constant rising and falling of the tide, sufficient potential for hydroelectric energy is present. In many countries including India, tidal energy is already produced.
(v) (d)

B.

12. The renewable resources are not able to regenerate and are depleting and on the other hand, the non-renewable sources are in the endangered zone. So, it is very essential for all to conserve our resources before the fight for survival begins. There are few words to live by in this situation and they are – Reduce, recycle, reuse and reforest.

13. Recharge wells are used to recharge the groundwater table. Here, casting tubes are drilled into the underlying bedrock when the permeability is low to increase the rate of penetration of run-off water to ground water table.

14. Problems associated with building dams are as follows-
i. Fragmentation and change of course rivers.
ii. Degradation of riverine ecosystems in downstream.
iii. Heavy social cost due to displacement of people and animals.
iv. Stabilization and creation of marshy lands in the nearby areas.
v. Methane emission in large reservoirs.

15. Mining takes place in four stages- Prospecting, Exploration, Development and Exploitation. Prospecting is the stage where location of minerals takes place.

16. Deforestation is one of the major problems of environment in present times. Living beings are dependent on the natural resource for abundant things. So it is essential for mankind to take care of this resource and regenerate it. Trees should be planted during rainy season. Strict punishment should be awarded on cutting of trees. On cutting of one tree, plenty more should be planted instead. This helps the habitat as well as to control soil erosion.

17. Match the following:

Magnetite is the ore of Iron.
(i) (d)

Argentite is the ore of Silver.
(ii) (a)

Galena is the ore of Lead.
(iii) (e)

Cinnabar is the ore of mercury.
(iv) (b)

Bauxite is the ore of Aluminium
(v) (c)

Glossary

Acid rain: Any precipitation or deposition having a pH lower than 5.6.

Acrosome: Covering of the head of the sperm.

Allantois: Sac-like structure that is developed from the gut of the embryo.

Alleles: Pair of contrasting traits that represent a character/trait.

Alveoli: Small balloon-like, thin-walled air sacs at the end of each bronchiole.

Amitosis: Mode of cell division in which the division takes place within the nucleus.

Ampulla: Part of the fallopian tube which lies next to the infundibulum.

Anemophily: Abiotic pollination in which pollen grains are carried from the anther of a flower to the stigma of a flower of another plant of same species by air.

Anoxybiotic organisms: Organisms that completely depend on anaerobic respiration for their energy needs.

Apoplast pathway: Passage of water and minerals through cell wall and intercellular spaces.

Areola: Circular pigmented area around the nipple.

Aster: A cellular structure shaped like a star, formed around each centrosome during cell division.

Autotrophic nutrition: Mode of nutrition in which an organism prepares its own food from simple inorganic material.

Binary fission: Splitting up of an organism into two parts that grow independently into new organisms.

Biodiversity: Wide variety of flora and fauna on Earth.

Biotic components: Living components in an ecosystem such as plants, animals, microorganisms and human beings.

Blastocyst: Stage in embryonic development that comes after morula which consists of trophoblast (outer layer) and an inner cell mass, also implantation occurs at this stage.

Blastulation: Stage of gestation when the morula develops into a blastocyst.

Bowman's capsule: Thin-walled (one-cell thick), round cup-like structure that lies in the cortex region of the kidney.

Breathing: Physical process that involves taking in of oxygen and releasing out carbon dioxide.

Bronchi: Two branches generated from trachea with each of them entering the lungs from their respective side.

Capacitation: Physiological changes that occur in the sperm which enable to fertilize the ovum.

Cellular respiration: Series of chemical reactions which occur inside the cell that involve breakdown of glucose to liberate energy.

Cerebral cortex: Outer layer of the cerebrum.

Cerebrospinal fluid: Clear, colourless fluid which is present between the inner two layers of meninges inside brain.

Cervix: Lowermost part of the uterus which leads into the next accessory female reproductive organ, which is vagina.

Chalaza: The location where the nucellus attaches to the integuments, opposite to the micropyle.

Chemoautotrophs: Organisms that produce their food by utilizing energy from chemical reactions.

Chiasmata: Point of contact between two non-sister chromatids of a homologous chromosome.

Chromomeres: Small bead-shaped structures that appear on the chromosome.

Chromonema: Chromatin fibre which is in the early stage of condensation.

Cleavage: Act or state of splitting or dividing of a cell, particularly during telophase of cell division.

Clitoris: Small projected part of the vulva present above the urethral opening.

Cohesive force: Force of attraction among the similar molecules.

Complementary base pairing: Kind of pairing of purines and pyrimidines of opposite polynucleotide strands.

Corpus luteum: Part of the follicle which appears like a yellow-coloured mass after the ovulation.

Cross-pollination: Transfer of pollen grains from the anther of a flower to the stigma of another flower of the same plant or different plant of the same species.

Cross: Mating between two individuals leading to the fusion of gametes.

Crossing over: Phenomenon of the exchange of segments of non-sister chromatids (genes) of homologous chromosomes.

Deglutition: Act or process of swallowing.

Dehiscence: Process of release of pollen grains by breaking the anther wall.

Dendrites: Tree-like highly branched extensions of cytoplasm of the cell body in neurons.

Dentition: Arrangement of teeth in a particular species.

Dialysis: Process by which the blood of a kidney patient is purified.

Diapedesis: Passage of blood cells inside the capillaries, commonly accompanying inflammation.

Dictyosomes: Stacks of flat membrane-bound cavities that together comprise the Golgi apparatus.

Diffusion: Process of movement of molecules from higher to lower concentrations until the concentrations become equal.

Diphyodont: An animal with two successive sets of teeth.

Diploid cell: Cell which contains two sets of chromosomes.

Double fertilization: Fertilization process characteristic of angiosperms in which one sperm cell of a pollen grain fertilizes with an egg cell and the second one fuses with two polar nuclei to produce a triploid body that gives rise to the endosperm.

Ecological pyramid: Diagrammatic representation of food chains by arranging the organisms at the various trophic levels.

Ecosystem: Community of living organisms and non-living components of the environment.

Ecotone: Area of transition where ecosystems overlap.

Embryogenesis: Entire process of development of a single-celled diploid zygote into a newborn child until its birth.

Emphysema: Respiratory disease in which the lung tissue involved in the exchange of respiratory gases gets impaired and the walls separating alveoli break.

Emulsification: Process in which large fat molecules are broken down into small, tiny droplets.

Endocytosis: Process through which materials move into the cell by engulfing food and other substances from the external environment.

Enzyme: Biological catalyst which acts only on its specific substrate.

Eosinophilia: Condition in which the number of eosinophils in per unit volume of blood increases due to some parasitic infection.

Epididymis: Long-coiled tube which acts as a temporary storage organ for spermatids.

Epiglottis: Leaf-like cartilaginous flap that covers the glottis to prevent the entry of food particles in the respiratory tract.

Epiglottis: Muscular flap-like structure at the opening of larynx.

Evolution: Orderly changes in the characteristics of groups of organisms over the course of generations.

Excretion: Process through which waste and toxic products are expelled from the body of an organism.

Exocytosis: Process through which materials move from inside to outside the cell.

Expiratory reserve volume: Additional volume of air that can be exhaled with maximum effort after normal expiration.

Faeces: Undigested matter of the ingested food.

Fallopian tube: Muscular tube that transports ovum from the ovary to the uterus.

Fermentation: Chemical process by which substances like glucose are broken down anaerobically.

Fertilization: Fusion of a sperm and ovum to form a diploid zygote.

Fertilization: Process in sexual reproduction which involves fusion of male and female gametes.

Flaccid cell: Plant cell that is limp through reduction of pressure inside the cell.

Food chain: Linear flow of energy between various components of the ecosystem.

Food web: Interlinking of various food chains.

Fraternal twins: Dizygotic twins formed when two different eggs or ova are fertilized by two different sperms.

Gene flow: New genetic combinations occur due to accidental migration of some individual organisms to far off places resulting in interbreeding between the migrant species with the closely related species of the new region.

Genes: Molecular units of heredity.

Genetics: Branch of biology that deals with the study of heredity and variations.

Geotropism: Movement of plant due to its growth under the influence of gravity.

Glomerular filtrate: Fluid that comes out of Bowman's capsule and enters the renal tubule.

Glomerulus: Network of blood capillaries present inside the outer cavity of Bowman's capsule.

Gluconeogenesis: Process of synthesis of glucose from non-carbohydrate source.

Glycolysis: Sequence of reactions for the breakdown of glucose to two molecules of pyruvic acid.

Graafian follicle: Matured follicle in which the ovum is present.

Guttation: Process by which excess water exudes from the leaves and is seen as water droplets on the leaf margins.

Haploid cell: Cell which contains only one set of chromosomes.

Haploid nucleus: A single set of chromosomes is present in the nucleus.

Heterotrophic nutrition: Mode of nutrition in which an organism depends on the other organisms for its food.

Homologous chromosomes: Two chromosomes of the pair that are similar in structure and are derived one from each parent.

Horticulture: Science of growing and cultivating plants.

Hybrid: Offspring produced by a cross between two individuals of same species that differ from each other at least in one character.

Hydrotropism: Growth of the part of a plant towards water.

Hymen: Thin membrane that partially closes the opening of the vagina.

Hyphae: Thread-like projections of the mycelium of a fungus.

Hypoxia: Condition in which the tissues of a region of a body or the whole body do not receive adequate oxygen.

Implantation: Process by which the blastocyst gets embedded and fixed to the endometrium of the uterus.

Infundibulum: Broad funnel-like structure that connects the ovary with the fallopian tube.

Inheritance: Transmission of characters and variations along the forthcoming generations.

Inspiratory reserve volume: Excess volume of air that can be inhaled by the deepest breath on top of the tidal volume.

Isthmus: Small, narrow, thick-walled, tube-like structure found at the junction of cervix and uterus.

Karyokinesis: Division of cell nucleus during mitosis.

Kinetochore: Small disc-like protein structure that allows the chromatids to be attached to a spindle fibre on a chromosome.

Labia minora: A pair of thin-folded skin covered by labia majora which protects the clitoris, and vaginal and urethral openings.

Lacteals: Lymph vessels of the small intestine which absorb digested fats.

Larynx: Cartilaginous cavity which contains twin ligamentous fold-like structures called vocal cords.

Lenticels: Small openings present in the woody stems for gaseous exchange.

Leydig cells: Interstitial cells that are present between the seminiferous tubules and whose main function is to produce testosterone.

Linkage: Phenomenon in which certain genes present on a chromosome are together carried on to daughter cell during meiotic cell division.

Lymph: Tissue fluid that is collected in lymphatic vessels.

Melanin: Pigment that gives human skin, hair and eyes their colour.

Menarche: Onset of menstrual cycle at the time of puberty.

Menopause: Point in time of a female which is marked by end of menstrual cycles.

Menstrual cycle: Process of maturation of the immature oocytes into mature ova and the subsequent events taking place in female reproductive system.

Metabolic activities: Physiological activities that are essential for the survival of living organisms.

Microsporogenesis: Formation of four haploid microspores from each microspore mother cell by meiotic cell division.

Micturition: Process of regulated expulsion of urine from the urinary bladder through the urethra.

Morula: Formation of multicellular embryo from the single-celled zygote.

Mountain sickness: Negative health effect due to high altitude caused by acute exposure to low amounts of oxygen.

Mutation: Sudden variations either in the number of chromosomes or in the structure of chromosomes appearing in an individual of a generation.

Myelin sheath: Multi-layered fatty substance that covers the axons of many neurons.

Nephron: Structural and functional unit of a kidney.

Nerves: Cable-like glistening white structures containing a bundle of neurons.

Neurotransmitters: Molecules of a chemical substance that transmit the impulse from one neuron to another through the synapse.

Non-myelinated axons: Axons without the myelin sheaths.

Non-sister chromatids: Chromatids of different chromosome.

Nucellus: Part of the ovule composed of nutritive tissues that act as the source of nutrition to the embryo formed after fertilization.

Nucleosome: Double helix of DNA bound by a histone polymer.

Oocyte: An immature female reproductive cell inside a follicle.

Organogenesis: Stage of gestation when the formation of different organs takes place in the embryo.

Osmoregulation: Process in which water and salt balance is maintained in the body by means of osmosis.

Osmosis: Movement of solvent (water) molecules from a solution of higher water concentration to a solution of lower water concentration through a semipermeable membrane.

Ostium: Aperture of infundibulum which collects ovum from the ovary.

Oxyhaemoglobin: Compound that is formed when haemoglobin combines with oxygen.

Parturition: Process of giving birth to the completely developed foetus.

Pedicle: Stalk-like structure that attaches flower to the shoot by means of a stalk.

Peristalsis: Process of involuntary movement of muscles of digestive tract for the transportation of food.

Phagocytosis: Process of engulfing and ingestion of particles by the cell to form a phagosome or food vacuole.

Phenotype: Expressed or observable characteristics of an organism.

Phosphorylation: Addition of inorganic phosphate to ADP to produce high-energy ATP molecule.

Photolysis: Splitting or decomposition of a chemical compound by means of light energy or photons.

Photosynthesis: Process through which green plants prepare carbohydrates from carbon dioxide taken from atmosphere and water from the soil in presence of sunlight.

Photosystem: Biochemical mechanism in plants by which chlorophyll absorbs light energy for photosynthesis.

Phototropism: Growth movement of the plant in response to light.

Pituitary gland: Endocrine gland situated in a bony structure in the middle of the base of the skull.

Plasmodesmata: Narrow channels that act as intercellular cytoplasmic bridges to facilitate communication and transport of materials between plant cells.

Pleura: Double-layered membrane enclosing lungs.

Pneumatophores: Specialized roots that emerge out of the water-logged soil to facilitate the aeration required for respiration.

Pollination: Transfer of pollen grains from the anther of a flower to the surface of the stigma of the same or another flower.

Pollutant: Substance or an energy introduced into the environment that has undesired effects on the natural ecosystem.

Presynaptic membrane: Membrane at the axon terminal of a neuron.

Primary pollutant: Pollutant that is directly emitted from the sources and enters the atmosphere.

Protandry: Condition when anther matures earlier than stigma.

Protogyny: Condition when carpel attains maturity earlier than anther.

Protoplasm: Living substance present in a cell.

Pseudopodia: Finger-like projections which help in the encircling of the food particle in *Amoeba*.

Pure breed: Variety of individuals in which a character remained unchanged in large number of successive generations.

Pyloric sphincter: Ring-like muscular valve which controls the passage of food from the stomach to intestine.

Rate of ventilation: Rate of respiration in terms of volume of air breathed in per minute.

Reflex action: An involuntary and almost instantaneous response to a stimuli.

Regeneration: Process of regrowth of an organism from its lost body part.

Residual volume: Volume of air that cannot be expelled from the lungs even with the maximum effort.

Ribonucleoproteins: Proteins which are structurally associated with RNA.

Scion: Portion of the stem of a plant which is cut in a slanting way.

Semen: Mixture of fluids secreted by the seminal vesicles, prostate gland and Cowper's glands which act as a medium for the transportation of sperms.

Serotonin: Chemical that transmits the messages from one area of the brain to another.

Serum: Plasma without fibrinogen.

Speciation: Origin of new species from an existing species.

Spermatids: Immature and non-motile sperms.

Spermatogenesis: Process in which haploid spermatozoa develop from germ cells in the seminiferous tubules of the testis.

Stolons: Stems that grow just below the soil surface or just on the surface of the ground.

Style: Long, narrow, tubular structure that acts as a passage for the entry of male gamete into the ovary.

Succus entericus: Intestinal juice secreted from the digestive glands embedded in the lining of small intestine.

Sunken stomata: Stomata found in plants of arid region, embedded at a greater depth of leaves.

Symplast pathway: Passage of water and minerals through the cytoplasm of the cells.

Synapse: Junction between the two nerve cells that facilitates the transmission of impulses from one neuron to another.

Synapsis: Pairing of homologous chromosomes during meiotic phase of cell division.

Synaptic cleft: Space between the two neurons across which a nerve impulse is transmitted by neurotransmitters.

Terrestrial ecosystem: Ecosystems that exist on land.

Thalamus: Flattened portion above the pedicel.

Thecodont: Dentition in which teeth are embedded in sockets.

Tissue respiration: Metabolic process by which oxygen reaches the body cells and carbon dioxide is released from them.

Trachea: Tube-like structure that provides the passage of air from the larynx to the lungs.

Transcription: Process of synthesis of RNA that is transferred to the ribosomes for the synthesis of proteins.

Transpiration: Loss of water from the surface of aerial parts of the plant mainly from the leaves.

Trophoblast: Layer of cells that forms the outer layer of the blastocyst.

Tubectomy: Permanent women contraception in which a portion of the fallopian tube is blocked.

Tunica albuginea: Dense and fibrous tissue which covers testes.

Turgid cell: Cell which is in state of being swollen, especially due to high fluid content.

Urethra: Tube-like structure which originates from urinary bladder.

Urinary system: System associated with the formation of urine in the kidneys.

Variation: Degree of differences between offspring and the parents.

Vasectomy: Male sterilization process in which vas deferens are cut out and tied.

Villi: Tiny finger-like structures that are projected inwards from the inner lining of the small intestine.

Vital capacity: Volume of air that a normal human being can exhale after the inhalation with the maximum effort.

White matter: Inner region of the cerebrum that contains axons of the neurons.

Zygote: Cell formed by the union of male and female gametes.

Photo Credits

CHAPTER 1

Page 1.3—HL Studios. Pearson Education Ltd; **Page 1.6**—alila. 123rf.com; **Page 1.9**—snapgalleria. 123rf.com; **Page 1.10**—alxhar (c) Shutterstock; **Page 1.10**—Oxford Designers & Illustrators Ltd. Pearson Education Ltd; **Page 1.10**—Tefi. Shutterstock; **Page 1.11**—BlueRingMedia. Shutterstock; **Page 1.12**—mikrostoker. 123rf.com; **Page 1.13**—sgame. Shutterstock; **Page 1.15**—udaix. Shutterstock; **Page 1.16**—123rf.com; **Page 1.16**—designua. 123rf.com; **P1.17**—Designua. Shutterstock; **Page 1.18**—sgame. Shutterstock

CHAPTER 2

Page 2.6—Oxford Designers & Illustrators Ltd. Pearson Education Ltd; **Page 2.6**—Designua. Shutterstock; **Page 2.7**—Ashray Shah. Shutterstock; **Page 2.8**—Ashray Shah. Shutterstock; **Page 2.8**—Ashray Shah. Shutterstock; **Page 2.9**—Ashray Shah. Shutterstock; **Page 2.9**—MichaelTaylor. Shutterstock; **Page 2.12**—Alila Medical Media. Shutterstock; **Page 2.13**—Oxford Designers & Illustrators Ltd. Pearson Education Ltd; **Page 2.14**— ellepigrafica.shutterstock

CHAPTER 3

Page 3.3—Mohammed Ali. Pearson India Education Services Pvt. Ltd; **Page 3.4**—udaix.shutterstock; **Page 3.4**—designua. 123rf.com; **Page 3.6**—BlueRingMedia. Shutterstock; **Page 3.7**—Valentina Moraru. Shutterstock; **Page 3.10**—designua. 123rf.com; **Page 3.11**—Oxford Designers & Illustrators Ltd. Pearson Education Ltd; **Page 3.14**—Oxford Designers & Illustrators Ltd. Pearson Education Ltd

CHAPTER 4

Page 4.4—Amit John. Pearson India Education Services Pvt. Ltd; **Page 4.5**—Amit John. Pearson India Education Services Pvt. Ltd; **Page 4.5**—Power_J. Shutterstock; **Page 4.6**—Mohd Suhail. Pearson India Education Services Pvt. Ltd; **Page 4.6**—BSIP SA / Alamy Stock Photo; **Page 4.6**—Amit John. Pearson India Education Services Pvt. Ltd; **Page 4.6**—Rattiya Thongdumhyu. Shutterstock; **Page 4.7**—Amit John. Pearson India Education Services Pvt. Ltd; **Page 4.8**—KPG_Payless.shutterstock; **Page 4.9**—frank60.shutterstock; **Page 4.9**—Madlen. Shutterstock; **Page 4.10**—Kazakov Maksim. shutterstock; **Page 4.10**—cloki. Shutterstock; **Page 4.10**—F.Neidl.shutterstock; **Page 4.11**—Volodymyr Nikitenko.shutterstock; **Page 4.11**—Jan Csernoch / Alamy Stock Photo; **Page 4.11**—Warayoo. Shutterstock; **Page 4.12**—123rf.com; **Page 4.12**—Mohd Suhail. Pearson India Education Services Pvt. Ltd; **Page 4.12**—Mohd Suhail. Pearson India Education Services Pvt. Ltd; **Page 4.17**—Kicky_princess.shutterstock; **Page 4.21**—Coleman Yuen. Pearson Education Asia Ltd; **Page 4.21**—Arvind Balaraman. Shutterstock; **Page 4.23**—Brian A Jackson. Shutterstock; **Page 4.23**—Mohd Suhail. Pearson India Education Services Pvt. Ltd; **Page 4.24**—Mohd Suhail. Pearson India Education Services Pvt. Ltd; **Page 4.25**—Kazakova Maryia. Shutterstock; **Page 4.25**—Designua.shutterstock; **Page 4.27**—Bogdan Wankowicz. Shutterstock; **Page 4.27**—Bogdan Wankowicz. Shutterstock

CHAPTER 5

Page 5.3—Pearson Education Ltd; **Page 5.4**—Oxford Designers & Illustrators Ltd. Pearson Education Ltd; **Page 5.5**—123rf.com; **Page 5.6**—Teguh Mujiono. Shutterstock; **Page 5.7**—Sapna Advertising Co. Pearson India Education Services Pvt. Ltd; **Page 5.7**—123rf.com; **Page 5.8**—Alila Medical Media. Shutterstock; **Page 5.8**—Peter Hermes Furian. Shutterstock; **Page 5.9**—udaix. Shutterstock; **Page 5.9**—Alila Medical Media. Shutterstock; **Page 5.10**—Blamb. Shutterstock; **Page 5.10**—Mohd Suhail. Pearson India Education Services Pvt. Ltd; **Page 5.11**—Tefi. Shutterstock; **Page 5.11**—David Litman. shutterstock; **Page 5.11**—Pearson Education, Inc.; **Page 5.12**—Designua. Shutterstock; **Page 5.12**—Alila Medical Media.shutterstock; **Page 5.13**—Alila Medical Media. Shutterstock; **Page 5.14**—GRei. Shutterstock; **Page 5.14**—Pearson Education Ltd; **Page 5.16**—Blamb. Shutterstock; **Page 5.16**—vetpathologist. Shutterstock; **Page 5.18**—Oxford Designers & Illustrators Ltd. Pearson Education Ltd; **Page 5.21**—123rf.com; **Page 5.22**—doethion. 123rf.com; **Page 5.22**—Teguh Mujiono. Shutterstock; **Page 5.23**—ellepigrafica.shutterstock; **Page 5.23**—snapgalleria. Shutterstock; **Page 5.24**—Alexander_P. Shutterstock; **Page 5.25**—Alila Medical Media.shutterstock; **Page 5.26**—Blamb. Shutterstock; **Page 5.28**—Alila Medical Media. Shutterstock; **Page 5.30**—Blamb. Shutterstock

CHAPTER 6

Page 6.4—Oxford Designers & Illustrators Ltd. Pearson Education Ltd; **Page 6.4**—Oxford Designers & Illustrators Ltd. Pearson Education Ltd; **Page 6.5**—HL Studios. Pearson Education Ltd; **Page 6.7**—123rf.com; **Page 6.7**—Alila Medical Media. Shutterstock; **Page 6.8**—Angallen Rogozha. Shutterstock; **Page 6.8**—Alila Medical Media. Shutterstock; **Page 6.9**—Oxford Designers & Illustrators Ltd. Pearson Education Ltd; **Page 6.10**—Designua. Shutterstock; **Page 6.10**—Oxford Designers & Illustrators Ltd. Pearson Education Ltd; **Page 6.11**—ellepigrafica.shutterstock; **Page 6.12**—Jakinnboaz.shutterstock; **Page 6.13**—ellepigrafica. Shutterstock; **Page 6.14**—Alila Medical Media. Shutterstock; **Page 6.16**—Designua. Shutterstock; **Page 6.17**—Pearson Education Ltd; **Page 6.17**—Timonina. Shutterstock; **Page 6.18**—Designua. Shutterstock; **Page 6.18**—Timonina. Shutterstock; **Page 6.19**—Designua. Shutterstock; **Page 6.19**—Scott Camazine / Alamy Stock Photo; **Page 6.20**—Designua. Shutterstock; **Page 6.20**—somersault1824.shutterstock; **Page 6.20**—Designua. Shutterstock; **Page 6.20**—jarun011. 123rf.com; **Page 6.21**—Designua. Shutterstock; **Page 6.21**—toeytoey. 123rf.com; **Page 6.21**—Designua. Shutterstock; **Page 6.21**—toeytoey. 123rf.com; **Page 6.22**—Scott Camazine / Alamy Stock Photo; **Page 6.22**—Alila Medical Media. Shutterstock; **Page 6.23**—Blamb.shutterstock; **Page 6.24**—Designua. Shutterstock; **Page 6.24**—Oxford Designers & Illustrators Ltd. Pearson Education Ltd; **Page 6.25**—Designua. Shutterstock; **Page 6.26**—Oxford Designers & Illustrators Ltd. Pearson Education Ltd; **Page 6.26**—BlueRingMedia. Shutterstock; **Page 6.27**—hfsimaging. 123rf.com; **Page 6.28**—designua. 123rf.com; **Page 6.29**—ODI/Alamy Stock Photo; **Page 6.30**—udaix. Shutterstock; **Page 6.31**—NelaR. shutterstock; **Page 6.33**—Alila Medical Media. Shutterstock; **Page 6.34**—Designua. Shutterstock; **Page 6.34**—Sebastian Kaulitzki. Shutterstock; **Page 6.34**—Alila Medical Media. Shutterstock; **Page 6.34**—CLUSTERX.shutterstock

CHAPTER 7

Page 7.3—Amit John. Pearson India Education Services Pvt. Ltd; **Page 7.4**—Devkant Gupta. Pearson India Education Services Pvt. Ltd; **Page 7.6**—ducu59us. Shutterstock; **Page 7.6**—Alila Medical Media. Shutterstock; **Page 7.8**—age fotostock / Alamy Stock Photo; **Page 7.10**—2516503. Shutterstock; **Page 7.11**—Oguz Aral. Shutterstock; **Page 7.12**—Suwin. Shutterstock; **Page 7.13**—ducu59us. Shutterstock; **Page 7.18**—Tefi. Shutterstock; **Page 7.19**—Alila Medical Media. Shutterstock; **Page 7.20**—udaix. Shutterstock; **Page 7.21**—medistock. Shutterstock; **Page 7.22**—Alila Medical Media. Shutterstock; **Page 7.23**—Alila Medical Media. Shutterstock; **Page 7.24**—udaix.shutterstock; **Page 7.24**—ann131313. Shutterstock

CHAPTER 8

Page 8.4—snapgalleria. Shutterstock; **Page 8.5**—mrhighsky. 123rf.com; **Page 8.5**—Tefi. Shutterstock; **Page 8.7**—extender01. 123rf.com; **Page 8.8**—Oxford Designers & Illustrators Ltd. Pearson Education Ltd; **Page 8.10**—designua. 123rf.com; **Page 8.10**—MedusArt. Shutterstock; **Page 8.12**—udaix. Shutterstock; **Page 8.13**—Designua. Shutterstock; **Page 8.14**—stihii. Shutterstock; **Page 8.14**—Alila Medical Media. Shutterstock; **Page 8.15**—Alila Medical Media. Shutterstock; **Page 8.16**—Oxford Designers & Illustrators Ltd. Pearson Education Ltd; **Page 8.18**—Alila Medical Media. Shutterstock; **Page 8.20**—Zuzanae. Shutterstock; **Page 8.21**—Alila Medical Media. Shutterstock; **Page 8.22**—Designua. Shutterstock; **Page 8.23**—Designua. Shutterstock; **Page 8.27**—Designua. Shutterstock; **Page 8.28**—Martin Shields / Alamy Stock Photo; **Page 8.28**—griffin024. 123rf.com; **Page 8.28**—Mohd Suhail. Pearson India Education Services Pvt. Ltd; **Page 8.28**—Pearson Education Ltd

CHAPTER 9

Page 9.5—Pearson Education Ltd; **Page 9.6**—Oxford Designers & Illustrators Ltd. Pearson Education Ltd; **Page 9.7**—Science History Images /Alamy Stock Photo; **Page 9.9**—Pearson Education Ltd; **Page 9.14**—Tamara Kulikova. Shutterstock; **Page 9.14**—Vilor. Shutterstock; **Page 9.16**—Le Do. Shutterstock

CHAPTER 10

Page 10.3—Designua.shutterstock; **Page 10.4**—Sander van Sinttruye. Shutterstock; **Page 10.5**—kongsak sumano.shutterstock; **Page 10.5**—Vecton.shutterstock; **Page 10.6**—Paul Looyen. Shutterstock; **Page 10.6**—2630ben. Shutterstock; **Page 10.7**—rixie. 123rf.com; **Page 10.7**—HL Studios. Pearson Education Ltd; **Page 10.9**—HL Studios. Pearson Education Ltd; **Page 10.10**—National Geographic Creative/Alamy Stock Photo; **Page 10.10**—clearviewstock. Shutterstock; **Page 10.10**—Lebendkulturen.de. Shutterstock; **Page 10.10**—peteretchells. 123rf.com; **Page 10.10**—MikhailSh. Shutterstock; **Page 10.10**—Vladimir Wrangel.shutterstock; **Page 10.13**—Sozaijiten; **Page 10.13**—Jajmo. Shutterstock; **Page 10.15**—Oxford Designers & Illustrators Ltd. Pearson Education Ltd; **Page 10.22**—motorolka. Shutterstock; **Page 10.22**—Martin Fowler / Alamy Stock Photo; **Page 10.22**— Zeljko Radojko. Shutterstock; **Page 10.22**—Sarycheva Olesia. Shutterstock; **Page 10.22**— Leftleg. Shutterstock; **Page 10.22**—Viktar Malyshchyts. Shutterstock; **Page 10.22**— Przemyslaw Ceynowa. Shutterstock

CHAPTER 11

Page 11.3—Kichigin.shutterstock; **Page 11.4**—Wangworn Sankamethawee. Shutterstock; **Page 11.4**—123rf.com; **Page 11.4**—Alison Hancock. Shutterstock; **Page 11.5**—Andre van der Veen. Shutterstock; **Page 11.5**—Andrey Armyagov. Shutterstock; **Page 11.5**—raweenuttapong. 123rf.com; **Page 11.5**—topseller. Shutterstock; **Page 11.5**—Dr. Morley Read. Shutterstock; **Page 11.7**—Vecton. Shutterstock; **Page 11.9**—Arvind Singh Negi/Red Reef Design Studio. Pearson India Education Services Pvt. Ltd; **Page 11.10**—ssuaphotos. Shutterstock; **Page 11.10**—Francey. Shutterstock; **Page 11.12**—Alexander Chaikin. Shutterstock; **Page 11.12**—Chaiyaporn Baokaew. Shutterstock; **Page 11.13**—Luzss. Shutterstock; **Page 11.14**—Nigel Cattlin / Alamy Stock Photo; **Page 11.14**—Pearson Education Ltd; **Page 11.17**—Vladeep. shutterstock; **Page 11.18**—nightman1965. 123rf.com; **Page 11.19**—Oxford Designers & Illustrators Ltd. Pearson Education Ltd; **Page 11.20**—b900. Shutterstock; **Page 11.24**—Designua.shutterstock

CHAPTER 12

Page 12.8—Image Source / Alamy Stock Photo; **Page 12.8**—Hemis / Alamy Stock Photo; **Page 12.9**—milena moiola / Alamy Stock Photo; **Page 12.12**—Geof Kirby / Alamy Stock Photo; **Page 12.13**—Sean Pavone / Alamy Stock Photo; **Page 12.14**—inga spence / Alamy Stock Photo; **Page 12.14**—Paco Ayala. 123rf.com; **Page 12.15**—Lyroky / Alamy Stock Photo